Accident Prevention Manual
ESSENTIALS

EDITORS:

PHILIP E. HAGAN, JD, MBA, MPH, ARM, CIH, CET, CHMM, CHCM, CHSP, CEM®

JOHN F. MONTGOMERY, PHD, CSP, CHMM

JAMES T. O'REILLY, JD

National Safety Council
Itasca, IL

NSC Press Editor: Deborah Meyer
Cover Design, Interior Design, and Composition: Jennifer Villarreal
Senior Director, Publications: Suzanne Powills
Cover Photos: (Top left) xerviar/iStock/Thinkstock; (top center) ndoeljindoel/iStock/
Thinkstock; (top right) rookman/iStock/Thinkstock; (bottom left) kemaltaner/iStock/
Thinkstock; (bottom center) bugphai/iStock/Thinkstock; (bottom right) Einariuss/
iStock/Thinkstock

DISCLAIMER

Although the information and recommendations contained in this publication have been compiled from sources believed to be reliable, the National Safety Council makes no guarantee as to, and assumes no responsibility for, the correctness, sufficiency, or completeness of such information or recommendations. Other or additional safety measures may be required under particular circumstances.

Copyright ©2014 by the National Safety Council
All Rights Reserved
Printed in the United States of America
18 17 16 15 14   5 4 3 2 1

Library of Congress Cataloging-in-Publication Data
Accident prevention manual essentials/editors, Philip E. Hagan, JD, MBA, MPH, ARM, CIH, CET, CHMM, CHCM, CEM, John F. Montgomery, PHD, CSP, CHMM, James T. O'Reilly, JD.
    pages cm
  Includes index.
    ISBN 978-0-87912-332-1 — ISBN 0-87912-332-X 1. Industrial safety. I. Hagan, Philip (Philip E.), editor. II. Montgomery, John F. (John Franklin), editor. III. O'Reilly, James T., editor. IV. National Safety Council.
  T55.A328 2014
  658.3'82--dc23

                              2014027637

                                                      Product Number: 12152-0000

Contents

Preface v

Definitions of Terms v

Acknowledgments vi

Contributors vi

1 Safety Culture 1

2 Regulatory Framework for Safety 21

3 Legal Implications for Safety 63

4 Injury and Illness Record Keeping, Incidence Rates, and Analysis . . 117

5 Identifying Hazards 131

6 Loss Control and Prevention 165

7 Safety and Health Training 197

8 The Computer and Internet as Safety Information Tools 241

9 Fire Protection 261

10 Electrical Safety 301

11 Construction Safety 325

12 Basics of Industrial Hygiene 355

13 Personal Protective Equipment (PPE) 375

14 Lab Safety 413

References 471

Index 489

PREFACE

The first edition of the *Accident Prevention Manual Essentials* continues a tradition begun in 1946 with the publication of the first *Accident Prevention Manual*. This Essentials manual brings to the safety/health/environmental professional the broad spectrum of topics, specific hazards, best practices, control procedures, resources, and sources of help known in the field today.

This first edition provides a broad coverage of essential topics from the Accident Prevention Manuals in order to make available a text that could be covered in a semester-long course. In addition, it provides a more concise look at safety requirements for those who want to get a quick overview of the safety field. Volunteer experts from many different subject areas have come together to make this book an important resource to be used in support of safety programs and related education. In addition to the expertise of National Safety Council volunteers and staff, we have received expert assistance in developing, writing, and reviewing from contributors representing various disciplines and from the editors, Philip E. Hagan, John F. Montgomery, and James T. O'Reilly. If you have different ideas and want them to be considered for the next edition, your suggestions are welcome and can be sent to the National Safety Council, 1121 Spring Lake Drive, Itasca, IL 60143, attn. Deborah Meyer. E-mail: deborah.meyer@nsc.org.

The audience served by this text is widespread, but the text's focus is primarily to provide a book that can be used for educational purposes.

DEFINITIONS OF TERMS

As the concerns and responsibilities of safety/health/environmental professionals expand, so must their ability to communicate and educate. Technical terms are defined in the text where they are used. However, the terms *incident* and *accident* deserve a special note. In the years since the original publication of this series, many theories of accident causation and definitions of the term *accident* have been advanced. The National Safety Council continues to work to increase awareness that an *incident* is a near-accident and that so-called *accidents* are not random events but rather preventable events. To that end, the term *incident* is used in its broadest sense to include incidents that may lead to property damage, work injuries, or both. The following definitions are generally used in this manual:

- **Accident**: That occurrence in a sequence of events that produces unintended injury, death, or property damage. Accident refers to the event, not the result of the event (see unintentional injury).

- **Incident:** An unintentional event that may cause personal harm or other damage. In the United States, OSHA specifies that incidents of a certain severity be recorded.
- **Near-miss incident:** For purposes of internal reporting, some employers choose to classify as "incidents" the near-miss incident; an injury requiring first aid; the newly discovered unsafe condition; fires of any size; or nontrivial incidents of damage to equipment, building, property, or product.
- **Unintentional injury:** The preferred term for accidental injury in the public health community. It refers to the result of an accident.

With proper hazard identification and evaluation, management commitment and support, preventive and corrective procedures, monitoring, evaluation, and training, unwanted events can be prevented.

ACKNOWLEDGMENTS

General Editor Phil Hagan thanks Karl Bourdeau, who was the first to tell him that he would write a book one day; Richard, Myrna and Linda Pifer, who have been both friends and always supportive throughout; and to sisters, Lisa and Judy, with brother-in-law, Scott, who have always been there for him.

General Editor John Montgomery thanks his wife Karen and memory of Christopher for their support and encouragement in the editing and rewrite of chapters. He also wishes to thank all chapter authors, contributors, and reviewers for their diligent review and manual updates.

General Editor Jim O'Reilly acknowledges the inspiration of Dr. William Mase, former Director, Division of Public Health Sciences, University of Cincinnati College of Medicine; and the invaluable assistance of his family, Carol, Jessie, and CB.

CONTRIBUTORS

The following safety, health, and environmental professionals have contributed to the first edition of the *Accident Prevention Manual Essentials* as editors, writers, and/or reviewers of chapters or sections. The National Safety Council very much appreciates the dedication and professional expertise they have contributed to the cause of safety, health, and environmental education.

Jairo Betancourt, has more than 25 years of experience in biomedical research and laboratory safety. His experiences include designing, implementing and managing laboratory safety programs for universities and research institutions both domestically and internationally.

He is an active member of the American Biological Safety Association (ABSA). Currently he is involved in the International Working Biosafety Group (IBWG, www.internationalbiosafety.org), the ABSA Philanthropy task force, and co-editor of the Biosafety Compendium. He frequently conducts education and training programs on biosafety and biosecurity in Spain and Latin American Countries throughout Central and South America (Colombia, Mexico, Dominican Republic, Venezuela, and Argentina).

John DeLaHunt, MBA, has more than 25 years experience in environmental health and safety and disaster preparedness. He is currently managing risk, insurance, fire, and life safety at the University of Texas–San Antonio. He co-edited the *Environmental Compliance Assistance Guide for College & Universities*. Mr. DeLaHunt writes a bi-monthly column on campus issues for the American Chemical Society's *Journal of Chemical Health & Safety* (JCHAS) and its predecessor *Chemical Health & Safety* (CHAS). Mr. DeLaHunt is active in the Campus Safety, Health & Environmental Management Association (CSHEMA), having served on the CSHEMA Executive Committee, the Government Relations committee, and the Newsletter Awards Committee. He graduated from Colorado College with a BA in chemistry and an MBA, with emphasis in finance and management, at the University of Colorado at Colorado Springs. E-mail: john_delahunt@msn.com.

Teddy Gil, BME, MBA, ASNT Level III ET, FAA A&P License, has held varying positions throughout his career, the most recent being process improvement and engineering consultant for Delta Air Lines, implementing executive leadership short fuse interior configuration upgrades and fabrication. He was also vice president of business development and quality for Global Integrated Security Services, providing risk assessments consulting, and training; vice president of people development and training for Air Serv Corp.; and leader of the Delta Air Lines Technical Operations Employee Council, responsible for implementing improvement and positive cultural changes throughout the organization for the more than 12,000 technical operations employees. Mr. Gil was also the presiding officer of Delta's Technical Operations Conflict Resolution Program from 2002 to 2004. In addition, he has had several articles published in *Inside the Minds* and in ExecBlueprints, including "Universal Lessons: Training the Global Workforce;" "Preparing for a New U.S. Administration in 2009;" "4 Key Factors to Consider and Maximizing the Power of the Workforce;" and "Managing Human Capital to Execute Strategy." E-mail: gilt@bellsouth.net.

Philip E. Hagan, JD, MBA, MPH, ARM, CIH, CET, CHMM, CHCM, CHSP, CEM®, lectures in the Department of Human Science at Georgetown University, Washington, DC, and is a national practice leader with Partner Engineering and Science Inc. In addition, he is the past director of safety for the National Waste & Recycling Association and director of safety and environmental management for Georgetown University. He is a practicing attorney specializing in safety-, environmental-, and business-related law issues. He has consulted internationally on risk, safety, and environmental management issues in Italy, Qatar, India, Turkey, Yemen, and China. He has co-authored texts on environmental and workplace safety, training, and indoor environmental quality; and he has been a general editor for the *Accident Prevention Manual for Business & Industry* for two editions, plus he was the lead editor on this Essentials text. In addition, he has presented to a diverse group of audiences on subjects ranging from hazardous waste disposal to business continuity and emergency management. He is a member of several American Bar Association (ABA) Committees dealing with environmental issues in business transactions, toxic torts, workers' compensation, and international environmental law. He has been a peer reviewer for various safety-related American National Standards Institute (ANSI) consensus standards and guidelines. He holds a BS from East Carolina University, an MPH from George Washington University, an MBA from Georgetown University, and a JD from the George Mason University School of Law. E-mail: Phil.Hagan@georgetown.edu.

Valienti Antonio Henry, MBA, is board certified in safety, and a Certified Lean Six Sigma Black Belt. Currently he is a senior manager of loss prevention and reduction at the University of Miami. In addition, Mr. Henry also maintains a consulting practice in both the private and public sectors, which includes the development of loss control and risk management programs using specialized Lean Six Sigma methodologies to maximize efficiency and decrease costs for diverse clients in the health care and financial sectors. He has an MBA in international business and finance from the University of Miami. E-mail: vhenry@miami.edu.

David Hibbard, MPH, CIH, is the director of environmental health and safety at the University of Kentucky. He has more than 25 years of combined experience in the military, regulatory, chemical manufacturing, and higher education sectors involving the implementation and management of health and safety and industrial hygiene programs. He holds a BS from East Carolina University and a master's degree in public health from Eastern Kentucky University. E-mail: dwhibb0@uky.edu.

Ken Kolosh, Manager, Statistics, National Safety Council, 1121 Spring Lake Drive, Itasca, IL 60143-3201. E-mail: ken.kolosh@nsc.org.

Patrick Lorimer, BS, MPH, has more than 25 years of experience in the health and safety industry and is currently the director of operations of the East Coast of Partner Engineering and Science Inc., an environmental consulting firm that covers all 50 states. He was past director of health, safety and environmental hygiene for PMK Group Inc., a large, New Jersey–based environmental engineering firm. Mr. Lorimer has worked as a corporate risk manager for a large regional health system and has presented many professional seminars in the field of health safety and environmental hygiene on topics ranging from indoor air quality and risk management to environmental management systems. He holds a BS from East Carolina University and a master's degree in public health from George Washington University. E-mail: plorimer@partneresi.com.

John F. Montgomery, PhD, CSP, CHMM, is the senior vice president of environmental safety and health for Air Serv Corp, with responsibility for 40 domestic and international stations. Prior to joining Air Serv, he was with American Airlines for 18 years, where he served as the corporate manager of ground safety, corporate manager/acting managing director of the environmental department, and the manager of the noise and emissions regulatory program. Prior to joining American, he was the corporate manager of safety and lost time at Sky Chefs; spent time in the industrial sector; and was an assistant professor/lecturer at several universities, including Texas A&M, University of Central Missouri, Central Oklahoma University, and Lamar University.

Dr. Montgomery holds three advanced degrees, including a doctorate of philosophy from Texas A&M University, and two professional certifications, including Certified Safety Professional (Safety) and Certified Hazardous Material Manager (Environmental). He is a frequent speaker at industry meetings and seminars; was an editorial advisor to *Safety+Health Magazine*; and served as a general editor for three editions of the two-volume *Accident Prevention Manual for Business & Industry*, in addition to this Essentials edition. He was also a contributor to the *Accident Prevention Manual for Environmental Management* (1995 and 2000). He served as the Chairman of the ATA Environmental Committee and was named rapporteur of the International Air Transportation Association (IATA) Emissions Sub Group, and a delegate to the United Nations' International Civil Aviation Organization. He was a contributor/reviewer for the United Nations' Intergovernmental Panel on Climate Change (IPCC) review of the effect of aircraft emissions on the environment. E-mail: DrJFMonty@sbcglobal.net

James T. O'Reilly, JD, College of Law and College of Medicine, University of Cincinnati, Cincinnati, Ohio, has authored 45 texts and 200 articles. His scholarly work was acknowledged in a March 2000, decision of the U.S. Supreme Court, quoting one of his textbooks as the "expert" in its field. He was formerly associate general counsel of Procter & Gamble Co., chair of the Local Emergency Planning Committee for Cincinnati, and has served as chair of the American Bar Association's Section of Administrative Law, 1996–1997. He also served as vice mayor of an Ohio city and as a member of the regional council of governments. He has acted as a general editor for both volumes of the the *Accident Prevention Manual for Business & Industry* for two editions in addition to this Essentials text. E-mail: joreilly@fuse.net.

Ralph Stuart, MS, CIH, CCHO, is chemical hygiene officer at Cornell University in Ithaca, New York. He has an MS from the University of Vermont in environmental engineering and has been active at the national level in laboratory safety innovations since 1989. These include development of professional health and safety Internet information resources, as well as the EPA Project XL regulatory reinvention project for laboratory chemical waste management. He is currently secretary of the Division of Chemical Health and Safety of the American Chemical Society and chair of the ACS Task Force on Laboratory Chemical and Waste Management. E-mail: rstuart@cornell.edu.

Treasa M. Turnbeaugh, PhD, MBA, CSP, CET, is the chief executive officer for the Board of Certified Safety Professionals (BCSP). She is responsible for the overall operations of the BCSP as well as its contribution to the safety, health, and environmental (SH&E) profession. Dr. Turnbeaugh is experienced in the SH&E field and in the field of professional certification. Additionally, Dr. Turnbeaugh brings experience and leadership in the business arena of both for-profit and not-for-profit organizations.

Dr. Turnbeaugh has more than 25 years of experience in the safety profession with experience in workers' compensation cost reduction, ergonomics, industrial hygiene, indoor air quality, behavior-based safety, cultural assessments, diagnostics and metrics, injury management, and safety process improvement. She is experienced in servicing a variety of industries including manufacturing, health care, gaming, higher education, agribusiness, and municipalities.

Dr. Turnbeaugh holds a PhD in health services research, with a minor in epidemiology, and a master's of public health degree from Saint Louis University; an MBA from Lindenwood University; and both a MS and BS in occupational safety and health, with a specialization in industrial hygiene, from Murray State University. She has held her CSP certification for more than 20 years and is a Certified Environmental, Safety, and Health Trainer.

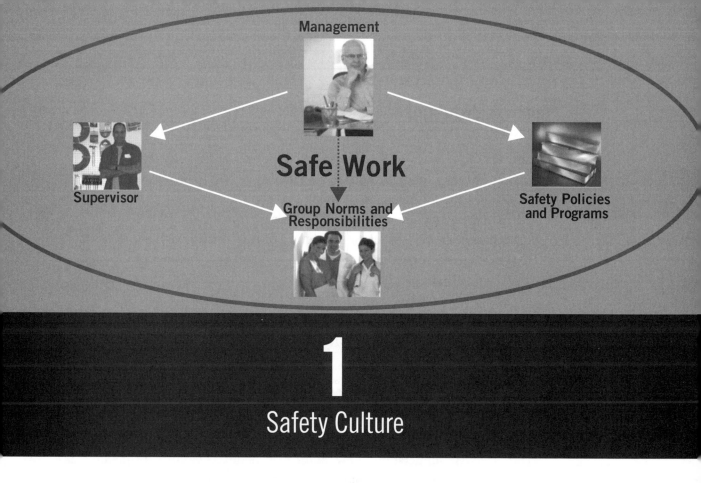

1

Safety Culture

- ❏ Explain how culture is defined as it relates to safety.
- ❏ Describe how culture can be used to enhance safety compliance in an organization.
- ❏ Identify the three fundamental levels at which culture manifests itself.
- ❏ Illustrate the difference between the terms *safety culture* and *safety climate*.
- ❏ Describe the elements common to a *successful safety culture*.
- ❏ Discuss ways to measure *safety culture* and *safety climate*.

DEFINING CULTURE

There are many ways to describe what comprises safety culture. The Safety Culture Maturity model espoused by Fleming (2000) provides one example and includes the following 10 elements:

- management commitment and visibility
- communication
- productivity versus safety
- learning organization
- safety resources
- participation
- shared perceptions about safety
- trust
- industrial relations and job satisfaction
- training.

However, to better understand *safety culture*, the safety and health professional needs to understand how *culture* is defined. Culture originated as a key concept in anthropology, but, management and organizational researchers have shown an interest in the area in an attempt to explain change within organizations.

Schein (1992) implies that culture can be changed and used to improve safety-related matters. He holds strong positions on organizational culture, as well as safety culture. His literature is the basis for many other researchers who have built their analytical approaches on his works. This chapter is based, in large part, on Schein's views on these areas of culture.

There are many definitions of culture and many include terms such as *shared perceptions, norms,* and *values.* The best-known and most succinct definition of organizational culture is that it is "the way we do things around here" (Schein, 1992). There are many academic definitions as well, but it is more important to understand the concepts behind those definitions.

In 1990, Schein posited that the problem with culture is that a set of people has to have had enough stability and common history to have allowed a culture to form. This means that some organizations will have no overarching culture because they have no common or long-term history. Other organizations can be presumed to have a strong culture because of a long, shared history or because they have shared important intense experiences. Please note that "strong culture" does not imply good, but is an indicator of the strength and intensity of the culture.

Culture is what a group learns over a period of time as that group solves problems of the external environment and internal integration. Such learning is simultaneously a behavioral, cognitive, and an emotional process (Schein, 1990).

Culture can now be further defined as a pattern of basic assumptions that is invented, discovered, or developed by a given group; it is learned as an organization copes with problems of external adaptation and internal integration that has worked well enough to be considered valid and, therefore, is to be taught to new members as the correct way to perceive, think, and feel in relation to those problems (Schein, 1990).

Once a group has learned to hold common assumptions, the resulting automatic patterns of perceiving, thinking, feeling, and behaving provide meaning, stability, and comfort. The anxiety that results from the inability to understand or predict events is reduced by the shared learning. The strength of a culture is derived in part from this anxiety-reduction factor. In a way, some aspects of culture are to the group what defense mechanisms are to the individual (Hirschhorn, 1987; Menzies, 1960; Schein, 1985).

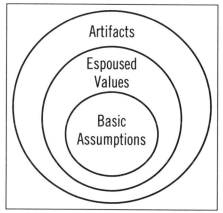

Figure 1–1. Fundamental Levels of Culture

There are three fundamental levels at which culture manifests itself: (1) observable artifacts, (2) espoused values, and (3) basic underlying assumptions (see Figure 1–1).

ARTIFACTS

Artifacts can be easily observed. Artifacts include how people address each other, dress codes, physical layout of the environment, emotional intensity, company records, and policies. These are the most superficial manifestations of culture. They may be apparent to the outside observer, but the values and assumptions behind these artifacts are much more difficult to identify and are, therefore, potentially misleading if used alone to draw conclusions about culture.

ESPOUSED VALUES

Espoused values are basically people's expressed beliefs. These espoused values will typically relate to the basic assumptions (discussed next), but may be in conflict if there is social pressure or motivation present. Management will say that safety is important, but only time and deeper probing will tell if this is a reality (Hale, 2006).

BASIC ASSUMPTIONS

Basic assumptions are the deep-rooted, unconscious perceptions, thought processes, feelings, and behaviors of a group. Deeply held assumptions often start out historically as values, but as they stand the test of time, they are gradually taken for granted and then take on the character of assumptions. They are no longer questioned and become less open for discussion. Such avoidance behavior occurs particularly if the learning was based on traumatic experiences in the organizational history. This often leads to the group counterpart of what would be repression in the individual and can help to explain why culture is so difficult to change (Schein, 1990).

Once the assumptions are understood, it is easier to determine the meanings of various behavioral and artifactual observations and understand how cultures can seem to be ambiguous or even self-contradictory (Martin and Meyerson, 1988). It is possible for a group to hold conflicting values that manifest themselves in inconsistent behavior while having complete consensus on underlying assumptions. It is equally possible for a group to reach consensus on the level of values and behavior and still develop serious conflict later because there was no consensus on critical basic assumptions. This is frequently observed in mergers or acquisitions where initial synergy is gradually replaced by conflict, leading to dissension and ultimately divestitures.

If we combine insider knowledge with outsider questions, assumptions can be brought to the surface, but the process of inquiry has to be interactive—with the outsider continuing to probe until assumptions have been discovered and validated. This will lead to a feeling of greater understanding on the part of both the outsider and the insiders.

The culture of a group can be defined as:

> A pattern of shared basic assumptions that the group learned as it solved its problems of external adaptation and internal integration that has worked well enough to be considered valid and, therefore, to be taught to new members as the correct way to perceive, think, and feel in relation to those problems. (Schein, 1992)

This definition presents three key concepts: how new members are socialized into the group, behavior, and the existence of multiple cultures within a single organization. Schein submits that how new members learn in an organization is more revealing than what they actually learn because this exposes deeper assumptions of the group. Schein's definition does not overtly mention behavior, but behavior reflects basic cultural assumptions as well. Further, he suggests that behavior is determined by how we perceive, think, and feel in relation to situational factors that arise from the immediate external environment. Finally, Schein does not mention size of the cultural group, but claims that organizations can have variations among the subgroups. Therefore, multiple cultures can coexist within the larger group. Some of these subcultures will typically be in conflict with other groups.

CLIMATE OR CULTURE

The terms *safety culture* and *safety climate* are often used interchangeably. However, these terms should be as different constructs that are subsets of an organization's overall culture (Mearns and Flin, 1999). Understanding the difference between these terms will allow the safety and health professional to differentiate what is observable and measurable versus what is highly subjective.

Generally speaking, culture is more complex than climate and includes the underlying assumptions, values, norms, and expectations of an organization. It has its roots in sociology and social anthropology, with an emphasis on symbols, myths, collective values, norms, and the interaction of groups (Mead, 1934). Researchers agree that culture is a valid measure for assessing organizations and making improvements. (Schneider, 1990; Schein, 1984; Cooke and Rousseau, 1988). However, culture cannot be easily measured nor easily interpreted.

Climate is a reflection of culture, often assessed by gathering information through questionnaires or surveys that provide a snapshot of individual perceptions, attitudes, and beliefs (Sarkus, 2001). Climate has its roots in social psychology as a reflection of culture and as the interaction between an individual and a situation (Ashforth, 1985; Killman, et al., 1985; Lewin, 1951; Rousseau, 1988; Schneider and Gunnarson, 1996). Climate focuses on individual perceptions related to the work environment. This concept is what most safety culture surveys—or, more properly, safety climate surveys—are based upon.

According to Dennison (1996), a way to differentiate between culture and climate is to view climate as a thermometer, reading the current temperature of an organization—a surface-level indicator. It leads to quantitative measures and standardized instruments with established reliability and validity. Climate is predicted to differ to a greater extent between groups than it does within a group.

Culture is analogous to a barometer, reading aspects of the weather system and measuring a deeper level of conditions that can aid in the prediction of changes in organizational patterns. Culture uses qualitative observation and in-depth interviews of organizational members. Culture is unique to a given organization, making comparisons across organizations and use of standardized tools of limited value (Schein 1985; 1990).

ORGANIZATIONAL CULTURE

The concept that organizational cultures contribute to the performance effectiveness of a company is not new. The well-known Hawthorne study from

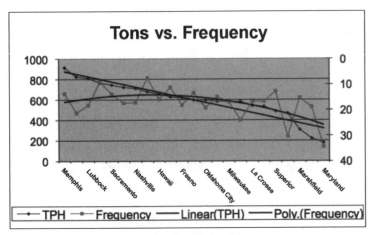

Figure 1–2. Cultural relationship of productivity to safety.

the late 1920s and early 1930s, observed and documented the social, technical, and ideological relations of employees (Roethlisberger and Dickson, 1946). Organizational culture has remained a topic of research and management interest in terms of exploring performance effectiveness, and degreed programs have been created to formalize this pursuit.

Figure 1–2 illustrates the relationship between performance effectiveness (productivity) and losses/safety. The relationship suggests that there is an organizational culture connection that ties low productivity to higher losses and higher productivity to lower losses. This relationship holds until the upper one-third of high productivity is reached, where it appears that a culture of productivity takes precedence over a culture of safety.

SAFETY CULTURE

The term *safety culture* first appeared in the 1987 Organization for Economic Cooperation and Development (OECD) Nuclear Energy Agency report on the 1986 Chernobyl disaster (INSAG, 1988). Subsequently, researchers believe that safety culture is a subcomponent of corporate culture (Westrum 1993; Hudson and van der Graaf, 2002) that affects the safety and health of the group members and others outside of the group as well. Safety culture affects and is affected by other operational processes and systems—it is inherently coupled to the overall corporate culture. Thus, any dominant subcomponent such as productivity, turnover, or quality will influence the safety processes and vice versa (Williams, 1991).

Creek (1995) suggested that a safety program will only be successful if it was an integrated part of the overall organizational culture; it has to "fit" the culture of the organization. Hansen (1993) agrees, stating that safety activities in most companies are treated as separate from and unrelated to other organizational activities, which is a limiting factor to the success of many safety efforts.

Hansen (1993) also identified the safety culture of an organization as crucial to safety performance success. He cited the National Institute of Occupational Safety and Health (NIOSH) studies from the 1970s that found "best practices" in safety—such as safety rules, safety committees, incident investigation, and safety promotions—were not factors of good safety performance companies versus poor ones. These studies did, however, show a significant correlation between safety performance and core management competencies, such as management commitment and the communication and feedback process with employees.

Hansen (1993) characterized a successful safety culture as one with humanistic employee relations policies and informal communications between management and employees in which feedback is encouraged and where methods to produce the product safely are built into the standard operating procedures. Organizations without a positive safety culture and with negative employee attitudes typically have poor management practices—which have caused such attitudes (Hansen, 1995). The responsibility for changing that culture is ultimately management's (Arden, 1993). Management must take an active and visible role in the safety program and in encouraging employee participation, input, and feedback. An example of active and visible management participation is for the plant manager to begin each management meeting with departmental accountability for safety (e.g., having managers report on safety performance in their departments).

Geller (1994) concurs that safety must be integrated into the overall corporate culture for sustained improvement in safety performance, thereby creating a "total safety culture." He further defines a *total safety culture* as an organization that creates an environment where everyone feels responsible and takes responsibility for their individual safety as well as that of others. He asserts that building a total safety culture requires continuous improvement in three areas: (1) environmental conditions, (2) personal factors (attitudes and beliefs), and (3) behavioral factors.

LEVELS OF POSITIVE SAFETY CULTURE

There are different levels of cultural maturity that organizations must navigate. Organizations with a more mature culture will address issues quickly, have open discussion as issues arise, and welcome new ideas as to how to address the issues. These organizations encourage active thinking and involvement from all levels of the organization. By contrast, those organizations with a less mature culture will address issues only when absolutely necessary and may only address the symptoms of the issue as opposed to the root causes.

Westrum (1993) differentiates an effective organization from an ineffective one by the organization's ability to handle issues that arise. Organizations must have a culture of conscious inquiry in order to ensure its safety. This indicates that individuals and groups are empowered to observe, inquire, and make their conclusions known to higher management. Individuals will participate in offering observations, conclusions, and suggestions when they believe that their thoughts will be considered and used in a constructive manner. Westrum also proposes that the "license to think" is one of the key features of an effective organization and links the license to think with what an organization empowers individuals to do.

The strength of the culture depends on how well information flows inside the organization, and Westrum (1993) divides organizations into three categories based on their flow of information (Figure 1–3). Westrum's ideas were expanded by Hudson (2001) and Hudson and van der Graaf (2002). They present an evolutionary model of safety culture and suggest that organizations can work their way from one level of maturity to the next (Figure 1–4).

PATHOLOGICAL	BUREAUCRATIC	GENERATIVE
Do not want to know.	May not find out.	Actively seek information.
Messengers are shot.	Listened to if they arrive.	Messengers are trained.
Responsibility is shirked.	Responsibility is compartmentalized.	Responsibility is shared.
Bridging is discouraged.	Bridging is allowed but neglected.	Bridging is rewarded.
Failure is punished or covered up.	Organization is just and merciful.	There is inquiry and redirection.
New ideas are actively crushed.	New ideas present problems.	New ideas are welcomed.

Figure 1–3. How organizations treat information.

Westrum, 1993

Hudson and van der Graaf (2002) present stair steps that begin with the *pathological culture.* This culture is ruled by the desire for status quo; such organizations do not care to understand why incidents happen nor how to prevent them. This aligns with Westrum's (1993) definition of a pathological culture. Next, Hudson and van der Graaf include the *reactive culture* in which much attention is given to safety—but only after an accident happens.

Hudson and van der Graaf's (2002) *calculative culture* is synonymous with Westrum's (1993) bureaucratic class in which the organization holds fast and hard to its rules and ignores signals of needed change. This organization is inspection- and audit-driven, and individuals assume all systems are in place for compliance purposes; individual participation will not make much difference. The next level of safety maturity as described by Hudson and van der Graaf is the *proactive culture,* in which the organization believes all safety systems are in place and adhered to but is still looking for ways to make continuous improvement (Hudson, 2001).

The final step of the safety culture maturity model (Hudson and van der Graaf, 2002), is the *generative culture*, where safety is no longer a separate issue, but is entirely integrated into the business and is a part of everyday business processes within the organization. Organizations at this level are learning organizations with an effective feedback system in place. This aligns directly with Westrum's (1993) generative level, where organizations welcome signals for change, look at change as an opportunity for overall system improvement, and are positive about making such changes for continuous improvement of the overarching business systems.

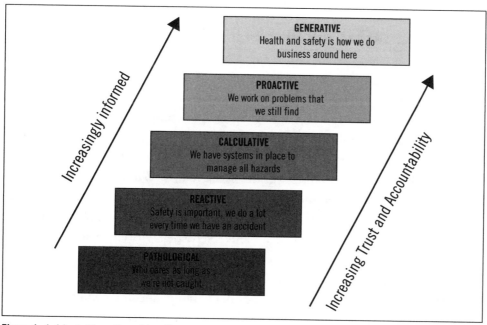

Figure 1–4. Adapted from the safety culture maturity model.

Hudson and van der Graaf, 2002

Reason (1997) identifies characteristics of a successful safety culture that would align well with the generative culture:

- *reporting culture*—one in which people are willing to report errors and near misses
- *just culture*—one of "no blame," where trust is present and individuals are encouraged or rewarded for providing safety information, but also where there is a clear line between acceptable and unacceptable behavior
- *flexible culture*—one that can take on different forms but that shows evidence of moving from a conventional hierarchical mode to a flatter structure
- *learning culture*—the ability and desire to draw correct conclusions from

its safety information and desires to implement major improvements when the need is evident.

Combined, these subcultures or characteristics create a well-informed organizational culture. Reason (1997) concluded that in most respects, an informed culture is a successful culture. Hudson (2001) interprets that the four characteristics given by Reason form a culture of trust. Thus, as organizations climb the safety maturity model, they are attempting to create a more informed culture—one that implies a culture rich in trust.

MEASURING SAFETY CULTURE/CLIMATE

The most popular way of measuring safety culture today is by using *safety culture perception surveys*. More correctly, they should be called *safety climate surveys* as discussed earlier in this chapter. For the purposes of this section, all surveys will be called perception surveys. Petersen (1989) espoused that safety perception surveys (or safety climate surveys) are important tools that can be used to measure safety program effectiveness. While perception surveys cannot measure attitudes and beliefs directly, they are the best means available to extrapolate information about attitudes and beliefs, which behaviorists propose affect behavior or actions. Conversely, behaviorists also believe that behaviors or actions performed repeatedly can affect a person's attitudes or beliefs. Hellriegel and Slocum (2004) state that general attitudes best predict general behaviors and specific attitudes best predict specific behaviors.

One issue with perception surveys is the lack of psychometrically sound measures for this purpose (McLain, 1995). There is confusion among safety practitioners about what a perception survey should be. Many people believe that asking a multitude of questions creates a sound, valid survey. Nothing could be further from the truth. This method will simply give answers to the questions asked and the way in which they were asked. A psychometrically valid survey is one that has been based on theory, has been tested many times, and has an acceptable level of validity and reliability. However, this is not a chapter on survey methods, so only the cursory elements of these factors are discussed.

A psychometric model is based on theory found from in an in-depth literature search. The theory helps establish constructs of measures and items. Figure 1–5 depicts the theoretical model of a safety culture. This model was developed based on literature review and many cumulative years of consulting experience. "Measures" are the categories of interest for research, and the "items" are the questions that collectively assist in making determinations about the measures (see Figure 1–6). Through advanced statistical calculations, a reliability score, or alpha score, can be developed for the measures. These alpha scores indicate the certainty to which the researcher believes he or she has asked the correct questions in the correct manner to explain what the measure indicates. An alpha score of 0.60 (60%) or better is considered a strong measure. Asking more questions does not necessarily make the measure construct stronger and could actually make it weaker. However, questions can be systematically removed and alpha scores recalculated to see if fewer questions affect the measures.

The advanced statistical procedure to develop the measure constructs and their reliability scores is called *factor analysis*. This is also a good technique for refining a survey to be more succinct as well as more reliable.

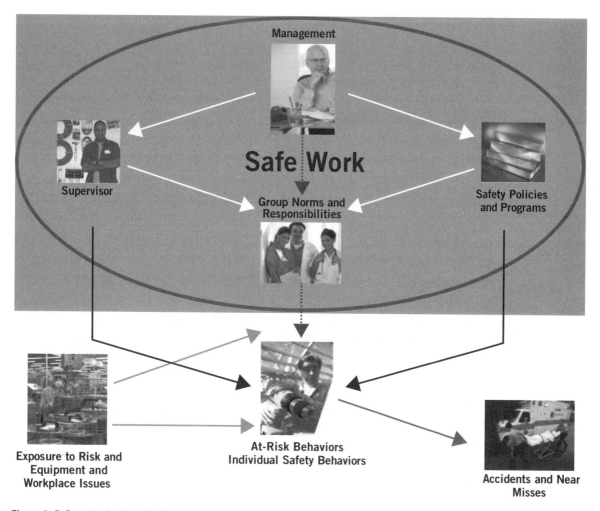

Figure 1–5. Example of a theoretical model of safety culture.

Measure

Management Trust	Strongly Disagree	Disagree	Slightly Disagree	Slightly Agree	Agree	Strongly Agree
Management can be trusted.	6%	16%	14%	24%	33%	7%
I trust management to tell me if I am in danger at work.	4%	12%	6%	18%	43%	18%
If I were hurt on the job, I trust management to treat me fairly.	4%	8%	11%	19%	42%	16%
I trust management to do what they say they are going to do.	8%	15%	13%	29%	32%	4%
I feel free to discuss safety concerns with management without the fear of having it used against me later.	2%	4%	9%	25%	47%	13%

Items

Figure 1–6. Example of measure and item construct—Alpha (0.79).

JOB SATISFACTION IMPACT

The research of the safety-specific climate gave way to considerations that underlying workplace issues may contribute to employee perceptions of safety. McLain (1995) proposed that perception of risk might contribute to the safety climate—that the perceived likelihood of being harmed in the workplace can affect psychological interpretations and perceptions, which thereby influence work attitudes and behaviors. More specifically, McLain researched the impacts of job satisfaction, satisfaction with physical working conditions, stress, and distraction from task performance. He did not speculate as to the direction of the relationship between perception of risk and job satisfaction, but this could be presumed to be an inverse relationship.

Extrapolating McLain's (1995) work, it might be assumed that the relationship of job satisfaction to safety climate is a positive one. Other researchers have shown a similar relationship as it relates to overall organizational climate and job satisfaction (Downey et al., 1974; James and James, 1992). Research by Bigoes (1986) and Greenwood and Wolf (1987) shows a significant relationship between employee attitudes and accident rates; they suggest that increasing job satisfaction is just as important as eliminating physical hazards in the workplace. Thus, a review of the literature reveals that many factors play a significant role in creating a safety climate. Unfortunately, the relationship of these factors is not a simple linear one.

Another tool that can be used to explain how these factors interrelate is *path analysis*. Path analysis can show the relationship of safety climate measures to one another, as well as the direction and relative strength of those relationships. Figure 1–7, indicates that 46% of the respondent's perceptions about job satisfaction are directly related to their trust in their supervisor and safety policies and procedures and are inversely related to their perception of their own at-risk behaviors. This example also shows an interesting relationship and role that supervisory trust has on job satisfaction.

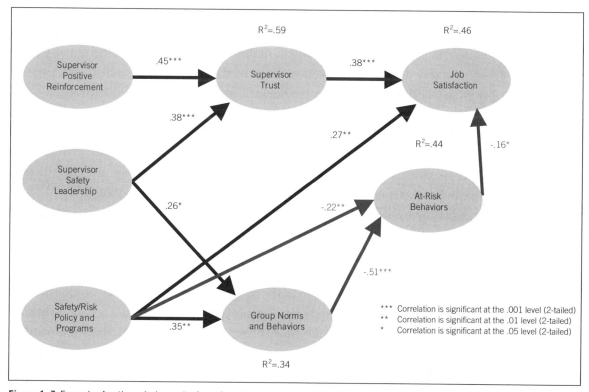

Figure 1–7. Example of path analysis results for safety climate measures.

TRUST IMPACT

Many researchers have proposed that trust plays a central role in safety culture (Hudson, 2003; Reason, 1997; Westrum, 1995). Helmreich and Merritt (1998) have stated that safety cultures are built on trust and that trust needs to exist at multiple levels: between workers, in supervisors, and in management. Mayer et al. (1995) studied the relationship of trust and perceived risk in the work environment. They found that if trust is greater than perceived risk, one employee may try to stop another from acting unsafely. If risk is greater than trust, the employee may not try to stop the other for fear of some sort of reprisal. However, the employee must trust both his or her co-worker and his or her management's commitment to safety in order to proceed with promoting safe behaviors. The willingness of employees to assume the role of "my brother's keeper" is often cited as a desirable indicator of a safe work culture, and based upon the preceding research, this willingness appears to be trust-dependent.

Burns (2004) also found a relationship between trust and self-reported safety behaviors. He found a positive relationship between an employee's trust in co-workers or his or her supervisor and whether the employee would then challenge that co-worker regarding unsafe acts. He also found a positive relationship between an employee's trust in a supervisor and whether the employee would report an incident or safety concern. Mayer and Davis (1999) suggest that ability, benevolence, and integrity are distinct factors of trustworthiness—and provide a solid framework from which to build trust.

Burns (2004) also suggested that in organizations with a hierarchical structure, hierarchy was an antecedent of trust. Turner (1987) predicted that employees trusted their co-workers more than their supervisors and trusted their supervisors more than senior managers. However, employees are typically not able to have as much regular interaction with senior management. This may help to explain why safety climate surveys usually show a discrepancy in perceptions based on the level of the organization answering the perception survey.

PLANNING THE SAFETY CLIMATE SURVEY

Before embarking on a safety survey, several factors should be considered. Management should understand that survey results will indicate one-third of what they already knew, one-third of what they suspected, and one-third of what they did not know. Management must also understand that if they survey an organization, there will be an implied promise to provide feedback and make changes based on the findings. If there is no feedback and no change, employees will lose trust in management and in the organization.

There are several key items to keep in mind when surveying:

- keep the data anonymous, report back only at the aggregated level
- decide how to analyze the data before surveying so the proper demographic data for stratification can be included
- survey response rates will be highest—about 80% to 90%—if the survey is proctored by an outside party and taken on company time; survey rates via the web usually yield about a 50% return rate; surveys mailed to homes usually yield a 20% to 30% return rate
- involve influential employees in the survey effort
- have management communicate the purpose and anonymity of the survey

- use survey tools that are psychometrically sound and have good reliability and validity
- never survey without feedback and action regarding the results.

GROUP BEHAVIOR

As alluded to, culture and subcultures lead to and are exhibited by group behavior. Interestingly, the 19th-century British anthropologist Edward Tylor defined culture as "socially patterned human thought and behavior" (Bodley, 1994). With this in mind, the individual is then either integrated into the group behavior or must choose to behave independently of the group. A driving factor in the individual's decision to comply with group cultural behavior is that of the individual's sense of belonging.

In order to change, people must first feel secure and solid in their belonging to the group—this includes leaders having a sense of belonging with the group as well. If there are signals that the group is not changing in the desired fashion, it will be very difficult for individuals to change due to the need for acceptance. If the signals indicate desired change is occurring, individuals will change with the group for continued acceptance.

CHANGING CULTURE

This chapter has so far established the importance of organizational culture and a safe work culture. How to measure the safety climate to get a sense of how the safety processes are perceived at various levels of the organization has been discussed. The need for improvement in several areas, including trust and overall job satisfaction, has also been described, and the importance of groups, group behavior, and leadership in terms of understanding our current culture and in making change has been determined. Now it is time to discuss how to actually make changes in the organization—which can be a daunting task.

First, the objectives for change must be established. It would be very difficult to make positive change in an organization if the company's present position and its ultimate goal are not known. Chaudron (2003) suggests that organizations need to go through a formal decision-making process that has four major components:
- levels, goals, and strategies
- measurement system
- sequence of steps
- implementation and organizational change.

LEVEL, GOALS, AND STRATEGIES

Deciding the level at which to begin is one of the most difficult decisions to make. Chaudron (2003) suggests that there are four levels of organizational change:

- shaping and anticipating the future (level 1)
- defining what business(es) to be in and the core competencies (level 2)
- structurally changing or reengineering processes (level 3)
- incrementally improving the processes (level 4).

MEASUREMENT SYSTEMS

Measurement is needed by all organizations to assess success of change and for continuous improvement. The measurement system needs to be implemented both before a change (which will help in directing the change) and after a change (to assess the success of the changes made). Measurement of culture/climate change can be in the form of perception surveys; daily observations; or downstream measures such as frequency of losses, severity of losses, productivity numbers, or quality measurements.

SEQUENCE OF STEPS

Chaudron (2003a) suggests that there are four basic options for implementation: (1) the whole organization is involved from the start and is intensively working at once on making the change; (2) divisions or business units go at their own pace and generally use an incremental approach; (3) business units implement the same things at about the same time schedule; and (4) a pilot project is featured in one division or business, so the organization can learn from its mistakes and successes and then apply those lessons to the rest of the organization.

IMPLEMENTATION AND ORGANIZATIONAL CHANGE

Some organizations involve employees from the beginning and allow employees to have influence over the strategic plans. Involving employees (and union representatives) from the start tends to reduce resistance to change—employee buy-in is critical to the success of culture change. The issue some organizations have with involving employees is the threat this creates to traditional hierarchies and power; such organizations tend to involve employees only at the implementation phase (Chaudron, 2003a).

Simon and Leik (1999) conclude that communication and feedback are the keys to a successful safety culture and successful culture change initiatives, leading to a safe work culture. Schein (1992) agrees that communication is a powerful mechanism for change and that managers should be responsible for systematically paying attention to how and what they communicate. Schein indicates that managers can change culture by:

- what they pay attention to, measure, and control on a regular basis
- how they react to critical incidents
- how they allocate scarce resources
- how they do role modeling, teaching, and coaching
- how they allocate rewards and resources
- how they recruit and select new members.

Many behavioralists would agree with these tenants, and as discussed in the next section on behavior-based safety, many of these factors are addressed within this process. What there is very little debate over, however, is the role that management must take in change initiatives. Management must understand the need for change, lead the change initiative, and model desired behaviors to achieve the desire outcomes.

BEHAVIORAL-BASED SAFETY AS A CHANGE CATALYST

One approach to affecting safety culture has been the use of behavior-based safety (BBS). While there are a number of BBS models that have gained recognition over the past decade, most are based on the same behavioral foundation. The foundation includes two commonly accepted principles:

1. It is desirable to focus on "upstream" or leading indicators.
2. Effective use of consequences can modify behaviors.

Traditionally, safety performance has been measured by the end results or the by-products of accidents and injuries—in other words, *lagging indicators.* These measures include OSHA injury rates, workers' compensation loss data, and the negative effects on production issues such as quality and productivity. These types of measures do not provide a reliable predicator of the upstream factors that can lead to employee injuries or human error potentials. Measuring only outcomes does not provide guidance on how to incrementally change the work environment. In addition, classic safety measures do not provide an effective feedback method to influence the actions a person can exhibit that may lead to on-the-job errors. As discussed earlier in this chapter, increased feedback is essential to a positive safety culture.

The primary objective of a behavioral-based safety system is to provide methods to analyze an organization's safety climate and catalog critical behaviors associated with specific tasks. The combination of an organizational climate assessment and the implementation of a systematic process for shaping individual behaviors can provide an organization with a powerful tool to change safety values and culture at both the individual and group level.

BBS is grounded in the psychology of B. F. Skinner (1953), who scientifically demonstrated a process of pinpointing, observation, measurement, and feedback for changing human behaviors. The well-researched benefits of a BBS process include the following:

1. Provide a system to measure upstream indicators of safe behaviors and a platform to provide individual feedback on safety performance.
2. Influence the development of a safe work culture in that everyone accepts responsibility for safety and does something about it on a daily basis.
3. Develop a methodology for safe work practices to be supported with reinforcing feedback from peers, managers, and members of a safety team.
4. Influence a culture where employees go beyond the call of duty to identify unsafe conditions and employee "at-risk" behaviors, and intervene to correct them.
5. Develop a foundation of positive recognition for safe behaviors.
6. Develop a system for identifying what the root causes and barriers to safe behavior are in the existing management system.
7. Develop an employee involvement mechanism that provides for employee input and participation and contributes to the overall safety process.
8. Integrate seamlessly with current systems in place for problem identification, problem solving, and continuous improvement.
9. Identify and address the final, common pathway for injuries occurring at the facility.
10. Identify and correct system-related issues that can force "at-risk" behaviors to occur.

The underlying philosophy of the behavioral approach is to give ownership of safety to the people at risk through involvement and leadership at all levels of the organization. Traditionally, safety has been managed by people who are not at risk directing those who are. It is a considerable change for organizations to acknowledge the role of the individual in the workplace and to imbue in that person a sense of control and ownership of his or her actions. At least initially, some organizations are not ready for this change, and it must be stressed that an environment needs to be developed that allows open communication between employees and supervisors/managers. Supervisors also must accept a more proactive and positive role. Rather than being in total control, they should become a lead figure in a team context—a facilitator. Some managers and supervisors may feel threatened by this perceived erosion of control and an empowered workforce. It is vital that they are involved, not isolated.

CONCLUSION

The process of observation and feedback continues until the employees reach a 90% to 100% target goal of safe behaviors on a given pinpoint and maintain that level of safe behavior for greater than a 30-day period. At that time, the safe behavior is said to be at "habit strength." Then another pinpoint is chosen, and the cycle begins again. This systematic approach to altering the work environment helps to implicitly and incrementally change the safe work culture. The process embeds the essential cultural elements of communication and feedback into the organization, thus giving the entire workforce the feeling of empowerment to affect change with their efforts.

The use of a BBS process can be a powerful tool to supplement existing safety management processes. Its concepts stem from pinpointing the safe behaviors an organization wants its employees to perform, observing and tracking the behaviors on a daily basis, and implementing a positive reinforcement system to recognize teams when they achieve desired behavioral change goals. Some have summarized the BBS process as "catching the employee doing it right." While this view might be somewhat simplistic, it does reflect the position that the proper use of consequences—especially positive reinforcement (R+)—can be effective in modifying behavior and, ultimately, affecting culture.

SUMMARY

Organizational culture and safety culture are undeniably important in creating a successful safe work environment. Many researchers agree as to the relevance and importance of culture in creating this success. However, what is not as clear is specifically which specific elements of an organization help to create or reinforce a positive safety culture. As stated earlier, Fleming's Safety Culture Maturity model includes the following elements:
- management commitment and visibility
- communication
- productivity versus safety
- learning organization
- safety resources
- participation
- shared perceptions about safety
- trust
- industrial relations and job satisfaction
- training.

It is generally recognized that organizations with positive safety cultures have been successful in convincing individuals within every level of the organization that safety is at least as important as other business outcomes, such as productivity and quality. As previously discussed within this chapter, one of the most important elements of a culture is "shared values," and if each individual does not share this belief and vision, the elevation of safety as a top priority will not occur, and by definition, a "world-class" safety culture will not exist. Merely stating within a safety policy statement that safety occupies the position of top priority will not, by itself, convince anyone of that assertion.

At a minimum, visible demonstration of management commitment, support, and involvement; genuine employee involvement; effective training and communication; appropriate budgeting and allocation of resources; and credible behavioral management will be necessary. Employees can be very perceptive and will readily differentiate between lip service and genuine commitment. If safety is managed in a fashion different from that used to manage operational aspects, the organization should not be surprised if the shared perceptions of safety do not correlate well with the company safety policy statement.

There are many ideas on what a safety culture and a positive safety process look like and how to arrive at that safe work culture. No two organizations need approach a safe work culture in the same fashion. This is a custom process and must be worked on by those internal to the organization. There are many consulting firms and cultural assessment tools that can assist in the change initiatives, but ultimately, the answers must be discovered and implemented by those within the organization—those who are part of the culture.

REVIEW QUESTIONS

1. List the 10 elements of the Safety Culture Maturity model.
2. What are three fundamental levels at which culture manifests itself?
3. Describe the difference between the terms "safety culture" and "safety climate."
4. Describe what tools can be used to measure Safety Climate in an organization.
5. Describe how behavioral-based safety can be used as a change catalyst.
6. Compare and contrast leading and lagging indicators.

Job Safety and Health

It's the law!

OSHA®
Occupational Safety
and Health Administration
U.S. Department of Labor

EMPLOYEES:
- You have the right to notify your employer or OSHA about workplace hazards. You may ask OSHA to keep your name confidential.

2

Regulatory Framework for Safety

LEARNING OBJECTIVES

❑ Understand the primary accountabilities tasked to the Occupational Safety and Health Administration (OSHA) by the Occupational Safety and Health Act.

❑ Compare and contrast the roles of both the National Institute of Occupational Safety and Health and OSHA.

❑ Describe the rights granted to both employers and employees under OSHA regulations.

❑ Understand general inspection procedures associated with an OSHA inspection.

❑ Be able to describe the administrative process for addressing an alleged violation under the Occupational Safety and Health Act.

❑ Understand that there are other safety regulations both in the United States and beyond our borders.

INTRODUCTION

A new national policy was established on December 29, 1970, when President Richard M. Nixon signed into law the Occupational Safety and Health Act (Public Law 91-596, found in 29 United States Code [USC] §§651–678). Congress declared that the purpose of this piece of legislation was "to assure so far as possible every working man and woman in the Nation safe and healthful working conditions and to preserve our human resources."

The OSH Act took effect on April 28, 1971. Coauthored by Senator Harrison A. Williams (D-NJ) and the late Congressman William Steiger (R-WI), the act is sometimes referred to as the Williams-Steiger Act. It is regarded by many as landmark legislation because it goes beyond the present workplace and considers long-term health hazards in the working environment of the future.

The information provided in Part I of this chapter focuses on federal OSHA programs. State OSHA programs may differ from the federal program in certain areas but are required to be equal to the federal requirements. However, unless specifically stated to the contrary, the recommendations in this chapter can be followed whether jurisdiction rests at the federal or state level.

On November 9, 1977, President Jimmy Carter signed into law the U.S. Mine Safety and Health Act of 1977 (subsequently referred to as the Mine Act), Public Law 95-164. The act became effective March 9, 1978, and is covered in Part II of this chapter.

The Mine Act is intended to ensure, so far as possible, safe and healthful working conditions for miners. It applies to operators of all types of mines, both coal and metal/nonmetal and both surface and underground. The Mine Act states that mine operators are responsible for preventing unsafe, unhealthful conditions or practices in mines that could endanger the lives and health of miners.

Mine operators are required to comply with the safety and health standards promulgated and enforced by the Mine Safety and Health Administration (MSHA), an agency within the U.S. Department of Labor. Like OSHA, MSHA may issue citations and propose penalties for violations. Unlike employees under the OSH Act, miners (employees) are subject to government sanctions for violating safety standards relating to smoking in or near mines and mining machinery. Similarly, employers and other supervisory personnel may be held personally liable for civil penalties and may be prosecuted criminally for violations of Mine Act standards.

PART I—LEGISLATIVE HISTORY OF OSHA

Historically, the enactment of safety and health laws had been left to the states. Before the 1960s, only a few federal laws (such as the Walsh-Healey Public Contracts Act and the Longshoremen's and Harbor Workers' Compensation Act) directed any attention to occupational safety and health. Several pieces of legislation passed by Congress during the 1960s, including the Service Contract Act of 1965, the National Foundation on Arts and Humanities Act, the Federal Metal and Nonmetallic Mine Safety Act, the Federal Coal Mine Safety and Health Act, and the Contract Workers and Safety Standards Act (Construction Safety Act), focused industry attention on occupational safety and health.

Each of these federal laws was applicable only to a limited number of employers. The laws either were directed at those who had obtained federal contracts or targeted a specific industry. Even collectively, all the federal safety legislation passed before 1970 was not applicable to most employers or employees. Up to that time, congressional action on occupational safety and health issues was, at best, sporadic, covering only specific sets of employers and employees. There was little attempt to establish the omnibus coverage that is a central feature of the OSH Act.

Proponents of a more significant federal role in occupational safety and health, mostly represented by organized labor, based their position primarily on the following:

1. With rare exceptions, the states failed to meet their obligation in regard to occupational safety and health. A few had reasonable or adequate safety and health legislation, but most states legislated safety and health only in specific industries. In general, states had inadequate safety and health standards, inadequate enforcement procedures, inadequate staff with respect to quality and quantity, and inadequate budgets.

2. In the late 1960s, approximately 14,300 employees were killed annually on or in connection with their job, and more than 2.2 million employees incurred a disabling injury each year as a result of work-related incidents. The injury/death toll was considered by most to be unacceptably high.

3. The nation's work-injury rates in most industries increased throughout the 1960s. Because the trend was moving in the wrong direction, proponents of federal intervention felt that national legislation would help reverse this trend.

The OSH Act evolved amid stormy controversy in both houses of Congress as the legislators debated state versus federal roles, industry versus government control, and the like. Such issues were responsible for sharply drawn lines between political parties and between the business community and organized labor. After three years of political tug-of-war, numerous compromises were made to allow passage of the OSH Act by both houses of Congress. By 2010, the Bureau of Labor Statistics reported that the number of workplace fatalities had fallen to about 4,500 or about 12 workers per day. At the same time, U.S. employment had almost doubled to more than 130 million workers at more than 7.2 million worksites. The rate of reported serious workplace injuries and illnesses also dropped markedly, from 11 per 100 workers in 1972 to 3.5 per 100 workers in 2010 (OSHA 3302-01R, 2013). The latest Bureau of Labor of Statistics data—from 2012—indicate that 4,628 workers were killed on the job in United States workplaces (www.bls.gov/iif/oshwc/cfoi/cfoi_revised12.pdf).

ADMINISTRATION

Administration and enforcement of the OSH Act are vested primarily with the Secretary of Labor, the Assistant Secretary of Labor for OSHA, and the Occupational Safety and Health Review Commission (OSHRC) as an appellate agency, which is discussed later. With respect to the enforcement process, the Secretary of Labor, through the Assistant Secretary, performs the investigation and prosecution aspects, and OSHRC performs the administrative adjudication portion, with possible appeal through the courts.

Research and related functions and certain educational activities are vested in the Secretary of Health and Human Services. These responsibilities, for the most part, are carried out by the National Institute for Occupational Safety and Health (NIOSH) established within the Department of Health and Human Services (DHHS). Compiling injury and illness statistical data is handled by the Bureau of Labor Statistics (BLS), a part of the U.S. Department of Labor (DOL).

To assist the Secretary of Labor, the act authorizes the appointment of an Assistant Secretary of Labor for Occupational Safety and Health. This position is filled by presidential appointment with the advice and consent of the Senate. The Assistant Secretary is the chief of the Occupational Safety and Health Administration (OSHA) established within the DOL. The Assistant Secretary acts on behalf of the Secretary of Labor. For the purposes of this chapter, OSHA is also synonymous with the term *Secretary of Labor* or *Assistant Secretary of Labor.*

The primary functions of the four major governmental units assigned to carry out the provisions of the act are described in this section on administration.

OCCUPATIONAL SAFETY AND HEALTH ADMINISTRATION

The Occupational Safety and Health Administration (OSHA) came into existence officially on April 28, 1971, the date the OSH Act became law. This agency was created by the DOL to discharge the department's responsibilities assigned by the act.

Major Areas of Authority

The OSH Act grants OSHA the authority, among other things, (1) to promulgate, modify, and revoke safety and health standards; (2) to conduct inspections and investigations and to issue citations, including proposed penalties; (3) to require employers to keep records of safety and health data; (4) to petition the courts to restrain imminent-danger situations; and (5) to approve or reject state plans for programs under the act.

The act also authorizes OSHA (1) to provide training and education to employers and employees; (2) to consult with employers, employees, and organizations regarding prevention of injuries and illnesses; (3) to grant funds to the states for identification of program needs and for plan development, experiments, demonstrations, administration, and operation of programs; and (4) to develop and maintain a statistics program for occupational safety and health.

Major Duties Delegated

In establishing OSHA, the Secretary of Labor delegated to the Assistant Secretary for Occupational Safety and Health the authority and responsibility for safety and health programs and activities of the DOL, including responsibilities derived from the following:

- Occupational Safety and Health Act of 1970
- Walsh-Healey Public Contracts Act of 1936, as amended
- Service Contract Act of 1965
- Public Law 91-54 of 1969 (construction safety amendments)
- Public Law 85-742 of 1958 (maritime safety amendments)
- National Foundation on the Arts and Humanities Act of 1965
- Longshoremen's and Harbor Workers' Compensation Act (33 USC §§901, 904)
- Federal safety program under 5 USC §7902.

Similarly, the commissioner of the BLS was delegated the authority and given responsibility for developing and maintaining an effective program for collection, compilation, and analysis of occupational safety and health statistics; for providing grants to the states to assist in developing and administering programs in such statistics; and for coordinating functions with the Assistant Secretary for Occupational Safety and Health.

The Solicitor of Labor is assigned responsibility for providing legal advice and assistance to the secretary and all officers of the department in the administration of statutes and Executive Orders relating to occupational safety and health. In enforcing the act's requirements, the Solicitor of Labor represents the secretary in litigation before OSHRC and, subject to the control and direction of the Attorney General, before the federal courts.

Federal OSHA is a small agency. Along with OSHA state plan inspectors, there are approximately 2,200 inspectors responsible for the health and safety of 130 million workers, employed at more than 8 million worksites around the nation—which translates to about one compliance officer for every 59,000 workers (OSHA FAQs). Its organization is explained on its website (www.osha.gov/as/opa/oshafacts.html). OSHA has established 10 regional offices in Boston, New York, Philadelphia, Atlanta, Chicago, Dallas, Kansas City, Denver, San Francisco, and Seattle. (See the Directory of Federal Agencies at the end of this chapter.) The primary mission of the regional office chief, known as the Regional Administrator, is to supervise, coordinate, evaluate, and execute all programs of OSHA in the region. Assisting the Regional Administrator are Assistant Regional Administrators for (1) training, education, consultation, and federal agency programs; (2) technical support; and (3) state and federal operations. (Some functions are combined in certain regions.)

Area offices have been established within each region, and each office is headed by an Area Director. The mission of the Area Director is to carry out the compliance program of OSHA within designated geographic areas. The area office staff carries out its activities under the general supervision of the Area Director with guidance of the Regional Administrator, using policy instructions received from the national headquarters. Federal enforcement of the OSH Act is carried out by the area offices in states that do not have an approved state plan. In states with an approved plan, the area office monitors state activities. (See "Federal–State Relationships" later in this chapter.) The states conducted 50,000 OSHA inspections in 2013, while federal OSHA inspected 39,000 sites (www.osha.gov/as/opa/oshafacts.html).

OCCUPATIONAL SAFETY AND HEALTH REVIEW COMMISSION

The Occupational Safety and Health Review Commission (OSHRC) is a quasi-judicial board of three members appointed by the president and confirmed by the Senate. OSHRC is an independent agency of the executive branch of the

U.S. government and is not a part of the DOL. The principal function of the commission is to adjudicate cases when an enforcement action taken by OSHA against an employer is contested by the employer, the employees, or their representatives.

OSHRC's actions are limited to contested cases. In such instances, OSHA first notifies the commission of the contested cases. The commission then hears all appeals on actions taken by OSHA concerning citations, proposed penalties, and abatement periods and determines the appropriateness of such actions. When necessary, the commission may conduct its own investigation and may affirm, modify, or vacate OSHA's findings.

There are two levels of adjudication within the commission: (1) the administrative law judge (ALJ), and (2) the three-member commission. All cases not resolved in OSHA informal proceedings are heard and decided by one of the commission's ALJs. The judge's decision can be changed by a majority vote of the commission if one of the members, within 30 days of the judge's decision, directs that the decision be reviewed by the commission members. The commission is the final administrative authority to rule on a particular case, but its findings and orders can be subject to further review by the courts. (For further information, see "Contested Cases" later in this chapter.)

The headquarters of OSHRC is located at 1120 20th Street NW, Washington, DC 20036 (oshrc.gov).

NATIONAL INSTITUTE FOR OCCUPATIONAL SAFETY AND HEALTH

The National Institute for Occupational Safety and Health (NIOSH) was established within the Department of Health and Human Services under the provisions of the OSH Act. Administrative headquarters for NIOSH is within the Centers for Disease Control and Prevention (CDC) in Atlanta, Georgia. NIOSH is the principal federal agency engaged in research, education, and long-term training related to occupational safety and health.

The primary functions of NIOSH are (1) to develop and establish recommended occupational safety and health standards; (2) to conduct research experiments and demonstrations related to occupational safety and health; and (3) to develop educational programs to provide an adequate supply of qualified personnel to carry out the purposes of the OSH Act.

Research and Related Functions

Under the OSH Act, NIOSH is responsible for conducting research for new occupational safety and health standards. NIOSH develops criteria for establishing these standards and transmits the criteria to OSHA. OSHA is responsible for the final setting, promulgation, and enforcement of the standards.

Education and Training

NIOSH also has the responsibility to develop (1) education and training programs aimed at providing an adequate supply of qualified personnel to carry out the purpose of the OSH Act; and (2) informational programs on the importance and proper use of adequate safety and health equipment. The long-term approach to an adequate supply of training personnel in occupational safety and health is found in colleges and universities and other institutions in the private sector. NIOSH encourages such institutions, by contracts and grants, to expand their curricula in occupational medicine, occupational health nursing, industrial hygiene, and occupational safety engineering.

Employer and Employee Services

Of principal interest to individual employers and employees are the technical services offered by NIOSH. The five main services are provided on request to NIOSH's Division of Technical Services, 4676 Columbia Parkway, Cincinnati, OH 45226 (800-232-4636; cdc.gov/NIOSH). These services are as follows:

1. *hazard evaluation*—onsite evaluations of potentially toxic substances used or found on the job
2. *technical information*—detailed technical information concerning health or safety conditions at workplaces, such as the possible hazards of working with specific solvents, and guidelines for use of protective equipment
3. *incident prevention*—technical assistance for controlling on-the-job injuries, including the evaluation of special problems and recommendations for corrective action
4. *industrial hygiene*—technical assistance in the areas of engineering and industrial hygiene, including the evaluation of special health-related problems in the workplace and recommendations for control measures
5. *medical service*—assistance in solving occupational medical and nursing problems in the workplace, including assessment of existing medically related needs and development of recommended means for meeting such needs.

NIOSH and the Mine Safety and Health Administration (MSHA) test and approve personal sampler units for coal-mine dust and respiratory protective devices, including self-contained breathing apparatus; gas masks; supplied-air respirators; chemical-cartridge respirators; and dust, fume, and mist respirators.

NIOSH representatives, although not authorized to enforce the OSH Act, are authorized to make inspections and to question employers and employees in carrying out the duties assigned to the DHHS under the act. NIOSH has both warrant and subpoena power, if necessary, to obtain the information needed for its investigations. It may also request access to employee records. However, it must obtain the consent of employees or use methods that maintain the employee's right to privacy concerning information in the records.

INJURY AND ILLNESS DATA

The responsibility for conducting statistical surveys and establishing methods used to acquire injury and illness data is placed with the Bureau of Labor Statistics. Questions regarding record-keeping requirements and reporting procedures can be directed to any of the OSHA regional or area offices.

ADVISORY COMMITTEES

The OSH Act established a 12-member National Advisory Committee on Occupational Safety and Health (NACOSH) to advise, consult with, and make recommendations to the Secretaries of Labor and Health and Human Services with respect to the administration of the act. Eight members are designated by the Secretary of Labor and four by the Secretary of Health and Human Services. Members include representatives from management, labor, occupational safety and health professions, and the public.

MAJOR PROVISIONS OF THE OSH ACT

This section discusses the provisions of the OSH Act with which employers are expected to comply. The act represents one of the most far-reaching efforts in U.S. history to provide safer, healthier, and cleaner conditions, not only for employees but also for communities living near office and manufacturing facilities and for consumers who use the products and services of these firms.

EMPLOYER RIGHTS

Under the OSH Act, an employer has the following rights:
- to seek advice and offsite consultation as needed by writing, calling, or visiting the nearest OSHA office
- to request and receive proper identification of the OSHA compliance safety and health officer (CSHO) before inspection
- to be advised by the CSHO of the reason for an inspection
- to have an opening and closing conference with the CSHO
- to file a Notice of Contest with the OSHA area director within 15 working days after receiving a citation notice and proposed penalty
- to apply to OSHA for a temporary variance from a standard if unable to comply because needed materials, equipment, or personnel are not avail-

able to make necessary changes within the required time
- to take an active role in developing safety and health standards through participation in OSHA Standards Advisory Committees, through nationally recognized standards-setting organizations, and through evidence and views presented in writing or at hearings
- if a small-business employer, to apply for long-term loans, if a small business employer, through the Small Business Administration (SBA) to help bring the establishment into compliance, either before or after an OSHA inspection
- to be assured of the confidentiality of any trade secrets observed by an OSHA compliance officer.

ONSITE CONSULTATION

Congress has authorized, and OSHA now provides through a state agency or private contractors, free onsite consultation services for employers in every state. The onsite consultants help employers identify hazardous conditions and determine corrective measures.

The service is available on employer request. Priority is given to businesses with fewer than 150 employees. These firms are generally less able to afford private-sector consultation. OSHA assigns higher priority to companies that use employees in highly hazardous jobs.

The consultative visit consists of an opening conference, a walk-through of the company's facility, a closing conference, and a written summary of findings.

During the walk-through, the consultant tells the employer which OSHA standards apply to company operations and what they mean. The employer is informed of any apparent violations of those standards and, where possible, is given suggestions on how to reduce or eliminate the hazard.

Because employers, not employees, are subject to legal sanctions for violating OSHA standards, the employer determines to what extent employees or their representatives will participate in the visit. However, the consultant must be allowed to confer with individual employees during the walk-through in order to identify and judge the nature and extent of hazards. No citations or penalties are issued, and OSHA is not notified of results except when an employer refuses to correct a serious hazard. Follow-up actions are taken to ensure that appropriate corrections are made.

VOLUNTARY PROTECTION PROGRAMS

OSHA developed several Voluntary Protection Programs (VPPs), including Star and Merit status, which offer recognition to facilities that satisfy detailed criteria for quality of systems and performance. These programs were held illegal by a federal court but remain in place as a voluntary option for firms wishing to participate. Their purpose is to emphasize the importance of, encourage the improvement of, and recognize excellence in employer-provided, site-specific occupational safety and health programs. These programs must not only meet, but exceed, the standards. When employers apply and are accepted, they are removed from the regular inspection list (except for valid formal employee complaints, fatalities, or catastrophic events).

The VPP consists of three programs: a Star program for the most fully compliant sites, a Merit program for sites that aspire to achieve OSHA Star status, and a Demonstration Project program for sites where alternate means of compliance are being demonstrated. OSHA's 32-page application booklet cautions the applicant that this is a "major undertaking" with a comprehensive examination of the site. The benefit that OSHA offers, in recognition of the additional paperwork and meetings undertaken for the voluntary programs, is that OSHA general inspections (other than "for cause" incident investigations) will be scheduled once every three years for Star program participants. Star recognition indicates special efforts and commitment for the company that has undergone the inspection and demonstrated its qualifications.

The federal courts struck down OSHA's separate Cooperative Compliance Program in April 1999 because it had not been subject to public rulemaking procedures, required for new rules. The industry objections, asserting that new extra workplace reporting and compliance obligations were being imposed by OSHA on companies, were accepted by the appeals court. OSHA did not choose to appeal further; the agency stated that it would continue to target high-hazard workplaces for inspections based on their record of injuries and illnesses.

EMPLOYEE RIGHTS

Although the employee has the legal duty to comply with all the standards and regulations issued under the OSH Act, many employee rights are also incorporated into the act. Because these rights may affect labor relations as well as labor negotiations, employers should also be aware of the employee rights contained in the act. These rights fall into three main areas related to (1) standards; (2) access to information; and (3) enforcement. With respect to standards:

1. Employees may ask OSHA to begin proceedings for adoption of a new standard or to amend or revoke an existing one.
2. Employees may submit written data or comments on proposed standards and may appear as an interested party at any hearing held by OSHA.
3. Employees may file written objections to a proposed federal standard and/or appeal the final decision of OSHA.

4. Employees must be informed when an employer applies for a variance of a promulgated standard.

5. Employees must be given the opportunity to participate in a variance hearing as an interested party and have the right to appeal OSHA's final decision.

With respect to access to information:

1. Employees have the right to information from the employer regarding employee protection and obligations under the act and to review appropriate OSHA standards, rules, regulations, and requirements, which the employer should have available at the workplace.

2. Employees whose jobs may have exposed them to chemicals, radiation, or other hazardous substances have an OSHA-protected right to information about the risks, precautions, and safe use of the substances. Three methods are prescribed in OSHA's Hazard Communication Standard: training must be given and records kept, Material Safety Data Sheets (MSDSs) must be available to workers concerning chemicals present in the workplace, and labels must be adequate to advise workers about container contents and safe use.

3. If employees are exposed to harmful materials in excess of levels set by the standards, the affected employees must be so informed by the employer, who must also tell them what corrective action is being taken.

4. If an OSHA inspector finds an imminent hazard during an inspection, the workers and the employer must be told. If the employer refuses to act, OSHA may seek a court order to protect workers against the danger.

5. On request, employees must be given access to their medical records and history of exposure to toxic materials or harmful physical agents that must be monitored or measured and recorded. Safety Data Sheets must be immediately available or accessible.

6. If a standard requires monitoring or measuring hazardous materials or harmful physical agents, employees must be given the opportunity to observe such monitoring or measuring.

7. Employees have the right of access to (1) the list of toxic materials published by NIOSH; (2) criteria developed by NIOSH describing the effects of toxic materials or harmful physical agents; and (3) industrywide studies conducted by NIOSH regarding the effects of chronic low-level exposure to hazardous materials.

8. On written request to NIOSH, employees have the right to obtain the determination of whether a substance found or used in the establishment is harmful.

9. On request, employees must be allowed to review the Log and Summary of Work-Related Injuries and Illnesses (OSHA Forms 300 and 300A) at a reasonable time and in a reasonable manner.

With respect to enforcement:

1. Employees have the right to confer in private with the CSHO and to respond to questions from the CSHO during an inspection of an establishment.

2. An authorized employee representative must be given an opportunity to accompany the compliance officer during an inspection to aid in such inspection. (This is commonly known as the "walkaround" provision.) Also, an authorized employee has the right to participate in the opening and closing conferences during the inspection.

3. An employee has the right to make a written request to OSHA for a complaint inspection if the employee believes that a violation of a standard threatens physical harm; the employee has the right to request that OSHA keep his or her identity confidential.

4. An employee who believes that a violation of the act has occurred has the right to notify OSHA or a compliance officer in writing of the alleged violation, either before or during an inspection of the establishment.

5. If OSHA denies an employee's request for a special inspection, the agency must notify the employee in writing that the complaint was not valid and explain the reasons for this decision. The employee has the right to object to such a decision and may request a hearing by OSHA.

6. If a written complaint concerning an alleged violation is submitted to OSHA and the compliance officer responding to the complaint fails to cite the employer for the alleged violation, OSHA must furnish the employee or an authorized employee representative with a written statement explaining the reasons for its final disposition.

7. If OSHA cites an employer for a violation, employees have the right to review a copy of the citation, which must be posted by the employer at or near the place where the violation occurred. If "systemwide" agreements are made, all locations will be notified.

8. An employee has the right to appear as an interested party or to be called as a witness in a contested enforcement matter before OSHRC.

9. If OSHA arbitrarily or capriciously fails to seek relief to counteract an imminent danger and an employee is injured as a result, that employee has the right to bring action against OSHA for relief as may be appropriate.

10. An employee has the right to file a complaint with OSHA within 30 days if the employee believes that he or she has been discriminated against as a result of asserting employee rights under the act.

11. An employee has the right to contest the abatement period fixed in the citation issued to the employer. This can be done by notifying the OSHA Area Director who issued the citation within 15 working days of the issuance of the citation.

THE OSHA POSTER

The OSHA poster (OSHA 3165) must be prominently displayed in a conspicuous place in the work environment where notices to employees are customarily posted. The poster informs employees of their rights and responsibilities under the act.

OCCUPATIONAL SAFETY AND HEALTH STANDARDS

The Act authorizes OSHA to promulgate, modify, or revoke occupational safety and health standards. The rules of procedure for promulgating, modifying, or revoking standards are spelled out in 29 CFR 1911. The current requirements are available at all OSHA area and regional offices and printed annually in the *Code of Federal Regulations*. OSHA is responsible for promulgating legally enforceable standards that may require conditions or the adoption or use of practices, means, methods, or processes that are reasonably necessary and appropriate to protect employees on the job. Employers are responsible for becoming familiar with the standards applicable to their firms and ensuring that employees have and use personal protective equipment required for safety. In addition, employers are responsible for complying with the act's general-duty clause. The *Code of Federal Regulations*, Title 29, is available online at gpoaccess.gov. Standards contained in Part 1910 apply to general industry, while those contained in Part 1926 apply to construction. Standards that apply to ship repairing, shipbuilding, shipbreaking, and longshoring are contained in Parts 1915 through 1918, respectively. Agricultural standards are contained in Part 1928. As new equipment, methods, and materials are developed, these standards are updated via modification.

OSHA standards incorporate by reference certain other standards adopted by industry organizations. Standards incorporated by reference in whole or in part include those adopted by the following organizations:

- American Conference of Governmental Industrial Hygienists
- American National Standards Institute
- American Petroleum Institute
- American Society of Agricultural Engineers
- American Society of Mechanical Engineers
- American Society for Testing and Materials
- American Welding Society
- Compressed Gas Association

- Crane Manufacturers Association of America
- The Fertilizer Institute
- Institute of Makers of Explosives
- National Electrical Manufacturers Association
- National Fire Protection Association
- National Institute for Occupational Safety and Health
- National Plant Food Institute
- Society of Automotive Engineers
- Underwriters Laboratories Inc.
- U.S. Department of Commerce
- U.S. Public Health Service.

OSHA has the authority to promulgate emergency temporary standards in situations in which employees are exposed to grave danger. Emergency temporary standards can take effect immediately on publication in the *Federal Register*. They will remain in effect until superseded by a standard promulgated under procedures described in the act. The law requires OSHA to develop a permanent standard no later than 6 months after publication of the emergency temporary standard. Any person adversely affected by any standard issued by OSHA has the right to challenge its validity by petitioning the U.S. Court of Appeals within 60 days after its promulgation.

INPUT FROM THE PRIVATE SECTOR

Occupational safety and health standards promulgated by OSHA will never cover every conceivable hazardous condition that could exist in any workplace. Nevertheless, new standards and modification of existing standards are of significant interest to employers and employees alike. Industry organizations along with individuals and employee organizations need to express their views in two ways; (1) by responding to OSHA's advance notice of proposed rulemaking, which usually calls for information on which to base proposed standards; and (2) by responding to OSHA's proposed standards, because most of the expertise and the technical competence lies within the private sector. To do less means that industry and employees are willing to let the standards-development process rest in the hands of OSHA.

Additional sources that OSHA uses to revise existing occupational safety and health standards or develop new ones are NIOSH criteria documents and standards advisory committees. These committees are appointed by the Secretary of Labor.

In order to promulgate, revise, or modify a standard, OSHA must first publish in the *Federal Register* a notice of any proposed rule that will adopt, modify, or revoke any standard and invite interested persons to submit their views on the proposed rule. The notice must include the terms of the new standard and provide an interval of at least 30 days (usually 60 days or more) from the date of publication for interested persons to respond. These persons may file objections to the rule and are entitled to a hearing on their objections if they request that one be held. However, they must specify the parts of the proposed rule to which they object and the grounds for such objection. If a hearing is requested, OSHA must hold one. Based on (1) the need for control of an exposure to an occupational injury or illness and (2) the reasonableness, effectiveness, and feasibility of the control measures required, OSHA may either issue a rule promulgating an additional standard or modify or revoke an existing standard.

VARIANCES FROM STANDARDS

On some occasions, for various reasons, standards cannot be met. In other cases, the protection already afforded by an employer to employees is equal or superior to the protection that would be provided if the standard were strictly followed. The OSH Act provides an avenue of relief from these situations by empowering OSHA to grant variances from the standards, provided that doing so would not degrade the purpose of the act. The detailed "Rules of Practice for Variances, Limitations, Variations, Tolerances, and Exemptions" are codified in 29 CFR 1905.11(b).

OSHA can grant two types of variances—temporary and permanent. Temporary variances are generally concerned with compliance with new standards. Employers may apply for an order granting a temporary variance if they can establish that (1) they cannot comply with the applicable standard because they do not have the personnel, equipment, or time to construct or alter facilities; (2) they are taking all available steps to protect employees against exposure covered by the standard; and (3) their own programs will effect compliance with the standard as soon as possible.

Employers may also apply for a permanent variance from a standard. Variance orders can be granted if OSHA finds that the employer has demonstrated, by a preponderance of evidence, that it will provide a place of employment as safe and healthful as the one that would exist if it complied with the standards.

An employer may request an interim order permitting either kind of variance until the formal application can be processed. Again, the request for an interim order must contain statements of fact or arguments why such interim order should be granted. If the request is denied, the applicant will be notified promptly and informed of the reasons for the decision. If the order is granted, all concerned parties will be informed and the terms of the order will be published in the *Federal Register*. In such cases, the employer must inform the affected employees about the interim order in the same manner used to inform them of the variance application.

Upon filing an employer's application for a variance, OSHA will publish a notice of such filing in the *Federal Register* and invite written data, views, and arguments regarding the application. Those affected by the petition may request a hearing. After review of all the facts, including those presented during the hearing, OSHA will publish its decision regarding the application in the *Federal Register*.

Beginning in the early 1980s, OSHA authorized its Regional Administrators to "interpret" standards in a way that essentially became variances for individual employers. Such interpretations had no effect on other employers and reflected specific conditions at a particular workplace. OSHA has also been issuing "clarifications" of standards for employers asking for deviation from standards. While granting less than 10% of employers' requests for variances since enforcement began, OSHA has issued about eight times as many clarifications.

RECORD-KEEPING REQUIREMENTS

Most employers covered by the OSH Act are required to maintain company records of all occupational injuries and illnesses. Regulations describing how to properly record and report injuries and illnesses are codified in 29 CFR 1904. Such records consist of the following:

- a log and summary of occupational injuries and illnesses, OSHA Form 200
- a supplementary record of each occupational injury or illness, OSHA Form 101 (or state form)
- an annual summary of the total number of occupational injuries and illnesses. This must be posted by February 1 of the following year and remain posted until March 1 (Figure 2–1).

For details concerning recording and reporting occupational injuries and illnesses, see Chapter 4, Injury and Illness Record Keeping, Incidence Rates, and Analysis. Current OSHA forms for record keeping are available from OSHA area and regional offices. In states with an OSHA-approved plan, employers should check for any additional record-keeping requirements.

OSHA has made an effort to relieve small businesses from many burdensome record-keeping requirements. As a

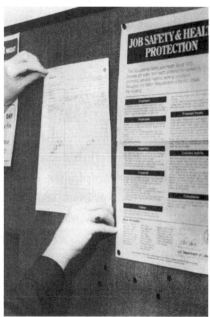

Figure 2–1. OSHA poster, "Job Safety and Health Protection," must be posted conspicuously at every plant, job site, or other facility.

result, most employers that had no more than 10 employees at any time during the calendar year immediately preceding the current calendar year need not comply with the record-keeping requirements. However, any employer, regardless of size, can be notified in writing by OSHA or BLS that the organization has been selected to participate in a statistical survey of occupational injuries and illnesses. The employer will then be required to maintain a log and summary and to make reports for the time specified in the notice. Further, no employer is relieved of the obligation to report any fatalities or multiple-hospitalization incidents to the nearest OSHA area office.

In 1996, most employers with 10 or fewer employees that engaged in retail trade, finance, insurance, real estate, and services were also exempted from most of the record-keeping requirements.

REPORTING REQUIREMENTS

Within 8 hours after an unintentional injury occurs that is fatal to one or more employees or that results in the inpatient hospitalization of three or more employees, the employer must report the incident either orally or in writing to the nearest Area Director of OSHA. In states with approved state plans, the report must be made to the state agency that has enforcement responsibilities for occupational safety and health. If an oral report is made, it shall always be followed with a confirming letter written the same day. The report must relate the circumstances of the incident, the number of fatalities, and the extent of any injuries.

WORKPLACE INSPECTION

Before the U.S. Supreme Court decision on the controversial *Barlow* case—*Marshall v Barlow's Inc.*, 436 U.S. 307 (1978)—the DOL's compliance safety and health officers could enter, at any reasonable time and without delay, any establishment covered by the OSH Act to inspect the premises and all its facilities. (See 29 CFR 1903.) However, since the Barlow decision, the OSHA compliance officer must obtain an inspection warrant and present it if the employer requires a warrant to permit an inspection.

Most employers readily consent to inspection and do not require an OSHA inspector to obtain a search warrant. OSHA's entitlement to a warrant does not depend on demonstrating probable cause to believe that conditions on the premises violate the OSHA regulations. Rather, the agency merely has to show that reasonable legislative or administrative standards for conducting an inspection have been satisfied. An organization needs to determine, well in advance, whether an inspection warrant will be requested. As a general rule, it is not advisable for the employer to refuse entry to a CSHO who has no inspection warrant. Such action only delays an inspection and increases the officer's suspicion about working conditions. In many of these cases, OSHA can obtain an inspection warrant within 48 hours; however, generally a longer period is involved.

The OSH Act authorizes an employer representative as well as an authorized employee representative, if one is designated, to accompany the CSHO during the official inspection of the premises and all its facilities. Employee representatives also have the right to participate in both the opening and closing conferences.

Usually the authorized employee representative is the union steward or the chairman of the employee safety committee. Occasionally there may be no authorized employee representative, especially in nonunion establishments. In this instance, the CSHO will select employees at random and confer with them on matters of safety and health and work conditions.

An employer should not refuse to compensate employees for the time spent participating in an inspection tour and for related activities such as attending the opening and closing conferences.

Inspection Priorities

OSHA has established priorities for assignment of staff and resources. The priorities are as follows:

1. *Investigation of imminent dangers*—Allegations of an imminent-danger situation ordinarily trigger an inspection within 24 hours of notification.
2. *Catastrophic and fatal*—Incidents will be investigated if they include any one of the following:
   ○ one or more fatalities
   ○ three or more employees hospitalized as inpatients
   ○ significant publicity and property damage
   ○ issuance of specific instructions for investigations in connection with a national office special program.
3. *Investigations of employee complaints*—Highest priority is given to complaints that allege an imminent-danger situation. Complaints reporting a "serious" situation are given high priority. If time and resources allow, the CSHO may attempt to inspect the entire workplace and not just the condition reported in the complaint, particularly if a high-hazard industry is involved.
4. *Programmed high-hazard inspections*—Industries are selected for inspection based on their death, injury, and illness incidence rates; employee exposure to toxic substances; and national and local inspection scheduling programs.

5. *Reinspections*—Establishments cited for alleged serious violations may be reinspected to determine whether the hazards have been abated, particularly if the employer does not provide adequate abatement information to OSHA.

General Inspection Procedures

The primary responsibility of the 1,100 OSHA inspectors and their state counterparts is to conduct an effective inspection to determine whether employers and employees are in compliance with the requirements of the standards, rules, and regulations promulgated under the OSH Act. OSHA inspections are almost always conducted without prior notice.

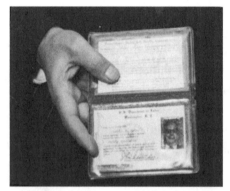

Figure 2–2. Bona fide OSHA compliance officers are equipped with official identification as shown here. The credentials are signed by the current or former Assistant Secretary of Labor for occupational safety and health. If in doubt about the validity of the credentials, the employer should contact the nearest OSHA area office, determine whether the area office has scheduled an inspection at the establishment in question, and verify the serial number on the credentials.

To enter an establishment, the CSHO presents proper credentials to a guard, receptionist, or other person acting in such a capacity. Employers should always insist on seeing and checking the CSHO's credentials carefully before allowing the individual to enter their establishment for the purpose of an inspection (Figure 2–2). Anyone who tries to collect a penalty or promotes the sale of a product or service is not a CSHO.

The CSHO will usually ask to meet with an appropriate employer representative. It is recommended that employers furnish written instructions to security, the receptionist, and other affected personnel regarding the CSHO's right of entry and initial treatment, whom should be notified, and to whom and where the CSHO should be directed to avoid undue delay.

Opening Conference

The CSHO will conduct a joint opening conference with employer and employee representatives. Where it is not practical to hold a joint conference, separate conferences are to be held for employer representatives. If there is no employee representative, then a joint conference is not necessary. When separate conferences are held, a written summary of each conference should be made and the summary provided on request to employer and employee representatives.

Because the CSHO will want to talk with the firm's safety personnel, these employees should participate in the opening conference. The employer representative who accompanies the CSHO during the inspection should also participate in the opening conference.

At the opening conference, the CSHO will do the following:

- inform the employer that the purpose of the officer's visit is to investigate whether the establishment, procedures, operations, and equipment are in compliance with OSH Act requirements
- give the employer copies of the act, standards, regulations, and promotional materials, as necessary
- outline in general terms:
  - the scope of the inspection
  - the records the officer wants to review
  - the officer's obligation to confer with employees
  - the physical inspection of the workplace
  - the closing conference
- if applicable, furnish the employer with a copy of any complaint(s) that is the basis for the inspection
- answer questions from those attending the conference.

In the opening conference, the employer representative should find out which areas of the establishment the CSHO wishes to inspect. In some cases the inspection may include areas of the facility in which trade secrets are maintained. If this is the case, the employer representative should orally request confidential treatment of all information obtained from such areas. The employer should follow up with a trade-secret letter to the CSHO requesting the officer to keep information identified in the letter strictly confidential. The CSHO should not discuss any part of this information or provide copies to any person not authorized by law to receive the data without prior written consent of the employer.

During the course of the opening conference, the CSHO may ask to review company records. The CSHO is authorized to review only the records required to be maintained by the OSH Act, regulations, and standards. In general, these records include the "OSHA Injury and Illness Log and Summary" [OSHA Form 300, available at www.osha.gov/recordkeeping/RKforms.html and the "Supplemental Record of Occupational Injuries and Illnesses" (OSHA Form 301)]. Such records should be made readily available to the OSHA inspector. Prompt, thorough, and complete cooperation in the inspection will always make a good impression.

The CSHO may request information about the employer's current safety and health program in order to evaluate it. Naturally, a comprehensive safety and health program that shows evidence of effective incident prevention will be impressive to all concerned.

The CSHO will also ask the employer whether workers of another employer (e.g., a maintenance or remodeling contractor) are working in or on the establishment. If so, the CSHO will give the authorized representative of those employees a reasonable opportunity to participate in the inspection of their work areas.

During the conference, the CSHO will meet with the employee's authorized representative and explain the person's rights. Generally, the representative will be an employee of the establishment inspected. However, the CSHO may judge that good cause has been shown to require a third party (such as an industrial hygienist or safety consultant) who is not an employee but is still an authorized employee representative to accompany the CSHO on the inspection to ensure an effective and thorough job. The final decision on this matter will rest with the CSHO.

The employer is not permitted to designate the employee representative. Employee representatives may change as the inspection process moves from department to department. The CSHO may refuse to allow any person to accompany him or her whose conduct interferes with a full, orderly inspection. If there is no authorized employee representative, the CSHO will consult with a reasonable number of employees concerning matters of safety and health in the workplace during the course of the inspection.

Inspection of Facilities

The CSHO will have the necessary instruments for checking items such as noise levels, certain air contaminants and toxic substances, and electrical grounding. During the course of inspection, the CSHO will note and usually record any apparent violation of the standards, including its location, and any comments regarding the violation. The officer will do the same for any apparent violation of the general-duty clause. These notes will serve as a basis for the Area Director's citations or proposed penalties. For these reasons, the employer representative should find out what apparent violations the CSHO has detected during the actual inspection of the facilities. The employer representative also should take the same notes as the CSHO during the inspection, including names of employees interviewed, so that the employer will have the same information as the CSHO.

The CSHO is only required to record apparent violations and is not required to present a solution or method of correcting, minimizing, or eliminating the violation. OSHA, however, will respond to requests for technical information regarding compliance with given standards. In such cases, the employer is urged to contact the regional or area office.

During the course of an inspection, the CSHO may receive a complaint from an employee regarding a condition alleged to be in violation of an applicable standard. The CSHO, even though the complaint is brought via an informal process, will normally inspect for the alleged violation.

In the course of a normal inspection, the CSHO may make some preliminary judgments regarding environmental conditions affecting occupational health. In such cases, the officer will generally use direct-reading instruments. Should this occur, and if proper instrumentation is available, it would be prudent for the employer to have qualified personnel at the establishment make duplicate tests in the same area at the same time under the same conditions. In addition, the employer representative should again take careful notes on the CSHO's methods as well as the results. If the inspection indicates a need for further investigation by an industrial hygienist, the CSHO will notify the Area Director, who may assign a qualified industrial hygienist to investigate further. If a laboratory analysis is required, samples will be sent to OSHA's laboratory in Salt Lake City and the results will be reported back to the Area Director. Initial inspections may also be originated by industrial hygienists with subsequent referrals to a CSHO. Photos and videos may be taken by the CSHO to document apparent violations.

Closing Conference

Upon completion of the inspection, the CSHO will hold a joint closing conference with employee representatives and representatives of the employer. If a joint conference is not possible, separate conferences will be held. Again, the employer's safety personnel should be present at the closing conference. At this time the CSHO will advise the employer and employee representatives of all conditions and practices that may constitute an apparent safety or health violation. The officer should also indicate the applicable section or sections of the standards that may have been violated.

The CSHO will normally advise that citations may be issued for alleged violations and that penalties may be proposed for each violation. The authority for issuing citations and proposed penalties, however, rests with the Area Director or the director's representative.

The employer will also be informed that the citations will fix a reasonable time for abatement of the violations alleged. The CSHO will attempt to obtain from the employer a reasonable estimate of the time required to control or eliminate the alleged violation. The officer will take such estimates into consideration when recommending a time for abatement. Although the employer is not required to do so, it may be advantageous to give the officer copies of any correspondence or orders concerning equipment to achieve compliance. This act of good faith may help establish a reasonable abatement period and may reduce the proposed penalty. The CSHO should also explain the appeal procedures with respect to any citation or any notice of a proposed penalty.

Informal Post-Inspection Conferences

Issues raised by inspections, citations, proposed penalties, or notice of intent to contest may be discussed at the request of an affected employer, employee, or employee representative at an informal conference held by the Area Director or his or her representative. Whenever the employer or employee representatives request an informal conference, both parties shall be afforded the opportunity to participate fully.

Follow-Up Inspections

Follow-up inspections will always be conducted for situations involving imminent danger and may be conducted where citations have been issued for serious, repeated, or willful violations. Follow-up inspections will be ordered at the discretion of the Area Director.

The follow-up inspection should be limited to verifying compliance of the conditions alleged to be in violation. The follow-up inspection is conducted with all of the usual formality of the original inspection, including the opening and closing conferences and the walkaround rights of the employer and employee representative.

VIOLATIONS

In addition to the general-duty clause, OSH Act occupational safety and health standards are used to determine alleged violations. There are five categories of violations: willful, serious, repeat, other than serious, and *de minimis* (very minor).

Willful Violations

The following definitions and procedures apply whenever the CSHO suspects that a willful violation may exist:

- A willful violation exists under the act when the evidence shows either an intentional violation of the act or plain indifference to its requirements.
- The violation need not be committed with a bad purpose or an evil intent to be deemed "willful." It is sufficient that the violation was deliberate, voluntary, or intentional as distinguished from inadvertent, accidental, or ordinarily negligent.
- The determination of whether to issue a citation for a willful or repeated violation will frequently raise difficult issues of law and policy and will require the evaluation of complex factual situations. Accordingly, a citation for a willful violation shall not be issued without consultation with the Regional Administrator, who shall, as appropriate, discuss the matter with the Regional Solicitor. A repeat violation is a subsequent violation of the same or a similar standard.

Serious Violations

A serious violation involves hazardous conditions that could cause death or serious physical harm to employees, and conditions that the employer knew, or should have known, existed.

OSHA's *Field Operations Manual* (Chapter IV, Violations) sets forth four steps for the CSHO to follow to determine whether a violation is serious or other than serious. Section 17(k) of the act provides that a serious violation shall be deemed to exist in a place of employment if there is a substantial probability that death or serious physical harm could result from a condition that exists, or from one or more practices, means, methods, operations, or processes that have been adopted or are in use, in such place of employment unless the employer did not, and could not with the exercise of reasonable diligence, know of the presence of the violation.

The CSHO shall take four steps to determine that a violation is serious. The first three steps determine whether there is a substantial probability that death or serious physical harm could result from an incident or exposure relating to the violative condition. (The probability that an incident or illness will occur is not to be considered in determining whether a violation is serious.) The fourth step determines whether the employer knew or could have known of the violation.

Apparent violations of the general-duty clause shall also be evaluated on the basis of these steps to ensure that they represent serious violations. The four elements the CSHO shall consider are as follows:

Step 1—the type of accident or health hazard exposure that the violated standard or the general-duty clause is designed to prevent.

Step 2—the type of injury or illness that could reasonably be expected to result from the type of accident or health hazard exposure identified in Step 1.

Step 3—whether the types of injury or illness identified in Step 2 could include death or a form of serious physical harm. Impairment of the body in which part of the body is made functionally useless or is substantially reduced in efficiency on or off the job. Such impairment may be permanent or temporary, chronic or acute. Injuries involving such impairment would usually require treatment by a medical doctor.

Step 4—whether the employer knew, or with the exercise of reasonable diligence could have known, of the presence of the hazardous condition. The knowledge requirement is met if it is determined that the employer actually knew of the hazardous condition that constituted the apparent violation. As a general rule, if the CSHO was able to discover a hazardous condition, it can be presumed that the employer could have discovered the same condition through the exercise of reasonable diligence.

Repeated Violations

An employer may be cited for a repeated violation if that employer has been cited previously for a substantially similar condition and the citation has become a final order.

Other-than-Serious Violations

This type of violation shall be cited in situations in which the injury or illness that would be most likely to result from a hazardous condition would probably not cause death or serious physical harm but would have a direct and immediate relationship to the safety and health of employees.

De Minimis *Violations*

De minimis violations refer to conditions that represent no immediate or direct threat to safety or health. *De minimis* is short for the legal maxim *De minimis non curat lex*, "The law does not concern itself with trifles." No written document is issued for such violations.

Identical Standard

Generally, similar conditions can be demonstrated by showing that in both situations the identical standard was violated.

Different Standards

In some circumstances, similar conditions can be demonstrated when different standards are violated.

CITATIONS

An investigation or inspection may reveal a condition that is alleged to be in violation of the standards or the general-duty clause. In such instances, the employer may be issued a written citation that describes the specific nature of the alleged violation, cites the standard allegedly violated, and fixes a time for abatement. The employer must prominently post each citation, or a copy thereof, at or near the place where the alleged violation occurred. All citations are issued by the Area Director or a designee and will be sent to the employer by certified mail.

A "Citation for Serious Violation" will be prepared to cover violations that fall into the "serious" category. This type of violation must be assessed a monetary penalty.

A citation used for other-than-serious violations may or may not carry a monetary penalty. A citation may be issued to the employer for employee actions that violate the safety and health standards (either serious or other).

A verbal notice, in lieu of a citation, is issued for *de minimis* violations that have no direct relationship to safety and health.

If an inspection has been initiated in response to an employee complaint, the employee or authorized employee representative may request an informal review of any decision not to issue a citation. However, employees may not contest citations, amendments to citations, penalties, or lack of penalties. Employees may contest the time for abatement of a hazardous condition specified in a citation. They also may contest an employer's *PMA*, which requests an extension of the abatement period. Employees must contest the PMA within 10 working days of its posting or within 10 working days after an authorized employee representative has received a copy.

Within 15 working days after the employer receives the citation, an employer may submit a written objection to the citation to OSHA. The OSHA Area Director then forwards the objection to OSHRC. Employees may request an informal conference with OSHA to discuss any issues raised by an inspection, citation, notice of proposed penalty, or employer's notice of intention to contest.

Upon receiving a citation, the employer must correct the cited hazard by the prescribed date. However, factors beyond the employer's reasonable control may prevent the work from being completed on time. In such a situation, the employer who has made a good-faith effort to comply may file for a PMA date.

The written petition should specify (1) all steps the employer took to achieve compliance; (2) the additional time needed to complete the work; (3) reasons additional time is needed; (4) all temporary steps being taken to safeguard employees against the cited hazard during the intervening period, (5) the fact that a copy of the PMA was posted prominently or at least near each place where a violation occurred; and (6) the employee representative (if there is one) who received a copy of the petition.

PENALTIES

Penalties may range to $7,000 for serious, other-than-serious, failure to abate (daily penalty amount), and posting violations and to $70,000 for repeated or willful violations. Willful violation penalties are no less than $5,000. Penalties are based on gravity of violation, good faith, size, and history of the employer. A "failure to abate" penalty may be a daily penalty for each day of failure to correct a violation past the stated abatement date.

EGREGIOUS POLICY

If OSHA considers the apparent violations flagrant, the agency, instead of grouping similar violations, may propose a separate penalty for each instance or employee exposed.

The factors used to determine the situation include the following:

- the number of worker fatalities, a worksite catastrophe, or a large number of similar injuries or illnesses
- a violation that results in high rates of injuries or illnesses
- whether the organization has an extreme history of workplace violations
- whether the employer seriously disregarded workplace safety and health responsibilities
- a large number of violations found at the worksite.

States can adopt their own penalty structure, which may even exceed the one set up under OSHA.

CONTESTED CASES

An employer has the right to contest any OSHA action. The employer may contest one or more of the following: a citation, a proposed penalty, a notice of failure to correct a violation, or the time allotted for abatement of an alleged violation. OSH Act regulations that cover procedures for contesting cases are codified in 29 CFR 2200. On the other hand, an employee or authorized employee representative may contest only the time allotted for an abatement of an alleged violation.

Subsequent to initiating a formal contest of a citation, employers should request an informal conference with the Area Director or the Area Director's representative. Many times, such informal sessions will resolve questions and issues, thus avoiding the formal contested case proceedings. The informal conference should occur within 15 working days of receipt of the violation and will not extend the Notice of Intent to Contest period. If the 15-day time period is exceeded, the citation will become a final order.

The informal conference will be attended by representatives from OSHA, the company, and the company's union representatives (if applicable). Conference members may be asked to obtain a more complete explanation of the violation cited by OSHA, to obtain an understanding of the specific standards cited in the violation, or to negotiate and enter into an informal settlement agreement. Other areas that may be discussed include the company's difficulty in meeting the abatement dates, employer defenses, problems concerning employee safety practices, and obtaining answers to any questions that the employer may bring to the table. The informal conference provides an opportunity for both sides to resolve the disputed citation and associated penalties in a relatively cordial atmosphere and is specifically intended to avoid the need for a more formal contest of the citation. The choice to contest the citation elevates the process to the OSHRC.

However, the informal conference may fail to resolve the dispute between OSHA and the employer. If the employer elects to contest the case, affected employees or the authorized employee representative are automatically deemed to be parties to the proceeding. In contesting an OSHA action, the employer must comply with the following rules that apply to a specific case:

1. The employer must notify the Area Office that initiated the action that the employer is contesting the case. This must be done within 15 working days after receiving OSHA's notice of proposed penalty; it should be sent by certified mail. If the employer does not contest within the required 15 working days, the citation and proposed assessment of penalties are deemed to be a final order of OSHRC and are not subject to review by any court or agency. As a result, the alleged violation must be corrected within the abatement period specified in the citation.

2. If any of the employees working at the site where the alleged violation exists are union members, a copy of the notice of contest must be served upon their union.

3. If employees who work on the site are not represented by a union, a copy of the notice of contest must either be posted at a place where the employees will see it or be served upon them personally.

4. The notice of contest must also list the names and addresses of parties who have been personally served a notice, or, if such notice is posted, it must contain the address of the posted location.

5. In some cases, the employees at the site of the alleged violation are not represented by a union and have not been personally served with a copy of the notice to contest. If so, posted copies must specifically advise the unrepresented employees that they may not be able to assert their status as parties to the case if they fail to properly identify themselves to the OSHRC or to the Hearing Examiner before the hearing begins or when it first opens.

6. There is no specific form for the notice of contest. However, such notice should clearly identify what is being contested—the citation, the proposed penalty, the notice of failure to correct a violation, or the time allowed for abatement—for each alleged violation or combination of alleged violations.

If the employer contests an alleged violation in good faith, and not solely for delay or variance of penalties, the abatement period does not begin until OSHRC enters the final order. When a notice of contest is received by an Area Director from an employer, an employee, or an authorized employee representative, the Director will file with OSHRC the notice of contest and all contested citations, notice of proposed penalties, or notice of failure to abate.

Ultimately, an administrative law judge (ALJ) will be assigned to the case and will conduct a hearing at a location reasonably convenient to those concerned. At the hearing, OSHA presents its case and is subject to a cross-examination by other parties. The party contesting then presents its case and is also subject to a cross-examination by other parties. Affected employees or an authorized employee representative may participate in the hearings. The decision by the ALJ will be based only on what is in the record. Therefore, if statements go unchallenged, they will be assumed to be fact.

After the hearings are completed, the ALJ will submit the record and a report with decisions to OSHRC. If no commissioner orders a review of an ALJ's decisions, they will stand as OSHRC's decision. If any commissioner orders a review of the case, the commission itself must render a decision to affirm, modify, or vacate the judge's decision. The commission's orders become final 15 days after issuance, unless stayed by a court order.

Any person adversely affected or aggrieved by an order of the commission may obtain a review of the order in the U.S. Court of Appeals. However, the person must seek a review within 60 days of the order's issuance.

SMALL-BUSINESS LOANS

The OSH Act enables small businesses to obtain economic assistance for health- and safety-related issues. It amends the Small Business Act to provide for financial assistance to small firms that must make changes to comply with the standards promulgated under the OSH Act or by a state under a state plan. Before approving any assistance, the Small Business Administration (SBA) must first determine that the small firm is likely to suffer substantial economic injury without financial help.

An employer can apply for a loan under one of two procedures: (1) before federal or state inspection in order to come into compliance or (2) after federal or state inspection to correct alleged violations.

When an employer has not been inspected and requests a loan to bring the establishment into compliance before an inspection, the employer must submit the following to the SBA:
- a statement of the conditions to be corrected
- a reference to the OSHA standards that require the employer to make corrections
- a statement of the firm's financial condition showing that a loan is needed.

The employer should submit this information to the nearest SBA field office along with any background material. The SBA will then refer the application to the appropriate OSHA Regional Office, Office of Technical Support. The OSHA Regional Office will review the application and advise SBA whether the employer is required to correct the described conditions in order to come into compliance and whether the proposed use of funds will accomplish the needed corrections. OSHA will initiate direct contact with the applicant only after clearance with the SBA.

If the employer is making an application after an inspection to correct alleged violations, the procedure is the same as before inspection, except that the applicant also must furnish the SBA with a copy of the OSHA citation(s). The SBA then refers the application to the OSHA Area Office that conducted the inspection. That office will notify the SBA whether the proposed use of loan funds will adequately correct cited violations.

Forms for loan applications may be obtained from any SBA field office. In some instances, private lending institutions will be able to provide the form for SBA/bank participation loans.

FEDERAL–STATE RELATIONSHIPS

The OSH Act encourages states to assume the fullest responsibility for administering and enforcing their own occupational safety and health laws. However, in order to assume this responsibility, such states must submit a state plan to OSHA for approval. If such a plan satisfies designated conditions and criteria, OSHA must approve the plan. The regulations pertaining to state plans for the development and enforcement of state standards are codified in 29 CFR 1902. The states and possessions listed in Figure 2–3 have approved plans.

The basic criterion for approval of state plans is that the plan must be "at least as effective as" the federal program. It was not Congress's intent to require that state programs be a mirror image of the federal program. Congress believed that rules for developing state plans should be flexible to allow consideration of local problems, conditions, and resources. The act provides for funding up to half the costs of the implementation of the state program.

A state plan must include any occupational safety and health issue (industrial, occupational, or hazard group) for which a corresponding federal standard has been promulgated. A state plan cannot be less stringent, but it may include subjects not covered in the federal standards. However, state plans that do not include issues covered by the federal program effectively surrender such issues to OSHA. For example, a state plan may cover all industry except

Alaska Department of Labor
PO Box 111149
Juneau, AK 99811
907-465-2700

Industrial Commission of Arizona
800 West Washington
Phoenix, AZ 85007
602-542-4661

California Department of Industrial Relations
455 Golden Gate Ave., San Francisco, CA 94102
415-972-8846

Connecticut Department of Labor
200 Folly Brook Boulevard
Wethersfield, CT 06109
860-263-6000

Hawaii Department of Labor and Industrial Relations
830 Punchbowl Street
Honolulu, HI 96813
808-586-8842

Indiana Department of Labor
402 West Washington, Room W-195
Indianapolis, IN 46204
317-232-2655

Iowa Division of Labor Services
1000 East Grand Avenue
Des Moines, IA 50319
515-242-5870

Kentucky Labor Cabinet
1047 U.S. Highway 127 South
Frankfort, KY 40601
502-564-3289

Maryland Division of Labor and Industry
Department of Labor, Licensing, and Regulation
1100 N. Eutaw St.
Baltimore, MD 21201
410-767-2241

Michigan Department of Labor
PO Box 30643
Lansing, MI 48079
517-322-1814

Minnesota Department of Labor and Industry
443 Lafayette Road
St. Paul, MN 55155
651-284-5050

Nevada Department of Industrial Relations
Division of Occupational Safety and Health
1309 Green Valley Parkway, Suite 200, Henderson, NV 89074
702-486-9044

New Mexico Environment Department
525 Camino de los Marquez
Santa Fe, NM 87505
505-476-8700

New York State Department of Labor
522 State Office Campus
Albany, NY 12240
518-457-3518

North Carolina Department of Labor
1101 Mail Service Center
Raleigh, NC 27699-1101
919-779-8560

Oregon OSHA
PO Box 14480
Salem, OR 97309
503-378-3272

Puerto Rico Department of Labor and Human Resources
Prudencio Rivera Martinez Building
505 Munoz Rivera Avenue
Hato Rey, PR 00918
787-754-2119

South Carolina Department of Labor
PO Box 11329
Columbia, SC 29211-1329
803-896-7665

Tennessee Department of Labor
220 French Landing Drive
Nashville, TN 37243
615-741-2793

Utah Occupational Safety and Health
PO Box 146650
Salt Lake City, UT 84114-6650
801-530-6010

Vermont Department of Labor and Industry
PO Box 488
Montpelier, VT 05601
802-828-2138

Virgin Islands Department of Labor
53A &54B Kronprindense Gade,
St. Thomas, USVI 00803
340-776-3700 x 2617

Virginia Department of Labor and Industry
Powers-Taylor Building, 13 South 13th Street
Richmond, VA 23219
804-371-2327

Washington Department of Labor and Industries
PO Box 44600
Olympia, WA 98504-4600
360-902-5495

Wyoming Department of Occupational Health and Safety
1510 E. Pershing Blvd. - West Wing
Cheyenne, WY 82002
307-777-7786

Figure 2–3. States with approved plans.

construction. If such is the case, the state surrenders its jurisdiction for safety and health programs in construction operations to OSHA, which is then obligated to enforce the federal standards for operations not covered by the state plan.

Following approval of a state plan, OSHA will continue to exercise its enforcement authority until it determines on the basis of actual operations that the state plan is indeed being satisfactorily carried out. If the implementation of the state plan is satisfactory during the first three years after the plan's approval, then the relevant federal standards and OSH Act enforcement of such standards no longer apply to issues covered under the state plan. This means that for the interim period when dual jurisdiction exists, employers must comply with both state and federal standards.

Although the state agencies administering the state plan are vitally concerned with its success, members of the state legislature do not always share their enthusiasm. The legislature not only must appropriate an adequate budget, but in many cases must pass legislation enabling the state agency to carry out all the functions incorporated in the state plan. At times the state agency responsible may fail to fully implement the state plan, and the state's performance falls short of being "at least as effective as" the federal program. In such instances, OSHA has the right and obligation to withdraw its approval of the state plan and once again assume full jurisdiction in that state.

PART II—MINE SAFETY AND HEALTH ACT AND OTHER PROGRAMS

Other parts of the regulatory structure for safety in the United States include the Mine Safety and Health Act among others. Europe has also developed a robust regulatory structure that in many ways parallels the development in the United States. Other nations, although not at the same stage of development, are realizing the importance of protecting both the worker and the environment and are developing regulatory infrastructure that mimics existing programs in the United States and Europe.

LEGISLATIVE HISTORY OF MSHA

Historically, the Bureau of Mines within the Department of the Interior administered mine safety and health laws. However, the bureau was eliminated at the end of 1995, and some of its functions were transferred to other sectors within the Department of the Interior. Before Congress passed the Mine Act, mine operators were governed by two separate laws: the Federal Coal Mine Safety and Health Act of 1969 and the Federal Metal and Nonmetallic Mine Safety Act of 1966. Under the U.S. Department of Labor, MSHA now administers mining safety laws.

Because the Bureau of Mines was also charged with promoting mine production, critics charged that this responsibility produced an inherent conflict of interest with respect to enforcement of safety and health laws. The establishment of the Mine Enforcement Safety Administration (MESA) in 1973 within the Department of the Interior failed to answer the criticism. Congress looked for alternative solutions, including the transfer of mine safety and health to the OSH Act. Finally, Congress resolved the issue by adopting the Mine Act, which repealed the Federal Coal Mine Safety and Health Act of 1969 and the Federal Metal and Nonmetallic Mine Safety Act of 1966.

ADMINISTRATION

The administration and enforcement of the U.S. Mine Safety and Health Act are vested primarily with the Secretary of Labor and the Mine Safety Health Review Commission. MSHA administers the investigation and prosecution aspects of the enforcement process. The Mine Safety and Health Review Commission, an independent agency created by the Mine Act, reviews contested MSHA enforcement actions.

The Mine Act distinguishes between health research and safety research. Miner health research and standards development is the responsibility of NIOSH, in cooperation with MSHA.

MINE SAFETY AND HEALTH ADMINISTRATION

The Mine Safety and Health Administration, located within the DOL, administers and enforces the Mine Act. MSHA is headed by the Assistant Secretary of Labor for Mine Safety and Health, who is appointed by the president with the advice and consent of the Senate. The Assistant Secretary acts on behalf of the Secretary of Labor. For the purposes of this chapter, MSHA is also synonymous with the term *Secretary of Labor* or *Assistant Secretary of Labor*.

MSHA is authorized to adopt procedural rules and regulations to carry out the provisions of the Mine Act. The agency also has the responsibility and authority to perform the following:

- promulgate, revoke, or modify safety and health standards
- conduct mine safety and health inspections
- issue citations and propose penalties for violations

- issue orders for miners to be withdrawn from all or part of the mine
- investigate mine accidents (as defined later under "Accident, Injury, and Illness Reporting")
- grant variances
- seek judicial enforcement of its orders.

Aiding the Assistant Secretary in carrying out the provisions of the Mine Act are, among others, (1) an Administrator for Coal Mine Safety and Health and (2) an Administrator for Metal and Nonmetal Mine Safety and Health. Each administrator is responsible for a Division of Safety and a Division of Health.

PART III—REQUIREMENTS BEYOND U.S. BORDERS

The rapid emergence of worldwide markets, the pace of technological and scientific change, and the sweeping social changes occurring around the world have all created a need for a uniform set of international safety and health standards. So far, Europe and the United States have led the way, although other nations are beginning to realize the importance of protecting the worker and the environment as they seek to industrialize their economies.

The goals of international standardization of safety and health regulations include the following:

- setting a common ground for market agreements and technological applications
- improving the quality and reliability of products and services
- protecting the user and/or the environment
- providing compatibility of goods and services.

Some of the more important regulations include those developed by the European Union and the International Organization for Standardization.

EUROPEAN UNION

The European Union (EU, formerly the EEC) has sought to create safety and health regulations that would afford the greatest protection for workers and consumers in member nations while providing uniform standards for all nations doing business either in western Europe itself or with western European nations. The countries involved are Austria, Belgium, Denmark, Finland, France, Germany, Greece, Ireland, Italy, Luxembourg, the Netherlands, Portugal, Spain, Sweden, and the United Kingdom. One standard, the Framework Directive (89/391/EEC) of June 12, 1989, encourages improvements in on-the-job safety and health of workers and describes the obligations of employers to ensure the safety and health of their employees. This standard has been adopted by EU countries and most nations doing business with these countries.

ISO 9000 SERIES

The ISO 9000 series applies to companies that export goods and products to the EU countries. These standards describe a process for establishing quality management and quality assurance in companies. The basic goal of the ISO 9000 series is to provide guidelines to help companies achieve consistency and uniformity of products or services throughout the entire chain of supply.

ISO 14000 SERIES

The ISO 14000 series is also related to establishing standards for quality assurance, aimed primarily at protecting the environment from the by-products of industrial processes. Companies can use their management systems developed under ISO 9000 regulations as a basis for establishing environmental management. ISO 14000 was phased in throughout the 1990s. The European Union has adopted the ISO standards as meeting the requirements of EU environmental standards.

SUMMARY

- OSHA's primary responsibilities are (1) to promulgate, modify, and revoke safety and health standards; (2) to conduct inspections and investigations and to issue citations, including proposed penalties; (3) to require employers to keep records of safety and health data; (4) to petition the courts to restrain imminent-danger situations; and (5) to approve or reject state plans for programs under the OSH Act.
- The Occupational Safety and Health Review Commission (OSHRC) is a quasi-judicial, three-member board that hears cases when OSHA actions are contested by employers or employees.
- The primary functions of NIOSH are (1) to develop and establish recommended occupational safety and health standards; (2) to conduct research experiments and demonstrations; and (3) to develop educational programs to provide qualified safety and health personnel.
- With some exceptions, the OSH Act applies to every employer in all 50 states and U.S. possessions that has one or more employees and that is engaged in a business affecting commerce. Under OSHA, the employer

has a general and specific duty to provide safe, healthy work environments and comply with all applicable standards. Employees, in turn, must comply with all standards that apply to their situation and conduct on the job.

- Sanctions are in the form of citations for violating standards and civil and criminal penalties if the employer failed to comply with duties under the act. OSHA can grant temporary and permanent variances from standards.

- Employers and employees are granted certain rights under OSHA regulations to seek advice and consultation with OSHA staff, participate in inspections, take an active role in developing safety and health standards, apply for financial assistance, and appeal or contest OSHA findings and decisions.

- OSHA requires employers to keep records of all occupational injuries and illnesses.

- General inspection procedures include an opening conference, a walk-through of the establishment, documenting alleged violations, interviewing workers, and a closing conference. Employers or employees can request informal post-inspection conferences to discuss problems and solutions. Follow-up inspections are conducted to ensure correction of alleged violations.

- All citations except those for *de minimis* violations must be posted near the place where the violation occurred. The employer can object to or contest a citation and petition for a modification of the time for correcting the violation. If a citation or penalty is not contested, it takes immediate effect.

- The informal conference may be used before the citation is formally contested. If the parties do not agree with the results of the informal conference, the employer may formally contest the citation to the Occupational Safety and Health Review Commission (OSHRC).

- The OSH Act encourages states to assume the fullest responsibility for administering and enforcing their own occupational safety and health laws.

- Employers must inform employees of any hazardous materials used in the workplace and train them in methods of handling these materials and self-protection.

- The Federal Mine Safety and Health Act of 1977 is intended to ensure safe, healthful working conditions for miners in all types of mines. Its primary duties are (1) to develop, revoke, or modify safety and health standards; (2) conduct inspections; (3) issue citations and propose penalties for violations; (4) order miners withdrawn from parts or all of mines;

(5) grant standard variances; and (6) seek judicial enforcement of its orders. MSHA has the authority to propose new standards, emergency temporary standards, or variances.

- Miners (employees) have the right to request inspections, accompany inspectors during their facility tour, observe monitoring procedures, gain access to their own medical and employment records, be informed of their exposure to toxic substances, contest any alteration in MSHA orders, and receive training for their jobs. Mine operators must comply with safety and health standards and are subject to sanctions if they fail to do so.
- Within 10 days of an incident, mine operators must file a report on the incident with the nearest MSHA district or subdistrict office. They must follow up with a report on their investigation of the incident's causes.
- Mine inspections are usually carried out without prior warning to the operator. The inspector will conduct an opening conference and a walk-through of the premises, document all alleged violations, and hold a closing conference.
- Inspectors or their supervisors can issue citations for violations. Penalties are assessed for each violation and for each day the violation remains uncorrected. Operators, miners, or others affected have 30 days in which to contest the citations either at an informal conference or through formal procedures.
- International and multinational regulations seek to create standards and guidelines to ensure the health and safety of workers, consumers, and the environment wherever companies operate across national boundaries.

DIRECTORY OF FEDERAL AGENCIES

THE OCCUPATIONAL SAFETY AND HEALTH ADMINISTRATION

National Headquarters:

Occupational Safety and Health Administration, U.S. Department of Labor, Department of Labor Building, 200 Constitution Avenue NW, Washington, DC 20210; 202-523-8017.

National Institute for Occupational Safety and Health, U.S. Department of Health and Human Services, 1600 Clifton Road NE, Atlanta, GA 30333; 404-639-3061.

Bureau of Labor Statistics, U.S. Department of Labor, 200 Constitution Avenue NW, Washington, DC 20210; 202-523-7943.

Occupational Safety and Health Review Commission, 1120 20th Street NW, Washington, DC 20036; 202-606-5380.

OSHA REGIONAL OFFICES

Region I (Connecticut, Maine, Massachusetts, New Hampshire, Rhode Island, Vermont)—JFK Fed. Bldg. E-340, Boston MA 02203; 617-565-9860.

Region II (New York, New Jersey, Puerto Rico, Virgin Islands)—201 Varick Street, Room 670, New York, NY 10014; 212-337-2378.

Region III (Delaware, District of Columbia, Maryland, Pennsylvania, Virginia, West Virginia)—Suite 740 West, 170 S. Independence Mall West, Philadelphia, PA 19106-3309; 215-861-4900.

Region IV (Alabama, Florida, Georgia, Kentucky, Mississippi, North Carolina, South Carolina, Tennessee)—61 Forsyth Street SW, Atlanta, GA 30303; 404-562-2300.

Region V (Illinois, Indiana, Michigan, Minnesota, Ohio, Wisconsin)—J. C. Kluczynski Federal Building, 230 South Dearborn Street, Chicago, IL 60604; 312-353-2220.

Region VI (Arkansas, Louisiana, New Mexico, Oklahoma, Texas)—555 Griffin Square Building, Griffin & Young Streets, Dallas, TX 75202; 972-850-4145.

Region VII (Iowa, Kansas, Missouri, Nebraska)—Two Pershing Square, 2300 Main Street, Suite 1010, Kansas City, MO, 64108; 816-283-8745.

Region VIII (Colorado, Montana, North Dakota, South Dakota, Utah, Wyoming)—Federal Building, 1999 Broadway, Suite 1690, Denver, CO 80202; 720-264-6550.

Region IX (Arizona, California, Hawaii, Nevada, Guam, American Samoa, Trust Territory of the Pacific Islands)—90 7th Street, Suite 18100, San Francisco, CA 94103; 415-625-2547.

Region X (Alaska, Idaho, Oregon, Washington)—1111 Third Avenue, Suite 715, Seattle, WA 98101-3212; 206-553-5930.

THE MINE SAFETY AND HEALTH ADMINISTRATION

Mine Safety and Health Administration, U.S. Department of Labor, Room 601, 1100 Wilson Boulevard, Arlington, VA 22209; 202-693-9400.

National Institute for Occupational Safety and Health, U.S. Department of Health and Human Services, 1600 Clifton Boulevard NE, Atlanta, GA 30333; 404-329-3061.

National Mine Safety and Health Academy, 1301 Airport Rd., Beaver, WV 25813-9426; 304-256-3257.

Mine Safety and Health Review Commission, 601 New Jersey Avenue NW, Washington, DC 20001; 202-434-9906.

COMPILATIONS OF REGULATIONS AND LAWS

The environmental health and safety professional should be familiar with two U.S. government publications:

- *Federal Register (FR)*
- *Code of Federal Regulations (CFR)*

They are published by the Office of the *Federal Register*, National Archives and Records Service, General Services Administration, and are available from the Superintendent of Documents, U.S. Government Printing Office, Washington, DC 20402. Every safety office should obtain them.

THE FEDERAL REGISTER

The *Federal Register*, published daily Monday through Friday, provides a system for making publicly available regulations and legal notices issued by all federal agencies. In general, an agency will issue a regulation as a proposal in the *Federal Register* followed by a comment period, and then will finally promulgate or adopt the regulation in the publication. References to material published in the *Federal Register* are usually in the format A FR B, in which A is the volume number, FR indicates *Federal Register*, and B is the page number. For example, 43 FR 58946 indicates volume 43, page 58,946.

THE CODE OF FEDERAL REGULATIONS

The *Code of Federal Regulations*, published annually in paperback volumes, is a compilation of the general and permanent rules and regulations that have been previously released in the *Federal Register*.

The CFR is divided into 50 different titles, representing broad subject areas of federal regulations—for example, Title 29—Labor; Title 40—Protection of Environment; Title 49—Transportation. Each title is divided into chapters (usually bearing the name of the issuing agency), and then further divided into parts and subparts covering specific regulatory areas. References are usually in the format 40 CFR 250.XX, meaning Title 40 CFR, Part 250 (Hazardous Waste Guidelines and Regulations), or 49 CFR 172.XX (Hazardous Materials Table and Hazardous Materials Communications Regulations). The "XX" refers to the number of the specific regulatory paragraph.

The *Code of Federal Regulations* is kept up to date by the individual issues of the *Federal Register*. These two publications must be used together to determine the latest version of any given rule or regulation.

REVIEW QUESTIONS

1. What was the purpose of the Williams-Steiger Act (OSH Act)?
2. Before the passage of the OSH Act, other pieces of national safety legislation had been passed in the United States; what was the main drawback of these pieces of legislation?
3. Labor was a strong proponent of giving the federal government a more significant role in occupational safety and health. On what did they base their position?
4. List the two organizations that are vested with the administration and enforcement of the OSH Act.
5. Name the quasi-judicial board of three members appointed by the president and confirmed by the Senate to adjudicate cases.
6. What are the primary functions of NIOSH?
7. List the five main technical services provided by NIOSH.
8. The final responsibility for compliance rests with the _____.
9. What are the two voluntary safety programs established by OSHA for companies that have exceptional safety programs?
10. In what publication are possible federal safety standards published before they are brought up for formal consideration to be enacted into law?
11. What two types of variances can OSHA grant?
12. Employers must report to OSHA within _____ after an unintentional injury occurs that is fatal to one or more employees or that results in the inpatient hospitalization of three or more employees.
13. Are compliance safety and health officers (CSHOs) required to present solutions or methods of correcting, minimizing, or eliminating a violation?
14. List the five categories of violations.
15. What four steps must a CSHO take to determine that a violation is serious?
16. How may an employer contest a violation?
17. How long should employee medical records be retained by employers?
18. What is the basic purpose of the hazard communication standard?
19. What does the quality of a hazard communication program depend on?
20. Who is responsible for the information on MSDSs?
21. Whom does the OSH Act cover, and who is excluded from its coverage?
22. What are the general duties of employers and employees under the OSH Act?
23. What is the purpose of the OSHA Voluntary Protection Programs?
24. What concepts must an organization have present to qualify as having an exemplary safety program?

25. What does the informal conference provide regarding a citation?
26. How does a state go about having a "state OSHA plan" approved?
27. How has the OSH Act given new visibility to occupational safety and health?

3

Legal Implications for Safety

LEARNING OBJECTIVES

- ❏ Identify potential legal issues faced by someone in the role of safety manager.
- ❏ Understand the scope of OSHA regulations.
- ❏ Understand the criteria for being cited under the General Duty Clause, Section 5(a)(1) of the OSH Act.
- ❏ Understand key elements of OSHA regulations that have the most significant regulatory impacts on the workplace based on the history of OSHA citations.
- ❏ Understand the process for maintaining injury and illness reports associated with OSHA record-keeping purposes using OSHA 300 Log or 301 Incident Report forms.

OVERVIEW

The safety environment is shaped by legal requirements from potential liability issues that arise from court proceedings associated with workplace torts and by the government regulatory arena. The court system addresses issues related to workers' compensation, negligence, and other related torts. Legislatures at both the federal and state levels (and sometimes municipal) promulgate regulations that govern safety practices in the workplace. The executive branches (e.g., president and governors) of government entities enforce those regulations through agencies like the Occupational Safety and Health Administration (OHSA) using the Occupational Safety and Health Act (OSH Act) or a similar regulation. The courts are used to interpret differences of opinion when two or more sides disagree on either the meaning or enforcement of a regulation.

The modern safety manager has five significant roles in dealing with an organization's legal obligations.

First, the safety manager uses knowledge based on experience, education, training, and instinct to facilitate compliance with safety programs while addressing legal liabilities associated with safety in the workplace. The work of the safety manager is an important part of protecting workers and avoiding liability associated with injuries, fatalities, and loss of customer confidence in the company.

Second, the role of the safety manager is usually to track and maintain relevant data in records that must be kept to satisfy regulatory obligations for the organization with regard to safety and environmental reporting requirements.

Third, the safety manager is a key member of the compliance team, a team that reduces exposure of the organization due to preventing work-related injuries and fatalities, avoiding potential adverse outcomes from government safety and health inspections, and implementing the requirements of new regulations and standards.

Fourth, the safety manager acts as a valued participant in addressing workers' compensation, arbitration, or litigation actions involving an organization and its operations.

And lastly, on the regulatory side, the safety manager keeps up with proposed regulation changes from the comment stage to implementation, in order to ensure that resulting regulations are reasonable, effective in addressing workplace hazards, and implemented in a timely manner.

SCOPE OF THE OCCUPATIONAL HEALTH AND SAFETY ACT

In general, the Occupational Safety and Health Act extends to employers and their employees in the 50 states, the District of Columbia, Puerto Rico, and all other territories under federal government jurisdiction. Coverage is provided either directly by the federal Occupational Safety and Health Administration or through an OSHA-approved state occupational safety and health program in states that have approved programs.

Each supervisor should know which set of regulations governs their workplace. Twenty-five states and the District of Columbia are covered by federal OSHA regulations. The other 25 states (see Table 3–A) and Puerto Rico and the Virgin Islands have their own regulatory plans that have been approved by the federal OSHA system and cover the private and in some cases, the public sectors.

The Connecticut, New Jersey, New York, and Virgin Islands plans cover public-sector (state and local government) employment only. This means that in these states, government workers would be covered by the state plan and private-sector employees would be covered by federal OSHA regulations.

In some cases, there will be regulatory requirements from other sources that will need to be followed. The Environmental Protection Agency (EPA), the Department of Transportation (DOT), and the Nuclear Regulatory Commission (NRC) are examples of potential sources of other regulatory requirements besides OSHA that may govern a workplace. The safety supervisor should ask his or her employer for support in determining which regulations are applicable if this has not already been done. This chapter deals primarily with OSHA regulations.

OSHA regulations can be found in Title 29 of the Code of Federal Regulations (CFR), Parts 1902–1990. These regulations cover general industry, maritime, construction, and agricultural workplaces. These regulations can be found at the osha.gov website.

Table 3–A is provided as a source of OSHA regulatory information for states with their own plans (some plans do not cover the whole working sector).

TABLE 3–A. List of State OSHA Regulations	
Alaska	Alaska Division of Labor Standards and Safety labor.state.ak.us/lss/home.htm
Arizona	Arizona Secretary of State www.ica.state.az.us/Divisions/osha/index.html
Connecticut	CONN-OSHA adopts federal OSHA regulations and standards identically
California	California DOSH www.dir.ca.gov/dosh/
Hawaii	Hawaii Standards hawaii.gov/labor/hiosh/

Illinois	Illinois Public Employee Only (PEO) State Plan was approved as a developmental plan www.illinois.gov/idol/Pages/default.aspx
Indiana	Indiana OSHA adopts federal OSHA regulations and standards identically
Iowa	Iowa OSH Administrative Rules www.iowaworkforce.org/labor/iosh/index.html
Kentucky	OSH Regulations www.labor.ky.gov/osh/
Maryland	Maryland Standards www.dllr.state.md.us/labor/mosh.html
Michigan	Standards and Legislation www.michigan.gov/miosha
Minnesota	Minnesota Standards and Regulations www.dli.mn.gov/MnOsha.asp
Nevada	Nevada Standards dirweb.state.nv.us/OSHA/osha.htm
New Jersey	See Regulations and Standards section lwd.dol.state.nj.us/labor/lsse/employer/Public_Employees_OSH.html
New Mexico	New Mexico Regulations www.nmenv.state.nm.us/Ohsb_Website/index.htm
New York	See Regulations and Standards section www.labor.state.ny.us/workerprotection/safetyhealth/DOSH_PESH.shtm
North Carolina	NCDOL Standards www.nclabor.com/osha/osh.htm
Oregon	Oregon OSHA Rules and Laws www.orosha.org/
Puerto Rico	Spanish translations of safety and health standards/Normas traducidas al español radicadas www.trabajo.pr.gov/prosha/index.asp
South Carolina	South Carolina www.llr.state.sc.us/Labor/Osha/index.asp
Tennessee	Tennessee Department of Labor and Workforce Development www.state.tn.us/labor-wfd/tosha.html
Utah	R614—Labor Commission, Occupational Safety and Health www.laborcommission.utah.gov/UOSH/index.html
Vermont	Vermont Standards www.labor.vermont.gov/Default.aspx?tabid=74
Virgin Islands	VIDOSH adopts federal OSHA regulations and standards identically
Virginia	Virginia Standards www.doli.virginia.gov
Washington	Washington Standards www.lni.wa.gov/Safety/default.asp
Wyoming	Wyoming OSHA Standards wydoe.state.wy.us/osha

Workplaces covered by these regulations should ensure that that the poster, "Job Safety and Health: It's the Law" (OSHA 3165), be displayed in a conspicuous place visible to employees and applicants to inform those persons of the protections afforded by the OSH Act. Federal government agencies must post a Federal Agency Poster. The poster is available for free from the OSHA Office of Publications. Reproductions or facsimiles of the poster shall be at least 8½ × 14 in. with 10-point type. Employers do not need to replace previous versions of the poster.

GENERAL DUTY CLAUSE

In many cases, there are specific regulations that govern different workplace activities. For those cases in which there are no specific regulations, there is Section 5(a)(1) of the OSH Act, often referred to as the *General Duty Clause.* The General Duty Clause requires employers to "furnish a place of employment that is free from recognized hazards which are causing or are likely to cause death or serious physical harm to employees." The General Duty Clause is used by OSHA inspectors to cite employers when hazards are identified that are not covered by other regulations. However, for the General Duty Clause to be used, the identified hazard needs to meet several criteria.

OSHA looks at the following when evaluating whether the General Duty Clause is applicable:

- There is no applicable OSHA standard for an identified hazard.
- The employer failed to keep the workplace free of a hazard to which employees of that employer were exposed.
- The hazard was recognized or should have been recognized:
  - The employer knows about the hazard as shown by written or oral statements made during or before an OSHA inspection.
  - The hazard is recognized by others in the same industry.
  - Just plain common sense indicates that any reasonable person would recognize the hazard.
- The hazard was causing or was likely to cause death or serious physical harm.
- There was a feasible and useful method to correct the hazard.

A general duty citation must involve both the presence of a serious hazard and exposure of the cited employer's own employees.

REQUIRED WRITTEN PLANS AND OTHER DOCUMENTATION

Regulations can take different forms, and their requirements can vary widely. Some require written plans or other forms of documentation that will serve as a guide for complying with the regulation. Common examples of regulations requiring written plans are 29 CFR 1910.1030(c)(1)(i) and 1910.1030(c)(1)(iii) (bloodborne pathogens), 29 CFR 1910.1200(e)(1) and 1910.1200(e)(4) (hazard communication), and 29 CFR 1910.146(c)(4) (permit-required confined spaces). Traditionally, these written programs have been kept in separate binders in appropriate work areas in order to comply with the standards. Generally, these written plans need to be readily available to employees or their representatives.

These written plans can be general in nature (such as the hazard communication program) or they can have very specific requirements (like those found in the bloodborne pathogens standard). Sometimes, the only requirement is that written records be maintained. Because computers are more common in the workplace now that in years past, OSHA will allow a written program to be in either paper or electronic format as long as the program meets all other requirements of the standard in question and is accessible by employees. This allows an employer to obtain significant benefits in consistency, ease of use, and accuracy in maintaining and updating the materials in a timely manner.

A partial listing of OSHA regulations with written components required in many workplaces includes the following:

OSHA Log 300, Recording and Reporting Occupational Injuries and Illness, § 1904
Emergency Action Plan, § 1910.38(a)
Fire Prevention Plan, § 1910.38(a)
Hearing Conservation, § 1910.95
Process Safety Management, § 1910.119
HAZWOPER, § 1910.120
Respiratory Protection, § 1910.134
Confined Spaces, § 1910.146
Control of Hazardous Energy, § 1910.147
Fire Extinguishers, § 1910.157
Toxic/Hazardous Substances (Subpart Z), § 1910.1000
Bloodborne Pathogens, § 1910.1030
Hazard Communication, § 1910.1200
Laboratory Standard, § 1910.1450

It is important for safety and health professionals to determine if regulations governing their workplace require written documentation. It is very difficult to comply with a regulation if there are written components and there is nothing available in writing. When an OSHA inspector visits, quite often the first area that is evaluated deals with those regulations with written requirements.

OVERVIEW OF SIGNIFICANT OSHA REGULATIONS

This chapter addresses those OSHA standards that are most likely to be encountered in a workplace setting.

Each supervisor should determine whether any OSHA regulations are applicable to their workplace. If this is the case, then an effective compliance program needs to be in place. The areas regulated by OSHA and discussed in this section are applicable in many workplace settings.

Fall protection, hazard communication, lockout/tagout, respiratory protection, machine guarding, electrical safety, powered industrial trucks, ladders, scaffolding, excavations, walking surfaces, process safety management of highly hazardous chemicals standard, and entry into confined spaces are examples of areas that frequently need to be addressed by an organization's safety program.

MOST FREQUENTLY CITED OSHA STANDARDS

The following standards are frequently cited by OSHA inspectors:
1. Fall Protection, § 1926.501
2. Hazard Communication, § 1910.1200
3. Scaffolding, § 1926.451
4. Respiratory Protection, § 1910.134
5. Electrical, Wiring Methods, § 1910.305
6. Powered Industrial Trucks, § 1910.178
7. Ladders, § 1926.1053
8. Lockout/Tagout, § 1910.147
9. Electrical, General Requirements, § 1910.303
10. Machine Guarding, § 1910.212

These and other important standards are addressed in the rest of the chapter.

FALL PROTECTION STANDARD

Fall protection must be provided at 4 ft in general industry, 5 ft in maritime, and 6 ft in construction.

There are a number of ways to protect workers from falls, including conventional systems such as guardrail systems, safety net systems, and personal fall protection systems (fall-arrest systems, positioning systems, and travel restraint systems), as well as through the use of safe work practices and training. The use of warning lines, designated areas, control zones, and similar systems are permitted by OSHA in some situations and can provide protection by limiting the number of workers exposed and instituting safe work methods and procedures. These alternative systems may be more appropriate than conventional fall protection systems when performing certain activities.

Whether conducting a hazard assessment or developing a comprehensive fall protection plan, thinking about fall hazards before the work begins will help to manage fall hazards and focus attention on prevention efforts. If personal fall protection systems are used, particular attention should be given to identifying attachment points and to ensuring that employees know how to properly don and inspect the equipment.

Fall protection in the construction industry is often cited by OSHA inspectors. In general, any employee working in a location that is unprotected and at least 6 ft or more above a lower level should be protected by the use of guardrail systems, safety net systems, or personal fall-arrest systems. In some cases, when performing leading edge work, precast concrete erection work, or residential construction work and if it is not feasible or creates a greater hazard than using one of these systems, then it is permissible to develop and implement a fall protection plan that meets the following requirements:

- It must be prepared by a "qualified person" and developed specifically for the worksite and be maintained up to date.
- Any changes to the fall protection plan need to be approved by a "qualified person."
- A copy of the fall protection plan needs to be at the job site.
- The fall protection plan shall be under the supervision of a competent person.
- The fall protection plan shall document following items:
  - The reasons the use of conventional fall protection systems (guardrail systems, personal fall-arrest systems, or safety net systems) will not work or why their use would create a greater hazard.
  - The other measures that will be taken to reduce or eliminate the fall hazard for workers who cannot be provided with protection from the conventional fall protection systems. This can be done by discussing the extent to which scaffolds, ladders, or vehicle-mounted work platforms can be used to provide a safer working surface and thereby reduce the hazard of falling.
- The fall protection plan shall identify each location where conventional fall protection methods cannot be used.
  - These locations shall then be classified as controlled access zones and defined by control lines or something similar to restrict access.
  - When control lines are used, they shall be erected not less than 6 ft (1.8 m) nor more than 25 ft (7.7 m) from the unprotected or leading edge, except when erecting precast concrete members.

- When erecting precast concrete members, the control line shall be erected not less than 6 ft (1.8 m) nor more than 60 ft (18 m) or half the length of the member being erected, whichever is less, from the leading edge.
- The control line shall extend along the entire length of the unprotected or leading edge, approximately parallel to the unprotected or leading edge and connected on each side to a guardrail system or wall.
- Where overhand bricklaying and related work is taking place, the controlled access zone shall be defined by a control line erected not less than 10 ft (3.1 m) nor more than 15 ft (4.5 m) from the working edge.

HAZARD COMMUNICATION STANDARD

OSHA's website indicates that more than 30 million American workers are exposed to hazardous chemicals in their workplaces. The OSHA Hazard Communication Standard (HCS) is intended to ensure that these workers and their employers are informed of the identities of these hazardous chemicals, associated health and safety hazards, and appropriate protective measures. Hazard communication is addressed in specific standards for the general industry, shipyard employment, marine terminals, longshoring, and the construction industry. The HCS covers some 650,000 hazardous chemical products found in more than 3 million establishments. As a supervisor, it is important to determine if employees in the workplace could be exposed to hazardous chemicals. Given the right (or wrong) conditions, most chemicals can be hazardous.

In general, the Hazard Communication Standard states that chemical manufacturers/importers must determine the hazards of each chemical product and communicate the hazard information to customers through labels and Safety Data Sheets (SDSs). The employers (and supervisors) then have the following responsibilities:

- Identify and list hazardous chemicals in their workplaces.
- Obtain SDSs and labels for each hazardous chemical.
- Develop and implement a written hazard communication program, which should include information on container labels, SDSs, and their availability and employee training.

Written Program

The written program does not have to be lengthy or complicated and must be available by request for employees and employees' designated representatives. The written hazard communication program should contain a list of the hazardous chemicals in each work area, how the employer will inform employees of nonroutine task hazards, and the hazards associated with chemicals in unlabeled pipes. If the workplace has multiple employers on site, it is necessary to ensure that information regarding hazards and protective measures be made available to the other employers on site as appropriate.

Labels

OSHA has updated the requirements for labeling of hazardous chemicals under its Hazard Communication Standard (HCS). As of June 1, 2015, all labels will be required to have pictograms, a signal word, hazard and precautionary statements, the product identifier, and supplier identification.

All containers of hazardous chemicals must be labeled, tagged, or marked with the identity of the material and must show hazard warnings appropriate for protecting employees. As long as the hazards of the chemicals are conveyed, the hazard warning can be any type of message using words, pictures, or symbols. Labels must be legible (they need to be clear to anyone who would be using the chemical).

There are some exceptions regarding container labels:

- Signs or placards can be posted that convey hazard information if there are stationary containers within a work area that have similar contents and hazards.
- Standard operating procedures, batch tickets, blend tickets, process sheets, and other similar written materials can be used instead of container labels on stationary process equipment if the same information is covered and readily available to employees in the work area.
- Portable containers into which hazardous chemicals are transferred from labeled containers and that are intended only for the immediate (within the immediate workshift) use of the employee who makes the transfer are permissible.
- Pipes or piping systems are not required to be labeled.

A sample revised HCS label, identifying the required label elements, is shown in Figure 3–1. Supplemental information can also be provided on the label as needed.

Safety Data Sheets

Each SDS must be in English (they can also be in other languages) and include information regarding the specific chemical identity of the hazardous chemical(s) involved and the common names. In addition, information must be provided on:

- identification and contact information for the organization responsible for preparing the SDS
- names, synonyms, and other identification information

Product Identifier
CODE _____
Product Name _____

Supplier Identification
Company Name_____
Street Address _____
City_____ State_____
Postal Code _____ Country _____
Emergency Phone Number _____

Precautionary Statements
Keep container tightly closed. Store in cool, well-ventilated place that is locked.
Keep away from heat/sparks/open flame. No smoking.
Only use nonsparking tools.
Use explosion-proof electrical equipment.
Take precautionary measure against static discharge.
Ground and bond container and receiving equipment.
Do not breathe vapors.
Wear protective gloves.
Do not eat, drink, or smoke when using this product.
Wash hands thoroughly after handling.
Dispose of in accordance with local, regional, national, and international regulations as specified.

In Case of Fire: Use dry chemical (BC) or carbon dioxide (CO_2) fire extinguisher to extinguish.

First Aid
If exposed, call the nearest Poison Center.
If on skin (on hair): Take off immediately any contaminated clothing.
Rinse skin with water.

Hazard Pictograms

**Signal Word
Danger**

Hazard Statement
Highly flammable liquid and vapor.
May cause liver and kidney damage.

Supplemental Information
Directions for use

_____
_____
_____

Fill Weight: _____   Lot Number: _____
Gross Weight: _____   Fill Date: _____
Expiration Date: _____

Figure 3-1. Sample Label

- physical and chemical characteristics of the hazardous chemical
- fire and exposure data
- health hazard information (including whether it is considered a carcinogen)
- exposure limits
- precautions for safe handling and use
- control methods
- emergency and first-aid procedures.

Copies of the SDSs need to be readily accessible to employees in their work areas. This means they have to be available during each workshift in case someone wants or needs to review the information on the SDS.

List of Hazardous Chemicals

The written plan needs to contain a list of all hazardous chemicals in the workplace. There should also be an SDS for each chemical on the list. If there are hazardous chemicals without an SDS, the supplier, manufacturer, or importer needs to be contacted to obtain the missing SDS. If the SDS is not received within a reasonable period of time, OSHA should be contacted. It is a good idea to document any actions in trying to obtain an SDS.

Employee Training

Employees exposed to hazardous chemicals in their work area need to receive training. This needs to occur at the time of initial assignment and/or whenever a new hazard is introduced into the work area. The training plan should cover the following elements and needs to have been updated by December 1, 2013:

- how the hazard communication program is implemented and how to read and interpret information in SDSs and on labels
- the hazards of the chemicals in the work area—hazards may be discussed by each chemical or by hazard categories, such as corrositivity or flammability
- measures that can be used to protect themselves from hazards
- procedures used to provide protection, such as engineering controls, work practices, and the use of personal protective equipment (PPE)
- methods and observations workers can use to detect the presence of a hazardous chemical to which they may be exposed—this could be from a smell or something as simple as identifying a spill from a container.

Trade Secrets—Medical Emergency

Sometimes, chemicals will come under the trade secret provision and the identity and ingredients will not be known. However, employers must immediately disclose the specific chemical identity of a hazardous chemical to a treating physician or nurse when the information is needed for proper emergency or first-aid treatment. If you need the information from the SDS, the chemical manufacturer, importer, or employer may obtain a written statement of need and a confidentiality agreement that will protect them for having to disclose the trade secret.

CONTROL OF HAZARDOUS ENERGY (LOCKOUT/TAGOUT) STANDARD

Approximately 3 million workers service equipment and face the greatest risk of injury if a lockout/tagout program is not properly implemented. *Lockout/tagout* (LOTO) refers to specific practices and procedures to safeguard employees from the unexpected energization or start-up of machinery and equipment or the release of hazardous energy during service or maintenance activities.

Compliance with the lockout/tagout standard (29 CFR 1910.147) prevents an estimated 120 fatalities and 50,000 injuries each year. Workers injured on the job from exposure to hazardous energy lose an average of 24 workdays for recuperation. In a study conducted by the United Auto Workers (UAW), 20% of the fatalities (83 of 414) that occurred among their members between 1973 and 1995 were attributed to inadequate hazardous energy control procedures—specifically, lockout/tagout procedures. Based on these statistics, it is clear that a supervisor should pay special attention to ensuring that an effective LOTO program is implemented throughout designated work areas.

Lockout/Tagout

Workers performing service or maintenance on machinery and equipment may be exposed to injuries from the unexpected energization, start-up of the machinery or equipment, or release of stored energy in the equipment. Thus, a LOTO standard requires the adoption and implementation of practices and procedures to shut down equipment, isolate it from its energy source(s), and prevent the release of potentially hazardous energy while maintenance and servicing activities are being performed. As long as minimum performance requirements are met, employers have the flexibility to develop lockout/tagout programs that are suitable for their respective facilities.

Program Elements

The LOTO program should cover the following elements: energy control procedures, employee training, and periodic inspections, to ensure that before service and maintenance are performed, machines and equipment that could unexpectedly start up, become energized, or release stored energy are isolated from their energy source(s) and rendered safe.

This program should cover performing servicing and/or maintenance on machines or equipment and workers who are exposed to the unexpected energization, start-up, or release of hazardous energy. "Unexpected" covers situations in which the servicing and/or maintenance is performed during ongoing normal production operations if an employee is required to remove or bypass machine guards or other safety devices. Unexpected also covers situations when an employee is required to place any part of his or her body into a point of operation or into an area on a machine or piece of equipment where work is performed or into the danger zone associated with the machine's operation.

Activities and operations covered by this standard include any servicing and/or maintenance of machines or equipment when the source of energy to the machines or equipment is electrical, mechanical, hydraulic, pneumatic, chemical, thermal, or other energy. This also includes activities like constructing, installing, setting up, adjusting, inspecting, modifying, maintaining, and/or servicing machines or equipment, including lubrication, cleaning or unjamming of machines or equipment, and making adjustments or tool changes where employees could be exposed to the unexpected energization or start-up of the equipment or release of hazardous energy.

Exceptions

This regulation does not cover work on cord- and plug-connected electrical equipment if the equipment is unplugged from the energy source and the authorized employee has exclusive control of the plug.

Another exception to this standard is when continuity of service is essential, shutdown of the system is impractical, documented procedures are followed, and employees are effectively protected by special equipment.

Lockout

Lockout is where placement of a lockout device on an energy-isolating device is used, in accordance with an established procedure, ensuring that the energy-isolating device and the equipment being controlled cannot be operated until the lockout device is removed. This would include the use of any device that uses positive means—such as a lock, blank flanges, and bolted slip blinds—to hold an energy-isolating device in a safe position, thereby preventing the energizing of machinery or equipment.

Tagout

Tagout is used where lockout is not feasible and placement of a tagout device on an energy-isolating device is used, in accordance with an established procedure, to indicate that the energy-isolating device and the equipment being controlled may not be operated until the tagout device is removed. This would include the use of any prominent warning device—such as a tag and a means of attachment—that can be securely fastened to an energy-isolating device to indicate that the machine or equipment to which it is attached may not be operated until the tagout device is removed.

Required Procedures

Employers must develop, document, and use specific procedures to control potentially hazardous energy when employees are servicing equipment or machinery. The procedures must outline the scope, purpose, authorization, rules, and techniques that the employer will use to control hazardous energy.

Periodic inspections should be performed at least annually to identify any deficiencies or deviations and correct them. Where lockout is used, the inspector must review each authorized employee's responsibilities under the procedure with that employee (group meetings are acceptable). Where tagout is used, the inspector must review both the authorized and affected employee's responsibilities with those employees for the energy control procedure being inspected and any additional training responsibilities.

Removing Lockout or Tagout Devices

Before lockout or tagout devices are removed, and energy restored, the work area must be inspected to ensure that nonessential items (e.g., tools, spare parts) have been removed and that all of the machine or equipment components are operationally intact.

The work area must be checked to ensure that all employees have been safely positioned or have cleared the area. In addition, all affected employees must be notified that the lockout or tagout devices have been removed before the equipment is energized.

Each lockout or tagout device must be removed from the energy-isolating device by the employee who applied the device. When the authorized employee who applied the lockout or tagout device is not available to remove it, that device may be removed under the direction of the employer, provided that specific procedures and training for such removal have been developed, documented, and incorporated into the employer's energy control program.

Training

The standard requires different levels of training for the three categories of employees:

- Authorized employees must receive training on the recognition of applicable hazardous energy sources, the type and magnitude of the energy available in the workplace, and the methods and means necessary for energy isolation and control.
- Affected employees must receive training on the purpose and use of the energy control procedure.
- Other employees (those whose work activities are or may be in an area where energy control procedures may be utilized) must be instructed about the procedure and the prohibition relating to attempts to restart or reenergize machines or equipment that are locked out or tagged out. Employers must train employees in the limitations of using tags instead of a lockout when addressing energy control measures.

If changes occur in a job or procedures or problems are identified, then employees should be re-trained. Training should be documented with a certificate that includes each employee's name and the dates of training and/or retraining.

RESPIRATORY PROTECTION STANDARD

An estimated 5 million workers are required to wear respirators in 1.3 million workplaces throughout the United States. Respirators protect workers against insufficient oxygen environments, harmful dusts, fogs, smokes, mists, gases, vapors, biological agents and sprays. These hazards may cause cancer, lung impairment, other diseases, or death.

Whenever possible, engineering controls should be used to control employee exposure to airborne hazards. When this is not feasible, a respiratory protection program should be instituted that complies with OSHA's respirator standard, 29 CFR 1910.134. This standard requires the use of respirators to protect employees from breathing contaminated and/or oxygen-deficient air when effective engineering controls are not feasible or while they are being instituted. Several other OSHA regulations also require the use of respirators.

Respirators shall be selected on the basis of hazards to which the worker is exposed (i.e., particulates, vapors, oxygen-deficiency, or combination). In addition, only respirators certified by National Institute for Occupational Safety and Health (NIOSH) shall be used. Certified respirators will be marked with "NIOSH," the manufacturer's name and part number, and an abbreviation to indicate the cartridge or filter type.

Samples of approval labels are shown in Figures 3–2 and 3–3.

PART 84 MATRIX APPROVAL LABEL
FPR P100 FILTER

DEF MANUFACTURING COMPANY
ANYWHERE, USA
1-800-555-1234

THESE RESPIRATORS ARE APPROVED ONLY IN THE FOLLOWING CONFIGURATIONS:			
TC-	PROTECTION[1]	RESPIRATOR	CAUTIONS AND LIMITATIONS[1]
84A-00X	P100	HALO 2000	ABDJMNO

1. PROTECTION

> P100-Particulate Filter (99.97% filtered efficiency level) is effective against all particulate aerosols.

2. CAUTIONS AND LIMITATIONS
   A—Not for use in atmospheres containing less than 19.5% oxygen.
   B—Not for use in atmospheres immediately dangerous to life or health.
   C—Do not exceed maximum use concentrations established by regulatory standards.
   J—Failure to use and maintain this product properly could result in injury or death.
   M—All approved respirators shall be selected, fitted, used and maintained in accordance with MSHA, OSHA, and other applicable regulations.
   N—Never substitute, modify, and, or omit parts. Use only exact replacement parts in the configuration specified by the manufacturer.
   O—Refer to user instruction and/or maintenance manuals for information about use and maintenance of these respirators.

Figure 3–2

PART 11 LABEL FOR HEPA FILTER

PERMISSIBLE

PERMISSIBLE PARTICULATE FILTER RESPIRATOR FOR DUSTS, FUMES, AND MISTS,
INCLUDING ASBESTOS-CONTAINING DUSTS AND MISTS, AND RADIONUCLIDES

MINE SAFETY AND HEALTH ADMINISTRATION
NATIONAL INSTITUTE FOR OCCUPATION
SAFETY AND HEALTH

APPROVAL NO. TC-21C-XXX

ISSUED TO
ABC Company
Anywhere, USA

LIMITATIONS

Approved for respiratory protection against dusts, fumes and mists having a 5mp-weighed average less than 0.05 milligram per cubic meter, including asbestos-containing dusts and mists, and radionuclides.

Not for use in atmospheres containing toxic gases or vapors.

Not for use in atmospheres immediately dangerous to life or health. Not for use in atmospheres containing less than 19.5% oxygen.

CAUTION

In making renewals or repair, parts identical with those furnished by the manufacturer under the pertinent approval shall be maintained.

Follow the manufacturer's instructions for changing filters.
The respirator shall be selected, fitted, used and maintained in accordance with the regulation of the Mine Safety and Health Administration, the Occupational Safety and Health Administration, and either application agencies.

MSHA/NIOSH Approval TC-21C-XXX
Issued to ABC Co. February 31, 1990

The approved assembly consists of the following part numbers:

000-000
000-000
etc.

Figure 3–3

When respirators are required in the workplace, a written respiratory protection program with worksite-specific procedures and elements for required respirator use is also required. The provisions of the program shall include procedures for selection, medical evaluation, fit testing, training, and use and care of respirators.

Fit Testing

Proper respirator size is determined through a *fit test*, which is a method used to select the right size and type of respirator for the user. Employees using negative-

or positive-pressure, tight-fitting facepiece respirators must pass an appropriate fit test using the procedures detailed in OSHA's respirator standard.

Fit testing all negative- or positive-pressure, tight-fitting facepiece respirators is required prior to initial use, whenever a different respirator facepiece is used, and at least annually thereafter. An additional fit test is required whenever there are changes in the user's physical condition that could affect respirator fit (e.g., facial scarring, dental changes, cosmetic surgery, or an obvious change in body weight). The employer must be fit tested with the same make, model, style, and size of respirator that will be used.

Employees using tight-fitting facepiece respirators are required to perform a user seal check each time they put on the respirator. A *user seal check* is a method to verify that the user has correctly put on the respirator and adjusted it to fit properly.

Manufacturers make several different sizes of respirators. Respirators may also vary in size from manufacturer to manufacturer. Users may be able to get a better fit by trying a respirator made by another manufacturer. In some cases, the use of powered air-purifying respirators may be appropriate. Employers must help employees find a suitable respirator.

Tight-fitting facepiece respirators must not be worn by employees who have facial hair that comes between the sealing surface of the facepiece and the face or that interferes with valve function. Respirators that do not rely on a tight face seal, such as hoods or helmets, may be used by bearded individuals.

Medical Evaluation

The employer must provide a medical evaluation to determine the employee's ability to use a respirator before the employee is fit tested or required to use the respirator in the workplace. Not all workers must be examined by a doctor. A physician or other licensed health care professional must perform the medical evaluation using the medical questionnaire contained in Appendix C of 29 CFR 1910.134 or an initial medical examination that obtains the same information.

Training must be provided to employees who are required to use respirators. The training must be comprehensive, understandable, and recur at least annually—and more often if necessary. This training should include at a minimum:

- why the respirator is necessary and how improper fit, use, or maintenance can compromise its protective effect
- limitations and capabilities of the respirator
- effective use in emergency situations
- how to inspect, put on and remove, use, and check the seals
- maintenance and storage

- recognition of medical signs and symptoms that may limit or prevent effective use.

Maintenance, Storage, and Replacement

The employer must provide for the cleaning and disinfecting, storage, inspection, and repair of respirators used by employees according to the procedures.

Some respirators are disposable and cannot be disinfected and are, therefore, assigned to only one person. Disposable respirators must be discarded if they are soiled, physically damaged, or reach the end of their service life. Replaceable filter respirators may be shared, but they must be thoroughly cleaned and disinfected after each use before being worn by a different person.

Respirators with replaceable filters are reusable, and a respirator classified as disposable may be reused by the same worker as long as it functions properly. All filters must be replaced whenever they are damaged, soiled, or causing noticeably increased breathing resistance (e.g., causing discomfort to the wearer). Before each use, the outside of the filter material should be inspected. If the filter material is physically damaged or soiled, the filter should be changed (in the case of respirators with replaceable filters) or the respirator discarded (in the case of disposable respirators). Always follow the respirator filter manufacturer's service-time-limit recommendations. Standard operating procedures for storing, reusing, and disposing of respirators that have been designated as disposable and for disposing of replaceable filter elements have to be developed.

Respirators must be stored to protect them from damage, contamination, dust, sunlight, extreme temperatures, excessive moisture, and damaging chemicals. They must also be packed or stored to prevent the facepiece and exhalation valve from deformation or damage. A good method is to place them in individual storage bins. Keep in mind that respirator facepieces can become distorted and the straps lose their elasticity if hung on a peg for a long time. Check for these problems before each use.

Storing the respirator in a plastic sealable bag after use is not considered a good practice. The respirator may be damp after use, and sealing prevents drying and encourages microbial growth. If plastic bags are used, respirators must be allowed to dry before storage.

When an employee uses a respirator voluntarily, an employer must implement those elements of the written respiratory protection program necessary to ensure that any employee using a respirator voluntarily is medically able to use that respirator and that the respirator is cleaned, stored, and maintained so its use does not present a health hazard to the user. Also, employers must provide the voluntary respirator users with the information contained in Appendix D of 29 CFR 1910.134.

Employers are not required to include in a written respiratory program those employees whose only use of respirators involves the voluntary use of filtering facepieces (dust masks).

MACHINE-GUARDING STANDARD

Moving machine parts have the potential to cause severe workplace injuries, such as crushed fingers or hands, amputations, burns, or blindness. Safeguards should be used for any machine part, function, or process that presents a danger that may result in an injury. When the operation of a machine or accidental contact could injure the operator or others in the vicinity, the hazards must be eliminated or controlled.

Machine-guarding hazards are addressed in specific standards for general industry, marine terminals, longshoring, and the construction and agriculture industries. The machine-guarding standard, 29 CFR 1910.212, provides general guarding requirements for machines and provides a blueprint for machine safety.

All machines consist of three fundamental areas:

- the point of operation
- the power transmission device
- the operating controls.

Despite all machines having the same basic components, safeguarding needs often differ due to varying physical characteristics and operator involvement.

The point of operation is where work is performed on the material, such as cutting, shaping, boring, or forming of stock. When a machine is in use, the point of operation is a place where an employee is potentially exposed to injury and needs to be guarded. The guarding device needs to conform with any appropriate standard or, in the absence of applicable specific standards, be designed and constructed so as to prevent the operator from having any body parts in the danger zone during the operating cycle.

The *power transmission apparatus* is all components of the mechanical system that transmit energy to the part of the machine performing the work. These components include flywheels, pulleys, belts, connecting rods, couplings, cams, spindles, chains, cranks, and gears. *Operating controls* refers to all parts of the machine that move while the machine is working. These can include reciprocating, rotating, and transverse moving parts, as well as feed mechanisms and auxiliary parts of the machine.

Operating controls are the input devices that the operator uses to activate or control the mechanical system. They need to be arranged such that a worker is protected from danger while operating the machinery. Often, additional safety devices are configured as part of the operating control process in order to enhance the safety of an operator in addition to required machine guards.

One or more methods of machine guarding needs to be provided to protect the operator and other employees in the machine area from hazards, such as those created by point of operation, ingoing nip points, rotating parts, flying chips, and sparks. Examples of guarding methods include barrier guards, two-hand tripping devices, electronic safety devices, and so forth.

Machine Guarding

The purpose of machine guarding is to protect the machine operator and other employees in the work area from potential hazards. Guards shall be affixed to the machine where possible and secured elsewhere if, for any reason, attachment to the machine is not possible.

Safeguards must meet minimum general requirements:
- The safeguard must prevent hands, arms, and any other part of a worker's body from making contact with dangerous moving parts.
- Workers should not be able to easily remove or tamper with the safeguard.
- The safeguard should ensure that no objects can fall into moving parts.
- If feasible, the machine should be able to be lubricated without removing the safeguards.

A fixed guard is a permanent part of the machine and is usually preferable to all other types of machine guarding because of its relative simplicity. It is not dependent upon moving parts to function. It may be constructed of sheet metal, screen, wire cloth, bars, plastic, or any other material that is substantial enough to withstand whatever impact it may receive and to endure prolonged use.

The safeguard must create no new hazards and create no interference for the worker. The guard shall be such that it does not offer an accident hazard in itself.

Additional Safety Measures

In some cases, additional measures will have to occur so that an operator can be protected. Use of safety devices may enhance the safety provided by a machine guard. It may:
- Stop the machine if a hand or any part of the body is inadvertently placed in the danger area.
- Restrain or withdraw the operator's hands from the danger area during operation.

- Require the operator to use both hands on machine controls, thus keeping both hands and body out of danger.
- Provide a barrier that is synchronized with the operating cycle of the machine in order to prevent entry to the danger area during the hazardous part of the cycle.

Special hand tools for placing and removing material without the operator placing a hand in the danger zone would be a good example of a safety device. Such tools shall not be used in place of other guarding required by this regulation but can only be used to supplement protection provided by a machine guard.

Eye and face protection must be provided to each employee when exposed to eye or face hazards from flying particles.

Training

A worker needs to know how and why to use a safeguarding system. The training should be specific and detailed. Operator training should involve instruction or hands-on training in the following:

- a description and identification of the hazards associated with particular machines
- the safeguards themselves, how they provide protection, and the hazards for which they are intended
- how to use the safeguards and why
- how and under what circumstances safeguards can be removed, and by whom (in most cases, repair or maintenance personnel only)
- when a lockout/tagout program is required
- what to do (e.g., contact the supervisor) if a safeguard is damaged, missing, or unable to provide adequate protection.

This kind of safety training is necessary for new operators and maintenance or setup personnel, when any new or altered safeguards are put in service, or when workers are assigned to a new machine or operation.

ELECTRICAL SAFETY STANDARDS

Electricity has long been recognized as a serious workplace hazard. The Occupational Safety and Health Administration of the U.S. Department of Labor (OSHA) considers electrical safety a high priority. The U.S. Bureau of Labor Statistics indicates that over the decade from 1992 to 2002, deaths due to electrical contact averaged almost 300 per year, and lost time injuries numbered more than 4,000 per year. OSHA's electrical standards are designed to protect employees exposed to dangers such as electric shock, electrocution, fires, and explosions. Electrical hazards are addressed in specific standards for the general industry, shipyard employment, and marine terminals.

OSHA has a brought additional requirements to the workplace to govern electrical work by revising 29 CFR 1910 Subpart S, Electrical Standard, which went into effect on August 15, 2007.

The final rule of this revision is partially based on Part I of NFPA 70E, Standard for Electrical Safety in the Workplace, 2000 edition, and NFPA 70, National Electrical Code, 2002 edition. This final rule revises OSHA's existing standard for electrical installations and focuses on safety in the design and installation of electric equipment in the workplace. It applies, as the previous standard did, to employers in general industry and in shipyard employment, longshoring, and marine terminals. It is important for supervisors who work with electricity to become familiar with relevant parts of NFPA 70E and NFPA 70.

Frequently Cited Standards Related to Electricity

In recent years, the following electrical standards have resulted in either frequent or costly citations:

- Electrical Systems Design, General Requirements, General Industry, § 1910.303
- Electrical, Wiring Methods, Components and Equipment, General Industry, § 1910.305
- Electrical, Hazardous (Classified) Locations, § 1910.307

In addition, OSHA has extended the ground-fault protection requirement to temporary receptacles used in construction activities performed in general industry. Ground-fault circuit-interrupter (GFCI) protection is required for all receptacle outlets on temporary wiring installations used during maintenance, remodeling, or repair of buildings, structures, or equipment or during other construction activities. A GFCI device will protect a worker by opening a circuit if currents going into and coming out of an electric circuit do not equal each other. This will prevent another current pathway—such as flow through a worker's body to ground—from causing injury to the worker.

To summarize, a supervisor should understand that electrical safety is a complex issue:

- There are new requirements based on a revised standard.
- It is important to ensure workers receive specialized education and training when working with electrical systems.
- Consensus standards can be used to help in the selection of the best method to achieve compliance with OSHA regulations.
- Some OSHA state plans are more restrictive than federal OSHA

requirements and, as such, may have adopted or incorporated consensus standards, but this is on a state-by-state basis and should be evaluated for each employer location.

- In most cases, electrical shock will be a recognized hazard that could cause—or likely cause—death or serious physical harm to employees. This means that electrical shock hazards not covered by existing regulations can be cited by use of the General Duty Clause described earlier.

POWERED INDUSTRIAL TRUCKS STANDARD

Requirements and Recommended Practices

OSHA requires that all forklifts be examined at least daily before being placed in service. Forklifts used on a round-the-clock basis must be examined after each shift.

The operator should conduct a pre-start visual check with the key off and then perform an operational check with the engine running. The forklift should not be placed in service if the examinations show that the vehicle may not be safe to operate. If a vehicle is in need of repair, defective or in any way unsafe, it should not be driven and should be taken out of service immediately. Any problems should be recorded on the appropriate documents and reported to a supervisor.

Preoperation Inspection

Before a vehicle is started, a preoperation (or pre-start) inspection that checks a variety of items, should occur. Each inspection should be specific for the following vehicles:

- electric forklifts
- internal combustion forklifts
- liquid propane forklifts

Operational Inspection

After completing the preoperation inspection, operators should conduct an operational inspection with the engine running.

The OSHA powered industrial truck standard lists a number of conditions under which a forklift must be removed from service. If the operator notes these conditions while driving, the driver must stop, park the vehicle and get assistance.

- Any powered industrial truck not in safe operating condition shall be removed from service. All repairs shall be made by authorized personnel.
- Defects when found must be immediately reported and corrected.
- Any vehicle that emits hazardous sparks or flames from the exhaust system

shall immediately be removed from service and not returned to service until the cause for the emission of such sparks and flames has been eliminated.

- When the temperature of any part of any truck is found to be in excess of its normal operating temperature, thus creating a hazardous condition, the vehicle shall be removed from service and not returned to service until the cause for such overheating has been eliminated.
- No truck shall be operated with a leak in the fuel system until the leak has been corrected.

Scheduled maintenance is critically important to the safe operation of a vehicle. Never operate a forklift requiring maintenance, and always ensure repair problems are reported to a responsible party. Never operate a vehicle that requires maintenance or is in any way thought to be unsafe.

- Keep industrial trucks in clean condition, free of lint, excess oil, and grease.
- Use noncombustible agents for cleaning trucks.

Training

The standard requires employers to develop and implement a training program based on the general principles of safe truck operation, the types of vehicle(s) being used in the workplace, the hazards of the workplace created by the use of the vehicle(s), and the general safety requirements of the OSHA standard. Trained operators must know how to do the job properly and do it safely as demonstrated by workplace evaluation. Formal (lecture, video, etc.) and practical (demonstration and practical exercises) training must be provided.

Employers must also certify that each operator has received the training and evaluate each operator at least once every 3 years. Prior to operating the truck in the workplace, the employer must evaluate the operator's performance and determine the operator to be competent to operate a powered industrial truck safely.

Refresher training is needed whenever an operator demonstrates a deficiency in the safe operation of the truck. Training shall consist of a combination of formal instruction (e.g., lecture, discussion, interactive computer learning, videotape, written material), practical training (demonstrations performed by the trainer and practical exercises performed by the trainee), and evaluation of the operator's performance in the workplace.

Training Program Content

Powered industrial truck operators shall receive initial training on the safe operation of a truck in the employer's workplace. Trainees may operate a powered industrial truck only:

- under the direct supervision of persons who have the knowledge, training, and experience to train operators and evaluate their competence
- where such operation does not endanger the trainee or other employees.

LADDER STANDARDS

Never use a ladder for any purpose other than the one for which it was designed. Ladders shall be inspected by a competent person for visible defects on a periodic basis and after any occurrence that could affect their safe use. Portable or fixed ladders with structural defects—such as, but not limited to, broken or missing rungs, cleats, or steps; broken or split rails; corroded components; or other faulty or defective components—shall either be immediately marked in a manner that readily identifies them as defective or be tagged with "Do Not Use" or similar language and shall be withdrawn from service until repaired.

The requirement to withdraw a defective ladder from service is satisfied if the ladder is:

- immediately tagged with "Do Not Use" or similar language
- marked in a manner that readily identifies it as defective
- blocked (such as with a plywood attachment that spans several rungs).

Other requirements for ladder use include the following:

- Position portable ladders so the side rails extend at least 3 ft above the landing.
- Secure side rails at the top to a rigid support and use a grab device when 3-ft extension is not possible.
- Make sure that the weight on the ladder will not cause it to slip off its support.
- Before each use, inspect ladders for cracked or broken parts such as rungs, steps, side rails, feet, and locking components.
- Do not apply more weight on the ladder than it is designed to support.
- Ladders shall not be moved, shifted, or extended while occupied.
- Use only ladders that comply with OSHA design standards listed in 29 CFR 1926.1053(a)(1).

Angle. Non-self-supporting ladders, which must lean against a wall or other support, are to be positioned at such an angle that the horizontal distance from the top support to the foot of the ladder is about one-fourth of the working length of the ladder.

In the case of job-made wooden ladders, that angle should equal about one-eighth of the working length. This minimizes the strain of the load on ladder joints that may not be as strong as on commercially manufactured ladders.

Rungs. Ladder rungs, cleats, or steps must be parallel, level, and uniformly spaced when the ladder is in position for use. Rungs must be spaced between 10 and 14 in. apart.

For extension trestle ladders, the spacing must be 8–18 in. for the base, and 6–12 in. on the extension section.

Rungs must be so shaped that an employee's foot cannot slide off and must be skid-resistant.

To Minimize Slipping or Falling

- Ladders are to be kept free of oil, grease, wet paint, and other slipping hazards.
- Wood ladders must not be coated with any opaque covering, except identification or warning labels on one face only of a side rail.
- Foldout or stepladders must have a metal spreader or locking device to hold the front and back sections in an open position when in use.
- When two or more ladders are used to reach a work area, they must be offset with a landing or platform between the ladders.
- The area around the top and bottom of ladder must be kept clear.
- Ladders must not be tied or fastened together to provide longer sections, unless they are specifically designed for such use.
- The top or top step of a stepladder shall not be used as a step.

The regulatory requirements for ladder use are relatively straightforward, but slips and falls from ladders continue to be a major source of injury in the workplace.

SCAFFOLDING STANDARD

The scaffolding standard has the following key provisions:

- Define a *competent person* and his or her responsibilities under the scaffolding standard:
  - "one who is capable of identifying existing and predictable hazards in the surroundings or working conditions, which are unsanitary, hazardous or dangerous to employees, and who has authorization to take prompt corrective measures to eliminate them."
- Define a *qualified person* and his or her responsibilities under the scaffolding standard:
  - "one who by possession of a recognized degree, certificate, or professional standing, or who by extensive knowledge, training, and experi-

ence has successfully demonstrated his or her ability to solve or resolve problems related to the subject matter, the work, or the project."

- Fall protection for employees is required at a 10-ft height above a lower level.
- Guardrail height:
  - The height of the top rail for scaffolds manufactured and placed in service before January 1, 2000, can be between 36 in. (0.9 m) and 45 in. (1.2 m).
  - The height of the top rail for scaffolds manufactured and placed in service after January 1, 2000, must be between 38 in. (0.97 m) and 45 in. (1.2 m). [When the crosspoint of crossbracing is used as a top rail, it must be between 38 in. (0.97 m) and 48 in. (1.3 m) above the work platform.]
  - Mid-rails must be installed approximately halfway between the top rail and the platform surface.
  - When a crosspoint of crossbracing is used as a mid-rail, it must be between 20 in. (0.5 m) and 30 in. (0.8 m) above the work platform.
- Erecting and dismantling—When erecting and dismantling supported scaffolds, a competent person must determine the feasibility of providing a safe means of access and fall protection for these operations.
- Training—Employers must train each employee who works on a scaffold on the procedures to control or minimize the hazards.
- Inspections—Before each work shift and after any occurrence that could affect the structural integrity, a competent person must inspect the scaffold and scaffold components for visible defects.
- Overhand bricklaying—A guardrail or personal fall-arrest system on all sides except the side where the work is being done must protect employees doing overhand bricklaying from supported scaffolds. The standards for aerial lifts have been relocated from 1926.556 to 1926.453.

Competent Person

In general, a competent person performs the following duties:
- Select and direct employees who erect, dismantle, move, or alter scaffolds.
- Determine if it is safe for employees to work on or from a scaffold during storms or high winds and to ensure that a personal fall-arrest system or windscreens protect these employees. (**Note:** Windscreens should not be used unless the scaffold is secured against the anticipated wind forces imposed.)

Qualified Person

The qualified person's duties include designing and loading scaffolds in accordance with the design.

Engineering Requirements

The standard requires a registered professional engineer to perform the design in some circumstances for suspension scaffolds. They should also design under the following circumstances:

- scaffolds that are to be moved when employees are on them
- when pole scaffolds over 60 ft (18.3 m) in height
- tube and coupler scaffolds are over 125 ft (38 m) in height
- fabricated frame scaffolds over 125 ft (38 m) in height above their base plates
- brackets on fabricated frame scaffolds used to support cantilevered loads in addition to workers
- outrigger scaffolds and scaffold components.

Each employee on a scaffold more than 10 ft (3.1 m) above a lower level should be provided with fall protection. In addition, a competent person must determine the feasibility and safety of providing fall protection for employees erecting or dismantling supported scaffolds.

Fall protection includes guardrail systems and personal fall-arrest systems. Guardrails and toeboards shall be installed on all open sides and ends of platforms more than 10 ft above the ground or floor, except needle beam scaffolds. Scaffolds 4–10 ft in height, having a minimum horizontal dimension in either direction of less than 45 in., shall have standard guardrails installed on all open sides and ends of the platform.

A personal fall-arrest system is a system used to arrest an employee in a fall from a working level. Personal fall-arrest systems include harnesses; components of the harness/belt, such as D-rings; and snap hooks, lifelines, and anchorage points.

Only a few of the requirements of 29 CFR 1926.451 are provided in this overview of the scaffolding standard, and there are many other requirements that a supervisor should be familiar with if working with scaffolding is part of a job's requirements.

At the minimum, a competent person should be involved in all phases of a scaffold job from design, erection, and operation to dismantling.

EXCAVATIONS STANDARD

Many construction projects involve excavations. *Excavation* means any manmade cut, cavity, trench, or depression in an earth surface, formed by earth removal.

Any site with excavation work occurring as part of the project should ensure inspections of excavations are conducted before construction begins, daily before each shift, as needed throughout the shift, and following rainstorms or other hazard-increasing events by a competent person.

As used here, a *competent person* is an individual who has training in soil analysis and use of protective systems; is knowledgeable about OSHA requirements; is capable of identifying existing and predictable hazards in the surroundings or working conditions that are unsanitary, hazardous, or dangerous to employees; and has authorization to take prompt, corrective measures to eliminate such hazards where identified. Prior to work with an excavation, the following issues must be addressed by a competent person:

- Evaluate soil and select appropriate protective systems.
  - *Protective system* means a method of protecting employees from cave-ins, from material that could fall or roll from an excavation face or into an excavation, or from the collapse of adjacent structures.
  - Protective systems include support systems, sloping and benching systems, shield systems, and other systems that provide the necessary protection.
- Construct protective systems in accordance with the standard requirements.
- Contact utilities (gas, electric) to locate underground lines, plan for traffic control if necessary, and determine proximity to structures that could affect choice of protective system.
- Test for low oxygen levels, hazardous fumes, and toxic gases, especially when gasoline engine–driven equipment is running or the dirt has been contaminated by leaking lines or storage tanks. Ensure adequate ventilation or respiratory protection if necessary.
- Provide safe access into and out of the excavation.
- Provide appropriate protections if water accumulation is a problem.
- Inspect the site daily at the start of each shift, following a rainstorm, or after any other hazard-increasing event.
- Keep excavations open the minimum amount of time needed to complete operations.

Trenches and excavations should be inspected daily for evidence of possible cave-ins, hazardous atmospheres, failure of protective systems, or other unsafe conditions.

Excavated material (spoils) can be hazardous if set too close to the edge of a trench/excavation. The weight of the spoils can cause a cave-in, or spoils and equipment can roll back on top of workers, causing serious injuries or death. Spoils and equipment should be set at least 2 ft back from the excavation. Retaining devices, such as a trench box, that will extend above the top of the trench should be used to prevent equipment and spoils from falling back into the excavation. Where the site does not permit a 2-ft setback, spoils may need to be temporarily hauled to another location.

Stairways, ladders, ramps, or other safe means of egress in all trenches that are 4 ft deep or more should be provided for egress. This means of egress should be positioned within 25 lateral feet of workers. Structural ramps that are used solely for access or egress from excavations must be designed by a competent person. When two or more components form a ramp or runway, they must be connected to prevent displacement and be of uniform thickness. Cleats or other means of connecting runway components must be attached in a way that would not cause tripping. Structural ramps used in place of steps must have a nonslip surface. Use earthen ramps as a means of egress only if a worker can walk them in an upright position and only if they have been evaluated by a competent person.

WALKING/WORKING SURFACES STANDARD

Slips, trips, and falls constitute the majority of general industry accidents. They cause 15% of all accidental deaths and are second only to motor vehicles as a cause of fatalities. The OSHA standards for walking/working surfaces apply to all permanent places of employment, except where only domestic, mining, or agricultural work is performed.

Walking/working surfaces are addressed in specific standards for the general industry, shipyard employment, marine terminals, longshoring, and the construction industry. For general industry, the following sections apply:

Walking/Working Surfaces, § 1910 Subpart D
Definitions, § 1910.21
General Requirements, § 1910.22
Guarding Floor and Wall Openings and Holes, § 1910.23
Fixed Industrial Stairs, § 1910.24
Portable Wood Ladders, § 1910.25
Portable Metal Ladders, § 1910.26
Fixed Ladders, § 1910.27
Safety Requirements for Scaffolding, § 1910.28
Manually Propelled Mobile Ladder Stands and Scaffolds (Towers), § 1910.29

Housekeeping

Housekeeping is a very important aspect of OSHA's Walking/Working Surfaces standard. OSHA requires that all places of employment, passageways, storerooms, and service rooms be kept clean and orderly and in a sanitary condition and, so far as possible, in a dry condition. Where wet processes are used, drainage shall be maintained, and false floors, platforms, mats, or other dry standing places should be provided where practicable. To facilitate cleaning, every floor, working place, and passageway shall be kept free from protruding nails, splinters, holes, or loose boards.

Aisles and Passageways

Where mechanical handling equipment is used, sufficient safe clearances shall be allowed for aisles, at loading docks, through doorways, and wherever turns or passage must be made. Aisles and passageways shall be kept clear and in good repairs, with no obstruction across or in aisles that could create a hazard. Permanent aisles and passageways shall be appropriately marked.

Covers and Guardrails

Covers and/or guardrails shall be provided to protect personnel from the hazards of open pits, tanks, vats, ditches, holes, and so forth.

Floor Loading Protection

In every building or other structure, or part thereof, used for mercantile, business, industrial, or storage purposes, the loads approved by the building official shall be marked on plates of approved design that shall be supplied and securely affixed by the owner of the building, or his or her duly authorized agent, in a conspicuous place in each space to which they relate. Such plates shall not be removed or defaced, but if lost, removed, or defaced, shall be replaced by the owner or his or her agent.

It shall be unlawful to place, or cause, or permit to be placed on any floor or roof of a building or other structure a load greater than that for which such floor or roof is approved by the building official.

Protecting Openings

OSHA's 29 CFR 1910.23 provides extensive guidelines for many situations in which there is an opening that could result in a fall if the opening were to be left unprotected. Included in OSHA's extensive list are stairway floor openings, ladderway floor openings or platforms, hatchway and chute floor openings, skylight floor openings and holes, pits and trapdoor floor openings; infrequently used wall openings where there is a drop of more than 4 ft, manhole floor openings, every temporary floor opening, every floor hole into which persons can accidentally walk, places where doors or gates open directly on a stairway, and those situations in which there is a hazard of materials falling through a wall hole. It would be a good idea for each supervisor to be familiar with both the unsafe conditions described by OSHA and the remedies for addressing those same conditions.

PROCESS SAFETY MANAGEMENT OF HIGHLY HAZARDOUS CHEMICALS STANDARD

OSHA Fact Sheet 93-45 does a good job of explaining the general requirements for complying with the Process Safety Management (PSM) of Highly Hazardous Chemicals (HHCs) standard, 29 CFR 1910.119. This standard is intended to prevent or minimize the consequences of a catastrophic release of toxic, reactive, flammable, or explosive HHCs from a process. A *process* is any activity or combination of activities, including any use, storage, manufacturing, handling, or onsite movement of HHCs. A process includes any group of vessels that are interconnected and separate vessels that are located such that a HHC could be involved in a potential release.

Application

The standard applies to a process that contains a threshold quantity or greater amount of a toxic or reactive HHC as specified in Appendix A of 29 CFR 1910.119. Also, it applies to 10,000 lb or greater amounts of flammable liquids and gases and to the process activity of manufacturing explosives and pyrotechnics.

Exceptions

The standard does not apply to retail facilities, normally unoccupied remote facilities, and oil- or gas-well drilling or servicing activities. Hydrocarbon fuels used solely for workplace consumption as a fuel are not covered if such fuels are not part of a process containing another HHC covered by the standard. Atmospheric tank storage and associated transfer of flammable liquids that are kept below their normal boiling point without benefit of chilling or refrigeration are not covered by the PSM standard unless the atmospheric tank is connected to a process or is sited in close proximity to a covered process such that an incident in a covered process could involve the atmospheric tank.

Process Safety Information

The standard requires compilation of written process safety information (PSI), including hazard information on HHCs, technology information, and equipment information on covered processes.

Employee Involvement

The standard requires developing a written plan of action regarding employee participation, consulting with employees and their representatives on the conduct and development of process hazard analyses and on the development of other elements of process safety management required under the rule. Employees and their representatives should be provided access to process hazard analyses and all other information required to be developed under the rule. Employees include worksite and contract employees.

Process Hazard Analysis

The standard specifies that process hazard analyses (PHAs) must be conducted as soon as possible for each covered process using compiled process safety information in an order based on a set of required considerations. At least 25% of initial process hazard analyses must have been completed by May 26, 1994; 50% by May 26, 1995; 75% by May 26, 1996; and 100% by May 26, 1997. Process hazard analyses must be updated and revalidated at least every 5 years and must be retained for the life of the process.

Operating Procedures

The standard requires that all operating procedures be in writing. The procedures must provide clear instructions for safely conducting activities involving covered process consistent with PSI. Steps for each operating phase, operating limits, safety and health considerations, and safety systems and their functions must be included. These procedures must be readily accessible to employees who work on or maintain a covered process. The need to be reviewed as often as necessary to ensure they reflect current operating practice and must implement safe work practices to provide for special circumstances such as lockout/tagout and confined space entry.

Training

Employees operating a covered process must be trained in the overview of the process and in the operating procedures addressed previously. This training must emphasize specific safety and health hazards, emergency operations, and safe work practices. Initial training must occur before assignment, or employers may certify that employees involved in the process as of May 26, 1992, have required knowledge, skills and abilities. Documented refresher training is required at least every 3 years.

Contractors

The standard identifies responsibilities of worksite employer and contract employers with respect to contract employees involved in maintenance, repair, turnaround, major renovation, or specialty work on or near covered processes. Contract employers are required to train their employees to safely perform their jobs and document that employees received and understood training. Contract employees need to know about potential process hazards and the worksite employer's emergency action plan. These employees must follow safety rules of the facility, and advise the worksite employer of the hazards contract work itself poses or hazards identified by contract employees.

Pre-start-up Safety Review

A safety review for new facilities and significantly modified work sites is mandated by the standard to confirm that the construction and equipment of a process are in accordance with design specifications; to ensure that adequate safety, operating, maintenance, and emergency procedures are in place; and to ensure process operator training has been completed. Also, for new facilities, the PHA must be performed and recommendations resolved and implemented before start-up. Modified facilities must meet the management of change requirement.

Mechanical Integrity

Requires the onsite employer to establish and implement written procedures for the ongoing integrity of process equipment, particularly those components that contain and control a covered process.

Hot Work

Hot-work permits must be issued for hot-work operations conducted on or near a covered process.

Management of Change

The worksite employer must establish and implement written procedures to manage changes except "replacements in kind" to facilities that effect a covered process. The standard requires the worksite employer and contract employers to inform and train their affected employees on the changes prior to start-up. Process safety information and operating procedures must be updated as necessary.

Incident Investigation

The standard requires employers to investigate as soon as possible (but no later than 48 hours after) incidents that did result or could reasonably have resulted in catastrophic releases of covered chemicals. The standard calls for an investigation team, including at least one person knowledgeable in the process involved, a contract employee when the incident involved contract work, and others with knowledge and experience to investigate and analyze the incident and to develop a written report on the incident. Reports must be retained for 5 years.

Emergency Planning and Response

The standard requires employers to develop and implement an emergency action plan. The emergency action plan must include procedures for handling small releases.

Compliance Audits

The standard calls for employers to certify that they have evaluated compliance with process safety requirements at least every 3 years. Prompt response to audit findings and documentation that deficiencies are corrected are required. Employers must retain the two most recent audit reports.

Trade Secrets

The standard sets requirements similar to trade secret provisions of the 1910.1200 Hazard Communication Standard requiring information required by the PSM standard to be available to employees (and employee representatives). Employers may enter into a confidentiality agreement with employees to prevent disclosure of trade secrets.

Although information from the OSHA Fact Sheet provides a good overview of the regulatory requirements for complying with the Process Safety Management of highly hazardous chemicals standard, compliance can only be ascertained by carefully addressing each of the provisions in the standard.

CONFINED SPACE ENTRY STANDARD

Since the Confined Space standard—29 CFR1910.146—applies to all of general industry, a performance-oriented standard was developed rather than a specification standard. Currently, construction, marine terminal, shipyard employment, and agriculture are not subject to the OSHA General Industry Permit-Required Confined Spaces regulation. However, employers in those industries should be aware that their workers are covered when they do work that falls under the general industry category. For example, maintenance, repair, and refurbishing work are covered under general industry rules even though done by "construction" contractors.

It is an employer's obligation to evaluate a workplace to determine if any spaces are permit-required confined spaces. The health and safety professional must first determine whether a space is a confined space. If it is a confined space, then he or she must determine if it is a permit-required confined space. If it is a permit-required confined space, then it must be determined whether full permit entry rules apply or less restrictive alternative entry rules apply.

A *confined space* is characterized by restricted means of entry/exit, size sufficient to contain a worker, and not specifically designed for worker occupancy. Many workplaces contain areas that are considered confined spaces because, while they are not necessarily designed for people, they are large enough for workers to enter and perform certain jobs. A confined space also has limited or restricted means for entry or exit and is not designed for continuous occupancy. Confined spaces include, but are not limited to, tanks, vessels, silos, storage bins, hoppers, vaults, pits, manholes, tunnels, equipment housings, ductwork, pipelines, and so forth.

OSHA uses the term *permit-required confined space* (permit space) to describe a confined space that has one or more of the following characteristics: contains, or has the potential to contain, a hazardous atmosphere; contains a material that has the potential to engulf an entrant; has walls that converge inward or floors that slope downward and taper into a smaller area that could trap or asphyxiate an entrant; or contains any other recognized safety or health hazard, such as unguarded machinery, exposed live wires, or heat stress.

A *permit-required space* is a confined space that has a potential hazard to health or life associated with it. Hazards may be the result of atmosphere or materials in the space or the result of the shape of the space.

In general, the Permit-Required Confined Spaces standard requires that the employer evaluate the workplace to determine if any spaces are permit-required confined spaces. If permit spaces are present, and workers are ever authorized to enter such spaces, a comprehensive permit space program must be developed, which is an overall plan/policy for protecting employees from permit space hazards and for regulating employee entry into permit spaces.

Permit spaces must be identified by signs, and entry must be controlled and limited to authorized persons. An important element of the requirements is that entry be regulated by a written entry-permit system and that entry permits be recorded and issued for each entry into a permit space. The standard specifies strict procedures for evaluation and atmospheric testing of a space before and during an entry by workers.

The standard requires that entry be monitored by an attendant outside the space and that provisions be made for rescue in the event of an emergency. The standard specifies training requirements and specific duties for authorized entrants, attendants, and supervisors. Rescue service provisions are required, and, where feasible, rescue must be facilitated by a nonentry retrieval system, such as a harness and cable attached to a mechanical hoist. Many would-be rescuers have become trapped by the same hazard requiring the rescue in the first place.

The OSHA Permit-Required Confined Spaces standard provides for alternative entry procedures (less stringent than full permit procedures) in cases where the only hazard in a space is atmospheric and the hazard can be controlled by forced air. The alternative procedure is allowed only in cases where specified requirements for substantiation and notification are met.

Many hazards related to uncontrolled releases of energy may be located in confined spaces, and any program should ensure that measures are available to assess potential hazards from the following:

- high-pressure fluids and gases
- mechanical energy
- oxygen deficiency
- toxics
- flammable materials
- engulfment
- wet/slick surfaces
- electrical energy.

OSHA requires the following elements be covered in a permit-required confined space entry program:

- identification and evaluation of confined spaces and permit-required confined spaces
- identification of hazards in those spaces
- procedures for controlling hazards
- written program
- permit system
- employee training
- record keeping
- rescue provisions.

A confined space is defined as a space that:

- is large enough and so configured that an employee can bodily enter and perform assigned work
- has limited or restricted means for entry or exit (e.g., tanks, vessels, silos, storage bins, hoppers, vaults, and pits are spaces that may have limited means of entry)
- is not designed for continuous employee occupancy.

A permit-required confined space has to meet the following four requirements:

- contains or has a potential to contain a hazardous atmosphere
- contains a material that has the potential for engulfing an entrant

- has an internal configuration such that an entrant could be trapped or asphyxiated by inwardly converging walls or by a floor that slopes downward and tapers to a smaller cross-section
- contains any other recognized serious safety or health hazard.

The next step is to evaluate potential hazards, which includes (but is not limited to) the following:

- oxygen deficiency, toxics, flammables/explosives
- engulfment, mechanical and electrical energy sources, release of materials, noise, wet/slick surfaces, falling objects, hot and cold temperatures.

Oxygen deficiency, which refers to oxygen levels below 19.5%, is a major potential hazard in confined spaces and is described in Table 3–B.

Table 3–B. Oxygen Deficiency Levels	
Oxygen Level (%)	*Effects*
16–12%	Deep breathing, accelerated heartbeat, impaired attention, impaired thinking, impaired coordination
14–10%	Very faulty judgment, very poor coordination, rapid fatigue from exertion that may cause permanent heart damage, intermittent breathing
≤10%	Nausea, vomiting, inability to perform vigorous movement or loss of all movement, unconsciousness followed by death
<6%	Spasmodic breathing, convulsive movements, death in minutes

Confined-space entry requires that specific procedures be developed to cover both pre-entry and entry activities. Pre-entry consists of evaluating potential hazards, organizing entry, and completing the written permit.

An entry process/system needs to include the following information and actions:

- work to be performed
- identity of individuals performing work
- time period
- identification and evaluation of potential hazards in the space
- completion of written permit
- equipment procurement
- permit review with team members
- rescue procedure(s)
- communication processes
- contact of rescue team if not at entry

- completion of LOTO procedures
- cleaning/purging atmosphere of any hazardous constituents
- ventilation system in place based on identified requirements
- documentation of atmospheric conditions
- entry to perform work
- exit with all entrants
- cancellation of permit by appropriate party
- entry equipment maintenance.

Procedures for multiple operations in the same space also need to be developed that cover incompatible jobs, oversight for the operation, notification procedures, scheduling, and an entry permit system. As needed, air monitoring devices, portable ventilation, appropriate personal protective equipment (PPE), communication devices, and retrieval equipment should be obtained prior to entry.

Additionally, other equipment might be specified when indicated, such as:
- explosion-proof lighting
- GFCI electrical protection
- nonsparking tools
- barriers to protect the opening
- entry harnesses
- nonentry retrieval.

Specific duties must be assigned to the entry team, including entry supervisor, authorized entrant, and attendant. The *authorized entrant* must be trained to understand hazards, possible health symptoms and consequences, the proper use of equipment, the importance of maintaining ongoing communication with the attendant, and to immediately leave the space when directed by a team member.

The *entry supervisor* must follow the procedures to end an entry, including the following: (1) notification to all team members that the entry has ended; (2) method(s) for notifying team members; (3) ensuring that equipment and materials have been removed from the space; and (4) securing the space to prevent unauthorized entry.

A review process should be carried out after each entry and periodically for appropriate confined spaces to ensure that procedures are appropriate and circumstances have not occurred that would require entry procedures to change.

Training for all confined entry personnel must be completed and documented. Retrain employees when there are changes in the program, workplace, or equipment; deviations during an entry; and inadequate knowledge observed.

No program, permit system, entrant, or rescue procedures are required if:
- the only hazard is a hazardous atmosphere *and*
- ventilation will be maintained to provide a safe atmosphere *and*
- documented through monitoring and inspections *and*
- entry will be only to verify atmosphere.

Reclassification to a *non-permit space* is allowed under the following conditions:
- no actual or potential atmospheric hazards
- entry space to eliminate hazards follows §§ 1910.146(d)–(k) of standard
- reclassification process needs to be documented.

Contractors

OSHA's Construction Safety and Health Regulations Part 1926 does not currently contain a permit-required confined space regulation. Subpart C, § 1926.21, Safety Training and Education, specifies training for personnel who are required to enter confined spaces and defines a "confined or enclosed space."

A *confined or enclosed space* means any space having a limited means of egress, which is subject to the accumulation of toxic or flammable contaminants or has an oxygen-deficient atmosphere. Confined or enclosed spaces include, but are not limited to, storage tanks, process vessels, bins, boilers, ventilation or exhaust ducts, sewers, underground utility vaults, tunnels, pipelines, and open top spaces more than 4 ft in depth such as pits, tubs, vaults, and vessels.

Contractors hired to enter confined spaces must be provided with the following information regarding the confined space by the host employer:
- the nature of the hazards involved
- the necessary precautions to be taken
- the use of protective and emergency equipment required.

Dual-entry missions should be coordinated between contractors and the employer. Contractors should be debriefed after entry.

Before allowing any employees to enter a confined space, the contractor should make sure that they have the following information from the host company: "dual-entry" coordination, contractor program elements, a list of hazards confronted or created during entry. This information should be shared with the contractor through a briefing and prior to entry.

OSHA's construction regulations also contain requirements dealing with confined-space hazards in underground construction (Subpart S), underground electric transmission and distribution work (§ 1926.956), excavations (Subpart P), and welding and cutting (Subpart J).

Further guidance may be obtained from American National Standard ANSI Z117.1-1989, Safety Requirements for Confined Spaces. This standard provides minimum safety requirements to be followed while entering, exiting, and working in confined spaces at normal atmospheric pressure. This standard does not pertain to underground mining, tunneling, caisson work, or other similar tasks that have established national consensus standards.

OSHA LOG 300: RECORDING AND REPORTING OCCUPATIONAL INJURIES AND ILLNESS STANDARD

Reporting work-related injuries, illnesses, or deaths does not mean someone was at fault or that an OSHA regulation has been violated. When an employee dies or three or more employees are admitted to a hospital from a work-related incident, an oral report to OSHA must occur within 8 hours. This can be done in person or over the phone (1-800-321-OSHA/800-321-6742).

Illnesses or injuries related to the workplace are recorded on OSHA Log 300. A current OSHA Log 300 can be downloaded from www.osha.gov. For an injury or illness to be recorded, it should be new, work related, and serious. *New injuries and illnesses* are defined as not being the same type or involving the same part of the body of an injury or illness that was recorded previously unless the injury or illness had completely recovered.

OSHA RECORD KEEPING

The purpose of this section is to provide the supervisor with information about the uses and benefits of record keeping for occupational injuries and illnesses, as well as how to comply with OSHA injury and illness record-keeping requirements. Types of records and reports, record-keeping requirements, and determination of recordability will be reviewed. Although the supervisor may not be the individual who maintains the OSHA record-keeping log, it is important to fully understand the requirements to be able to assist the individual who makes the final determination for record keeping.

The OSH Act of 1970 requires covered employers to prepare and maintain occupational injury and illness records. The OSH Act and record-keeping regulations in 29 CFR 1904 provide specific recording and reporting requirements.

There are many specific OSHA standards and regulations that require record maintenance and retention of medical surveillance, inspections, exposure monitoring, and other activities not covered here. Companies are responsible for keeping informed of current OSHA regulations at all times.

The purpose of this rule (Part 1904) is to require employers to record and report work-related fatalities, injuries, and illnesses.

Note: Recording or reporting a work-related injury, illness, or fatality does not mean that the employer or employee was at fault, that an OSHA rule has been violated, or that the employee is eligible for workers' compensation or other benefits.

All employers covered by the Occupational Safety and Health Act (OSH Act) are covered by these Part 1904 regulations. States that operate their own job safety and health programs have adopted comparable record-keeping regulations that have been in effect since January 1, 2002. States must have the same requirements for which injuries and illnesses are recordable and how they are recorded. Other provisions may be different as long as they are as stringent as the federal requirements. Employers in some state plan states may be subject to more stringent reporting requirements (e.g., California requires that every case of "serious injury or illness" be reported).

However, most employers do not have to keep OSHA injury and illness records unless OSHA or the Bureau of Labor Statistics (BLS) informs them in writing that they must keep records. For example, employers with 10 or fewer employees and business establishments in certain industry classifications are partially exempt from keeping OSHA injury and illness records.

Note: All employers covered by the OSH Act must continue to report any workplace incident resulting in a fatality or the hospitalization of three or more employees within 8 hours to the nearest office of the OSHA Area Director by telephone or in person (no voice mail messages allowed). If no one answers at the area office, call the OSHA toll-free telephone number: 1-800-321-OSHA (6742).

This rule promotes improved employee awareness and involvement in the record-keeping process, providing workers and their representatives with access to information on record-keeping forms and increasing awareness of potential workplace hazards. Employee privacy concerns have been addressed—the former rule had no privacy protections covering the log used to record work-related injuries and illnesses.

The rule uses a question-and-answer format written in plain language and uses checklists and flowcharts to provide easier interpretations of record-keeping requirements. Employers are afforded more flexibility in using computers and telecommunications technology to meet record-keeping requirements. The term *lost workdays* was eliminated, and the record keeping focuses on days away or days restricted or transferred. Calendar days are used for counting instead of workdays.

The company executive must sign and certify that the 300A Form is accurate.

EXEMPTIONS FOR RECORDING INJURIES AND ILLNESSES

OSHA has identified two categories of *exemptions* that may affect a company's obligation to record injuries and illnesses sustained by its employees: exemption for size and exemption for low-hazard industries. However, remember that all employers must report to OSHA any workplace incident that results in a fatality or the hospitalization of three or more employees.

If a company has 10 or fewer employees at all times during the last calendar year, it does not need to keep OSHA injury and illness records unless OSHA or the BLS informs you in writing.

- The partial exemption for size is based on the number of employees in the entire company.
- To determine if a company is exempt because of size, the company's peak employment during the last calendar year must be determined. If the company had no more than 10 employees at any time in the last calendar year, it qualifies for the partial exemption for size.

EXEMPTION FOR LOW-HAZARD INDUSTRIES

If a business establishment is classified in a specific low-hazard retail, service, finance, insurance, or real estate industry, it does not need to keep OSHA injury and illness records unless the government asks the company to keep the records.

- All employers, however, must report any workplace incident to OSHA that results in a fatality or the hospitalization of three or more employees.
- The partial industry classification exemption applies to individual business establishments. If a company has several business establishments engaged in different classes of business activities, some of the company's establishments may be required to keep records, while others may be exempt.

OSHA RECORD-KEEPING FORMS

The injury and illness records required by OSHA's record-keeping rule are an important source of information for OSHA, employers, and employees. OSHA requires completion of the following forms:

- OSHA 300 Log: Log of Work-Related Injuries and Illnesses
- OSHA 300-A Summary Form: Summary of Work-Related Injuries and Illnesses

- OSHA 301 Incident Report: Injury and Illness Incident Report

Note: There are penalties for failure to comply with OSHA record-keeping obligations.

The OSHA 300 Log of Work-Related Injuries and Illnesses (Form 300), is used to classify work-related injuries and illnesses and to note the extent and severity of each case.
  - When an incident occurs, use the log to record specific details about what happened and how it happened.

The OSHA 300-A Summary of Work-Related Injuries and Illnesses is a separate form (Form 300A) that shows the totals for the year in each category.
  - Each covered employer must complete the summary at the end of the year and post it for 3 months (February 1 to April 30).
  - The employer must review the records at year-end for accuracy before summarizing them.

Additional certification of accuracy by a company executive and additional data on the average employment and hours worked at the establishment are also required.

The OSHA 301 Injury and Illness Incident Report (OSHA Form 301) or equivalent form must be completed for each injury or illness recorded on Form 300.
  - This form or an equivalent must be filled out within 7 calendar days after information is received that a recordable work-related injury or illness has occurred. Some state workers' compensation, insurance, or other reports may be acceptable substitutes.
  - To be considered an equivalent form, any substitute must contain all the information asked for on Form 301.
  - According to Public Law 91-596 and 29 CFR 1904, OSHA's record-keeping rule, this form must be kept on file for 5 years following the year to which it pertains.
  - If the supervisor is unsure whether a case is recordable, he or she should call the local OSHA office for help. When in doubt, record it. It can always be lined out later.

Note: Federal OSHA requires other types of record keeping for many other reasons. For example, some OSHA regulations require training records documenting that training was conducted and understood. It is beyond the scope of this chapter to discuss those various record-keeping requirements.

Each employer that is required to keep records of fatalities, injuries, and illnesses must record each fatality, injury, and illness that:

- is work-related
- is a new case
- meets one or more of the general recording criteria (see Figure 3–4).

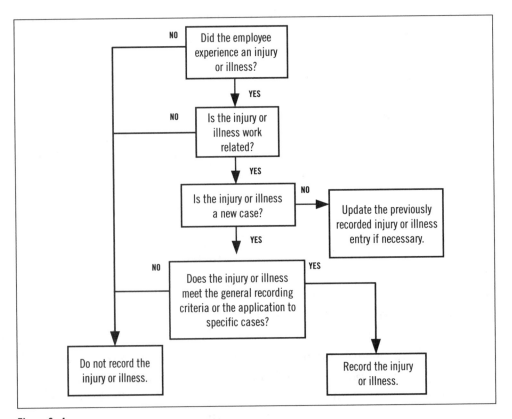

Figure 3–4

DETERMINING WORK RELATEDNESS AND OSHA RECORDABILITY

There are a number of points to consider in the process of accurately determining whether an injury or illness is work related.

When an Injury or Illness Is Not Considered Work Related

An injury or illness is considered *work related* if an event or exposure in the work environment caused or contributed to the condition or significantly aggravated a preexisting condition.

- Work relatedness is presumed for injuries and illnesses resulting from events or exposures occurring in the workplace, unless an exception specifically applies.

- The work environment includes the establishment and other locations where one or more employees are working or are present as a condition of their employment.

Definition of the Work Environment

OSHA defines the *work environment* as "the establishment and other locations where one or more employees are working or are present as a condition of their employment. The work environment includes not only physical locations, but also the equipment or materials used by the employee during the course of his or her work."

Situations in which an Injury or Illness Occurs in the Work Environment and Is Not Considered Work Related

An injury or illness occurring in the work environment that falls under one of the following exceptions is not work related, and therefore is not recordable:

A company is *not* required to record injuries and illnesses if the injury or illness:

- Occurred when the employee was present in the work environment as a member of the general public rather than as an employee.
- Involves signs or symptoms that surface at work, but result solely from a non-work-related event or exposure that occurs outside the work environment.

An injury or illness that occurs in the work environment is not considered work related when it meets with the following criteria:

- Results solely from voluntary participation in a wellness program or in a medical, fitness, or recreational activity such as blood donation, physical examination, flu shot, exercise class, racquetball, or baseball.
- Is solely the result of an employee eating, drinking, or preparing food or drink for personal consumption. (Example: If the employee is injured by choking on a sandwich while in the employer's establishment, the case would not be considered work related.)

Note: If the employee is made ill by ingesting food contaminated by workplace contaminants (such as lead) or gets food poisoning from food supplied by the employer, the case would be considered work related.

- Is solely the result of an employee doing personal tasks (unrelated to his or her employment) at the establishment outside of the employee's assigned working hours.

- Solely results from personal grooming, self-medication for a non-work-related condition, or is intentionally self-inflicted.
- Is caused by a motor vehicle accident and occurs on a company parking lot or company access road while the employee is commuting to or from work.
- Is the common cold or flu.

Note: Contagious diseases such as tuberculosis, brucellosis, hepatitis A, or plague are considered work related if the employee is infected at work.

- Is a mental illness. Mental illness will not be considered work related unless the employee voluntarily provides the employer with an opinion from a physician or other licensed health care professional with appropriate training and experience (psychiatrist, psychologist, psychiatric nurse practitioner, etc.) stating that the employee has a mental illness that is work related.

Injuries or Illness while Traveling

Injuries and illnesses that occur while an employee is on travel status are work related if, at the time of the injury or illness, the employee was engaged in work activities "in the interest of the employer." Examples of such activities include travel to and from customer contacts; conducting job tasks; and entertaining or being entertained to transact, discuss, or promote business (work-related entertainment includes only entertainment activities being engaged in at the direction of the employer).

New Cases

An employer must consider an injury or illness a new case to be evaluated for recordability if the employee:

- Has not previously experienced a recorded injury or illness of the same type that affects the same part of the body.
- Previously experienced a recorded injury or illness of the same type that affected the same part of the body but had recovered completely (all signs/symptoms of the previous injury or illness had disappeared) and an event or exposure in the work environment caused the injury or illness, or its signs or symptoms, to reappear.

Recordable Injuries and Illnesses

Work-related injuries and illnesses that result in the following must be recorded:

- death
- loss of consciousness
- days away from work

- restricted work activity or job transfer
- medical treatment beyond first aid.

Any significant work-related injury or illness that is diagnosed by a physician or other licensed health care professional must be recorded. Any work-related case involving cancer, chronic irreversible disease, a fractured or cracked bone, or a punctured eardrum must also be recorded.

Additional Criteria

A company must also record work-related injuries and illnesses that meet any of the following additional criteria:

- any needlestick injury or cut from a sharp object that is contaminated with another person's blood or other potentially infectious material
- any case requiring an employee to be medically removed under the requirements of an OSHA health standard
- tuberculosis infection evidenced by a positive skin test or diagnosed by a physician/other licensed health care professional after exposure to a known case of active tuberculosis
- an employer's hearing test (audiogram) reveals:
  - the employee has experienced a standard threshold shift (STS) in hearing in one or both ears (averaged at 2,000, 3,000, and 4,000 Hz)
  - the employee's total hearing level is 25 dB or more above audiometric zero (also averaged at 2,000, 3,000, and 4,000 Hz) in the same ear(s) as the STS.

DEFINITIONS OF MEDICAL TREATMENT AND FIRST AID

The following information from OSHA defines medical treatment and first aid by providing a variety of examples that will assist in classification.

Medical Treatment

Medical treatment means the management and care of a patient to combat disease or disorder. The following are not considered medical treatment and are not recordable:

- visits to a doctor or other health care professional solely for observation or counseling
- diagnostic procedures, such as x-rays and blood tests, including the administration of prescription medications used solely for diagnostic purposes (e.g., eye drops to dilate pupils)
- any procedure that can be labeled first aid.

First Aid

If the incident required only the following types of treatment, consider it *first aid*. Do not record the case if it involves only:

- using a nonprescription medication at nonprescription strength
- administering tetanus immunizations (immunizations such as Hepatitis B vaccine or rabies vaccine, are considered medical treatment)
- cleaning, flushing, or soaking wounds on the skin surface
- using wound coverings such as bandages, Band-Aids™, gauze pads, or the like or using butterfly bandages or Steri-Strips™ (other wound coverings such as sutures, staples, etc., are considered medical treatment)
- using hot or cold therapy
- using any nonrigid means of support, such as elastic bandages, wraps, nonrigid back belts, and so forth (devices with rigid stays or other systems designed to immobilize parts of the body are considered medical treatment)
- using temporary immobilization devices while transporting an accident victim (splints, slings, neck collars, back boards)
- drilling a fingernail or toenail to relieve pressure or draining fluid from a blister
- using eye patches
- removing foreign bodies from the eye using only irrigation or a cotton swab
- removing splinters/foreign material from areas other than the eye by irrigation, tweezers, cotton swabs, or other simple means
- using finger guards
- using massages (physical therapy or chiropractic treatment are considered medical treatment for record keeping)
- drinking fluids for relief of heat stress.

RESTRICTED WORK ACTIVITY

Situations may arise in the workplace that are defined as *restricted work activity*. To handle these situations effectively, it is important to understand the parameters of restricted work, as defined by OSHA, as well as how to count the number of days of restricted work activity or the number of days away from work.

Deciding if the Case Involves Restricted Work

Restricted work activity occurs when, as the result of a work-related injury or illness, an employer or health care professional keeps, or recommends keeping, an employee from doing the routine functions of his or her job or from working the full workday that the employee would have been scheduled to work before the injury or illness occurred.

Routine Job Function

A *routine job function* is defined as work activities the employee regularly performs at least once per week.

How to Count the Number of Days of Restricted Work Activity or Number of Days Away from Work

- Count the number of calendar days the employee was on restricted work activity or was away from work as a result of the recordable injury or illness.
- Do not count the day on which the injury or illness occurred in this number.
- Begin counting days from the day the incident occurs.
- If a single injury or illness involved both days away from work and days of restricted work activity, enter the total number of days for each.
- Stop counting days of restricted work activity or days away from work once the total of either—or the combination of both—reaches 180 days.

CLASSIFYING INJURIES AND ILLNESSES

The information from OSHA in Table 3–C defines injuries and illnesses by providing a variety of examples that will assist in classification.

Table 3–C. Injuries and Illnesses	
Classifying Injuries	*Classifying Illnesses*
An *injury* is any wound or damage to the body resulting from an event in the work environment. *Examples:* Cut, puncture, laceration, abrasion, fracture, bruise, amputation, insect bite, electrocution, or a thermal, chemical, electrical, or radiation burn. Sprain and strain injuries to muscles, joints, and connective tissues are classified as injuries when they result from a slip, trip, fall, or other similar accidents.	The following list provides a summary of major types of *illnesses*: • Musculoskeletal disorders (MSD illnesses) are disorders of the muscles, nerves, tendons, ligaments, joints, cartilage, or spinal discs. MSDs do not include disorders caused by a slip, trip, motor vehicle accident, fall, or other similar accidents. • Skin diseases or disorders are illnesses involving the worker's skin that are caused by work exposure to chemicals, plants, or other substances. • Respiratory conditions are illnesses associated with breathing hazardous biological agents, chemicals, dust, gases, vapors, or fumes at work. • Poisoning includes disorders evidenced by abnormal concentrations of toxic substances in blood, other tissues, other bodily fluids, or the breath that are caused by the ingestion or absorption of toxic substances into the body. • Noise-induced hearing loss is defined for record-keeping purposes as a change in the hearing threshold relative to the baseline audiogram of an average of 10 dB or more in either ear at 2,000, 3,000, and 4,000 Hz, and the employee's total hearing level is 25 dB or more above audiometric zero (also averaged at 2,000, 3,000, and 4,000 Hz) in the same ear(s). • All other occupational illnesses.

SUMMARY

The following is an at-a-glance overview on how to handle situations that require a supervisor to assess a case involving an employee injury and illness. It should be remembered that records are not only a requirement by OSHA. OSHA's record-keeping rule results in important information for employers and employees as well.

What to do
- Within 7 calendar days after receiving information about a case, decide if the case is recordable under the OSHA record-keeping requirements.
- Determine whether the incident is a new case or a recurrence of an existing one.
- Establish whether the case is work related.
- If the case is recordable, complete the OSHA 301 form.

Note: Use OSHA's Injury and Illness Report (Form 301) or an equivalent. Some state workers' compensation, insurance, or other reports may be acceptable substitutes, as long as they provide the same information as OSHA Form 301.

How to work with the 300 Log
- Identify the employee involved unless it is a privacy concern case as described later.
- Identify when and where the case occurred.
- Describe the case, as specifically as possible.
- Classify the seriousness of the case by recording the most serious outcome associated with the case, with column J (Other Recordable Cases) being the least serious and column G (Death) being the most serious.
- Identify whether the case is an injury or illness. If the case is an injury, check the injury category. If the case is an illness, check the appropriate illness category.

Circumstances under which the employee's name should not be entered on OSHA Form 300

Consider the following types of injuries or illnesses to be privacy concern cases. In these cases, do *not* enter the employee's name on the OSHA 300 Form. Instead, enter "privacy case" in the space normally used for the employee's name. Keep a separate, confidential list of the case numbers and employee names for the establishment's privacy concern cases so that the cases can be updated and, if requested, the information provided to the government.

- an injury or illness to an intimate body part or to the reproductive system
- an injury or illness resulting from a sexual assault
- a mental illness
- a case of HIV infection, hepatitis, or tuberculosis
- a needlestick injury or cut from a sharp object that is contaminated with blood or other potentially infectious material (see 9 CFR Part 1904.8 for definition)
- other illnesses, if the employee independently and voluntarily requests that his or her name not be entered on the log.

Note: Musculoskeletal disorders (MSDs) are not considered privacy concern cases.

What to do if the outcome changes after the case is recorded
If the outcome or extent of an injury or illness changes after recording the case, simply draw a line through the original entry or, if desired, delete or white-out the original entry. Then write the new entry where it belongs. Remember, it is important to record the most serious outcome for each case.

When to post the Form 300A Summary
The Summary only—not the Log—must be posted by February 1 of the year following the year covered by the form, and it must be remain posted until April 30 of that year.

How long to keep the Log and Summary on file
The Log and Summary must be kept for 5 years following the year to which they pertain.

Sending the forms to OSHA at the end of the year
These completed forms do not need to be sent to OSHA unless OSHA specifically requests them.

There are many more regulations that a workplace has to comply with, but these are a few that affect a majority of workplaces. For questions regarding a regulation, sources of help include internal company resources, associations, the Internet, and the regulatory agencies that are enforcing the regulations.

REVIEW QUESTIONS

1. List five of the top-cited OSHA workplace violations.
2. For a company to be cited using the General Duty Clause, name the five criteria that must exist.
3. What is the definition of a confined space?
4. What is the definition of a permit-required confined space?
5. When recording information on the OSHA 300 Log or 301 Incident Report forms, how is a routine job function defined?
6. Name three regulations that require written programs.
7. What are the recent changes to labeling under the Hazard Communication Standard, 29 CFR 1910.1200?
8. True or False: OSHA has extended the ground-fault protection requirement to temporary receptacles used in construction activities performed in general industry.

Form 300 (Rev. 01/2004)

f Work-Related Injuries and Illnesses

employee health and must be used in a manner that
protects the confidentiality of employees to the extent
possible while the information is being used for
occupational safety and health purposes.

Year 20___

U.S. Department of Lal
Occupational Safety and Health Administr

Form approved OMB no. 1218-

rmation about every work-related death and about every work-related injury or illness that involves loss of consciousness, restricted work activity or job transfer,
k, or medical treatment beyond first aid. You must also record significant work-related injuries and illnesses that are diagnosed by a physician or licensed health
ou must also record work-related injuries and illnesses that meet any of the specific recording criteria listed in 29 CFR Part 1904.8 through 1904.12. Feel free to
ngle case if you need to. You must complete an Injury and Illness Incident Report (OSHA Form 301) or equivalent form for each injury or illness recorded on this
re whether a case is recordable, call your local OSHA office for help.

Establishment name _____

City _____   State _____

erson		Describe the case				Classify the case					Enter the number of days the injured or ill worker was:		Check the "Injury" colum choose one type of illnes				
e's name	(C) Job title (e.g., Welder)	(D) Date of injury or onset of illness	(E) Where the event occurred (e.g., Loading dock north end)	(F) Describe injury or illness, parts of body affected, and object/substance that directly injured or made person ill (e.g., Second degree burns on right forearm from acetylene torch)		CHECK ONLY ONE box for each case based on the most serious outcome for that case:		Remained at Work			Away from work	On job transfer or restriction	(M)	Injury	Skin disorder	Respiratory condition	Poisoning	Hearing loss
						Death (G)	Days away from work (H)	Job transfer or restriction (I)	Other record-able cases (J)		(K)	(L)		(1)	(2)	(3)	(4)	(5)
		___/___ month/day				☐	☐	☐	☐		___ days	___ days		☐	☐	☐	☐	☐
		___/___ month/day				☐	☐	☐	☐		___ days	___ days		☐	☐	☐	☐	☐
		___/___ month/day				☐	☐	☐	☐		___ days	___ days		☐	☐	☐	☐	☐
		___/___ month/day				☐	☐	☐	☐		___ days	___ days		☐	☐	☐	☐	☐
		___/___ month/day				☐	☐	☐	☐		___ days	___ days		☐	☐	☐	☐	☐
		___/___ month/day				☐	☐	☐	☐		___ days	___ days		☐	☐	☐	☐	☐
		___/___ month/day				☐	☐	☐	☐		___ days	___ days		☐	☐	☐	☐	☐
		___/___ month/day				☐	☐	☐	☐		___ days	___ days		☐	☐	☐	☐	☐

4

Injury and Illness Record Keeping, Incidence Rates, and Analysis

LEARNING OBJECTIVES

- ❏ Describe records of work-related employee injuries and illnesses required by OSHA, state compensation authorities, and insurers.

- ❏ Identify types of incident reports and injury records used to evaluate the effectiveness of safety programs.

- ❏ Describe the elements found in an effective incident surveillance system.

- ❏ List and describe the statistical measures used in injury data analysis.

- ❏ Understand the sources of information for statistics used in both numerators and denominators in calculating incident rates.

INTRODUCTION

In this chapter, the terms *incident* and *injury* are restricted to occupational injuries and illnesses. In other chapters, *incident* is used in its broad meaning: unplanned, undesired events that interrupt the completion of an activity and that may include property damage or injury.

The Williams-Steiger Occupational Safety and Health Act of 1970 (OSH Act) requires most U.S. employers to maintain specific records of work-related employee injuries and illnesses. Some employers are required to maintain injury and illness records under regulations issued by other federal agencies, such as the Mine Safety and Health Administration (MSHA) and the Federal Railroad Administration (FRA). In addition to these records, many employers also are required to make reports to state workers' compensation authorities. Similarly, insurance carriers may require reports for their records. Occupational injury and illness reports and records are now required of nearly every establishment by its management or the government.

Safety personnel are faced with two tasks—maintaining records required by law and by their management, and maintaining records useful to an effective safety program. Unfortunately, the two are not always synonymous. A good occupational safety and health program requires more data than that contained in most standard federal and state record-keeping systems.

INCIDENT RECORDS

Records of incidents and injuries are essential to maintain efficient and successful safety programs, just as records of production, costs, sales, and profits and losses are essential to efficient and successful business operations. Records supply the information necessary to transform haphazard, costly, ineffective safety work into a planned safety program that controls both the conditions and the acts that contribute to incidents. Good record keeping is the foundation of a scientific approach to occupational safety.

USES OF RECORDS

A good record-keeping system can help the safety professional in the following ways:
- Provide safety personnel with the means for an objective evaluation of their incident problems and with a measurement of the overall progress and effectiveness of their safety program.
- Identify high-incident-rate units, facilities, or departments and problem areas so extra effort can be made in those areas.

- Provide data for an analysis of incidents pointing to specific causes or circumstances, which can then be attacked by specific countermeasures.
- Create interest in safety among supervisors or team leaders by furnishing them with information about their departments' incident experience.
- Provide supervisors and safety committees with hard facts about their safety problems so their efforts can be concentrated.
- Measure the effectiveness of individual countermeasures, and determine whether specific programs are doing the job they were designed to do.
- Assist management in performance evaluation.

RECORD-KEEPING SYSTEMS

The system presented in this section is a model that can be used to provide the basic items necessary for good record keeping. It is designed to dovetail with the present record-keeping requirements of the OSH Act and attempts to avoid a duplication of effort on the part of personnel responsible for keeping records and filing reports. Some of the forms presented in this section are also constructed with data-processing methods in mind. In general, a self-coding check-off form can save time for both the person who fills out the report and the person who tabulates and processes the data.

A well-designed form takes into account the person who will fill it out and the way in which the form will be processed. An incident report should accomplish three things: establish all causes contributing to the incident, reveal questions the investigator should ask to determine all environmental and human causes, and provide a means of accumulating incident data. Such a form is more likely to be filled out accurately and will present fewer problems for those who process and analyze the data.

In addition to the system presented here, which is primarily a manual, paper-based system, a number of computer-based record-keeping systems are available. Such systems greatly facilitate data analysis; some can be integrated into training management programs.

INCIDENT REPORTS AND INJURY RECORDS

To be effective, preventive measures must be based on complete and unbiased knowledge of the causes of incidents. The primary purpose of an incident report is to obtain such information, not to fix blame. The completeness and accuracy of the entire incident record system depend on information in the individual incident reports. Therefore, management must be sure that the forms and their purpose are understood by those who must fill them out. Such employees should be given necessary training or instruction.

First-Aid Report

The collection of injury data generally begins in the first-aid department. The first-aid attendant or nurse fills out a report for each new case. Copies are sent to the safety department or safety committee, the worker's supervisor, and other departments as management may wish.

Incident Investigation Report

It is recommended that the supervisor make a detailed report about each incident, even when only a minor injury or no injury is the result. For purposes of the OSHA Log of Work-Related Injuries and Illnesses (Form 300), only reports that meet the minimum severity level need to be separated and recorded. Minor injuries occur in greater numbers than serious injuries, and records of these injuries can help pinpoint problem areas. By working to alleviate these problems, workers and management can prevent many serious injuries. Minor injuries should not be regarded lightly, however. Complications may arise from these injuries, and their result can be quite serious.

Supervisors or team leaders should complete the supervisor's incident investigation report form as soon as possible after an incident occurs. They should send copies of these reports to the safety department and to other designated persons. Information concerning activities and conditions that preceded an occurrence is important to prevent future incidents. This information is particularly difficult to get unless it is obtained promptly after the incident occurs.

Employee Injury and Illness Record

After cases are closed, the first-aid report and the supervisor's report are filed by source of injury (type of machine, tool, material, etc.), type of event or exposure, or another factor that will facilitate use of the reports for incident prevention. The supervisor needs to document the experience of individual employees. Particularly in large facilities where supervisors have many people working for them, they may not remember the total number of injuries—especially if the injuries are minor—incurred by individual employees. An employee injury card, therefore, fills a real need. It provides space to record such factors as date of injury, classification, costs, and lost workdays.

Because of the importance of the human factor in incidents, much can be learned about incident causes from studying employee injury records. If certain employees or job classifications have frequent injuries, a study of employee working procedures, physical and mental abilities, training, job assignments, working environment, and the instructions and supervision given them may reveal as much as a study of incident locations, agencies, or other factors. An increase in the frequency of incidents involving an employee bears further investigation.

PERIODIC REPORTS

The forms just discussed are prepared when incidents occur; they are used to record the incidents and preserve information about contributing circumstances. Periodically, management should summarize this information and relate it to department or facility exposure in order to evaluate safety programs and to identify the principal incident causes.

Monthly Summary of Injuries and Illnesses

Managers and supervisors should prepare a monthly summary of injuries and illnesses to reveal the current status of incident experience. This monthly summary of injury and illness cases (Figure 4–1) allows for tabulating monthly and cumulative totals and computing OSHA incidence rates. Space is also provided for yearly totals and rates. This form would be filled out on the basis of the individual report forms that were processed during the month or from OSHA Form 300, Log of Work-Related Injuries and Illnesses (Figure 4–2).

MONTHLY SUMMARY OF INJURIES AND ILLNESSES, 19___

Company _____ Plant _____ Department _____

| Period | Average Number of Employees | Number of Employee-Hours Worked | Costs (Compensation, other) | OSHA Recordable Cases[1] | | | | | | Total Case Incidence Rate[2] | Lost Workdays Incidence Rate[2] | First Aid Cases |
				Deaths	Lost Workday Cases	Nonfatal Cases Without Lost Workdays	Total Cases	Total Lost Workdays			
Jan.											
Feb.											
2 mo.											
Mar.											
3 mo.											
Apr.											
4 mo.											
May											
5 mo.											
Jun.											
6 mo.											
Jul.											
7 mo.											
Aug.											
8 mo.											
Sep.											
9 mo.											
Oct.											
10 mo.											
Nov.											
11 mo.											
Dec.											
Year											

[1] Refer to OSHA Log for numbers of cases: Deaths, columns 1+8; Lost Workday Cases, cols. 2+9; Nonfatal Cases Without Lost Workdays, cols. 6+13; Total Lost Workdays, cols. 4+5+11+12. Total Cases equals Deaths plus Lost Workday Cases plus Nonfatal Cases Without Lost Workdays.
[2] Incidence rate is number of "Total Cases" or "Total Lost Workdays" multiplied by 200,000 and divided by "Number of Employee-Hours Worked."

Figure 4–1. Results of the safety program can be gauged from data on this Monthly Summary of Injuries and Illnesses form. Rates computed for the month, year to date (cumulative), and year permit comparisons between time periods, and between departments, facilities, and companies during the same period. Changes in the classification of injuries and other adjustments can be easily made.

Figure 4–2. The Log of Work-Related Injuries and Illnesses, OSHA Form 300, is used to record injuries or illnesses that result in fatalities or lost workdays, require medical treatment, involve loss of consciousness, or restrict work or motion. Because forms are subject to change, be sure to ask your OSHA area office for the latest forms and instructions.

The monthly summary should be prepared as soon after the end of each month as the information becomes available, but not later than the 20th of the following month.

Annual Report

Every establishment subject to the OSH Act is obliged to post its annual summary by February 1 for 30 days. The cumulative totals on OSHA Form 300, Log of Work-Related Injuries and Illnesses, serve as the annual report. Establishments designated as part of the BLS annual survey also must report these figures to the requesting agency.

For management purposes, however, the annual report fulfills a more direct function. Managers and others prepare monthly summaries of injuries and illnesses primarily to show the trend of safety performance during the year. However, annual reports are prepared to compare data for the longer periods with data from previous years and with data from similar organizations and from the industry as a whole.

When annual records are closed, OSHA requires that the anticipated future lost workdays (both days away from work and days of restricted work activity) be recorded. Then, when a case becomes final, the records can be corrected to show the actual days lost.

USES OF REPORTS

Reports to Management

Management must monitor the incident experience of its company. Therefore, monthly and other periodic summary reports showing the results of the safety program should be furnished to the responsible executives. Such reports do not need to contain details or technical language. They can be supplemented by simple charts or graphs to compare current incident rates with historical trends and the rates of other companies in the industry.

In a large company, departmental data help the executives visualize incident experience in various facility operations and provide a yardstick for better evaluation of progress made in the elimination of incidents. It can be particularly valuable to compare cost figures, if they can be obtained, for different periods.

Bulletins to Supervisors

Supervisors are primarily interested in their own department and workers. One of the most effective ways to create and maintain the interest of supervisors in incident prevention is to keep them informed about the incident records of their departments. Department injury rates based on sufficient amounts of exposure reflect the effectiveness of the supervisors' safety activities.

Bulletin Board Publicity

Posting a variety of materials on bulletin boards is one of the best ways to maintain employee interest in safety. Incident records furnish many items, such as the following:

- no-injury records
- unusual incidents
- frequent causes of incidents
- charts showing trends in incidents
- simple tables comparing departmental records.

THE CONCEPT OF BILEVEL REPORTING

As mentioned earlier in this chapter, each company has different incident problems from those of organizations in other industries and even within the same industry. As a result, no individual form or set of forms can possibly include all of the information necessary to fully investigate the causes of all incidents. With this in mind, and because long forms are rarely welcomed or completed accurately, the concept of bilevel reporting has arisen.

The basic idea behind bilevel reporting is that further details about specific types of incidents are required in addition to the general information contained in the standard report form (such as the supervisor's incident report form). To obtain this additional data, a supplementary form, containing a few specific questions about the incident type under investigation, is prepared and made available. This supplementary form is then filled out and attached to the regular report, but only for incidents that the investigator needs to analyze in detail.

OSHA RECORD-KEEPING REQUIREMENTS

OSHA record-keeping requirements are subject to change and interpretation periodically. To be sure that you are using the most current and accurate rules, consult the record-keeping section of the OSHA website (www.osha. gov/recordkeeping/index.html) or contact a regional or area OSHA office. The *OSHA Recordkeeping Handbook* may be downloaded from the website or requested from an OSHA office. The handbook contains agency-approved policy, record-keeping rules, frequently asked questions, and letters of interpretation. Record-keeping forms may also be downloaded from the site.

In addition to the record-keeping requirements of 29 CFR 1904 of the

Code of Federal Regulations, many specific OSHA standards and regulations require maintenance and retention of records of medical surveillance, exposure monitoring, inspections, and other activities and incidents, and the reporting of certain information to employees and to OSHA.

AN INCIDENT SURVEILLANCE SYSTEM

Most safety and health professionals recognize that the OSHA record-keeping system does not provide enough information about what is going on in the workplace to effectively manage a safety and health program. The developers of the American National Standard for Occupational Safety and Health Incident Surveillance, ANSI Z16.5-1998, recognized that for most organizations, the development, implementation, and evaluation of safety and health programs requires information on incidents well beyond government case-recording requirements. Z16.5 provided a comprehensive approach to incident surveillance. It defined a set of events and exposures that formed the basis of a comprehensive surveillance system. It gave the safety and health professional all the information required to meet government agency record-keeping requirements *plus* a uniform method to document events and exposure that could indicate potential or emerging safety and health hazards before they resulted in recordable cases. The standard was withdrawn for administrative reasons and is no longer in print, but the concepts embodied there are still valid and are presented here.

The key concept in Z16.5 is that information should be documented about many different kinds of events and exposures in the workplace, all of which are of interest to the safety and health professional. From this large database of "documentable events," the professional may select those cases that must be recorded on the OSHA Log or reported to workers' compensation authorities or insurance carriers. The standard defines the input to the database—that is, what should be documented. The output from this database is determined by the recording requirements of the database users. An important advantage of the Z16.5 system is that it puts the employer in control of the data and makes it easier for him or her to respond to the changing data requirements of outside agencies.

Z16.5 provided guidance on how to document events and exposures; how to collect the data; how to summarize the data; and how to analyze the data on injuries/illnesses, sentinel incidents, and costs including statistical measures. The statistical measures help to separate random variation from caused variation, which helps the safety and health professional to focus on the most important issues. Application of the concepts taken from the standard is highly recommended for organizations that want to create a state-of-the-art surveillance system.

INJURY DATA ANALYSIS

The traditional approach to incident investigation has been to expend the greatest amount of time and effort on the most severe and least frequent types of injuries/illnesses. By expanding the database to include "sentinel incidents," an employer is able to monitor a larger base and thereby be better positioned to determine whether the system is stable, improving, or deteriorating.

Sentinel incidents may be seen as precursors to possible injuries and may have the same complex set of root causes as more serious events. Sentinel incidents may include actions or lack of actions remote as well as near (in time) that result in the breakdown of the system that releases energy and causes injury or illness.

STATISTICAL MEASURES

Some common statistical categories of documentable occupational injuries/illnesses are listed here. Other categories may be used for statistical measures as well.

- death
- injuries/illnesses resulting in permanent disability
- injuries/illnesses resulting in days away from work
- injuries/illnesses resulting in days of restricted work activity
- injuries/illnesses involving both days away from work and days of restricted work activity
- medical treatment cases
- organizational levels (e.g., corporate, region, division, location, department, operation, etc.)
- operational function (e.g., maintenance/repair, assembly, paint, etc.)
- day, shift, time
- energy source, energy released, contact with energy.

INCIDENCE RATES

Safety performance is relative. Only when a company compares its injury experience with that of its entire industry, or with its own previous experience, can it obtain a meaningful evaluation of its safety accomplishments. To make such comparisons, a method of measurement is needed that will adjust for the effects of certain variables contributing to differences in injury experience. Injury totals alone cannot be used for two reasons.

First, a company with many employees may be expected to have more injuries than a company with few employees. Second, if the records of one company include all the injuries treated in the first-aid room, while the records of a similar company include only injuries serious enough to cause lost time, obviously the first company's total will be larger than the second company's figure.

A standard procedure for keeping records, which provides for these variables, is included in the OSHA record-keeping requirements. First, this procedure uses incidence rates that relate injury and illness cases, and the resulting days lost, to the number of employee-hours worked; thus, these rates automatically adjust for differences in the hours of exposure to workplace hazards. Second, this procedure specifies the kinds of injuries and illnesses that should be included in the rates. These standardized rates, which are easy to compute and to understand, have been generally accepted in industry, thus permitting the necessary and desired comparisons.

A chronological arrangement (time series) of these rates for a company will show whether its level of safety performance is improving or worsening. Within a company, the same sort of time series by departments not only will show the trend of safety performance for each department, but will also reveal to management other information to make safety programs more effective. If it is found, for example, that the trend of incidence rates in a company is up, a review of the rate trends by department may reveal that this change is accounted for by the rates of just a few departments. With the sources of the highest company rates isolated, management can concentrate safety efforts at these points.

A comparison of current incidence rates with those of similar companies and with those of the industry as a whole serves a critical function. This step provides the safety professional with a more accurate perspective on the company's safety performance than could be obtained by reviewing historical trends.

An "incidence rate" may be calculated for any or all of the preceding categories, as well as other categories of cases. The incidence rate, IR, is defined as the number of cases per 100 full-time equivalent employees per year. It is calculated by multiplying the number of cases (N) occurring in a given employee population by 200,000 and then dividing by the total number of employee-hours (H) worked by all employees in the given population. The number 200,000 is equivalent to 100 employees working 40 hours a week for 50 weeks. The general formula is

(1) $IR = (N \times 200,000)/H.$

If rates are calculated for part of a year, such as quarterly or monthly, the same formula is used and the 200,000 factor remains the same.

It is important that the employee-hours used in the denominator of the incidence rate formula cover the same group of employees (establishment, department, etc.) and the same time period as the injuries/illnesses used in the numerator.

The following example gives the formula for the incidence rate for cases involving days away from work:

Incidence rate of cases involving days away from work =
(number of cases involving days away from work $\times$ 200,000) $\div$ H

where H is employee-hours. This is a common incidence rate used for evaluating safety and health programs, for comparing experience between organizations, and for tracking trends over time.

SEVERITY MEASURES

Measures of severity should be calculated for temporarily disabling injuries/illnesses using the appropriate number of days away from work. The total number of days counted in the particular category should be divided by the number of cases in that category to derive an average severity or average number of days lost per lost-time case.

(2) Average days away from work $= \dfrac{\text{Total number of days away from work}}{\text{Total number of days-away-from-work cases}}$

An alternative method would be to derive an "incidence rate of days away from work" (either calendar or scheduled) using the following formula:

(3) Incidence rate of days away from work = (Total number of days away from work $\times$ 200,000) $\div$ H

where H is employee-hours.

For employers with a large work force, a death rate per 10,000 workers should also be calculated. This is not recommended for most employers because fatalities are usually rare events. The formula is:

Death rate = (Number of Deaths $\times$ 200,000) $\div$ Number of hours worked

where DR is the death rate, D is the number of deaths, and H is employee-hours.

SENTINEL INCIDENT INCIDENCE RATES

Rates for documentable incidents other than occupational injuries/illnesses should be calculated. However, the appropriate exposure measure used in the rate denominator may not be employee-hours and the constant in the numerator may not be 200,000.

For traffic incidents involving highway vehicles, an appropriate rate would be incidents per million vehicle-miles (or kilometers) traveled. The formula is:

(4) Vehicle incident rate $= \dfrac{\text{Number of incidents} \times 1{,}000{,}000}{\text{Vehicle-miles (or kilometers)}}$

For other sentinel incidents, the appropriate exposure measure may be hours of operation, or number of units produced (in industry standard units), or some other applicable measure. The general formula for a sentinel incident incidence rate is:

(5) Sentinel incident incidence rate $= \dfrac{\text{Number of sentinel incidents} \times K}{\text{Number of exposure units}}$

where K is a suitable constant chosen by the user so that the rate is greater than zero and less than 100.

Examples of industry-specific Serious Injury Incidence Rate (SIIR) measures for costs are cents per ton of coal, cents per acre of farm crop, cents per vehicle-mile, or cents per item manufactured.

SUMMARY

- Companies must maintain records of work-related employee injuries and illnesses as required by OSHA, state compensation authorities, and insurers. Good record-keeping systems provide data to evaluate incident problems and safety program effectiveness, identify high-incident-rate areas, create interest in safety, enable the company to concentrate efforts on more serious incident problems, and measure effectiveness of countermeasures against hazards and unsafe practices.
- The primary purpose of an incident report is to obtain accurate, objective information about the causes of incidents in order to prevent incidents from reoccurring.
- OSHA incident rates help companies compare their safety performance with the performance of previous years or of the entire industry to evaluate their safety programs.

REVIEW QUESTIONS

1. Safety personnel must maintain records for what two reasons?
2. List five of the seven ways a good record-keeping system can help the safety professional.
3. In which department does the collection of injury data generally begin?
   a. the human resources department
   b. the safety department
   c. the first-aid department
   d. the department where the accident occurred
5. Which nonsafety professional should make a detailed report of each incident?
   a. the human resources director
   b. the medical staff supervisor
   c. the legal department manager
   d. the injured worker's supervisor
5. How often should managers and supervisors prepare a summary of injuries and illnesses?
   a. after every 10 occurrences
   b. weekly
   c. monthly
   d. quarterly

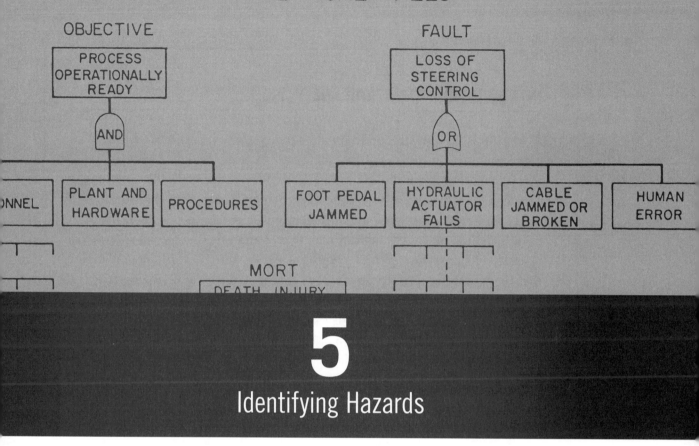

5

Identifying Hazards

INTRODUCTION TO HAZARD ANALYSIS

A hazard is an unsafe condition or activity that, if left uncontrolled, can contribute to an unintentional injury or illness. Before hazards can be controlled, they must be identified. This identification of hazards can be accomplished through a systematic hazard analysis program that includes job safety analysis, inspection, measurement and testing, and incident investigation. Including all four functions means that analysis is performed before the operation begins, during the life cycle of the operation, and after indications that the system has broken down. This chapter covers the following topics:

- the system safety process
- the philosophy and methods of hazard analysis
- the benefits and major components of job safety analyses
- planning and conducting inspections.

SYSTEM SAFETY

System safety is a deliberate attempt to find patterns of operation that lead to safer, more precise, and predictable results.

The need for system safety is rooted in the economic considerations of production. Unwanted incidents with associated injuries and illnesses incur increased costs and decrease profits. Companies have found that it is more cost effective to correct actions before they lead to injuries and illnesses. The profit motive is the underlying force in system safety, but legal issues, ethical motives, and regulatory directives also play a role.

PROFIT MOTIVE

Incidents produce direct and indirect losses that must be absorbed by a company. The direct losses of resources affect not only property but personnel. The loss of an aircraft due to an incident represents a decrease in the revenue potential of an airline. Fewer aircraft represent fewer passenger-revenue miles. The loss of personnel can leave an airline without qualified workers required for the operations, and training new employees represents a loss in the revenue stream of a company.

The indirect costs of an incident can be devastating to a company. The legal costs related to an aircraft incident, for example, can dramatically decrease the profits earned by a company. But the greatest costs can be to an airline's reputation. One only needs to look at the case of ValuJet, a low-cost airline that had a plane crash into the Everglades due to safety issues in 1996. The company never recovered, and by the end of 1997 it was no longer in business. Absolute safety is not cost effective and perhaps not possible in most cases. For a company to achieve no risk of an incident would require that it cease its operations. People must accept that risk is inherent in any venture. An amount of risk that is tolerable to the consumer and a producer must be achieved.

LEGAL VULNERABILITY

Consumers and employers are held accountable in the roles they play in an incident. Criminal and civil law can weigh heavily against those who are responsible. In the 1970s, Ford Motor Company marketed a vehicle with a known design defect: the Ford Pinto. The Pinto had a flawed fuel tank design that would cause it to ignite if the car was hit from behind. To rectify the design for 11 million cars and 1.5 million light trucks with Pinto-like fuel tank design would cost $11 each, for a total expenditure of $137 million. Ford chose to save the $11 it would have cost to rectify the problem. Because of its decision, the Ford Motor Company was held liable for the deaths caused by Pinto crashes, which led to the most expensive recall in automotive history.

ETHICAL MOTIVES

Sophisticated societies for the enhancement of professional conduct have existed for centuries. Professional societies and licenses were created to provide uniform methods of scrutinizing the management and behavior of service providers. In the past, these societies lacked the organizational strength to effectively develop systems of safety. Today, organizations such as the American Consulting Engineers Council are guided by codes of ethics:

> Engineers shall hold paramount the safety, health, and welfare of the public in the performance of their professional duties.

DIRECTIVES

Regulatory directives can specify how companies will proceed in the development of their safety systems. The airline industry, for example, is controlled by Title 14 of the *Code of Federal Regulations* (14 CFR). These regulations lay out in specific terms how the aviation industry will conduct its business and safety systems. The development of airworthy transport aircraft is specified in Federal Aviation Regulation (FAR) 25.1309 (b): "The airplane systems and associated components, considered separately and in relation to other systems, must be designed so that:

1. The occurrence of any failure condition which would prevent the continued safe flight and landing of the airplane is extremely improbable, and

2. The occurrence of any other failure conditions which would reduce the capability of the airplane or the ability of the crew to cope with adverse operating conditions is improbable."

Organizations can have many directives to follow from many different regulatory schemes. For example, the airline industry must comply not only with 14 CFR but with other pieces of legislation such as the Consumer Product Safety Act, the Federal Hazardous Substances Act, and the Flammable Fabrics Act. Federal or organizational directives can influence the emphasis a company places on the development of safety systems.

SYSTEM SAFETY TERMS

The difficulty in designing safety systems is partly due to the fluid nature of the activities in which one participates. In order to have a foundation from which to build, the tools and techniques to be used must be identified. Many industries have their own definitions for describing safety, but some are common throughout the safety world:

- *System*—A formation of personnel, procedures, materials, tools, equipment, facilities, and software. The elements of this composite entity are used together in the intended operation or support environment to perform a given task or achieve a specific production, support, or mission requirement (MIL-STD-882).
- *Safety*—Freedom from conditions that cause death, injury, occupational illness, or damage to or loss of equipment or property, or damage to environment (MIL-STD-882).
- *Management*—The process of allocating scarce or limited resources to achieve identified goals.
- *System safety*—The application of engineering and management principles, criteria, and techniques to optimize safety within the constraints of operational effectiveness, time, and cost throughout all phases of the system life cycle (MIL-STD-882).
- *Risk*—An expression of the probability/impact of a mishap in terms of hazard severity and hazard probability (MIL-STD-882).
- *Mishap*—An unplanned event or series of events that result in death, injury, occupational illness, or damage of equipment or property or damage to environment (MIL-STD-882).

HOW IS SYSTEM SAFETY DESIGNED?

The development of system safety should be derived from and supported by the mission statement of a company. Without the full support of management and personnel, a safety program will lack effectiveness. System safety programs must actively identify, verify, and rectify areas of risk, reducing it to a level that is acceptable to both the company and its stakeholders. The risk involved must be identified as early as possible, before it escalates to an unmanageable level. Once the risk is identified, it must be investigated to find its point of origin, solution, and potential for cross-contamination into other areas of operation. The final phase must implement any recommendations in accordance with the findings of the investigation. This final phase is also a starting point because the cycle must continue to maintain an effective and dynamic safety program that will provide optimum solutions for the risks at hand.

MISHAP MODELS

Potential mishaps (incidents or risks) are analyzed using various mishap models. One traditional model is called *Henrich's Domino Theory*. Incidents involve a sequence of the following five general factors:

1. environment of the risk
2. fault of a person
3. unsafe act or condition
4. accident
5. injury.

The analogy is that if one of the steps/dominoes is set in motion and they are allowed to continue to fall, then the result will be an accident. Eliminating any of the factors involved should stop the sequence.

Another mishap model assumes that mishaps are the result of multiple causes and is called the *all/multiple cause model*. This model assumes that a chain or a series of causes must take place before a mishap can occur. Underlying assumptions in this model include the following:

- Single-cause mishaps are extremely rare.
- Identifying single causes provides limited preventive options.
- Mishaps normally have both technical and management causes.
- Technical causes identify deficiencies in the operational system.
- Management causes identify deficiencies in the management system that allowed the operational deficiencies to exist.

A system safety model, however, is in place before a mishap occurs and proactively prevents unintended incidents. One model, the *risk management cycle*, consists of six distinct elements that can be analyzed to provide a means by which system safety can be achieved (Figure 5–1).

1. Identify hazards.

2. Assess risks.
3. Develop and evaluate control measures.
4. Make control decisions and assume residual risk.
5. Implement control measures.
6. Evaluate effectiveness of control measures.

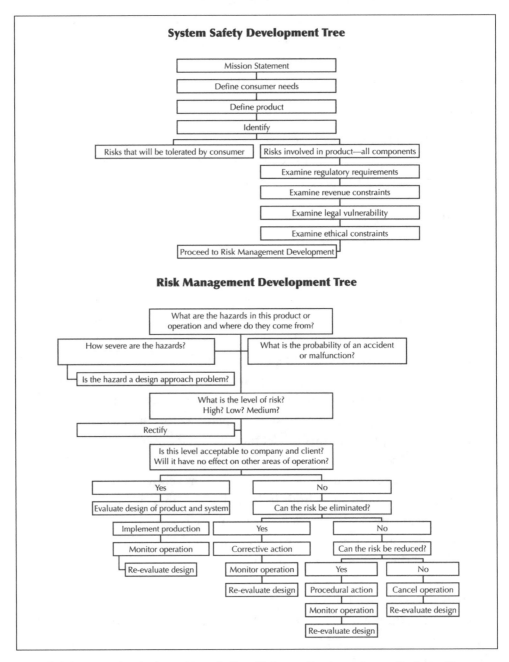

Figure 5–1. A system safety development tree, starting with the overall system and proceeding to specific management of risks.

Because system safety is a deliberate attempt to find patterns of operation that lead to safer, more precise, and more predictable results, it can function only with the cooperation of all who participate within the system. It is a dynamic relationship whereby the interactions of people and their environment must constantly be analyzed to maintain a safe and efficient environment. What is paramount and must be determined is the level of risk that will be accepted by the producer and consumer. Other approaches to identifying and preventing hazards are discussed in the next section.

HAZARD ANALYSIS

Hazard analysis is an analysis performed to identify and evaluate hazards in order to eliminate or control them. Data from hazard analysis can be regarded as a baseline for future monitoring activities. Before the workplace is inspected to ensure that environmental and physical factors fall within safe ranges, hazards inherent in the system must be discovered (i.e., hazard identification). Hazard analysis has proven to be an excellent tool to identify and evaluate hazards in the workplace.

Analyzing a problem or situation to obtain data for decision making is not new. Workers and their supervisors constantly make assessments—even if unconsciously—about their work to guide their actions. Written analyses carry the process one step further by providing the means to document hazard information, providing a historical basis for future decisions.

WHAT IS HAZARD ANALYSIS?

Hazard analysis is an orderly process used to acquire specific hazard and failure data pertinent to a given system. A popular adage holds that "most things work out right for the wrong reasons." By providing data for informed management decisions, hazard analysis helps things work out right for the right reasons. The method forces those conducting the analysis to ask the right questions and helps answer them. By locating the hazards that are the most probable and/or have the severest consequences, hazard analyses provide information needed to establish effective control measures. Analytic techniques help the investigator decide what facts to gather, determine probable causes and contributing factors, and arrange orderly, clear results.

What are some uses for hazard analysis?

- It can uncover hazards that have been overlooked in the original design, mockup, or setup of a particular process, operation, or task.
- It can locate hazards that developed after a particular process, operation, or task was instituted.

- It can determine the essential factors in and requirements for specific job processes, operations, and tasks.
- It can indicate what qualifications are prerequisites to safe and productive work performance.
- It can indicate the need for modifying processes, practices, operations, and tasks.
- It can identify situational hazards in facilities, equipment, tools, materials, and operational events (e.g., unsafe conditions).
- It can identify ergonomic problems through anthropometrics and workstation design (e.g., worktable heights, chairs, reaching capabilities).
- It can identify work practices responsible for incident situations (e.g., deviations from standard procedures).
- It can identify exposure factors that contribute to injury and illness (e.g., contact with hazardous substances, materials, or physical agents).
- It can identify physical factors that contribute to incident situations (e.g., noise, vibration, insufficient illumination).
- It can determine appropriate monitoring methods and maintenance standards needed for safety.
- It can determine the possible results of failures/incidents, people or property exposed to loss, and the potential severity of injury or loss.
- It can identify hazards in new equipment or processes before an employee is exposed to them.

FORMAL METHODS OF HAZARD ANALYSIS

Formal hazard analytical methods can be divided into two broad categories: inductive and deductive.

Inductive Method

The inductive analytical method uses observable data to predict events and outcomes within a particular system. It postulates how the component parts of a system will contribute to the success or failure of the system as a whole. Inductive analysis considers a system's operation from the standpoint of its components, their failure in a specific operating condition, and the effect of that failure on the system.

The inductive method forms the basis for such analyses as failure mode and effect analysis (FMEA) and operations hazard analysis (OHA). In FMEA, the failure or malfunction of each component is considered, including the mode of failure. Management can trace throughout the system the effects of the hazard(s) that led to the failure and evaluate the ultimate impact on task performance.

Once the inductive analysis is completed and the critical failures requiring further investigation are detected, then the fault tree analysis will facilitate an inspection (see "Deductive Method"). The job safety analysis (JSA) section discussed later in this chapter also uses the inductive method for determining the safety risks and components of various jobs.

Deductive Method

If inductive analysis reveals what can happen, deductive analysis shows how. It postulates failure of the entire system and then identifies how the components could contribute to the failure.

Deductive methods use a combined-events analysis, often in the form of decision trees. The positive tree shows the requirements for success. Positive trees are less commonly used than fault trees because they can easily become a list of "should," and subsequent moralizing could make it difficult to reach an endpoint.

Fault trees are reverse images of positive trees and show ways troubles can occur. The analyst selects an undesired event, then diagrams in tree form all the possible factors that can contribute to the occurrence of the undesired event. The branches of the tree continue until they reach independent factors. The analyst can then determine probabilities for the independent factors occurring.

The fault tree requires a thorough analysis of a potential event and involves listing all known sources of failure. It is a graphic model of the various parallel and sequential combinations of system component faults that can result in a single, selected system fault. Figure 5–2 illustrates three types of analytical trees.

Analytical trees have three advantages:
1. They accomplish a thorough analysis without wordiness. Using known data, the analyst can identify the single and multiple causes capable of inducing the undesired event.
2. They make the analytical process visible, allowing for the rapid transfer of hazard data from person to person and from group to group, with few possibilities for miscommunication during the transfer.
3. They can be used as investigative tools. By reasoning backward from the incident (the undesired event), the investigator can reconstruct the system and pinpoint the elements responsible for the undesired event.

Cost-Effectiveness Method

The cost-effectiveness method can be used as part of either the inductive or deductive approach. The cost of system changes made to increase safety is compared with the decreased costs of fewer serious failures or with the increased efficiency of the system. Cost-effectiveness is frequently used to decide among several systems, each capable of performing the same task.

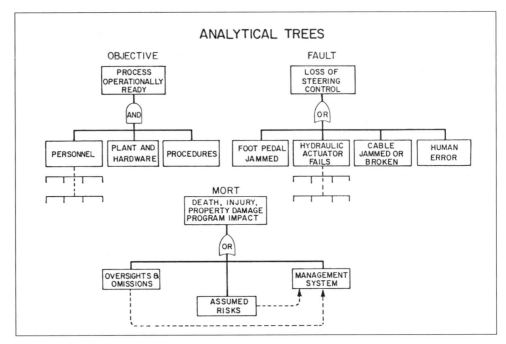

Figure 5–2. Analytical trees are nothing but "structured common sense." Trees are of two major types—objective or positive trees, which emphasize how a job should be done properly, and fault trees, which chart things that can go wrong and produce a specific failure. A fault tree structured for one job can often be generalized to cover a wide variety of jobs. The MORT diagram describes the ideal safety program in an orderly, logical manner. It is based on three branches: (1) a branch dealing with specific oversights and omissions at the worksite; (2) a branch that deals with the management system that establishes policies and makes the entire system go; and (3) an assumed-risk branch visually recognizing that no activity is completely risk-free and that risk management functions must exist in any well-managed organization.

Printed with permission from Professional Safety, February 1977.

Choosing a Method

To decide what hazard analytical approach is best for a given situation, the hazard control specialist will want to answer five questions:

1. What is the quantity and quality of information desired?
2. What information already is available?
3. What is the cost of setting up and conducting analyses?
4. How much time is available before decisions must be made and action taken?
5. How many people are available to assist in the hazard analysis, and what are their qualifications?

Conducting a hazard analysis can be expensive. Before a hazard analysis technique is chosen, it is important to determine what information is needed and how important it is.

It is beyond the scope of this manual to go into detail regarding other applications of system safety (Johnson, 1980).

WHO SHOULD PARTICIPATE IN HAZARD ANALYSIS?

A hazard analysis, to be fully effective and reliable, should represent as many different viewpoints as possible. Each person familiar with a process or operation has acquired insights concerning problems, faults, and situations that can cause unintentional injuries. These insights need to be recorded, along with those of the person initiating the hazard analysis—usually the safety professional. Input from workers and employee representatives can be extremely valuable at this stage.

WHAT FACTORS NEED TO BE ANALYZED?

All machines, equipment, processes, operations, and tasks in any establishment or facility are good candidates for hazard analysis because they have the potential to cause incidents. Eventually, hazard analyses should be completed for all jobs, but the most potentially threatening should have immediate attention. In determining which processes, operations, and tasks receive priority, those making the decisions should take the following factors into consideration:

- *Frequency of incidents*—Any operation or task with an associated history of repeated incidents is a good candidate for analysis, especially if different employees have the same kind of incident while performing the same operation or task.

- *Potential for injury*—Some processes and operations can have a low incident frequency but a high potential for major injury (e.g., tasks on a grinder conducted without a tool rest or tongue guard).

- *Severity of injury*—A particular process, operation, or task can have a history of serious injuries and be a worthy candidate for analysis, even if the frequency of such injuries is low.

- *New or altered equipment, processes, and operations*—As a general rule, whenever a new process, operation, or task is created or an old one altered (because of machinery, equipment, or other changes), the safety professional or supervisor should conduct a hazard analysis. For maximum benefit, the hazard analysis should be done while the process or operation is in the planning stages. No equipment should be put into regular operation until the safety professional has checked it for hazards, studied its operation, installed any necessary additional safeguards, and developed safety instructions or procedures. Adhering to such a procedure ensures that managers can train employees in hazard-controlled, safe operations and help prevent serious injuries and exposures.

- *Excessive material waste or damage to equipment*—Processes or operations producing excessive material waste or damage to tools and equipment are candidates for hazard analysis. The same problems causing the waste or damage could also, given the right situation, cause injuries.

One of the first steps in hazard and incident analysis is performing job safety analyses. They can be specifically tailored to individual jobs or categories of jobs in the workplace. This next section describes the nature of the job safety analyses and how they can be conducted.

JOB SAFETY ANALYSIS

Job safety analysis (JSA) is a procedure used to review job methods and uncover hazards that (1) may have been overlooked in the layout of the facility or building and in the design of the machinery, equipment, tools, workstations, and processes; (2) may have developed after production started; or (3) resulted from changes in work procedures or personnel.

A JSA can be written as shown in Figure 5–3. In the left column, the basic steps of the job are listed in the order in which they occur. The middle column describes all hazards, both those produced by the environment and those connected to the job procedure. The right column gives the safe procedures that should be followed to guard against the hazards, prevent potential injuries, and perform the job correctly. (See Figure 5–4 for a list of instructions printed on the back of JSA forms published by the National Safety Council.)

For convenience, both the JSA procedure and the written description are commonly referred to as JSA. Health hazards are also considered when making a JSA.

BENEFITS OF JSA
The principal benefits of a JSA include the following:
- reducing the frequency of injuries
- reducing the severity of injuries
- providing information to develop effective training programs
- instructing the new person on the job
- preparing for planned safety observations
- giving pre-job instruction on irregular jobs
- reviewing job procedures after incidents occur
- studying jobs for possible improvement in job methods.

A JSA can be done in three basic steps. However, before initiating this analysis, management must first carefully select the job to be analyzed.

SELECTING THE JOB
A job is a sequence of separate steps or activities that together accomplish a

JOB SAFETY ANALYSIS	JOB TITLE (and number if applicable): Banding Pallets		DATE:	☒ NEW
INSTRUCTIONS ON REVERSE SIDE		PAGE_1_ OF_2_ JSA NO._105_	00/00/00	☐ REVISED
	TITLE OF PERSON WHO DOES JOB: Bander	SUPERVISOR: James Smith	ANALYSIS BY: James Smith	
COMPANY/ORGANIZATION: XYZ Company	PLANT/LOCATION: Chicago	DEPARTMENT: Packaging	REVIEWED BY: Sharon Martin	
REQUIRED AND/OR RECOMMENDED PERSONAL PROTECTIVE EQUIPMENT: Gloves - Eye Protection - Long Sleeves - Safety Shoes			APPROVED BY: Joe Bottom	

SEQUENCE OF BASIC JOB STEPS	POTENTIAL HAZARDS	RECOMMENDED ACTION OR PROCEDURE
1. Position portable banding cart and place strapping guard on top of boxes.	1. Cart positioned too close to pallet (strike body & legs against cart or pallet, drop strapping gun on foot.)	1. Leave ample space between cart and pallet to feed strapping - have firm grip on strapping gun.
2. Withdraw strapping and bend end back about 3".	2. Sharp edges of strapping (cut hands, fingers & arms). Sharp corners on pallet (strike feet against corners).	2. Wear gloves, eye protection & long sleeves - keep firm grip on strapping - hold end between thumb & forefinger - watch where stepping.
3. Walk around load while holding strapping with one hand.	3. Projecting sharp corners on pallet (strike feet on corners).	3. Assure a clear path between pallet and cart - pull smoothly - avoid jerking strapping.
4. Pull and feed strap under pallet.	4. Splinters on pallet (punctures to hands and fingers.) Sharp strap edges (cuts to hands, fingers, and arms).	4. Wear gloves - eye protection - long sleeves. Point strap in direction of bend - pull strap smoothly to avoid jerks.
5. Walk around load. Stoop down. Bend over, grab strap, pull up to machine, straighten out strap end.	5. Protruding corners of pallet, splinters (punctures to feet and ankles).	5. Assure a clear path - watch where walking - face direction in which walking.
6. Insert, position and tighten strap in gun.	6. Springy and sharp strapping (strike against with hands and fingers).	6. Keep firm grasp on strap and on gun - make sure clip is positioned properly.

Figure 5–3. This sample of a completed JSA shows how hazards and safe procedures are identified to help reduce the occurrence of injuries.

work goal. Some jobs can be broadly defined by what is accomplished—for example, making paper, building a facility, and mining iron ore. On the other hand, a job can be narrowly defined in terms of a single action, such as turning a switch, tightening a screw, and pushing a button. Such broadly or narrowly defined jobs are unsuitable for JSA.

Jobs suitable for JSA are those assignments that a line supervisor may make. Operating a machine, tapping a furnace, and piling lumber are good subjects for job safety analyses because they are neither too broad nor too narrow.

Jobs should not be selected at random—those with the worst injury experience should be analyzed first if JSA is to yield the quickest results. In fact, some companies make such selections the focal point of their incident prevention program.

Selection of jobs to be analyzed and establishment of the order of analysis should be guided by the following factors:

INSTRUCTIONS FOR COMPLETING JOB SAFETY ANALYSIS FORM

Job Safety Analysis (JSA) is an important accident prevention tool that works by finding hazards and eliminating or minimizing them *before* the job is performed, and *before* they have a chance to become accidents. Use your JSA for job clarification and hazard awareness, as a guide in new employee training, for periodic contacts and for retraining of senior employees, as a refresher on jobs which run infrequently, as an accident investigation tool, and for informing employees of specific job hazards and protective measures.

Set priorities for doing JSAs: jobs that have a history of many accidents, jobs that have produced disabling injuries, jobs with high potential for disabling injury or death, and new jobs with no accident history.

Here's how to do each of the three parts of a Job Safety Analysis:

SEQUENCE OF BASIC JOB STEPS

Break the job down into steps. Each of the steps of a job should accomplish some major task. The task will consist of a *set* of movements. Look at the first *set* of movements used to perform a task, and then determine the next logical *set* of movements. For example, the job might be to move a box from a conveyor to a shelf in the storage area. How does that break down into job steps? Picking up the box from the conveyor and putting it on a handtruck is one logical set of movments, so it is one job step. Everything related to that one logical set of movements is part of that job step.

The next logical *set* of movements might be pushing the loaded handtruck to the storeroom. Removing the boxes from the truck and placing them on the shelf is another logical set of movements. And finally, returning the handtruck to the receiving area might be the final step in this type of job.

Be sure to list *all* the steps in a job. Some steps might not be done each time—checking the casters on a handtruck, for example. However, that task is a part of the job as a whole, and should be listed and analyzed.

POTENTIAL HAZARDS

Identify the hazards associated with each step. Examine each step to find and identify hazards—actions, conditions and possibilities that could lead to an accident.

It's not enough to look at the obvious hazards. It's also important to look at the entire environment and discover every conceivable hazard that might exist.

Be sure to list health hazards as well, even though the harmful effect may not be immediate. A good example is the harmful effect of inhaling a solvent or chemical dust over a long period of time.

It's important to list *all* hazards. Hazards contribute to accidents, injuries and occupational illnesses.

In order to do part three of a JSA effectively, you must identify potential and existing *hazards*. That's why it's important to distinguish between a hazard, an accident and an injury. Each of these terms has a specific meaning:

HAZARD—A potential danger. Oil on the floor is a *hazard*.

ACCIDENT—An unintended happening that may result in injury, loss or damage. Slipping on the oil is an *accident*.

INJURY—The *result* of an accident. A sprained wrist from the fall would be an injury.

Some people find it easier to identify possible accidents and illnesses and work back from them to the hazards. If you do that, you can list the accident and illness types in parentheses following the hazard. But be sure you focus on the *hazard* for developing recommended actions and safe work procedures.

RECOMMENDED ACTION OR PROCEDURE

Using the first two columns as a guide, decide what actions are necessary to eliminate or minimize the hazards that could lead to an accident, injury, or occupational illness.

Among the actions that can be taken are: 1) engineering the hazard out; 2) providing personal protective equipment; 3) job instruction training; 4) good housekeeping; and 5) good ergonomics (positioning the person in relation to the machine or other elements in the environment in such a way as to eliminate stresses and strains).

List recommended safe operating procedures on the form, and also list required or recommended personal protective equipment for each step of the job.

Be specific. Say *exactly* what needs to be done to correct the hazard, such as, "lift, using your leg muscles." Avoid general statements like, "be careful."

Give a recommended action or procedure for *every* hazard.

If the hazard is a serious one, it should be corrected immediately. The JSA should then be changed to reflect the new conditions.

Figure 5–4. Use these instructions for preparing a JSA.

- *Frequency of incidents*—The greater the number of unintentional injuries associated with the job, the greater its priority claim for a JSA.
- *Rate of disabling injuries*—Every job that has had disabling injuries should be given a JSA, particularly if the injuries prove that prior preventive action was not successful.
- *Severity potential*—Some jobs may not have a history of injuries but may have the potential for producing severe injury.
- *New jobs*—Changes in equipment or in processes obviously have no history of injuries, and thus their injury potential may not be fully appreciated. A JSA of every new job should be made as soon as the job has been created. Analysis should not be delayed until injuries or near misses occur.

After the job has been selected, the three basic steps in making a JSA are as follows:

1. Break the job down into successive steps or activities and observe how these actions are performed.

2. Identify the hazards and potential injuries. This is the critical step because only an identified problem can be eliminated.

3. Develop safe job procedures to eliminate the hazards and prevent the potential injuries.

BREAKING THE JOB DOWN INTO STEPS

Before the search for hazards begins, a job should be broken down into a sequence of steps, each describing what is being done. Avoid two common errors: (1) making the breakdown so detailed that an unnecessarily large number of steps results; or (2) making the job breakdown so general that basic steps are not recorded.

To do a job breakdown, select the right worker to observe—an experienced, capable, and cooperative person who is willing to share ideas. If the employee has never helped out on a job safety analysis, explain the purpose (to make a job safe by identifying and eliminating or controlling hazards) and show him or her a completed JSA. Reassure the employee that he or she was selected because of experience and capability.

Observe the employee perform the job and write down the basic steps. Consider videotaping the job as it is performed for later study. To determine the basic job steps, ask "What step starts the job?" Then ask, "What is the next basic step?" and so on.

Completely describe each step. Any possible deviation from the regular procedure should be recorded because this irregular activity may lead to an incident.

To record the breakdown, number the job steps consecutively as illustrated in the first column of the JSA training guide shown in Figure 5–5. Each step tells what is done, not how.

The wording for each step should begin with an action word such as *remove, open,* or *weld.* The action is completed by naming the item to which the action applies—for example, *remove extinguisher* or *carry to fire.*

Check the breakdown with the person observed and agree on what is done and the order of the steps. Thank the employee for helping to enhance workplace safety.

IDENTIFYING HAZARDS AND POTENTIAL INCIDENT CAUSES

Before filling in the next two columns of the JSA (Potential Hazards and Recommended Action or Procedure), begin the search for hazards. The purpose is to identify all hazards—both those produced by the environment and those connected with the job procedure. Each step, and thus the entire job, must be made safer and more efficient. To do this, ask these questions about each step:

JOB SAFETY ANALYSIS WORK SHEET
JOB: Using a Pressurized Water Fire Extinguisher

WHAT TO DO (Steps in sequence)	HOW TO DO IT (Instructions) (Reverse hands for left-handed operator.)	KEY POINTS (Items to be emphasized. Safety is always a key point.)
1. Remove extinguisher from wall bracket.	1. Left hand on bottom lip, fingers curled around lip, palm up. Right hand on carrying handle palm down, fingers around carrying handle only.	1. Check air pressure to make certain extinguisher is charged. Stand close to extinguisher, pull straight out. *Have firm grip, to prevent dropping on feet.* Lower, and as you do remove left hand from lip.
2. Carry to fire.	2. Carry in right hand, upright position.	2. Extinguisher should hang down alongside leg. (This makes it easy to carry and reduces possibility of strain.)
3. Remove pin.	3. Set extinguisher down in upright position. Place left hand on top of extinguisher, pull out pin with right hand.	3. Hold extinguisher steady with left hand. Do not exert pressure on discharge lever as you remove pin.
4. Squeeze discharge lever.	4. Place right hand over carrying handle with fingers curled around operating lever handle while grasping discharge hose near nozzle with left hand.	4. Have firm grip on handle to steady extinguisher.
5. Apply water stream to fire.	5. Direct water stream at base of fire.	5. Work from side to side or around fire. After extinguishing flames, play water on smouldering or glowing surfaces.
6. Return extinguisher. Report use.		

Figure 5–5. This JSA worksheet shows how to break down a job and analyze hazards and procedures.

- Is there a danger of striking against, being struck by, or otherwise making harmful contact with an object?
- Can the employee be caught in, by, or between objects?
- Is there a potential for a slip or trip? Can the employee fall on the same level or to another?
- Can strain be caused by pushing, pulling, lifting, bending, or twisting?
- Is the environment hazardous to safety or health?

Close observation and knowledge of the particular job are required if the JSA is to be effective. The job observation should be repeated as often as necessary until all hazards and potential causes for incident or injury have been identified.

When inspecting a particular machine or operation, ask the question, "Can an injury occur here?" If yes, then develop more specific questions.

Questions will be of most value if they are incorporated into an inspection form that can be filled out at regular intervals. Even though a question may not at first seem to apply to a specific operation, on closer scrutiny it may be found to apply. Using a checklist is a good way to make sure nothing is overlooked.

To complete column 2 of the JSA, the analyzer should list all potential causes for incidents or injuries and all hazards yielded by a survey of the machine or operation. Record the type of potential cause of injuries and the agents involved. For example, to note that the employee may injure a foot by dropping a fire extinguisher, write down *struck by extinguisher*.

Again, check with the observed employee after the hazards and potential causes of injuries have been recorded. The experienced employee will probably offer additional suggestions. Also check with others experienced with the job. Through observation and discussion, the analyzer can develop a reliable list of hazards and potential injuries.

DEVELOPING SOLUTIONS

The final step in a JSA is to develop a recommended safe job procedure to prevent the occurrence of incidents. The principal solutions are as follows:
1. Find a new way to do the job.
2. Change the physical conditions that create the hazards.
3. Change the work procedure.
4. Reduce the frequency (particularly helpful in maintenance and materials handling).

To find an entirely new way to do a job, determine the work goal of the job, and then analyze the various ways of reaching this goal to see which way is safest. Consider work-saving tools and equipment.

If a new way cannot be found, then ask this question about each hazard and potential injury cause listed: "What change in physical condition (such as change in tools, materials, equipment, layout, or location) will eliminate the hazard or prevent the potential injury?"

When a change is found, study it carefully to find other benefits (such as greater production or time saving) that will accrue. These benefits are good selling points and should be pointed out when proposing the change to higher management.

To investigate changes in the job procedure, ask the following questions about each hazard and potential injury cause listed: "What should the employee do—or not do—to eliminate this particular hazard or prevent this potential injury?" "How should it be done?" Because of his or her experience, in most cases the supervisor can answer these questions.

Answers must be specific and concrete if new procedures are to be any good. General precautions—"be alert," "use caution," or "be careful"—have limited value. Answers should precisely state what to do and how to do it. The recommendation, "Make certain the wrench does not slip or cause loss of balance," is incomplete. It does not tell how to prevent the wrench from slipping. Here, in contrast, is an example of a recommended safe procedure that tells both what and how: "Set wrench properly and securely. Test its grip by exerting a light pressure on it. Brace yourself against something immovable or take a solid stance with feet wide apart before exerting full pressure. This prevents loss of balance if the wrench slips."

Some repair or service jobs have to be repeated often because a condition needs repeated correction. To reduce the need for such repetition, ask, "What can be done to eliminate the cause of the condition that makes excessive repairs or service necessary?" If the cause cannot be eliminated, then ask, "Can anything be done to minimize the effects of the condition?"

However, reducing the frequency of a job contributes to safety only in that it limits the exposure. Every effort should still be made to eliminate hazards and to prevent injuries through changing physical conditions, revising job procedures, or both.

A job that has been redesigned may affect other jobs and even the entire work process. Therefore, the redesign should be discussed not only with the worker involved, but also with co-workers, the supervisor, the facility engineer, and others who are concerned. In all cases, however, check or test the proposed changes by observing the job after discussing the changes with those who do the job. Their ideas about the hazards and proposed solutions can be of considerable value. They can judge the practicality of proposed changes and perhaps suggest improvements. These discussions are more than just a way to check a JSA. They are safety contacts that promote awareness of job hazards and safe procedures.

USING JSA EFFECTIVELY

The major benefits of a JSA come after its completion. However, benefits are also to be gained from the development work. While conducting a JSA, supervisors learn more about the job they supervise. When employees are encouraged to participate in job safety analyses, their safety attitudes improve and their knowledge of safety increases. As a JSA is worked out, safer and better job procedures and safer working conditions are developed. But these important benefits are only a portion of the total benefits listed at the beginning of this discussion.

When a JSA is distributed, the supervisor's first responsibility is to explain its contents to employees and, if necessary, to give them further individual training. The entire JSA must be reviewed with the employees concerned so that they will know how the job is to be done—without injuries.

The JSA can furnish material for planned safety contacts. All steps of the JSA should be used for this purpose. The steps that present major hazards should be emphasized and reviewed again and again in subsequent safety contacts.

New employees on the job must be trained in the basic job steps, taught to recognize the hazards associated with each job step, and instructed in the necessary precautions. There is no better guide for this training than a well-prepared JSA. (See Chapter 7, Safety and Health Training, for further discussion of job instruction training.)

Occasionally, the supervisor should observe employees as they perform the jobs for which analyses have been developed. The purpose of these observations is to determine whether employees are doing the jobs in accordance with the safe job procedures. Before making such observations, the supervisor should prepare by reviewing the appropriate JSA to keep in mind the key points to observe.

Whenever an incident occurs on a job covered by a JSA, the JSA should be reviewed to determine whether it needs revision. If the JSA is revised, all employees concerned with the job should be informed of the changes and instructed in any new procedures.

When an incident results from failure to follow JSA procedures, the facts should be discussed with all those who do the job. It should be made clear that the incident would not have occurred had the JSA procedures been followed.

All supervisors are concerned with improving job methods to increase safety and health, reduce costs, and step up production. The JSA is an excellent starting point for questioning the established way of doing a job. In addition, study of the JSA may well suggest ideas for improvement of job methods.

Once the hazards are known, the proper solutions can be developed. Some solutions may be physical changes that eliminate or control the hazard, such as placing a safeguard over exposed moving machine parts. Others may be job procedures that eliminate or minimize the hazard, such as safe piling of materials. If these solutions do not completely or sufficiently control the hazard, personal protective equipment may be necessary to safely perform the job (see Chapter 13, Personal Protective Equipment (PPE)). A combination of these solutions may also provide a safe work environment.

The first stage of the hazard and incident analysis procedure is inspection. Management must know what problems and potential injury causes may be present in the workplace and what unsafe procedures or practices workers may be performing.

INSPECTION

Inspection should be conducted in an organization to locate and report existing and potential unsafe conditions or activities that, if left uncontrolled, have the capacity to cause injuries in the workplace.

PHILOSOPHY BEHIND INSPECTION
Depending on the conditions surrounding the process, an inspection can be viewed negatively as

- fault-finding, with the emphasis on criticism

or positively as

- fact-finding, with the emphasis on locating hazards and developing plans for eliminating hazards that can adversely affect safety and health.

The second viewpoint is more effective. This viewpoint depends on two factors: (1) performance indicators adequate for measuring a particular situation; and (2) comparison of what is with what ought to be (Firenze, 1978). Failure to analyze inspection reports for causes of system defects ultimately means the failure of the monitoring function. Corrective action may fix the specific item but fail to fix the system.

PURPOSE OF INSPECTION

The primary purpose of inspection is to detect potential hazards so they can be corrected before an unintentional injury or illness occurs. Inspection can determine conditions that need to be corrected or improved to bring operations up to acceptable standards, from both safety and operational standpoints. Secondary purposes are to improve operations and thus to increase efficiency, effectiveness, and profitability.

Although management ultimately has the responsibility for inspecting the workplace, authority for carrying out the actual inspecting process extends throughout the organization. Obviously supervisors, foremen, and employees fulfill an inspection function, but so do departments as diverse as engineering, purchasing, quality control, human resources, maintenance, and medical.

TYPES OF INSPECTION

Inspection can be classified as one of two types, continuous or interval inspection.

Continuous Inspection

This process is conducted by employees, supervisors, and maintenance personnel as part of their job responsibilities. Continuous inspection involves noting an apparently or potentially hazardous condition or unsafe procedure and either correcting it immediately or making a report to initiate corrective action. Continuous inspection of personal protective equipment is especially important.

This type of inspection is sometimes called informal because it does not conform to a set schedule, plan, or checklist. However, critics argue that continuous inspection is erratic and superficial, that it does not get into out-of-the-way places, and that it misses too much. The truth is that both continuous and interval inspections are necessary and complement one another.

As part of their job, supervisors make sure that tools, machines, and equipment are properly maintained and safe to use and that safety precautions are being observed.

Toolroom employees regularly inspect all hand tools to be sure that they are in safe condition. Foremen are often responsible for continuously monitoring the workplace and seeing that equipment is safe and that employees are observing safe practices. When foremen or supervisors inspect machines at the beginning of a shift, a safety inspection must be part of the operation.

Continuous inspection is one ultimate goal of a good safety and health program. It means that each individual is vigilant, alert to any condition having incident potential, and willing to initiate corrective action.

However, in some instances, the supervisor's greatest advantage in continuous inspection—familiarity with the employees, equipment, machines, and environment—can also be a disadvantage. Just as an old newspaper left on a table in time becomes part of the decor, a hazard can become so familiar that no one notices it. The supervisor's blind spot is particularly likely to occur with housekeeping and unsafe practices. Poor housekeeping conditions may be overlooked because the deterioration is gradual and the effect is cumulative. A similar phenomenon may occur with unsafe practices, such as employees not following established production procedures.

In addition, no matter how conscientious the supervisors are, it is difficult to be completely objective. Inspections of their areas reflect personal and vested interests, knowledge and understanding of the production problems involved in the area, and concern for the employees. A planned periodic inspection of their areas by another supervisor can be used to audit their efforts. Furthermore, the supervisors who inspect another area may return to their own sections with renewed vision. Having looked at the trees day in and day out, they need occasionally to take the long view and see the forest.

Though this section is devoted primarily to discussing planned inspections, continuous inspections should be regarded as a cooperative, not a competitive, activity.

Interval Inspections

Planned inspections at specific intervals are what most people regard as "real" safety and health inspections. They are deliberate, thorough, and systematic procedures that permit examination of specific items or conditions. They follow an established procedure and use checklists for routine items. These inspections can be any one of three types: periodic, intermittent, and general.

Periodic inspection includes inspections scheduled at regular intervals. They can target the entire facility, a specific area, a specific operation, or a specific type of equipment. Management can plan these inspections weekly, monthly, semiannually, annually, or at other suitable intervals. Items such as safety guard mountings, scaffolds, elevator wire ropes (cables), two-hand controls, fire extinguishers, and other items relied on for safety require frequent inspection. The more serious the potential for injury or damage, the more often the item should be inspected.

Periodic inspections can be of several different types:

- inspections by the safety professional, industrial hygienist, and joint safety and health committees
- inspections for preventing incidents and damage or breakdowns (checking mechanical functioning, lubricating, etc.) performed by electricians, mechanics, and maintenance personnel; sometimes these persons are asked to serve as roving inspectors
- inspections by specially trained certified or licensed inspectors, often from outside the organization (e.g., inspection of boilers, elevators, unfired pressure vessels, cranes, power presses, fire-extinguishing equipment). These are often mandated inspections required by regulatory agencies, manufacturers, underwriters, or management
- inspections done by outside investigators or government inspectors to determine compliance with government regulations.

The advantage of periodic inspection is that it covers a specific area and allows detection of unsafe conditions in time to provide effective countermeasures. Measurement data collected at regular intervals indicate degenerative trends. The staff or safety committee periodically inspecting a certain area is familiar with operations and procedures and therefore quick to recognize deviations. A disadvantage of periodic inspection is that deviations from accepted practices are rarely discovered because employees are prepared for the inspectors.

Intermittent inspections are those made at irregular intervals. Sometimes the need for an inspection is indicated by incident tabulations and analysis. If a particular department or location shows an unusual number of incidents or if certain types of injuries occur with greater frequency, the supervisor or manager should call for an inspection. When construction or remodeling is going on within or around a facility, an unscheduled inspection may be needed to find and correct unsafe conditions before an intentional injury or illness occurs. The same is true when a department installs new equipment, institutes new processes, or modifies old ones.

Another form of intermittent inspection is that made by the industrial hygienist when a health hazard is suspected or present in the environment. It usually involves the following tasks:

- sampling the air for the presence of toxic vapors, gases, radiation, and particulates
- sampling physical stresses such as noise, heat, and radiation
- testing materials for toxic properties
- testing ventilation and exhaust systems for proper operation.

Intermittent inspections may be initiated because of the following reasons:
- increase in injury or illness rates in an area
- reports from employees in an area
- management directive
- reports of hazards from other departments, companies, manufacturers, or regulatory agencies
- random selection
- incident/severity potential
- reaction to an event (e.g., injury, threat of sabotage, severe weather warning).

A general inspection is usually planned and often covers places not inspected periodically. This includes areas no one ever visits and where people rarely get hurt, such as parking lots, sidewalks, fencing, and similar outlying regions.

PLANNING AND CONDUCTING AN INSPECTION

An effective safety and health inspection program requires the following elements:
- sound knowledge of the facility
- knowledge of relevant standards, regulations, and codes
- systematic inspection steps
- a method of reporting, evaluating, and using the data.

An effective program begins with analysis and planning. If inspections are casual, shallow, and slipshod, the results will reflect the method. Before instituting an inspection program, these five questions should be answered:
1. What items need to be inspected?
2. What aspects of each item need to be examined?
3. What conditions need to be inspected?
4. How often must items be inspected?
5. Who will conduct the inspection?

HAZARD CONTROL INSPECTION INVENTORY

To determine what factors affect the inspection, a hazard control inspection inventory can be conducted. Such an inventory is the foundation on which a program of planned inspection is based. It resembles a planned preventive maintenance system and yields many of the same benefits.

Management should divide the entire facility—yards, buildings, equipment, machinery, vehicles—into areas of responsibility. These areas, once determined, should be listed in an orderly fashion. The analyst may develop a color-coded map or floor plan of the facility. Large areas or departments can be divided into smaller areas and assigned to each first-line supervisor and/or the hazard control department's inspector.

WHAT ITEMS NEED TO BE INSPECTED?

Once specific areas of responsibility have been determined, managers should inventory areas of responsibility that could impact safety and health.

There are many sources of information about items to be inspected, especially employees in an organization. For instance, maintenance employees know what problems can cause damage or shutdowns. The workers in the area are qualified to point out causes of injury, illness, damage, delays, or bottlenecks. Medical personnel in the organization can list problems causing job-related illnesses and injuries. Manufacturers' manuals often specify maintenance schedules and procedures and safe work methods.

It is important to remember, however, that federal and state or provincial laws, codes, and regulations usually set up minimum requirements only. To comply with company policy and ensure a safe working environment, management must often exceed these regulatory requirements. Some OSHA publications indicate not only what standards are required but also what violations are most frequent. These same sources are helpful in the next step—determining critical factors to be inspected.

WHAT CONDITIONS NEED TO BE INSPECTED?

The unsafe conditions for each part to be inspected should be described specifically and clearly. A checklist question that reads "Is ___ safe?" is meaningless because it does not define what makes an item unsafe. Inspectors should describe the elements that contribute to an unsafe condition and not simply list unsafe conditions for each item. Usually, conditions described by physical descriptions can be indicated by such words as *jagged, exposed, broken, frayed, leaking, rusted, corroded, missing, vibrating, loose,* or *slipping.*

Checklists serve as reminders of what to look for and as records of what has been covered. They can be used to structure and guide inspections. They also allow on-the-spot recording of all findings and comments before they are forgotten. In case an inspection is interrupted, checklists provide a record of what has and has not been inspected. Otherwise, inspectors may miss items or conditions they should examine or may be unsure, after inspecting an area, that they have covered everything. Good checklists also help in follow-up work to make sure hazards have been corrected or eliminated.

Many types of monitoring checklists are available, varying in length from thousands of items to only a few. These checklists are useful in determining which standards or regulations apply to individual situations. Once the applicable standards are identified, the organization can tailor a checklist to its needs and uses and enter it into the computer system for action and follow-up.

The Centers for Disease Control of the U.S. Department of Health and Human Services (DHHS) have devised a suggested checklist for the safety evaluation of shop and laboratory areas. The worksheet is referenced to the OSHA General Industry Standards.

Merely running through a checklist, however, does little to locate or correct problems. The checklist must be used as an aid to the inspection process, not as an end in itself. Of course, any hazard observed during inspection must be recorded, even though it is not part of the checklist. Sample inspection checklists from various companies are available at the National Safety Council website (nsc.org). These are used with computer follow-up on inspection results, actions to be taken, and corrections made.

The amount of detail included in the checklist will vary, depending on the inspector's knowledge of the relevant standards and the nature of the inspection. An experienced inspector with thorough knowledge of the standards will need only a few clues as a reminder of items to be inspected. Checklists for infrequent inspection generally will be more detailed than daily or weekly ones.

The format of a checklist should include columns to indicate either compliance or action date. Space also should be provided to cite the specific violation, a way to correct it, and a recommendation that the condition receive more or less frequent attention. Whatever the format of the checklist, space should be provided for the inspector's signature and the inspection date.

Checklists can be prepared by the safety and health committee, by the safety director, or by a subcommittee that includes engineers, supervisors, employees, and maintenance personnel. The safety professional and the department supervisor should monitor checklist development and make sure all applicable standards are covered. In their final form, the checklists should conform to the inspection route.

Choosing the inspection route means inspecting an area completely and thoroughly while avoiding the following:

- time-consuming backtracking and repetitions

- long walks between items
- unnecessary interruptions of the production process
- distraction of employees.

Often, a closed-loop inspection will give good results. Sometimes, it is valuable to follow the production path of the material being processed.

It is important to remember that a checklist is a tool and should be used only to support the safety process. Once unsafe conditions have been identified, it is important to provide workable solutions for addressing the situation in a safe manner.

HOW OFTEN MUST ITEMS BE INSPECTED?

The frequency of inspection is determined by four factors:

1. What is the loss severity potential of the problem? The inspector should ask, "If the item or critical part fails, what injury, damage, or work interruption will result?" The more severe the loss potential, the more often the item should be inspected. For instance, a frayed wire rope on an overhead crane block has the potential to cause a much greater loss than does a defective wheel on a wheelbarrow. Therefore, the rope needs to be inspected more frequently than the wheel.

2. What is the potential for injury to employees? If the item or critical part fails, how many employees will be endangered and how frequently? The greater the probability for injury to employees, the more often the item should be inspected. For example, a stairway continually used by many people needs to be inspected more frequently than one seldom used.

3. How quickly can the item or part become unsafe? The answer to this question depends on the nature of the part and the conditions to which it is subjected. Equipment and tools used frequently can become damaged, defective, or worn more quickly than those rarely used. An item located in a particular spot can be exposed to greater damage than an identical item in a different location. The faster an item can become unsafe, the more frequently it should be inspected.

4. What is the past history of failures? What were the results of these failures? Maintenance and production records and incident investigation reports can provide valuable information about how frequently items have failed and the results in terms of injuries, damage, delays, and shutdowns. The more often an item has failed in the past and the greater the consequences, the more it needs to be inspected.

The Occupational Safety and Health Administration, the Mine Safety and Health Administration (MSHA), the Federal Aviation Administration (FAA), the Nuclear Regulatory Commission (NRC), the Environmental Protection Agency (EPA), and other federal, state, provincial, and local regulatory agencies require periodic inspections. Consult the regulations and the agency responsible for enforcement for current information regarding inspection criteria and intervals. Frequency of inspections should be described in specific terms—for example, before every use, when serviced, daily, monthly, quarterly, yearly.

WHO WILL CONDUCT THE INSPECTION?

Answering the four previous questions—the items to be inspected, the aspects of each item to be inspected, the conditions to be inspected, and the frequency of inspections—will help determine who is qualified to do the inspection. No individual or group should have exclusive responsibility for all inspections. Employees who perform these inspections will benefit from training in hazard recognition. Some items will need to be inspected by more than one person. For example, although an area supervisor may inspect an overhead crane weekly and maintenance personnel inspect it monthly, the operator of the crane will inspect it before each use. When grinding wheels are received, they are inspected by the stockroom attendant, but they must be inspected again by the operator before each use.

As part of the hazard control inspection inventory, management should assign responsibility for each inspection.

Safety Professionals

Clearly, the safety professional should spearhead the inspection activity. During both individual and group inspections, the professional can educate others in inspection techniques and hazard identification by using on-the-spot examples and firsthand contact. Supervisors, foremen, stewards, and safety and health committees can be shown what to look for when making inspections. The organization's fire protection representative or industrial hygienist usually works with the hazard control specialist in conducting inspections.

Company or Facility Management

Safety inspections should be considered part of the duties of company or facility management. By participating in inspections, management demonstrates its commitment to maintaining a safe working environment. But the psychological effect of inspection by senior executives goes beyond merely showing an interest in safety. When employees know that management is coming to inspect their area, conditions that seemed "good enough" suddenly appear unsatisfactory and are quickly corrected.

First-Line Supervisor or Foreman

Because supervisors and foremen spend practically all of their time in the shop or facility, they are continually monitoring the workplace. At least once a day, supervisors need to check their areas to see that (1) employees are complying with safety regulations; (2) guards and warning signs are in place; (3) tools and machinery are in safe condition; (4) aisles and passageways are clear and proper clearances maintained; and (5) material in process is properly stacked or stored.

Employees

As mentioned previously, employee participation in continuous inspection is one goal of an effective hazard control program. Before beginning the workday, the employee should inspect the workplace and any tools, equipment, and machinery that will be used. Any defects the employee is not authorized to correct should be reported immediately to the supervisor. Action resulting from this report must be reported to the employee to encourage further participation.

Joint Safety and Health Committees

Joint safety and health committees (discussed in Chapter 6, Loss Control and Prevention) conduct inspections as part of their function. They give equal consideration to factors that could cause incidents, fires, and adverse health exposures. By periodically visiting areas, members may notice changed conditions more readily than someone who is there every day. Another advantage provided by the committee is the members' various backgrounds, experience, and knowledge represented.

If the committee is large, the territory should be divided among teams of manageable size. Large groups going through the facility are unwieldy and distracting.

Other Inspection Teams

If there is no safety and health committee, a planned, formal inspection is still necessary. Management should assign an inspection team that is multi-disciplined and includes the hazard control specialist, production manager, supervisor, employee representative, fire-prevention specialist, and industrial hygienist. The important point is that inspections should be directed by a responsible executive who has the authority to ensure that the work is carried out effectively.

Outside inspectors sometimes are needed to perform inspections. For example, insurance company safety engineers and local, state or county, and federal inspectors may lend their expertise to specific inspections.

Contractors' Inspection Services

For some technical systems, notably sprinkler systems, contracting companies furnish inspection services. Companies without either qualified safety professionals or a well-established maintenance program can avail themselves of such services.

RECORDING HAZARDS

Inspectors should locate and describe each hazard found during inspection. A clear description of the hazard should be written down, with questions and details recorded for later use. It is important to determine which hazards present the most serious threat and are most likely to occur. The hazard-ranking scheme described in Chapter 6, Loss Control and Prevention, will simplify the job of classifying hazards.

WRITING THE INSPECTION REPORT

Every inspection must be documented in a clearly written report furnished by the inspector. Without a complete and accurate report, the inspection would be little more than an interesting sightseeing tour. Inspection reports are usually one of three types:

1. *Emergency*—Made without delay when a critical or catastrophic hazard is probable. Using the classification system described in Chapter 6, Loss Control and Prevention, this category would include any items marked IA or IIA.
2. *Periodic*—Covers unsatisfactory nonemergency conditions observed during the planned periodic inspection. This report should be made within 24 hours of the inspection. Periodic reports can be initial, follow-up, final, or a combination of all three.
3. *Summary*—Lists all items of previous periodic reports for a given time.

FOLLOW-UP FOR CORRECTIVE ACTION

After the inspection report has been written and disseminated, the inspection process starts to return benefits. The information acquired and the recommendations made are valueless unless management takes corrective action. Information and recommendations provide the basis for establishing priorities and implementing programs that will reduce unintentional injuries, improve conditions, raise morale, and increase the efficiency and effectiveness of the operation.

In making recommendations, inspectors should be guided by four rules:

1. *Correct the cause whenever possible.* Do not merely correct the result, leaving the problem intact. In other words, be sure the disease and not just the symptom is cured. If the inspector or supervisor does not have the authority to correct the real cause, the inspector should bring it to the attention of the person who does.

2. *Immediately correct everything possible.* If the inspector has been granted the authority and opportunity to take direct corrective action, he or she should take it. Delays risk injuries.

3. *Report conditions beyond one's authority and suggest solutions.* Inform management of the condition, the potential consequences of hazards found, and solutions for correction. Even when nothing seems to come of a recommendation, it can pay unexpected dividends.

4. *Take intermediate action as needed.* When permanent correction takes time, the hazard should not be ignored. Inspectors or supervisors should take any temporary measures they can, such as roping off the area, locking and tagging out equipment or machines, or posting warning signs. These measures may not be ideal, but they are better than doing nothing.

PREPARING THE INCIDENT INVESTIGATION REPORT

Chapter 4, Injury and Illness Record Keeping, Incidence Rates, and Analysis, outlines specific ways to record and classify data: how to identify key facts about each injury and the incident that produced it, how to record facts on a form that facilitates analysis and reveals patterns and trends, how to estimate incident costs, and how to comply with regulatory record-keeping requirements.

An unintentional injury in any organization is of significant interest to employees, who will ask questions that reflect their concerns. Is there any potential danger to those in the immediate vicinity? What caused the incident? How many people were injured? How badly?

Those who investigate incidents should answer these questions truthfully and avoid covering up any facts. On the other hand, they must be certain that they are authorized to release information, and they must be sure of their data.

Because the incident report is the product of the investigation, it should be prepared carefully and adequately to justify the conclusions reached. It must be issued soon after the incident. When a report is delayed too long, employees may feel left out of the process. If a final report must be postponed pending detailed technical analysis or evaluation, then management should issue an interim report providing basic details of the investigation.

Summaries of vital information on major injury, damage, and loss incidents should be distributed to department managers. Such summaries should include information on incident causes and recommended action for preventing similar incidents. Management should maintain incident and statistical report files as dictated by company policy.

Supervisors need to keep employees informed of significant injuries and preventive measures proposed or executed. Posting incident reports is one way to make information available.

IMPLEMENTING CORRECTIVE ACTION

The preceding section on inspection emphasized that hazard control benefits accrue only after the inspection report is written and disseminated. Until corrective action is initiated, any recommendations—no matter how earnest, thorough, and relevant—remain "paper promises."

The same is true of incident investigation when it is used as a monitoring technique. Viewed from the perspective of hazard control, incident investigation serves as a monitoring function only when it provides the impetus for corrective action.

SUMMARY

- Monitoring, a vital management tool, is a set of observation and data-collection methods used to detect and measure deviations from plans and procedures in current operations. It involves hazard analysis, job safety analysis, inspection, measurement and testing, and incident investigation.
- Inductive or deductive hazard analysis is an orderly process used to acquire specific hazard and failure data pertinent to a given system. Factors such as frequency of incidents; potential for injury; severity of injury; new or altered equipment, processes, and operations; and excessive material waste or damage to equipment determine which tasks or processes are analyzed.
- Job safety analyses are the first step of hazard analysis. JSAs are used to identify and analyze potential hazards and causes of incidents within each job or within specific categories of jobs.
- The primary purpose of inspection is to detect potential hazards so they can be corrected before an incident occurs. Continuous inspections are a routine part of the job. Planned inspections are more formal procedures that may be periodic, intermittent, or general. Inspectors report all hazards—classifying and describing them carefully—and recommend corrective actions.

- Measurement and testing methods are used to monitor chemical, physical, biological, and ergonomic hazards. Four monitoring systems are used: personal, environmental, biological, and medical.
- Standards used to establish health and safety limits include Threshold Limit Values (TLVs), time-weighted averages (TWAs—exposures averaged over a set time, usually 8 hours), short-term exposure limits (STELs—exposure limits are usually higher than TLVs or PELs but are used to evaluate much shorter time periods), permissible exposure limits (PELs), and action levels (ALs). Measurements are divided into the problem definition phase, the problem analysis phase, and the solution phase.
- Incident investigations are conducted to determine direct causes, uncover contributing incident causes, prevent similar incidents, document facts, provide information on costs, and promote safety.
- Incidents must be investigated immediately to ensure accurate details and to preserve evidence. Investigators can be supervisors, safety professionals, special committees, or health and safety committees.
- Investigators must examine all human, situational, and environmental factors in determining incident causes and apply the five-step method for interviewing incident victims and witnesses. An investigation report should be issued as soon as possible and contain recommendations for corrective action.

REVIEW QUESTIONS

1. Define hazard analysis.
2. List the two formal methods of hazard analysis.
3. In determining which hazard analysis approach to use for a given situation, the hazard control specialist will need to answer which five questions?
4. In order to decide which processes, operations, and tasks receive priority, what are the five factors that need to be analyzed?
5. Define job safety analysis (JSA).
6. After a job has been selected for analysis, what are the three basic steps in conducting a JSA?
7. Inspecting is the first stage of the hazard and incident analysis procedure. What is the general purpose of an inspection?
8. List and briefly explain the two types of inspections.

9. The toolroom employee examines all tools before sending them out to be used. What is this type of inspection called?
    a. general
    b. intermittent
    c. continuous
    d. periodic
10. Gathering information about standards, regulations, and codes is the first step in determining what items need to be inspected. What sources of information are available to assist in this process?
11. List the four factors that determine the frequency of inspections.
12. Name and briefly define the four kinds of monitoring systems.
13. The toxicity of a material refers to
    a. its potential for being a health hazard.
    b. its capacity to produce injury or harm.
    c. a standard measure of percentage of particles.
    d. all of the above
14. Define threshold limit values (TLVs).
15. Define permissible exposure limits (PELs).
16. List the six main outcomes of an incident investigation.
17. Why is it important to investigate incidents immediately?

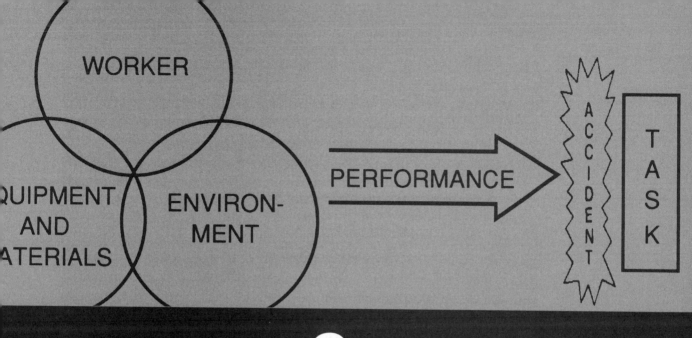

6

Loss Control and Prevention

LEARNING OBJECTIVES

- ❏ Develop an understanding of elements related to incident causation, using after-the-fact and before-the-fact analysis.
- ❏ Develop a working definition of what constitutes a hazard.
- ❏ Develop an understanding of theories and remedies related to liability in the workplace.
- ❏ Name and describe the primary objectives underlying workers' compensation laws.
- ❏ Determine what workers' compensation covers and limitations on that coverage.
- ❏ Understand the roles and support that a safety committee can provide to an organization.
- ❏ Identify what methods can be used to evaluate risk related to safety hazards.
- ❏ Understand the various roles of support functions in an organization for addressing risk—from housekeeping to purchasing.

INTRODUCTION

Before the concept of loss control was developed, accidents were regarded as either chance occurrences or acts of God—a view still held by some—or as an inherent consequence of production. Such approaches accept accidents as inevitable and, therefore, yield no information about causation and prevention. Control strategies are limited to mitigating the consequences of the occurrence.

In the early days of loss control, accident prevention activities focused on the human element. Findings indicated that a small proportion of workers accounted for a significant percentage of accidents. Control strategies were devised to reduce human error through training, education, motivation, communication, and other forms of behavior modification. During World War II, industrial psychology was aimed at matching employees to particular jobs. Personnel screening and selection were seen as the primary ways to prevent accidents. However, accident proneness and other behavior models have a glaring weakness: although they are useful for understanding human behavior, they do not consider the interaction between the worker and the other parts of the system.

The 1950s and 1960s saw the emphasis change to engineering and control programs aimed at machines and equipment. Further, the implementation of the Occupational Safety and Health Act of 1970 (OSH Act) emphasized preventing accidents through control of the work environment and the elements of the workplace. This act, along with other legislation, specified compliance by employers with promulgated safety and health standards and other rules and regulations.

In the 1980s and 1990s, there was a realization that even with all of the above, "accidents" still occurred. Focus returned to an emphasis on the human element, and the commitment and culture of the organization were important issues. Clearly, emphasis on any one area does not bring about permanent reduction of unintentional injuries and losses. A balance between applying all feasible engineering and control programs aimed at machines and equipment and applying human behavior modification, motivation, and training techniques must be achieved.

In the 1990s, the National Safety Council continued to work to increase awareness that an incident is a near accident, and that so-called accidents are not random events, but rather preventable events. The council changed its mission statement to eliminate the word "accident":

> The mission of the National Safety Council is to educate and influence society to adopt safety, health, and environmental policies, practices, and procedures that prevent and mitigate human suffering and economic losses arising from preventable causes.

To further increase awareness that so-called accidents are preventable, the council has tried to reduce use of the word *accident* in its publications, substituting more specific terms such as *unintentional injury* or *accidental injury*.

During the late 1990s to the present time, the council further clarified its mission statement to read:

> The mission statement of the National Safety Council is to saves lives by preventing injuries and deaths at work, in homes, and on the roads through leadership, research, education and advocacy.

Unintentional injury or *accidental injury* is the preferred term in the public health community. It refers to the result of an accident.

With proper hazard identification and evaluation, management commitment and support, preventive and corrective procedures, monitoring, evaluation, and training, most unintentional injuries can be prevented.

MANAGEMENT OVERSIGHT AND OMISSION

Over the past few decades, many organizations seeking to reduce hazards have focused on system defects, which result from management's lack of oversight or omission, or on malfunction of the management system. A balanced approach to loss control looks at each component of the system and includes such weaknesses as inadequate training and education, improper assignment of responsibility, unsuitable equipment, and failure to fund hazard control programs. Because managers are responsible for the design, implementation, and maintenance of systems, management errors can result in system defects.

EXAMINING INCIDENT CAUSATION

There are several basic approaches to examining how incidents are caused. These basic approaches include after-the-fact, before-the-fact, critical-incident technique, and safety sampling.

After-the-Fact

This approach relies on examining incidents after they have occurred to determine the cause and to develop corrective measures. Evaluation of past performance uses information derived from incident and inspection reports, workers' compensation data, and insurance audits. This approach is too often used only after a serious incident has resulted in injury or damage or system ineffectiveness. Furthermore, incident frequency and severity rates do not answer the crucial questions of how, what, why, and when incidents or near misses occur.

Before-the-Fact

This method relies on inspecting and systematically identifying and evaluating the nature of undesired events in a system. One such method is the critical-incident technique.

Critical-Incident Technique

The critical-incident technique measures safety performance and identifies practices or conditions that need to be corrected through direct observations of human behavior. This technique can identify the cause of an incident before the loss occurs. To obtain a representative sample of workers exposed to hazards, management selects workers from various departments of the facility. An interviewer questions workers who have performed particular jobs within certain environments. They are asked to describe only those existing hazards and unsafe conditions they are aware of. These are called *incidents*. Management then classifies incidents into hazard categories and identifies problem areas. The investigative team can also analyze the management systems that should have prevented the occurrence of unsafe practices or the existence of unsafe conditions. The technique can lead to improvements in loss control program management.

The critical-incident technique relies on five major components. The first step is to determine the incident and then, second, to evaluate the facts related to the incident, which involves collecting the details of the incident from the participants. When all of the facts are collected, the third step is to identify the issues contributing to the incident cause. Following this step, a decision can be made on how to resolve the issues based on various possible solutions. The final component is the evaluation, which will determine if the solution selected will solve the root cause of the situation and resolve the problems. This final aspect is most critical.

The procedure needs to be repeated because the worker-equipment-environment system is not static. Repeating the technique with a new sample of workers can reveal new problem areas and measure the effectiveness of the incident-prevention program.

Safety Sampling

Also called *behavior* or *activity sampling*, safety sampling is another technique that uses the expertise of those within the organization to inspect, identify, and evaluate hazards. This method relies on personnel—usually management or safety staff members—who are familiar with operations and are well trained in recognizing unsafe practices. While they make rounds of the facility or establishment, they record both the number and type of safety defects they observe on a safety sampling sheet.

Safety personnel or managers should make observations at different times of the day, on a planned or random basis in the actual work setting, and throughout the various parts of the facility. In a short time, they can easily convert observations to a simple report showing what specific unsafe conditions exist in which areas and which supervisors and foremen need help in enforcing good work practices. The information is unbiased and, therefore, irrefutable. What has been recorded is what has been observed. This may also determine the need for further or recurrent training of employees.

INCIDENTS AND LOSS CONTROL

This section focuses on the definition of hazards, their effects on the workplace, and efforts by management, safety professionals, and employees to control them. The more that management and workers realize that safety involves day-to-day teamwork and mutual support, the closer a company will come to achieving its safety goals.

DEFINITION OF HAZARDS

A workable definition of *hazard* is any existing or potential condition in the workplace that, by itself or by interacting with other variables, can result in deaths, injuries, property damage, and other losses. This definition carries with it two significant points:

1. A condition does not have to exist at the moment to be classified as a hazard. When the total hazard situation is being evaluated, *potentially* hazardous conditions must be considered.

2. Hazards may result not only from independent failure of workplace components, but also from one workplace component acting on or influencing another. For instance, if gasoline or another highly flammable substance comes in contact with sulfuric acid, the reaction created by the two substances produces both toxic vapors and sufficient heat for combustion.

Hazards are generally grouped into two broad categories: those dealing with safety and injuries, and those dealing with health and illnesses. However, hazards that involve property and environmental damage must also be considered.

EFFECTS OF HAZARDS ON THE WORK PROCESS

In a well-balanced operation, workers, equipment, and materials are brought together in the work environment to produce a product or to perform a service.

When operations go smoothly and time is used efficiently and effectively, production is at its highest.

When an incident interrupts an operation, it sets in motion a different chain of events and carries its own price tag. An incident is an unplanned, undesired event, not necessarily resulting in injury, but damaging to property and/or interrupting the activity in process. An incident increases the time needed to complete the job, reduces the efficiency and effectiveness of the operation, and raises production costs. If the incident results in injury, materials waste, equipment damage, or other property loss, there is a further increase in operational and hidden costs and a decrease in effectiveness.

MANAGEMENT SUPPORT

A program of loss control should be an integral part of the management process. Such a program provides hazard control with management tools such as programs, procedures, audits, and evaluations. Sometimes, hazard control program teams neglect the basics in their rush to be competitive and innovative, to deal with complex employee relations issues and government involvement, and to address the technical aspects of the programs. A program of hazard control ensures that safety fundamentals also will be addressed. These basics include sound operating and design procedures, operator training, inspection and test programs, and communicating essential information about hazards and their control.

A loss control program establishes facility-wide safety and health standards and coordinates responsibilities among departments. For example, if one department makes a product and another distributes it, they share responsibility for hazard control. The producer knows the nature of the process, its apparent and suspected hazards, and how to control the hazards. The producer and the distributor are responsible for making sure this information does not end with the production department, but is available to the purchaser or the next unit in the manufacturing process.

Coordination is also important when manufacturing responsibility is transferred from one department to another (as when a pilot program becomes a complete manufacturing unit). In addition, when a process is phased out, departments need to coordinate efforts to ensure that personnel who know the hazards are retained throughout the phase-out and that appropriate hazard control activities continue until the end.

SAFETY MANAGEMENT AND PRODUCTIVITY IMPROVEMENT

The process of identifying and eliminating or controlling hazards in the workplace is one way of making the best use of human, financial, technological, and physical resources. Optimizing these resources results in higher productivity. Here, *productivity* is defined as producing more output with a given level of input resources.

Loss control—like productivity, quality, costs, and personal relations—is a strategic process. To be effective, it must be integrated into the day-to-day activities and management systems of the organization and must become institutionalized—an operating norm and a strategic part of the organization's culture.

There are other similarities between efforts aimed at hazard control and productivity improvement. To achieve both objectives, an organization must intelligently manage its financial and human resources and use the most appropriate technology. It must illustrate innovative, enlightened, and efficient use of its facilities, equipment, materials, and work force, and have a trained, educated, and skilled work force.

An incident interrupts the production process. It not only increases the time needed to complete a production task, but may also reduce the efficiency and effectiveness of the overall operation and increase production costs. Sometimes, a succession of interruptions, or one long one, prevents the production schedule or desired product quality from being met. Such conditions make it difficult to attract new business.

Production Accomplishment and Control

Control of an operation, by definition, means keeping the system on course and preventing problems from occurring. However, it also implies some allowance for variations within the system, provided they remain within controlled limits. Any production system has built-in control limits, both upper and lower. These limits provide direction and also any acceptable leeway for the system's operation.

There are many aspects to control, including control over the quality of products and services, personnel, capital, energy, materials, and the facility environment. Each of these factors interacts with the other factors to produce the desired effect.

Determining Incident Factors

In order to set realistic goals for its process, the organization should first determine the major factors likely to cause loss of control. It should then identify the location, importance, and potential effects. Control measures can then be instituted to help reduce risk and potential losses. Factors responsible for incident losses may be identified by either inspection or detailed hazard analyses. The control measures may be administrative changes, some type of process innovation or machine safeguarding, personal protective equipment, or training. In addition to the control measures, monitoring systems should be used to continuously assess the effectiveness of these hazard-reducing controls. The results of the monitoring systems should result in changes to processes to abate potential hazards by incorporating changes to systems or production.

PROTECTING AGAINST LIABILITY

TYPES OF LIABILITY

When an unintentional incident causes injuries, legal liability may result. This discussion of the liability consequences of unintentional incidents is brief and general; consult legal counsel for advice before making important decisions. After a discussion of the types of liability, this section briefly explores the protections available to avoid those risks.

Civil Liability of Organizations and Potential Damages

The challenge for the safety professional within a company or organization is often to "do more with less." When he or she asks management to invest more in order to achieve more protection against hazards, the safety professional often is asked, "What's at stake for us if we don't do this?" The focus of this section is an outline of the legal system's consequences for lapses, omissions, or misconduct in the handling of health and safety protections that result in injuries.

Civil Tort Remedies. The U.S. system of awarding damages against people responsible for causing injury takes its name from the French and English legal systems, which used the term *tort* to describe an action that was wrong or harmful, and against which some legal consequence such as a jury verdict for damages may be awarded. The law of torts has evolved in the United States for dual purposes: as a compensation for losses and as a deterrent to misconduct. The tort law system focuses on whether the defendant who caused the harm was at fault. In some cases, the legal system has imposed "strict liability without fault" for a narrow range of hazardous activities. The U.S. system allows more civil cases to be won for larger amounts of monetary damages than other nations, but it remains difficult for the injured individual to prevail if legal liability is not proven.

Often, proving legal liability is a matter of showing that someone was negligent. Negligence is typically the failure to exercise the care toward others that a reasonable person would exercise in similar circumstances or taking action when a reasonable person would not. Most jurisdictions recognize three different levels of negligence:

- *Simple negligence* is the failure to use the degree of care an ordinary person would exercise to avoid hurting another person.
- *Gross negligence*, a higher level of negligence, is action that shows indifference to others and shocks fair-minded people, with the result of neglecting the safety of others.
- *Willful and wanton negligence*, the third and most egregious level of negligence, occurs when one acts consciously with reckless indifference to the consequences and when knowledge of existing circumstances and conditions indicates that the conduct would probably cause injury to another.

The Elements of a Negligence Action. A typical formula for evaluating negligence in a civil context requires that the following five elements be proved by a "preponderance of the evidence"—in which *preponderance of the evidence* simply means that it was more likely than not that the defendant was at fault.

- The defendant owed a duty to the plaintiff (or a duty to the general public, including the injured party).
- The defendant violated that duty.
- A plaintiff must prove that the defendant's actions actually caused the plaintiff's injury. This is often referred to as "but-for" causation. In other words, but for the defendant's actions, the plaintiff's injury would not have occurred.
- As a result of the defendant's violation of that duty, the plaintiff suffered injury.
- The injury was a reasonably foreseeable consequence of the defendant's action or inaction, and the defendant's actions actually caused the injury—but for the defendant's actions, the injury would not have occurred.

In claims of liability, usually the difficult element to prove is *causation*—a showing that the injury was a proximate result of what the defendant did, and not the result of some other person's actions. It is essential for a plaintiff, the person suing, to show that the harm was caused by this particular defendant—for example, by its truck hitting the delivery driver or its pile of boxes falling on a warehouse visitor.

This legal concept of *negligence* in the context of the safety professional means that a duty existed for the company, employer, shipper, and so on to take reasonable steps to avoid injury to workers, users, carriers, and so on, but the duty was breached.

The following situations could support a finding of negligence:

- failure to safeguard a machine or process against the foreseeable failure that causes an injury, such as omitting a guard screen on a machine that stamps metal
- removing a safety device on a machine, thus creating a hazardous situation for workers who might have been protected by the previous design of the machine
- maintaining facilities, premises, grounds, and so on in an unsafe condition that is not reasonable, so that people who work or visit there may be harmed by slipping, falling, or otherwise encountering unexpected dangers
- failure to supervise employees, allowing the poorly trained or poorly managed worker to cause harm—for example, by reckless driving of a vehicle on which the employee had no safety training
- negligent selection of employees that places the visitor or customer in a hazardous situation—for example, an employee with a history of erratic, violent behavior assigned as an armed security guard
- *Negligence per se* is a legal doctrine that holds a company or person liable for damages if an applicable law or rule was violated and, as a result, the injury occurred. Not all laws and rules are affected by this doctrine, and not all states follow it in the same way. Often *negligence per se* is used as evidence in evaluating the concept of negligence.

Organizational Liability. The Latin phrase *respondeat superior* is used in modern negligence law to impose on an employer the liability and associated obligation to pay damages if one of its workers causes harm to another person during his or her assigned duties, such as a driver hit by a recklessly operated dump truck. The law's attribution of liability to the company that owns the truck recognizes that people, not anonymous concepts such as a corporation, do the work that earns the money for the company; the company acts through people when it selects, hires, trains, and disciplines employees; and so the company or organization is held accountable for the actions of its employees.

A later subsection of this chapter discusses the individual liability of supervisors and co-workers when injuries occur at the workplace.

Punitive Damages. After an injury occurs, a retrospective look at its causes may show such reckless misconduct by the company or employer that a severe penalty should be used to deter future misconduct. Different states have used different norms for the jury award of these extra punishments, called *punitive damages,* because their goal is to punish the perpetrator rather than to compensate the victim. In simplest generalization, a company faces punitive damage liability if its actions are so sharply different from the socially acceptable behavior of similar companies that the misconduct is shocking. The result of such extremely careless or intentionally harmful actions is the severe harm caused to these injured people, whom the jury sees in this particular lawsuit. The response to the act is a jury award of money that the jury hopes will punish the offending company and deter misconduct in the future.

Intentional Torts. The employer responsible for an injury may, in extreme cases, face lawsuits by injured workers or their families, asserting that the danger was so severe and obvious that the company intended that workers be vulnerable to injury. These *intentional tort* cases are an exception to workers' compensation in states where they have been allowed. Because the normal standard of workers' compensation laws bars lawsuits, a worker who claims an intentional tort must bear a heavy burden to prove that the employer was aware that a serious or fatal injury would be likely to result if the worker were forced to undertake the risky task. Some states require a showing that it was substantially certain that injury would occur from the dangerous task or hazardous equipment.

Administrative Penalties Against Organizations

Managers who need some incentive to invest in safety programs should consider government's role as well as the court system's potential effects. In a system that is roughly parallel to the "fault"-based tort liability system, government agencies can impose administrative penalties and fines against an organization when an injury has been caused by the actions or omissions of the company. These administrative sanctions are discussed in this section according to the federal agency responsible; parallel systems for imposing penalties exist under state laws, as well, especially where the state enforces occupational safety and health programs under a "state OSHA plan."

These government penalty systems in virtually all cases apply to the company or organization and not to the individual supervisors or managers. For example, if a crane collapses at a job site and workers are injured, the federal Occupational Safety and Health Administration (OSHA) will investigate. The OSHA inspection may result in a recommended penalty of $80,000 against the crane service company. After a hearing before an administrative law judge of the Occupational Safety and Health Review Commission, the penalty may be upheld, reduced, or dismissed entirely. The $80,000 federal penalty acts as a punishment for not following safety requirements imposed by OSHA; OSHA expects that its penalties will be publicized as a deterrent to other crane companies as well.

Statutory Penalties as an Argument for Preventive Efforts

The government imposition of penalties for violations of safety rules has a benefit to society, augmenting the deterrent effect of the civil tort system described earlier. The safety professional who asks for more company effort or resources may want to study the recent history of similar organizations that were hit with large OSHA penalties. Financially oriented company managers who see the fines imposed on other companies may become more receptive to investing in a safety device or a training course for employees.

The OSHA Penalties. The most relevant penalty system is that of the federal OSHA and the state systems that carry out the same congressional mandate. OSHA civil penalties are imposed by area office directors after review of the facts found by OSHA inspectors. These include "willful" violations, the most severely punished forms of violations; "serious" violations, in which a health risk or injury potential may have caused significant harm; and routine, less-than-serious violations, usually of paperwork omissions or record-keeping errors. Penalties can range from a few thousand dollars to millions of dollars, depending on the number of workers affected, the harm created by the violation, and other factors.

The OSHA penalty becomes final and payment is due, unless the employer makes a timely request for a hearing. The hearing request must be made within 15 days or the total fine must be paid—so employers have to react quickly to respond to the OSHA letter announcing the decision to charge a penalty for certain violations. The employer can request an informal hearing during this 15-day period with the OSHA Area Director and possibly settle the citation(s) much as in the U.S. court system.

Other Federal Penalties. Beyond OSHA, other federal agencies also have civil penalty systems. The Mine Safety and Health Administration follows the OSHA model closely and applies to workers in surface and underground mines and processing facilities.

The Environmental Protection Agency (EPA) can impose large fines for the handling of chemicals that are regulated by several of its programs. For example, the Toxic Substances Control Act (TSCA) regulates the handling of experimental batches of new chemicals, whereas agricultural workers on a farm must be protected against exposures to certain hazardous pesticide sprays that are regulated by the Federal Insecticide, Fungicide, and Rodenticide Act (FIFRA). The EPA can impose huge penalties for improper handling of asbestos in building demolition, for the misuse of certain refrigerant gases that may affect stratospheric ozone, or for air pollution or water pollution violations that result from an industrial illness.

The Department of Transportation (DOT) can impose penalties for various types of violations. Rail and highway carriers are subject to penalties for unsafe practices. The Federal Aviation Administration (FAA) closely regulates airline workplace safety conditions, as well as the safe transport of freight and cargo by air. The DOT also levies fines and penalties for mishandling of shipments containing hazardous materials; a poor label or a false statement on shipping papers can draw a fine of thousands of dollars. DOT penalties seek to deter accidental injuries to workers who ship, move, and receive packages of chemicals and other potentially harmful cargoes.

The federal Consumer Product Safety Commission (CPSC) can impose fines of more than $1 million when a product intended to be used by consumers violates one of the CPSC's mandatory product safety standards, or when the producer fails to comply with the CPSC's requirement for immediate reporting of substantial product hazards. A lawn tractor made for consumers that causes accidental amputations is an example of a product for which the reporting of adverse effects is encouraged through the use of federal administrative penalties.

The federal Nuclear Regulatory Commission's role in safe handling of radioactive materials and the Food and Drug Administration's control on laser products used in workplaces also include civil administrative penalties. Both agencies use their detailed technical standards as the basis for charging violators. For example, factories whose measurement equipment includes radioisotopes, x-ray devices, or sophisticated laser machines can expect that incidents involving such equipment will be the subject of investigations, and possibly enforcement penalties, by these federal agencies.

Civil penalties are also the means by which the states enforce their reporting, record-keeping, and safety-protection rules. After an incident injures a worker, the state agencies responsible for safe workplaces may investigate and may impose a penalty against the employer.

Citizen Suits/Private Rights of Action. When a facility contractor, visitor, guest, or passerby is injured by actions of the company or organization, a lawsuit may result that includes the negligence arguments discussed in the preceding section. In some circumstances, the injured person can use special clauses in regulatory laws to also charge that the defendant owes damages for violating a government rule. This charge adds to the claim that the company or organization must pay the normal tort law damages. But only a minority of laws have been written to provide an extra basis on which to recover for losses by victims. For example, a neighbor may argue that a factory's fuel tank leak ruined its adjacent stream property and also that damages should be awarded under the state water pollution laws as a "private enforcement" of the state-wide water quality rules. Because these vary so widely across programs, states, and government agencies, it is simply enough to remind managers that when a violation occurs, the opponents may include not only the government but also local residents seeking to collect on the consequences of the violation.

Criminal Liabilities

Criminal law exists to punish and deter offenders, whose actions harm society, including those persons who are victims of the offense. Assault, robbery, and other crimes are well known; most workplace injuries involve no criminal liability at all. Unlike the long history of development of civil damages in tort cases for private remedies, the use of criminal sanctions for workplace injury cases is a recent phenomenon. Criminal law is the public's enforcement mechanism, and not the individual's or company's means of getting revenge against people who caused harm. Using criminal sanctions for the prosecution of harm caused by industrial incidents reflects a modern U.S. trend to deter mistakes by adding to the negative consequences of unintentional injuries and losses. One who wishes to prevent liability should be aware that the extra power of criminal enforcement may serve as a tougher sanction against the company and managers—so an investment in cautious compliance makes sense.

This section will discuss the potential for criminal liability consequences of an industrial incident. Only a tiny percentage of injury cases lead to these prosecutions. Of those, only a small percentage ever get to trial because settlement by *plea bargain* is so widely used in criminal cases. The reader should keep in mind that state or federal prosecutors must show the jury proof that goes *beyond a reasonable doubt* before a conviction can be secured. The standard of *beyond a reasonable doubt* is the highest level of proof that is required in the U.S. judicial system. The particular law sets the standard of what actions are criminal—for example, willfully exposing workers to radiation. To the extent possible, defense attorneys will argue that the action or omission by the defendants was not willful, intentional, or otherwise criminal beyond a reasonable doubt, but was merely a mistake due to some level of negligence.

No generalizations can be made about the severity of criminal penalties. Federal sentencing guidelines impose prison sentences of predetermined length for certain classes of crimes, but additional months of prison time can be included in the sentence if the defendant met certain criteria of concealment or recklessness. State laws give trial judges more leeway to select from a range of possible sentences. In general, a criminal conviction for a violation related to an industrial injury will result in prison terms under the federal system but may receive probation under the state sentencing program.

Criminal Remedies versus a Company or Organization. A corporation is legally treated as a "person" under state and federal laws, and it can be fined or penalized in criminal trials, even though the organization itself cannot be sent to jail. The industrial event that leads to criminal indictments against a company will probably also result in charges against supervisors, facility managers, the chief executive, and others.

Criminal Prosecution versus a Company for Negligence. When a criminal law forbids a company from allowing or requiring certain actions by employees, the company could be criminally charged when its actions were negligent. The jury would be asked by the prosecutor to find, beyond a reasonable doubt, that the company's actions were below the level at which a reasonable company would have undertaken this task. For example, a radio tower construction worker's fatal fall may result in a charge that the company negligently failed to comply with a state safety law governing construction safeguards.

Criminal Prosecution versus an Individual for Willful Actions. The criminal prosecution of a supervisor or manager at an industrial site for a safety-related violation of laws is a rare event. The prosecutor will conduct interviews, gather evidence, and try to reconstruct the scene. If the incident was the result of actions or commands by a supervisor that were more than merely negligent, the individual may be criminally charged. These individual prosecutions are unusual, but they offer some deterrence against future incidents.

Criminal Prosecution versus an Individual for Strict-Liability Offenses. A law that seeks to deter managers from allowing injuries to happen may impose *strict liability*, which means the jury can convict the individual with no proof of his or her fault or knowledge of the specifics of the action. For example, a company CEO who is responsible for operating a factory that uses laser-cutting tools could be criminally liable for violating the safety standards for lasers that are set by the Food and Drug Administration (FDA). Strict liability means the prosecutors could win a conviction without needing to prove that the CEO had personal knowledge or involvement with the laser equipment, but only that the violation occurred.

Criminal Prosecution versus an Individual for Fraud or Concealment. If an injury occurs and the employer tries to cover up the causes of the incident, a prosecutor can criminally charge the responsible officials with obstruction of justice, violations of the relevant safety statute, or other crimes. Fraud is a deliberate concealment of a material fact from one who has a right to accurate disclosure, such as the federal safety inspectors who inquire about a trench collapse injury at a construction site. The chances of criminal liability being imposed are greatly increased if the government inspectors believe that the company management has lied about the facts or altered records—for example, to falsely claim that required training had been given to the injured worker.

Individual Civil Liability

Protecting the company or organization against liability will be the principal task of safety managers. But in what circumstances will the individual supervisor, manager, or worker be successfully sued for damages, in addition to cases brought against the company?

When the injury situation arises inside a company's own workplace, and the injured person is also employed by the same company, then state workers' compensation law generally bars the "fellow servant" (co-worker) from winning such a suit.

In the case of a serious injury in which insurance covers the defendant company (or the company is large and self-insured), damages will probably be imposed on the company or organization, and most of the time, the injured person will settle with that company rather than pursue a separate lawsuit against one individual employee. When the injury appears to have been the result of misconduct by the employee, the normal practice is to sue both the company and the employee, in case the company successfully avoids being held liable. It would be rare that a company is held not liable but its supervisory employee or manager is held liable.

Negligence is the primary claim for damages lawsuits against individuals, as discussed earlier. The duty is owed by the individual, and the injury arises from that person's acts or omissions. The proof of causation is even more difficult because the claim asserts that this particular employee of the defendant company caused this particular harm.

Assault is the civil charge that alleges some physical contact by the named individual against the injured plaintiff. A tavern patron's claim of assault against a bouncer may be the simplest analogy. Unlike negligent failures to act, some direct adverse act by the defendant was done that harmed this individual person.

Statutory violations such as the OSHA and EPA civil penalty cases discussed earlier are rarely, if ever, brought against individuals. The exception may be in a discrimination claim under which a partially disabled worker alleges that a particular supervisor violated her rights by refusing to correct an unsafe situation at work.

Workers' Compensation

Civil tort liability lawsuits brought against employers in the courts for workplace injuries would be a major problem for both employers and injured workers if no alternative system had been developed to channel these injury claims. The state laws that have created systems of postinjury payments for injured workers, called *workers' compensation systems*, are a compromise that balances the rights of workers with those of employers. Employers have won the right to pay some level of compensation instead of being sued for damages by their workers if they are injured on the job. In most workplace injury cases, the law bars workers from suing their employer if the injury fits within the state workers' compensation system. Workers get an assurance of predictable, understandable health care benefits and payments for lost work time, but give up the right to sue employers, in virtually all workplace injury situations. Compensation checks come from the state fund to the worker; employers pay insurance premiums corresponding to a formula that takes into account the risk aspects of the particular employment.

Objectives of Workers' Compensation. A U.S. Chamber of Commerce publication, *Analysis of Workers' Compensation Laws*, published annually, cites these six basic objectives underlying workers' compensation laws:

1. Provide adequate, equitable, prompt, and sure income and medical benefits to work-related accident victims, or income benefits to their dependents, regardless of fault.
2. Provide a single remedy and reduce court delays, costs, and workloads arising out of personal injury litigation.
3. Relieve public and private charities of financial drains—incident to uncompensated industrial accidents.
4. Eliminate payment of fees to lawyers and witnesses as well as time-consuming trials and appeals.
5. Encourage maximum employer interest in safety and rehabilitation through an appropriate experience-rating mechanism.
6. Promote frank study of causes of accidents (rather than concealment of fault), reducing preventable accidents and human suffering.

Income Replacement. The first objective listed for workers' compensation is to replace the wages lost by workers who are disabled because of a job-related injury or illness. According to this objective, the replacement should be adequate, equitable, prompt, and sure.

To be adequate, the program should replace lost earnings (present and projected, including fringe benefits), minus expenses such as taxes and job-related transportation costs that would not continue. The worker, however, should share a proportion of the loss in order to provide incentives for rehabilitation and accident prevention. A two-thirds replacement ratio is found in most state statutes.

To be equitable, the program must treat all workers fairly. According to one concept of fairness, most workers should have the same proportion of their wages replaced. However, workers with a low wage may need to receive a high proportion of their lost wages in order to sustain themselves and their families. High-income workers who can afford to purchase private individual protection may have their weekly benefits limited to some reasonable maximum. However, if workers' compensation insurance is regarded primarily as a wage-replacement program, few people should be affected by this maximum.

The first objective also includes medical and vocational rehabilitation and return to productive employment. To achieve this goal, workers should receive quality medical care at no cost—care that will restore them as much as possible to their former physical condition. If complete restoration is impossible, workers should receive vocational rehabilitation that will enable them to maximize their earning capacity. Finally, the system should provide incentives for disabled workers and prospective employers to help employees return to productive employment as quickly as possible.

One of the objectives of workers' compensation is to allocate the costs of the program among employers and industries according to the degree to which they are responsible for the losses. Such an allocation is considered equitable because each employer and industry pays its fair share of the cost. In the long run, this allocation shifts resources from hazardous industries to safe industries and from unsafe employers within an industry to safe employers. Eventually, employers with the most unsafe operations will be driven out of the marketplace.

Critics argue that workers' compensation costs account for such a small part of overall operating expenses that they have little, if any, effect on a firm's resource allocation. As a result, unsafe employers would not need to resort to higher prices, and they would remain in the marketplace.

Major Characteristics. Compensation laws can be elective or compulsory. Under an elective law, the employer may accept or reject the act. However, if an employer rejects the act, it loses the three common-law defenses—assumption of risk, negligence of fellow employees, and contributory negligence. This means that in practice all the laws can be considered "compulsory." A compulsory law requires each employer to accept its provisions and provide for benefits specified.

Most jurisdictions require employers to obtain insurance or to prove financial ability to carry their own risk. Six states, two U.S. territories, and most provinces require employers to contribute to a monopolistic fund operated by the state or provincial agency. In some instances, employers may qualify as self-insurers. Thirteen states permit employers to purchase insurance either from a competitive state fund or from a private insurance company.

Covered Employment. Although most of the state workers' compensation laws apply to both private and public employment, none of the laws covers all forms of employment and occupation. For example, a few states restrict compulsory coverage to so-called hazardous occupations. Many laws exempt employers having less than a specified number of employees, usually less than three or four in any one location. Most of the laws also exclude workers in farming, domestic service, and casual employment. Many laws contain other exemptions, such as employment in charitable or religious institutions.

Federal workers are covered by the Federal Employees' Compensation Act (FECA). Employees of the District of Columbia are covered by the District of Columbia Workers' Compensation Act, which went into effect in 1982. Its provisions closely follow those of FECA.

Two other major groups excluded from coverage by compensation laws are interstate railroad workers and maritime employees. Railroad workers whose duties involve any aspect of interstate commerce are covered by the Federal Employers' Liability Act (FELA). Maritime workers are subject to the Jones Act, which applies provisions of the FELA to seamen.

The Federal Employers' Liability Act is not a workers' compensation law. Instead, it gives an employee the right to charge an employer with negligence and prevents the employer from pleading the common-law defense that the worker is a fellow servant or assumes part of the risk; moreover, the act substitutes the principle of comparative negligence for the common-law concept of contributory negligence.

It is not known how many state and local employees are covered by workers' compensation or provided with such protection voluntarily by their employers. All states (as well as Puerto Rico, Guam, and the District of Columbia) provide some coverage of public employees, but the extent of the benefits varies widely. Some laws specify no exclusions or exclude only such groups as elected or appointed officials. Others limit coverage to employees of specified political subdivisions or to employees engaged in hazardous occupations. In still others, the extent of coverage is left entirely up to the state or to the city or political subdivision employing government workers. Certain other groups, such as the self-employed, unpaid family members, volunteers, and trainees, generally are not protected by workers' compensation.

Limitations on Coverage. In view of the fact that some of the exemptions or exclusions in many state laws have persisted to this day, it may be helpful to review some of the reasons behind the original limitations. Nearly all state acts were prepared and enacted in the face of constitutional challenges and the outright opposition of certain business or government interests. Thus, each act was the result of political compromises.

Initially, workers' compensation was hailed as an innovation that would introduce greater certainty into the calculation and payment of benefits in contrast to the common-law system. Under common law, workers could sue employers and, if successful, might be ensured of adequate payment; however, those who lost would be left with nothing but debts. To reduce this risk, the workers' compensation law specified the benefits that would be paid to all regardless of fault. Although the outcome of workers' compensation cases is far more certain in ordinary suits in which negligence must be shown, the law is not "automatically" applied.

In part, this remaining uncertainty arises from the wide variety of permanent partial-disability cases that the schedules do not cover satisfactorily. Two factors usually prompt compensation litigation: one is uncertainty about whether an accident arose out of and in the course of employment; the other is the extent of disability. As workers' compensation comes to encompass more of the ailments to which the general population may be susceptible, it becomes difficult to separate impairments that are work related from those that are not. In addition, legal skills and medical judgment are required to assess the extent of disability in such difficult cases as occupational diseases, injuries to the soft tissue of the back, heart conditions, or situations in which the only evidence before the commission may be a subjective complaint.

Covered Injuries. Workers' compensation is intended to provide coverage only for certain work-related conditions and not for all of an employee's health problems. Statutory definitions and tests have been adopted to distinguish between conditions that are compensable and those that are not. All jurisdictions, when drafting workers' compensation laws, relied to some extent on the English legal system (or on other statutes based on the English model). Even though the statutory language of these laws is remarkably similar, there are variations in terminology and differences in interpretation; as a result, a condition considered compensable in one state may be held noncompensable in others.

The statutes usually limit compensation benefits to personal injury caused by accidents arising out of and in the course of employment. Although this restriction presents four distinct tests that must be met, in practice these tests are often considered in pairs: the "personal injury" and "by accident" requirements in one set, and the "arising out of" and "in the course of" requirements in the other.

For the first pair of tests, if interpreted narrowly, personal injury would refer solely to bodily harm, such as a broken leg or a cut, whereas the "by accident" test would refer to the cause, such as a blow to the body or an episode of excessive or improper lifting. In practice, however, the distinctions are often blurred. The "by accident" concept is a carryover from English law. Early judicial interpretations of English law made it quite clear that the "by accident" requirement was intended to deny compensation to those who injured themselves intentionally. A number of U.S. jurisdictions, however, have applied the test in order to narrow the range of unintentional injuries that must be compensated.

For the second pair of tests, "in the course of" employment would generally be an issue of time, place, and circumstance. If an injury occurs on the job or at the employer's place of business during normal working hours, the injury will usually be considered in the course of employment. Typically, "arises out of" employment would hinge on whether there is a causal connection between the injury and employment. The term "arising out of and in the course of employment," applied by almost every jurisdiction, is meant to clearly define the relationship between employment and an injury or disease for an employee to be eligible for workers' compensation. The phrase obviously lacks precision. Often it is quite difficult to determine whether a given set of facts can support an award of compensation.

"Exclusive Remedy" for Work-Related Disabilities. Before workers' compensation laws were enacted in the states, an employee, in order to recover damages for a work-related injury, had to prove some degree of fault or negligence on the employer's part. Under what is now known as the *quid pro quo of workers' compensation law,* employers accepted, or were required to accept, responsibility for injuries arising out of and in the course of employment without regard to fault. In exchange, employees gave up the right to sue employers for unlimited damages. These agreements are usually referred to in the state acts as *exclusive remedy* provisions, a term that is quite misleading.

WORKERS' COMPENSATION MAY NOT BE EXCLUSIVE REMEDY

In no state are workers' compensation benefits necessarily the only remedy available to an injured worker. Depending on the wording of the applicable statute, workers may bring a negligence action against their employer, fellow workers, another contractor on the same job, or some other entity or individual who caused the compensable injury. For example, workers may sue the manufacturer of a piece of equipment that caused an injury. So, neither liability nor remedy is perfectly exclusive in all workers' compensation cases.

Two concepts that are broadening the exclusive remedy provision are (1) the expansion of the dual-capacity doctrine; and (2) the intentional-tort exception.

Under the first concept, an injured employee can sue an employer for an injury—even if it arose out of and in the course of employment—if the injury was caused by the employer's product or a service available to the public. (Example: A driver of a tire company delivery truck who is injured when a defective tire, made by the employer, causes the truck to have an accident. Or a hospital employee who, after an accident on the job, is injured as the result of negligent treatment by one of the hospital's medical staff.) In both cases, the injury did not occur as a result of the employer/employee relationship, but rather through a relationship more akin to that of a supplier or service provider and the public.

In relatively few cases, workers have been able to bypass the exclusive-remedy approach of workers' compensation laws. These "intentional tort" claims are exceptional, and each state's highest court will set the parameters for satisfying the narrow prerequisites. To generalize, a worker must show that the employer knew of a grave risk; acted recklessly in sending the worker into danger, even though the employer knew that an injury was substantially likely; and the worker was, in fact, harmed. Unlike the conventional workers' compensation remedy that does not pin blame or allocate responsibility for the accident, these cases usually involve the employer's conscious or willful indifference to a hazard that resulted in a worker's serious injury.

Subrogation of Workers' Compensation. Some of the workers' compensation cases that result in payments to injured workers also reflect a harm that was attributable to a third person, not just the employer or the worker. In these cases, the product supplier, the machine builder, the other vehicle in a collision, and so on may be sued in civil tort liability. The damages awarded against that person must in many cases be paid back to the state insurance fund from which compensation payments had been made. This is called *subrogation*, in which the injured person receives payment and the one who contributed to the injury is held liable to pay damages and to reimburse the state fund.

PREVENTION STRATEGIES

Historically, the most successful efforts to prevent liability have been through a proactive program that uses audits, training, monitoring, and continual revisions of the internal compliance efforts of the organization. Incident prevention is discussed throughout this text, and of course no liability arises if no incidents occur.

The best alternative means of avoiding criminal liability is an effective internal monitoring and self-auditing system, such as has been suggested by the U.S. Sentencing Commission's guidelines, that will justify reduction of criminal sentences in case a violation is prosecuted. An organization's best efforts to avoid violating criminal laws can include classroom and video-training sessions, internal and external audits of the quality and effectiveness of internal compliance systems, and top management's expressed commitment to comply with the law. The company should consult with legal counsel regarding methods by which self-audit systems can provide some level of protection against prosecutions.

The best alternative means for reducing civil tort liability is to invest in safeguards that will minimize losses, such as smoke detectors, and that will mitigate the losses that could occur, such as fire suppression equipment near fuel tank farms. The safeguard investment reduces the risk of punitive damages for flagrant or reckless conduct. If an incident occurs, the immediate postincident response should be appropriate and not adversarial to the injured people, in order to reduce their interest in aggressive pursuit of damages.

INCIDENT CAUSES AND THEIR CONTROL

Close examination of each incident shows that it can be attributed, directly or indirectly, to an oversight, omission, or malfunction of the management system regarding one or more of the following three items (refer also to the discussion later in this chapter):
1. unsafe practices or procedures; either the worker or another person
2. situational factors, such as facilities, tools, equipment, and materials
3. environmental factors, such as noise, vibration, temperature extremes, and illumination.

If an adequate line management hazard control system is properly designed for the organization's workers, equipment, and environment, then the likelihood of injuries occurring in the workplace is greatly reduced.

UNSAFE PRACTICES OR PROCEDURES

An unsafe practice is generally described either as a human action departing from prescribed hazard controls or job procedures or practices, or as an action causing a person unnecessary exposure to a hazard. Both workers and management can cause injuries by commission; for example, a worker may sharpen a wood gouge on a grinder without placing the tool on the grinder's rest. In this case, management should ask questions such as, "Was the worker trained properly or pressured to rush the job?" or "Were procedures enforced?" Conversely, a supervisor contributes to the cause of an incident by omission when failing to have an oil spot on the floor wiped up.

An unsafe practice often is a deviation from the standard job procedures. Examples of such actions include the following:

- using equipment without authority
- operating equipment at an unsafe speed or in another improper way
- removing safety devices, such as guards, or rendering them inoperative
- using defective tools.

Unsafe practices also can be a deviation from safety rules or regulations, instructions, or job safety analyses. Why the deviation occurred is the real issue. When implementing a hazard control program, emphasis should be placed on the countermeasure that when implemented, will prevent the identified cause from leading to the incident.

Many incidents are the result of someone deviating from the standard job procedures, doing something prohibited, or failing to do something that should be done. In other situations, however, the worker unfairly becomes the target for criticism when other factors actually caused the mishap.

An important first step in loss control is distinguishing between worker error and supervisory error, then addressing what caused the system to break down. Don't just look for a "scapegoat"; look for the cause(s). Human error is reduced when:

- supervisors and workers know the correct methods and procedures to accomplish given tasks
- workers demonstrate a skill proficiency before using the particular piece of equipment
- higher management and supervisors consider the relationship between worker performance and physical characteristics and fitness
- the entire organization gives top priority and continuous regard to potentially dangerous situations and the corrective action necessary to avoid unintentional injuries
- supervisors provide proper direction, training, and surveillance. The supervisor must be aware of the worker's skill level with each piece of equipment and process and adjust the supervision of each worker accordingly. The supervisor shapes worker attitudes and actions by letting employees know that nothing less than safe work practices and the safest possible workplace will be accepted.

SITUATIONAL FACTORS

Situational factors are another major cause of unintentional injuries. These factors are materials that make incidents likely, and unsafe operations, tools, equipment, and facilities. Examples are unguarded, poorly maintained, and defective equipment; ungrounded equipment that can cause shock; equipment without adequate warning signals; poorly arranged equipment, buildings, and layouts that create congestion hazards; and equipment located in positions that expose more people to a potential hazard.

ENVIRONMENTAL FACTORS

The third factor in incident causation is environmental—that is, the way in which the workplace directly or indirectly causes or contributes to incident situations. Environmental factors fall into four broad categories: human, chemical, biological, and ergonomic.

Human Factors

Noise, vibration, radiation, illumination, and temperature extremes are examples of factors that can influence or cause injuries and illnesses. Operations on a machine lathe, for example, may produce high noise levels that prevent workers from hearing other sounds and impair communication with others or may damage the workers' hearing over time. Thus, workers may be unable to warn one another of a hazard in time to avoid an incident.

Chemical Factors

Classified under this category are toxic gases, vapors, fumes, mists, smokes, and dusts. In addition to causing illnesses, these often impair a worker's skill, reactions, judgment, or concentration. A worker exposed to the narcotic effect of some solvent vapors, for example, may experience a loss of judgment and fail to follow safe procedures.

Biological Factors

Biological factors refer to items capable of making a person ill through contact with bacteria, viruses, fungi, or parasites. For example, workers may suffer boils and inflammations caused by staphylococci and streptococci or experience groin itch caused by parasites.

PRINCIPLES OF LOSS CONTROL

Loss control is the function directed toward anticipating, recognizing, evaluating, and eliminating, or at least controlling, the potentially negative effects of occupational hazards. These hazards generally result from human errors and from the situational and environmental aspects of the workplace (Firenze, 1978). The primary function of a loss control system is to locate, assess, and set effective preventive and corrective measures for elements that are detrimental to operational efficiency and effectiveness.

The process exists on three levels:

1. national—laws, regulations, exposure limits, codes, and standards of governmental, industrial, and trade bodies
2. organizational—management of the hazard control program, safety and health committees, task groups, teams, and so on
3. component—worker-equipment-environment.

Loss control can be thought of as "looking for defects." First, there are fewer defects, or failures, than successes. Second, it is easier to agree on what constitutes failure than on what constitutes success. Failure is the inability of a system or a part of a system to perform as required under specified conditions for a specific length of time. The causes of failures often can be determined by answering a series of questions. "What can fail?" "How can it fail?" "How frequently can it fail?" "What are the effects of failure?" "What is the importance of the effects?" The manner in which a system, or portion of a system, can exhibit failure is commonly known as the *mode of failure*.

The opposite of failure is not necessarily total success. After all, totally error-free performance is an ideal state, not a reality. Rather, the opposite of failure is the minimum acceptable success. This is the condition in which operations are run with a minimum number of losses and interruptions, keeping efficiency and effectiveness of the operation within acceptable limits of control.

Management builds into each of its systems lower and upper limits of control. Each of these interfacing subsystems—maintenance, quality control, production control, personnel, and purchasing, to name a few—is designed to move the system within acceptable limits toward its objective. This concept of keeping operations within acceptable limits gives substance and credibility to the process of loss control. In addition to familiarizing management with the full consequences of system defects, loss control can pinpoint hazards before failures occur. The anticipatory character of loss control increases productivity.

PROCESSES OF LOSS CONTROL

The processes of an effective loss control program should be directed toward evaluating, eliminating, and preventing workplace hazards. Management and safety officials can implement many preventive measures when designing a loss control program. An effective loss control program can be relatively simple but should include at least the following elements:

1. hazard identification and evaluation
2. ranking hazards by risk
3. management decision making
4. establishing preventive and corrective measures
5. monitoring
6. evaluating program effectiveness, including employee evaluation and/or corrective action and recurrent training.

HAZARD IDENTIFICATION AND EVALUATION

The first step in a comprehensive loss control program is to identify and evaluate workplace hazards. These hazards are associated with machinery, equipment, tools, operations, materials, and the physical facility.

Hazard analysis is a way to acquire meaningful hazard information and a thorough knowledge of the demands of a particular task. Analysis probes operational and management systems to uncover hazards that (1) may have been overlooked in the layout of the facility or the building and in the design of machinery, equipment, and processes; (2) may have developed after production started; or (3) may exist because original procedures and tasks were modified.

The greatest benefit of hazard analysis is that it forces those conducting the analysis to view each operation as part of a system. In doing so, they assess each step in the operation while keeping in mind the relationship between steps and the interaction between workers and equipment, materials, the environment, and other workers. Other benefits of hazard analysis include (1) identifying hazardous conditions and potential incidents; (2) providing information with which effective control measures can be established; (3) determining the level of knowledge and skill as well as the physical requirements workers need to execute specific shop tasks; and (4) discovering and eliminating unsafe procedures, techniques, motions, positions, and actions.

The topic of hazard analysis—its underlying philosophy, the basic steps to be taken, and its ultimate use as a safety, health, and decision-making tool— will be treated in Chapter 5, Identifying Hazards.

RANKING HAZARDS BY RISK (SEVERITY, PROBABILITY, AND EXPOSURE)

The second step in the loss control process is to rank hazards by risk. Such ranking takes into account the consequence (the severity), the probability, and the exposure index. The purpose of this second process is to address hazards according to the principle of "worst first." Ranking provides a consistent guide for corrective action, specifying which hazardous conditions warrant immediate action, which have secondary priority, and which can be addressed in the future.

Once safety personnel or others have ranked hazards according to their potential destructive consequences, the next step is to estimate the probability of the hazard resulting in an incident situation. Quantitative data for ranking hazards probability are desirable, but almost certainly they will not be available for each potential hazard being assessed. Whatever quantitative data exists should be part of the risk-rating formula used to estimate probability. Qualitative data—estimates based on experience—are a necessary supplement to quantitative data.

After estimating both consequence and probability, the next and final step is to estimate worker exposure to the hazard. This can be done by assigning a single risk number or risk assessment code (RAC). After assigning a numerical ranking for severity, frequency, and probability, the job task is evaluated according to the assigned criteria and the point values are added. This produces a single number that allows for a risk ranking. There are many types of RACs. The RAC described in this paragraph combines the three evaluations into a single scale that provides a ranking for job tasks, making it easier to select specific job tasks to analyze. Management can use these values to select particular jobs for immediate analysis (Figure 6–1). The RAC rating scale is a guideline and is not intended to be used as an absolute measurement system.

Job Task	Severity 1–4 points	Exposure 1–3 points	Probability 1–3 points	Total
Conduct grinding mill area preshift inspection	3	2	2	7
Start complete grinding circuit	2	1	2	5
Start particle size monitor	4	2	3	9
Change steel rods	3	2	2	7
Routine rod mill shutdown	2	1	2	5
Charge rod mill with ore	2	2	2	6

Figure 6–1. Sample ranking system.

MANAGEMENT DECISION MAKING

The third step involves providing management with full and accurate information, including all possible alternatives, so managers can make intelligent, informed decisions concerning loss control. Such alternatives include recommendations for training and education, better methods and procedures, equipment repair or replacement, environmental controls, and—in rare cases where modification is not enough—recommendations for redesign. Information must be presented to management in a way that clearly states the actions required to improve conditions. The person who reports hazard information must do so in a manner that promotes, rather than hinders, action.

After management's decision makers receive hazard reports, they normally have four alternatives:

1. Take no action.
2. Modify the workplace or its components.
3. Redesign the workplace or its components.
4. Discuss the hazard and possible methods of elimination with affected workers.

When management chooses to take no positive steps to correct hazards uncovered in the workplace, it usually is for one of three reasons:

1. Management feels that it cannot take the required action. Immediate constraints—be they financial, crucial production schedules, or limitations of personnel—loom larger than the risks involved in taking no action.
2. Management is presented with limited alternatives. For example, it may receive only the best and most costly solutions with no less-than-totally-successful alternatives to choose from.
3. Management does not agree that a hazard exists. However, the situation can require additional consultation and study to resolve any problem.

When management chooses to modify the system, it does so with the idea that its operation is generally acceptable but, with the reported deficiencies corrected, performance will be improved. Examples of modification alternatives are the acquisition of machine guards, personal protective equipment, or ground-fault circuit interrupters to prevent electrical shock; a change in training or education; a change in preventive maintenance; isolating hazardous materials and processes; replacing hazardous materials and processes with nonhazardous or at least less-hazardous ones; and purchasing new tools.

Although redesign is not a popular alternative, it is sometimes necessary. When redesign is selected, management must be aware of certain problems. Redesign usually involves substantial cash outlay and inconvenience. For example, assume that the air quality in a facility is found to be below acceptable standards. The only way to correct this situation is to completely redesign and install the facility's general ventilation system. The cost and inconvenience can be formidable.

Another problem is the fact that the new designs usually contain hazards of their own. For this reason, whenever redesign is offered as an alternative, those making the recommendation must establish and execute a plan to detect problems in design and the early stages of construction so hazards can be eliminated, reduced, or controlled.

One way to expedite decision making regarding actions for loss control is to present findings clearly so that management understands the nature of the hazards, their location, their importance, the necessary corrective actions, and the estimated cost. Figure 6–2 shows a record of occupational safety and health deficiencies and illustrates one approach for recording and displaying hazard information for decision making. It indicates the hazard ranking, the specific location and nature of the hazard, and what costs are likely to be incurred. It also clearly states the recommended corrective action. At a glance, it shows whether the corrective action has been taken and the final cost.

RECORD OF OCCUPATIONAL SAFETY AND HEALTH DEFICIENCIES

Location ___Shipping___   Pete Varga
                                                                                    Inspector

Deficiency No.	Date Recorded	Description of Hazardous Condition	Specific Location	Identification of Acceptable Standard	Hazard Rating		Corrective Action	Estimated Cost of Correction	Date Deficiency Corrected	Resources Used for Correction
					Conse-quence	Proba-bility				
S - 1	12/11/9-	Ungrounded Tools and Equipment	Throughout Shop	OSHA; Subpart S National Electrical Code, Article 250; 4S	I	A	Provide receptacles with the 3–prong outlet. Test each to make certain it is grounded. Make sure that all tools (other than double-insulated) have a grounding plug.	$5,000	1/9/9-	$4,900

Figure 6–2. One approach to recording and displaying hazard information for decision making.

Reprinted with permission from RJF Associates, Inc.

ESTABLISHING PREVENTIVE AND CORRECTIVE MEASURES

After the safety team or others have identified and evaluated hazards and provided data for informed decisions, the next step involves implementing control measures.

Controls are of several kinds:

1. *elimination,* or physically removing a hazard—the most effective hazard control (e.g., moving a device that produced excessive noise to a location away from employees)
2. *substitution,* or replacing something that produces a hazard (similar to elimination) with something that does not produce a hazard (e.g., replacing lead-based paint with a water-based paint)

3. *engineering* (isolation of source; lockout procedures; design, process, or procedural changes; monitoring and warning equipment)
4. *administrative* (personnel, management, monitoring, limiting worker exposure, measuring performance, training and education, housekeeping and maintenance, purchasing)
5. *personal protective equipment* (body protection, fall protection, and so on). See Chapter 13, Personal Protective Equipment (PPE).

MONITORING

The fifth step in the process of hazard control deals with monitoring activities to locate new hazards and assess the effectiveness of existing controls. Monitoring includes inspection, industrial hygiene testing, and medical surveillance. These subjects are covered in Chapter 5, Identifying Hazards.

Monitoring is necessary (1) to ensure that hazard controls are working properly; (2) to ensure that modifications have not so altered the workplace that current hazard controls can no longer function adequately; and (3) to discover new or previously undetected hazards.

EVALUATING PROGRAM EFFECTIVENESS

The final process in hazard control is to evaluate the effectiveness of the safety and health program. Evaluation involves answering the following questions: "What is being done to locate and control hazards in the facility?" "What benefits are being received—for example, reduction of injuries, workers' compensation cases, and damage losses?" "Is operational efficiency and effectiveness enhanced by the safety and health program?" "What employee evaluation, corrective actions, and recurrent training are occurring?"

The evaluation team examines the program to see whether it has accomplished its objectives (effectiveness evaluation) and whether they have been achieved in accordance with the program plan (administrative evaluation, including such factors as schedule and budget). Evaluation must be adapted to (1) the time, money, and kinds of equipment and personnel available for the evaluation; (2) the number and quality of data sources; (3) the particular operation; and (4) the needs of the evaluators.

Effectiveness criteria include the number and severity of injuries to workers compared with work hours, the cost of medical care, material damage costs, facility damage costs, equipment and tool damage or replacement costs, and the number of days lost from injuries or illnesses.

One indicator of the effectiveness of a hazard control program is the experience rating given a company by the insurance carrier responsible for paying workers' compensation claims. Experience rating is a comparison of the actual losses of an individual (company) risk with the losses that would be expected from a risk of such size and classification. Experience rating determines whether the individual risk is better or worse than the average and to what extent the premium should be modified to reflect this variation. Experience modification is determined in accordance with the experience rating plan (ERP) formula, which has been approved by the insurance commissioners in most states. Loss frequency is penalized more heavily than loss severity because it is assumed that the insured can control small losses more easily than less frequent, severe losses.

REVIEW QUESTIONS

1. Give three of the five benefits of hazard analysis.
2. What is the purpose of ranking hazards by risk?
3. What types of negligence liability does a company assume when it takes on a contractor role inside a workplace, such as by repairing equipment or providing specialized mechanical service?
4. When can injured workers sue their employers?
5. What federal government programs regulate workplace safety?
6. Is proof of the manager's knowledge of the action necessary when the action violates a law with "strict liability" penalty provisions?
7. What extra risks do government contractors face from violations of federal safety rules?
8. Name the three major areas where hazardous conditions can be either eliminated or controlled and give an example of each.

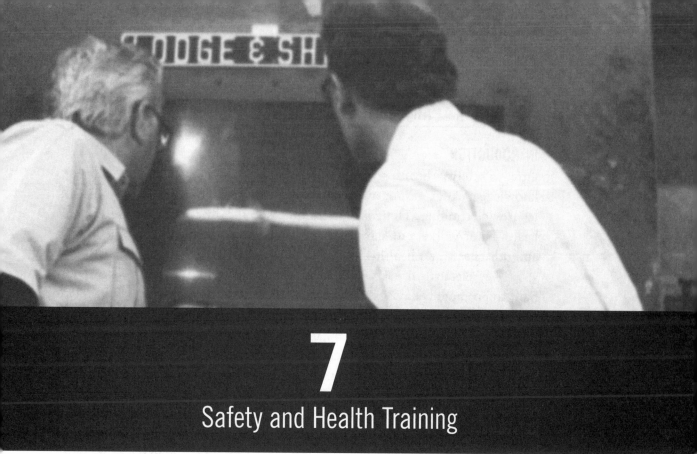

7

Safety and Health Training

LEARNING OBJECTIVES

- ❑ Identify in writing the goals of a successful safety and health training program.
- ❑ Discuss the immediate, short-term, and long-term benefits of safety training by describing various components and differences of these benefits.
- ❑ Identify the components of a safety orientation program and discuss their overall value to a safety culture.

TRAINING AS PART OF THE SAFETY AND HEALTH PROGRAM

INTRODUCTION

Often, a safety or health problem can be caused by lack of appropriate attitude, knowledge, skills, and/or awareness. One solution to mitigate this problem is to provide training. The goal for training specifically tailored for safety and health is for workers to learn and apply techniques that will keep themselves and others safe and healthy.

A key element in every successful safety and health program is training built to promote behaviors, skills, knowledge, and/or awareness as they relate to the accident prevention and the occupational safety and health program within the organization. Workers must have proper training specific to the organization to do their jobs safely and efficiently.

The responsibility for implementing and conducting employee training rests with management. Management must recognize that for the organization to achieve its objective of providing a safe and healthy workplace, employees must perform work at a certain competency level and meet certain minimum expectations and performance objectives. Therefore, management must establish goals that are tailored for all levels of the organization from top management, to supervisors/line managers, to safety professionals, to front-line employees. These goals then need to be incorporated into the appropriate training programs for each level. An organization's safety and health program must include:

- training in the proper methods of leadership and supervision to hold personnel accountable to the safety and health requirements/policies/procedures
- safety professional training on how to detect, eliminate, and/or control hazards; investigate accidents; and handle emergency situations
- targeted training based on the position held within the organization.

The safety and health program must also be reviewed on a regular basis and reconciled with current training to ensure that it meets all regulatory training obligations and complements or supports the goals and objectives of the company. The following will provide more specifics in relation to the definition of training, its benefits, choosing training as a solution, how the safety professional supports training objectives, and the characteristics of effective safety and health training programs.

TRAINING DEFINITION

Training is often confused with education. *Education* focuses on information that may or may not be used to improve a process or a specific task on the job. It can be present based, but it is more commonly focused on future applications, with a theoretical emphasis rather than a process-oriented emphasis. Merriam-Webster defines training as "a process by which someone is taught the skills that are needed for an art, profession, or job." In business organizations, training is primarily focused on enhancing performance in a work setting by targeting changes to an individual's behavior, skills, knowledge, aptitude, and/ or awareness. Hence, the goal of effective training in a business is to provide learning that leads to improved on-the-job performance. Training is one specific solution to meet a safety or health need caused by inappropriate behaviors, lack of needed skills, knowledge or aptitude, and awareness. It focuses on the present, providing information on the process necessary to accomplish a task, objective, or goal. It provides the why only to the extent that people need to know the information.

BENEFITS OF TRAINING

Training benefits can be categorized into immediate, short-term, and long-term benefits. It should be noted that a well-rounded safety and health program will have benefits that will have far-reaching implications—well beyond just safety and health. The benefits of safety and health training include but are not limited to:

Immediate:
- increased awareness
- increased knowledge
- increased skill level
- increased aptitude
- increased confidence
- reduced complacency.

Short term:
- increased employee satisfaction
- improved moral
- improved performance
- improved decision making.

Long term:
- reduced employee turnover
- reduced OSHA recordable incident rates
- reduced total incident rate

- reduced lost time
- reduced lost workday rates
- decreased severity rate
- increased return on training investment
- improved productivity.

These benefits will culminate in improved business performance directly affecting the bottom line and the organization's financial performance.

TRAINING AND NONTRAINING SOLUTIONS

Sometimes, a training program is not needed in order to affect on-the-job performance. Millions, perhaps billions, of dollars are wasted every year because leadership takes the easy road by concluding that training will solve a problem that in reality requires an all-together-different solution. In many situations, the solution may be a nontraining solution or a combination of training and nontraining solutions. Nontraining solutions are actions taken to resolve safety and health problems that do not require training. The following are some hypothetical examples of nontraining solutions:

- A supervisor may offer an incentive to the employee with the best overall safety record.
- A construction company may require the use of cut-resistant gloves while working.
- A manufacturing facility may require the use of safety glasses in the assembly division beyond a certain point where manufacturing is being completed.
- The engineering department may redesign the work flow of a manufacturing site to decrease the number of injuries caused by people walking near heavy machinery.
- A company may institute a program to stretch and flex at the beginning of the workday to reduce stress and strains.

It is important to analyze the problems and assess training needs before making decisions about solutions. The following are some analyses to consider using when assessing training needs, deficiencies, or requirements:

- safety and health deficiency/problem analysis (aka root cause analysis)
- organizational impact analysis
- performance analysis
- procedural analysis
- strengths, weaknesses, opportunities, and threats analysis (SWOT)
- root cause analysis

- training needs analysis
- course content delivery method and organizational analysis.

When facing safety and health challenges, management should consider all training and nontraining alternatives. Much of the return on investment in training occurs because of inadequate analysis of the safety and health problem/deficiency leading up to the incident. One example to consider is the frequency of the task being performed. A thorough root cause analysis followed by a training needs analysis will provide information such as whether a worker failed to remember all the steps (or perhaps the task is too complex to perform from memory). In situations such as provided in the preceding examples, nontraining solutions, such as the following specified processes and procedures, are more effective than continued training without any changes.

When considering what actions to take to resolve a problem, it is important to consider the repetition/frequency of the task accomplishment, whether there was sufficient follow-up after the initial completion of training to prevent the introduction of bad behaviors, and whether the task is very repetitive, whereby complacency may become a contributing factor. Therefore, the more complex and nonfrequent a task is, the more imperative is to have established, written processes and procedures. Examples of process and procedures include:

- Safety Data Sheets (formerly known as Material Safety Data Sheets), sections on protection information, special precautions, spill/leak procedures
- flowcharts
- checklists
- diagrams
- troubleshooting guides
- decision tables
- reference manuals
- help desks or hotlines.

Training and nontraining problems or needs and their related solutions can generally be categorized as (1) selection and assignment, (2) information and practice, (3) environment, and (4) motivation/incentive defined as follows:

1. *Selection and assignment* refers to considerations and processes used to hire people and assign them specific responsibilities and on-the-job tasks. This area includes improving the hiring selection process by identifying the best candidate for the task performance, thus minimizing related safety and health issues.

2. *Information and practice* is the act of providing all necessary informa-

tion and developing the skills needed to use safe work practices. This area includes clearly communicating tasks, goals, and instructions and providing feedback, training, job aids, guided practice, and experience. This is the only area that can sometimes be improved through a training solution because effective training provides many opportunities for skill development.

3. *Environment* refers to all day-to-day influences on performance. These include, but are not limited to, equipment, floor plan, access to tools, working relationships with others, and working relationships with the safety professionals of the organization. For example, in work areas where people should wear safety goggles but may forget, a sign can be posted showing the proper use of safety goggles. Or, if walkways are located near areas where heavy machinery is used, the engineering department may redesign the work flow of the site to decrease the potential for injuries.

4. *Motivation/incentive* refers to any link between safety and rewards for safe behavior, such as bonuses, pay increases, contest prizes, and team competition. For example, a supervisor may offer a bonus to the employee with the best overall safety record. In safety training, in particular, the reduced risk of injury and even death is a potential motivator.

TRAINING ROLES OF THE SAFETY PROFESSIONAL

A safety professional has four primary functional areas:

1. Anticipate, evaluate, and identify hazardous conditions and practices.
2. Develop hazard control designs, methods, procedures, and programs.
3. Implement, administer, and advise on hazard control programs.
4. Audit, measure, and evaluate the effectiveness of hazard control programs.

The role of a safety professional is very broad and one of the drivers that has led to specializations within functional areas. This chapter's focus is on the role of a safety professional as it relates to training. The role of training lies primarily within the third functional area: *implement, administer, and advise on hazard control programs*. This function involves directing and assisting in the design, development, implementation, and evaluation of training materials and/or courses. Additionally, the safety professional is responsible for overseeing and conducting (or assisting with) courses related to safety and health. The safety professional may be required to coordinate the function of training development with internal or external instructional designers, purchase materials, contract with a trainer, or coordinate the entire training function. No matter the role, it is important to have a clear idea of the training goals, based on the needs of the company or facility and the workers—hence the need for the safety professional to utilize training analysis, design, and development subject matter experts to ensure best practices are implemented.

DEVELOPING THE TRAINING PROGRAM

Unless training is the safety professional area of specialization, the safety professional should work with internal or external training subject matter experts (SMEs) who use generally accepted instructional systems design (ISD). Instructional designers utilize ISD models such as the Dick and Carey model, and the Analysis, Design, Development, Implementation, and Evaluation (ADDIE) model. These two models differ in sequence and interaction but share the major categories described in the ADDIE model. As illustrated in Figure 7–1, the Training Cycle model differs slightly from the ADDIE model because a continuous evaluation process is incorporated to ensure the training is always evaluated to the desired outcome(s). The development processes and major activities, including the Training Cycle primary categories, are as follows:

- analysis/identifcation
- design
- development
- implementation
- evaluation/maintenance
- continuous improvement loop/performance evaluation.

Each of these major categories will have subcategories that will include tasks such as training needs analysis, written performance objectives analysis, outline of content, selection of training delivery method, duration and recurrent frequency (if any), testing/assessment, and evaluation, which would include the competency levels required to indicate whether the performance objectives were achieved. Once completed, the primary categories are all independently evaluated and reanalyzed as required to ensure all aspects of the category have been addressed. Following the flow of the Training Cycle (see Figure 7–1), an evaluation of the Training Cycle system is accomplished as a last step and on an ongoing basis to ensure that it meets or exceeds the desired results. This is sometimes referred to as the maintenance step, whereby evaluations are analyzed and improvements made based on the outcomes of the analysis. This process is directly tied to the safety professional's four primary functional areas, especially the first; *anticipate, evaluate, and identify hazardous conditions and practices.*

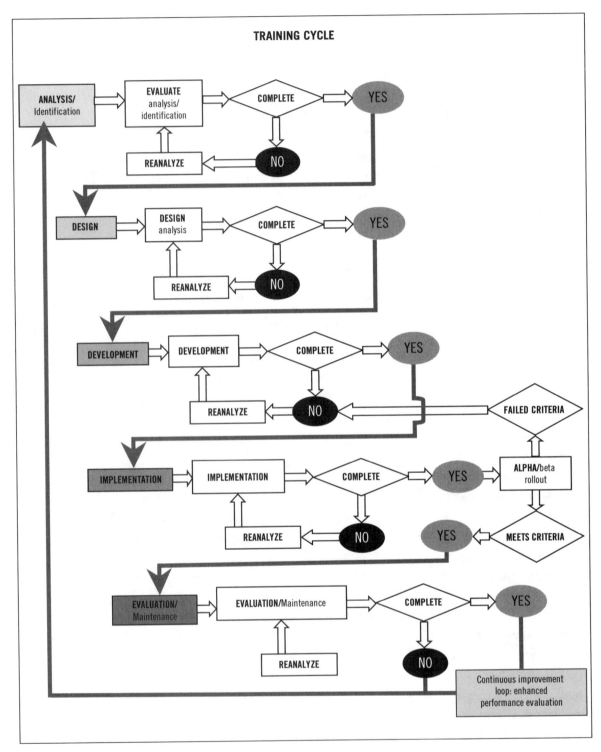

Figure 7–1. The Training Cycle

ANALYZE/IDENTIFY

In this category, the primary focus is on the foundational aspects of what will ultimately constitute the bulk of the decisions that will drive training content and delivery. In order to create an effective safety training program, the safety professional must first begin with analyzing and identifying the objective of the training to be designed. For example, is the training developed in response to a regulatory requirement, to an increased risk associated with a task, to part of a performance improvement initiative, to specific training as it relates to a safety and health program, or to training related specifically to a job or task?

The objective can be as simple as a new regulatory requirement requiring that a certain number of hours of training be provided to employees performing certain jobs or tasks. In these cases, much of the course curriculum/topics to be covered will likely be provided. More difficult cases require more in-depth investigation, such as cases where management has set new, more aggressive goals to reduce on-the-job injuries and lost workdays. In these cases, more detailed analysis is required to determine current worker performance and compare it to desired worker performance to identify training needs and goals. The curriculum will then need to be developed specifically for the intended purpose of improving current worker performance as it relates to the goal. For cases where the curriculum is not predefined, a broad range of analysis may be required as previously discussed in the "Training and Nontraining Solutions" section.

For the purposes of this chapter, analysis specifically related to training will be covered, but it is important to note that the safety professional has many other methods of analysis available that may be relevant and require incorporation into the analysis/identification category of the Training Cycle for the training outcome to have maximum impact. In completing a training needs analysis, any additional analysis will be reviewed and incorporated. Even in the event that the required training is a regulatory requirement with all aspects of the training defined, the training needs analysis will provide the basis for the analyze/identify category from Figure 7–1.

Training Needs Analysis

In order to create an effective safety training program, the safety professional needs to assess current worker performance and compare it to desired worker performance in order to identify training needs and goals related to identified deficiencies—hence the need to have learning and performance objectives as previously discussed. A training needs analysis is important to an organization because it helps to:

- distinguish between training and nontraining requirements
- distinguish and understand the problem or need before designing a solution
- save time and money by ensuring that solutions address the problems that need to be solved
- identify factors that will affect the training before its development.

A training needs analysis is the process of determining the *who, what, when, where,* and *why* elements associated with performing a work process safely. Key points to be considered when completing the training needs analysis include the following:

- knowledge and skills
- capacity
- standards
- measurement
- feedback
- conditions
- incentives.

The analysis ensures that training addresses identified performance gaps in relation to safety or health issues. Identifying specific training needs is the first phase of developing training that will ensure an effective and cost-efficient deployment. In analyzing training needs, the safety professional determines who may need training, what specifically they need to be trained to do, when they need to be trained, where they need to be trained, and why they need the training. This may be done by answering the following questions:

- Who does the job?
- What do they do in their jobs?
- When do they do the job?
- Where do they do the job?
- Why do they do the job?
- How do they do the job?

Primarily, training needs are analyzed by monitoring performance through observations, interviews, quality scores, audits, and questionnaires to determine the specifics of the problem or need that must be addressed through the required training. The training needs analysis may also show that other, nontraining solutions are necessary.

When a regulatory agency is not involved, the safety professional must determine whether training is even needed before creating a complete picture of the training need, which may in fact only be perceived. This is one of the main reasons safety professionals must understand nontraining solutions. In the initial stages of an assessment, the safety professional must always consider the many options that could solve the problem. Training for the sake of training can and often does increase employee frustration, lower morale, and possibly increase nonperformance and lack of compliance. Alternatively, mandated regulatory training is often seen as noncritical and nonessential by employees. In some cases, if a training needs analysis is not accomplished, training is provided to personnel who would not be required to receive it by regulation. This can serve to diminish and negatively affect the overall reputation of the safety and health programs, training programs, and employees' perception of the organization.

In the training needs analysis phase, the safety professional should identify training goals—framed by statements that describe how the training will satisfy the safety and health need or solve the problem, as well as state the general purpose of the training. Training goals provide direction for further analysis and help develop learning objectives. Training goals are also valuable tools for the safety professional to use in communicating the purpose of training to others. A training goal should clearly describe how the training will solve the safety or health problem. If the training needs analysis identified nontraining solutions, the goals must describe how the nontraining solution will solve the safety or health problem.

While the training goals and objectives are being identified, the safety professional/training developer should also identify the specific characteristics of the learners (workers) who will be involved in the training. This is the identification stage of the training development cycle's analysis/identify category. These characteristics include general demographics; learners' preferences, attitudes, knowledge, skills, and language and reading comprehension level; and previous experiences. The results of the analysis/identification include the following:

- specific characteristics that will influence the design and delivery of the training (also called an audience identification/description)
- recommendations on how the design of the training will accommodate the specific characteristics of learners.

Key points to be considered when completing a training needs analysis include the following:

- knowledge and skills
- capacity
- standards
- measurement

- feedback
- conditions
- incentives.

Training focused on the effectiveness of influencing behavior and solving the problem is performance based. *Performance-based training* is a learning experience (training) that is implemented to encourage a specific behavioral change or to solve a specific on-the-job problem. Performance-based training can be measured or evaluated by analyzing a worker's performance. This training is directly related to the job the worker is expected to perform, linked to the organization's safety and health goals, measured and evaluated by the worker's observable performance, and created using a systematic approach similar to what is illustrated in Figure 7–1. A *performance analysis* should be conducted by a safety and health professional for each specific job/task to determine what knowledge, skills, and attitudes people need to develop to meet the safety and health goals.

Two other types of analyses conducted in the needs assessment phase are job analysis and setting analysis.

- *Job analysis* is the process used to determine the procedures, decisions, knowledge, and skills required for a worker to perform a job function.
- *Setting analysis* is the process of identifying specific characteristics of the training environment (where training will occur) that will affect training.

Ideally, it is best to obtain setting information before designing the training. However, this is not always possible. The training course should be flexible enough to be delivered in a variety of settings. Once all analysis has been completed, it can then be used to determine what the training is seeking to change, improve, or re-enforce as it relates to the particular job/task, also known as *performance objectives*.

Written Learning and Performance Objectives

Objectives are especially critical in the safety and health arena because there is too much risk (potential for injury, illness, or loss of life) to workers to allow a "hit-or-miss" approach. Additionally, a vast amount of time and money is potentially wasted if training objectives are not determined in advance and training is conducted simply to place a check mark as having performed it. With the completion of the analysis and determination of the general or specific areas in which the learner needs to show proficiency, the learning and performance objectives can be developed. The importance of the learning and performance objectives cannot be understated and is usually considered the most critical step in the instruction system design. Learning and performance objectives provide the safety professional with a structure or framework for developing training that allows for everyone involved with the training—as well as those invested in the training—to know what needs to be taught, what is expected to be learned, and the performance associated with the learning. They also help determine whether the training is worth the investment in time and money. Objectives are also important guides in the following areas:

- selection and development of course content
- selection and development of learning activities
- measurement of the learner's performance.

Unlike goals, objectives are measurable and observable. Objectives differ from learning activities in that they describe the results themselves, not how to get results in the classroom. The four parts of an effective objective (sometimes referred to as the *ABCD method* of objective writing) are as follows:

- Audience (learners)—always identify the audience,
- Behavior—identify what learners must do in order to demonstrate mastery,
- Condition—identify what learners will be given or not given in order to perform the behavior.
- Degree—specify how well the audience members (learners) must perform the behavior.

Thus, objectives are important for training programs because they provide a measurable end point for performance (or behavior), they help learners identify the performance areas being evaluated, and they inform learners how they will be evaluated. Typically, objectives have three primary parts that include the job/task or observable action, the environment/conditions, and the standard to which the job/task must be performed given the condition parameters. Each of these parts can be defined as follows:

- *Job/task* (observable action) is defined as what the learner must be able to do.
- *Environment/conditions* is defined as the environment and/or conditions where the job/task is expected to occur.
- *Standard* is defined as the quantity and/or quality performance element that is considered acceptable.

When possible, the standard performance should have some value identified for achieving success (often 100% if the objective does not specify a level). Performance can be measured in terms of quantity, quality, or both. The current philosophy behind loss control supports measuring quality and quantity. Because of human nature, safeguards should be implemented to provide for the highest achievable performance level on a continuous basis within the training program development as well as for the job/task that the training aims to provide, set, and/or change in terms of the behavior. Once this determination is made, then the level of proficiency required to satisfactorily complete the training program can be determined. For example, if a training program has been developed for the use of a radioactive material in the performance of radiographic tests, is 75% an acceptable standard or level of competency? In this case—specifically, in relation to training to prevent actual exposure to the radioactive material outside its contained area—100% proficiency is required to ensure the safety and health of everyone on the team and all those who may be in the general area. Would the same standard or level of competency be required for a training program on the safe handling of food? These are the questions that the safety professional needs to answer and reevaluate on a continuous basis in relation to the performance outcome/goals that have been originally set by the organization and the regulatory requirements for minimum levels of acceptable safety standards.

DESIGN

In this category, the primary focus is on the design of the course, which includes course delivery, course content, major sections, and course sequence. Additionally, the safety and health or contracted instructional systems design professional identifies instructional goals, chooses training media, and most important, chooses the sequence in which workers will learn new information and skills. This work is based on the analysis/identification stage, which includes training needs analysis results, an audience analysis, and specific performance-based objectives.

After selecting the course delivery method(s), the types of training materials required can be determined. A major carryover from the analysis/identification stage is the written learning and performance objectives that are now expanded to include subcategories (as required) that meet the overall learning and performance objectives. The design category cannot be fully addressed without the analysis category having been properly and thoroughly completed because the design phase hinges on the outcomes of the analysis section. The design section should take advantage of all available resources—such as company policy and procedures manuals, regulatory brochures, and pamphlets—in the design of the training.

The use of written policies and procedures manuals has been a traditional means of providing information to new employees. The company should exercise care in preparing the manuals to ensure that the information is complete and easy to understand and that all rules are enforced. Policies and procedures manuals should cover items such as first aid, personal protective equipment, electrical safety, and housekeeping. These manuals can be used as key references by the participants during training and should be used as the major source for references as the training is designed and developed. References should always be included in materials to ensure proper source recognition and credibility.

The design stage includes but is not limited to the following:
1. literacy level consideration
2. adult learning needs
3. training delivery method selection
4. evaluation design.

Literacy Levels

Many workers read, write, use math skills, comprehend information, and use problem-solving abilities at a level called *low literacy* or *mid-literacy*. *Low literacy* generally refers to workers whose skills and/or abilities are at or below a fourth-grade level. *Mid-literacy* generally refers to workers whose skills and/or abilities are at a fifth- to eighth-grade level.

Workers with low or mid-literacy may have trouble understanding large amounts of information that is presented in complex textbooks, manuals, and lectures. This must be taken into consideration when designing and delivering safety and health training programs. For instance, training material can be modified to be written at a fourth- or fifth-grade reading level or to rely on less printed material. Use of symbols and illustrations in safety and health training and promotion can minimize the risk of the message being misunderstood. Incorporating course assessments announced as part of the course objectives also helps provide feedback on comprehension and appropriate competency target levels. (See "Testing/Assessment and Evaluation" later in this chapter.) Therefore, while the analysis phase determines the specific target audience as it relates to the job/task, the design phase must take into consideration and determine the appropriate literacy levels for the training design. For safety and health professionals, the primary audience (barring a few exceptions) will normally be adult learners. Thus, proper consideration of adult learning needs should be considered when designing training.

Adult Learning Needs

A major factor in the success of training is the extent to which adult learning needs are taken into consideration. Safety and health issues can be technical and difficult to learn. Also, many may see safety and health training as a disruption in their busy workday that does not really relate or add value to the work they are doing. To keep participants motivated and involved in safety and health training, the participants' learning needs must be considered. To accomplish this, adult learning principles must be used in the design and delivery of training. Different people learn using a variety of modalities. Training programs that incorporate a combination of methods based on adult learning concepts such as hearing, seeing, and doing is key when designing and delivering training programs.

The following percentages demonstrate potential learning retention based on the type of sensory concepts designed into the training program:

- reading—10%
- hearing—20% (20% of humans are auditory learners)
- seeing—30% (30% of humans are visual learners)
- hearing and seeing—50%
- speaking—70%
- speaking, hearing, and touching or doing an activity—90%.

Additionally, research conducted by the National Training Laboratories in Bethel, Maine, found retention percentages as represented in Figure 7–2 based on a culmination of various methods of teaching and the average retention rates. Therefore, it is important to understand and apply all available adult learning concepts into the development and implementation of a training program.

More generally applicable are four needs common to all adult learners. This information is adapted from Clay Carr, a widely respected training professional and author of the book, *Smart Training: The Manager's Guide to Training for Improved Performance*. These principles are generally accepted by most adult learning experts:

1. **Need to know why (WIFM):** Adults need to know why they are learning a particular topic or skill because they need to apply learning to immediate, real-life challenges. This is also known as the WIFM statement, or "What's in it for me?"
2. **Need to apply experience:** Adults have experience that they apply to all new learning.
3. **Need to be in control:** Adults need to be in control of their learning.
4. **Need for success:** Adults want to learn things that will make them more effective and successful.

These principles should be applied to any safety and health training developed, contracted, or designed for electronic learning applications.

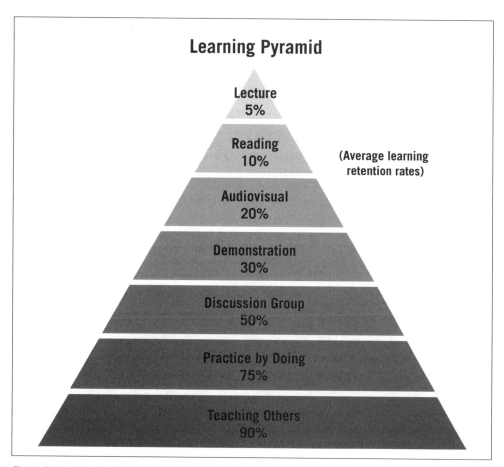

Figure 7–2. Learning Pyramid

Need to Know Why (WIFM). Adults need to know why they are learning a particular topic or skill because adults relate to the learning better once they understand why the training is advantageous. They also want to know how the training or learning can be applied immediately to real-life challenges. Therefore, they will often learn best when the following is true:

- They see clear demonstrations of how the training directly applies to their jobs.
- They have opportunities to apply the new information or skill to solve problems during the training.
- They have opportunities to think about how the new information or skill can be used.

An example of meeting this need is a supervisor demonstrating how to safely operate machinery; providing real-life experiences and observations on the importance of proper use, including examples of accidents, illnesses, and injuries associated with improper use; and then providing feedback while watching workers operate the machinery.

Need to Apply Experience. Adults have experience that they apply to all new learning and the following factors support the learning process:

- They have opportunities to share their experiences during training, using comparison and contrast, relationships, and association of ideas.
- They have opportunities to think about how the new information or skill relates to their past, present, or future experiences.
- Their experience, and opinions formed from their experience, is taken seriously by the facilitator.

For example, during training on personal protective equipment (PPE), provide time for participants to talk about their own PPE practices at their facility. They can also share their observations on the practices of their co-workers. Allow discussions on challenges, hardships, dislikes, concerns, and any other negative information, and be prepared to provide positive solutions or negative action result examples that further support the need and requirement to wear PPE. These discussions not only are healthy but also increase the credibility and awareness of the participants. Always work to resolve issues and concerns by answering honestly and following up as required on unanswered questions.

Need to Be in Control. Adults need to be in control of their learning and will learn best when there is some semblance of perceived control:

- They choose, or at least influence, the training they receive.
- They are in a flexible learning environment.
- They are actively involved in the learning process rather than passive receivers of information (the facilitator is a guide for the learning experience).
- They have opportunities to voice concerns and see them addressed, and can take part in activities such as group discussions, role-playing, and simulations.

For example, at a fluorescent light factory, workers are involved in a safety and health committee. Their responsibilities include assessing workers' needs for training, identifying appropriate training solutions, and evaluating the training once it has been delivered. Committee members are actively involved in the training and promote it both as part of the committee and as engaged workers.

Need for Success. Adults want to learn things that will make them more effective and successful, so benefits need to be part of the process:

- They should know why they are taking the training and how it will benefit them.
- They should be able to ask and answer these questions: "What is in it for me (WIFM)?" "How will it help me get ahead?" "What hazards will it help me control?"

An example of meeting this need is a safety management techniques course that includes action planning for future personal and professional development. A clearly stated and articulated objective at the beginning of every course or section is paramount and helps set the stage for all the learners by answering the WIFM question. Hence, while the analysis/identification stage defines the learning and performance objectives, the design stage may further break down those defined overall learning and performance objectives into more detailed objectives that relates to specific topics needed to create the basis/foundation to achieve the overall learning and performance goals.

Training Delivery Method Selection

Once the training needs analysis has been completed and the performance objectives have been written, the safety professional should carefully consider the most effective delivery method based on the audience. In selecting the delivery method, the safety professional may consider analyzing the return on investment to determine the most cost-effective training delivery approach. This analysis is not necessarily the best, but it will show the economic impact of the different options. The safety professional should consider the following when selecting the delivery method type:

- return-on-investment analysis
- delivery method yielding the highest performance results
- audience skill and literacy level.

This list is not inclusive and should be used as a general guide. Safety and health risks as well as regulatory requirements are also important factors.

There are three major types of performance-based training delivery methods:

1. *Instructor-led training*—This training can be presented in one of two ways. The first is presented in a classroom-like setting in which everyone follows the pace set by the instructor (also commonly called facilitator-led or trainer-led training). This type of training generally includes participant materials. The second is presented via an online platform

such as Online Meeting or WebEx. This platform mimics the classroom-like training except that the training is all conducted via a computer through the use of presentation slides, video, webcams, and interactive use of computer software that all participants see and is controlled by the trainer or facilitator. The trainer has the ability to pass on the control and has additional functionality that is not available to the participants.

2. *Self-paced training*—This is usually completed on an individual basis by working through a textbook and/or workbook. Self-paced training may also be completed through computer-based/web-based training or computer-assisted instruction, in which the learner is guided through the course through the use of a computer or online software. The software provides the course content, guides learning activities, and administers tests. Computer-based/web-based training, as part of a learning management system, can also provide the safety professional with a quick list of who has completed the training, and some programs can provide tests, scores, time to complete, number of attempts, and lowest and highest scores achieved. Computer software and the data available to the safety professional continue to evolve and expand, making analysis of the training much easier and more in-depth.

3. *Structured on-the-job training*—This training, also called on-the-job training (OJT), is similar to instructor-led training in that it is conducted by an instructor, but it is conducted at the learner's workplace. The instructor is usually a trained supervisor or employee who acts as a coach or guide. This type of training may or may not include participant materials, but it does incorporate all resources normally used during the course of completing the task(s) to be performed.

Evaluation Design

Evaluations are a necessary tool in eliciting information that can then be used to determine required changes to the training program design and its effectiveness and can be referred to as a major source of information. Constructing a questionnaire requires care and diligence to ensure that the questions asked are pertinent, are useful, and provide enough detail to enable tabulation and additional analysis. There are four primary types of information that can be discerned using questionnaires:

1. behaviors—what people do
2. attributes—personal and demographical characteristics
3. beliefs—what people think, attitudes opinions, etc.
4. knowledge—what people know and understand.

Evaluation design should always be accomplished such that the ISD, safety and health professional, and management personnel have direct input to maximize data collection with purposeful information gathering. The evaluation design itself must be tailored to the culture of the organization and must consider all aspects of the training design such as literacy, adult learning concepts, and the like.

TRAINING METHODS

Training methods falls under the design stage of the Training Cycle. Instruction system designers as well as safety and health professionals can select one of several different training methods when preparing a program. Each method has strengths and weaknesses. The technique selected should be determined by the objectives to be met, type of student participation, time allocated, facility being used, and equipment available. Everyone learns at different speeds and through different methods. Trainers must have the training and teaching skills to address these elements of human behavior. The following are the three most common types of training techniques used in industry:

1. on-the-job training (OJT)
   a. job instruction training (JIT)
   b. coaching
   c. internship
   d. apprenticeship
   e. mentoring
2. group methods
   a. conference/meeting/tailgating
   b. brainstorming
   c. case studies
   d. incident process
   e. facilitated discussion
   f. role-playing
   g. lecture
   h. question-and-answer (Q&A) sessions
   i. simulation
3. individual methods
   a. drill
   b. demonstration
   c. testing
   d. video-based training
   e. computer-assisted training

f. reading

g. independent study

h. seminars and short courses.

These methods are discussed in detail in the following sections.

On-the-Job Training

On-the-job training (OJT) is widely used because it allows for the workers to be productive during the training period. However, three considerations must be addressed when using OJT:

1. The trainer must possess proper training skills and be trained on the OJT being provided.
2. A training program should be developed to ensure that all workers are trained in the same way to perform their tasks in the safest and most productive manner.
3. Adequate time must be allotted to the trainer and trainee to be sure the subject is well covered and thoroughly understood.

Advantages to on-the-job training include the fact that additional resources and/or tools are not needed because the training is accomplished with resources and equipment normally used during the course of performing the job. On-the-job training is normally conducted where the job is performed, which provides further trainee familiarity and increased comfort in completing the job function. On-the-job training also has inherent disadvantages; most notably, the trainer must be well trained and vigilant while performing the job tasks, especially for work involving safety-sensitive tasks.

Job Instruction Training. A variation of OJT is known as *job instruction training* (JIT), also referred to as the four-point method. Instruction is broken down into four simple steps:

1. preparation
2. presentation
3. performance
4. follow-up.

This method of OJT has been highly successful. Workers are taught each job skill from a formal schedule of training. The program is adjusted to each student so that workers learn one task before beginning the next. In all training programs, selection of the trainer is critical to program success. The one-on-one relationship between trainer and trainee allows for better consistency and communication. In the four-point method, this trainer–trainee relationship works in the following ways:

Step 1: *Preparation.* The trainer puts the workers at ease. The trainer explains the job and determines what the workers currently know about the subject. This stage also includes preparation of the proper learning/ working environment.

Step 2: *Presentation.* The trainer demonstrates the work process. The student watches the performance and asks questions. The trainer should present the steps in sequence and stress all key points.

Step 3: *Performance.* The worker performs the task under close supervision (Figure 7–3). The trainer should identify any discrepancies in work performance and note good performance. The worker should explain the steps being performed. This ensures that the worker not only can perform the task, but understands how and why the task is done. This stage continues until the trainer is satisfied with the worker's competence at the job.

Step 4: *Follow-up.* The trainer and/or the supervisor must monitor the worker's performance to be sure the job is being performed as instructed and to answer any questions the worker may have.

Figure 7–3. Employee Training
This supervisor is explaining an enclosed operation to one of his workers. The supervisor is instructing the worker in the correct and safe operation of of the machine and will make frequent follow ups on his progress until certain of his performance.

Of the various OJT methods, JIT is probably the most flexible and direct. By practicing, the trainee is expected to develop and apply the learned skills in a typical work environment while under the guidance of a trained worker/ trainer. The trainer must know the job thoroughly; be a safe worker; and have the patience, skill, and desire to train.

The advantages of training in the JIT method are as follows:

1. The worker can be more easily motivated because the training/guidance is personal.
2. The trainer can identify and correct deficiencies as they occur.
3. Results of the training are immediately evaluated because the worker is performing the actual job on actual equipment. The work performed can be judged against reasonable standards.
4. Training is practical, realistic, and demonstrated under actual conditions. Workers can easily ask questions.

Timing is an important element in this type of training. The trainee can receive help when needed, and the trainer can provide feedback as the training progresses. The trainer can also determine when the trainee is ready to move on to new levels of training. It may be helpful to prepare a chart of tasks or subjects for which workers must receive training. This chart will make it easier to keep track of workers' training progress and the levels of competence they achieve.

Coaching. Other methods of OJT can be used, with the most common known as coaching or the buddy system. This system is considered effective in some situations, but the following challenges are associated with it:

- Trainers may be selected for their availability rather than for their training skills. A trainer who lacks basic teaching skills can undermine the entire orientation of a new worker.
- Each trainer may have his or her own way of performing the tasks being taught. This lack of continuity can make it difficult to control hazards in the workplace and can lead to frequent accidents.
- Key elements of orientation can be overlooked in the training program and may not be realized until an incident or accident occurs.
- Poor techniques or bad habits can be spread from one worker to another. Shortcuts or safety violations can be demonstrated to new workers as the "way we do it."
- Safety performance may not be emphasized during the training. Job performance should never be separated from safety standards in any training provided to workers.

Advantages and disadvantages of job instruction training mirror those previously covered under "On-the-Job Training" earlier in this chapter.

Internship. *Internships* are usually short-duration programs that last no more than one year. They are normally accomplished after the completion of an academic portion of a program but sometimes integrated into the last portion of the program. These programs are unlike an apprenticeship program and are normally comprised of two different entities working together to provide a collated program of study for completion of a degree or certification. Successful completion of the internship is required to meet the requirements of the degree or certificate to enable the learner advance into the workforce.

Apprenticeship. *Apprenticeship* training combines both the on-the-job training discussed earlier along with additional training specific to the job/task being performed. Unlike internships, apprenticeship programs can be much longer in duration, lasting anywhere from more than one year to upwards of four years. This type of training is sometimes referred to as *dual training* because of the training delivery combination of on-the-job (practical) training and dedicated instruction usually consisting of in-class training but also including online, computer-based, web-based, or self-paced programs. Apprenticeships also differ from internships in that the worker is usually paid, with salary increases associated with satisfactory completion of each level within the program. The Office of Apprenticeship within the Department of Labor's Employment and Training Administration provides a number of registered apprenticeship programs that are available for special incentives. These apprenticeships are approved by the government and may be eligible to receive tax benefits and workforce development grants. Registered apprenticeship programs offer career training in diverse areas, including carpentry, dentistry, and law enforcement.

Mentoring. *Mentoring* is a one-on-one professional relationship in which an experienced person (mentor) provides direct and personal guidance to assist another person (mentored person) in developing specific skills and knowledge to enhance the less-experienced mentored person in his or her professional and personal growth. While mentoring is, in many cases, an organizationally driven initiative, the mentor seldom receives training on mentoring. Like training, mentoring is a skill that is gained through training and experience. It is a long process and not one that should be used if immediate results are sought. Mentorships can last years as the mentored individual works toward the level of competency usually sought after for, say, higher-level leadership positions. For the scope of a safety and health professional, mentoring should be done frequently and with very defined and achievable goals and objectives.

Group Methods

Group techniques encourage participation from a selected audience. These methods allow trainees to share ideas and evaluate information and, depending on the organization, could include being actively involved in the planning and implementation of company policy. Several types of group training are used, but all require skilled facilitators to be successful.

Conference/Meeting/Tailgating. The *conference method* of training is widely used in business and industry for education-sharing purposes. This method is readily accepted because of the knowledge each participant brings to the group. In this process, sometimes called *meetings*, the trainer/facilitator controls the flow of the session as participants share their knowledge and experience. The skill of the facilitator can mean the success or failure of these sessions. Facilitators must use various techniques to draw information and opinions from members. The number of people involved should be limited to allow open discussion from all participants. The opinions of each member should be recorded, and a summary of the group's conclusions should be provided to those who were involved as well as to those who should be kept abreast of the information.

The conference technique is also a valuable method of problem solving. There are several situations in which a safety professional can use the knowledge and expertise of members of the organization to address safety and health issues. At the beginning of the conference, members should identify their goals and expectations for the session. For example, if a conference has been called to identify possible solutions to a safety and health concern, the group must understand that they are to make recommendations only, not to establish policy or procedures. By defining the actual role of the conference at the start, the group can avoid misconceptions and misdirection. When a group is asked to make recommendations, the members should be kept informed of the results of those recommendations.

If management fails to establish these ground rules and provide follow-up information, the conference members may feel that their efforts are ineffective. On the other hand, proper control and guidance of a conference can ensure its success and make it a gratifying experience for the participants.

This method has several advantages, including participation of the entire group and the fact that small groups can reach consensus. Disadvantages are that large groups may discourage participation by all participants, the group needs to have a purpose(s) that most can agree on, and complete consensus may be difficult if not impossible to reach in large groups.

Brainstorming. *Brainstorming* is a technique of group interaction that encourages each participant to present ideas on a specific issue. The method is normally used to find new, innovative approaches to issues. Typically, there are four ground rules:

1. Ideas presented are not criticized.
2. Freewheeling creative thinking and building on ideas are positively reinforced.
3. As many ideas as possible should be presented quickly.
4. Combining several ideas or improving suggestions is encouraged.

A recorder should be selected to document the ideas presented. The moderator should control the flow of suggestions, cut off negative comments, and solicit ideas from each member.

The advantage of brainstorming is that it allows ideas to be developed quickly, encourages creative thinking, and involves everyone in the process. Ideas from the group can go beyond old stereotypes or the "way it's always done," but the success of this method depends on the maturity level of the group. Additionally, the technique can lead to unfocused ideas—hence the need to limit the sessions to short durations to prevent straying from the known reality of ideas that have true potential of solving the problem.

Case Studies. *Case studies* are written descriptions of business decisions or problems that learners will use as a basis for demonstrating predetermined skills and knowledge. They have two distinct advantages. First, case studies provide an opportunity for learners to use skills and knowledge acquired during the course. Second, case studies can serve as an evaluation tool for trainers to measure the degree of proficiency attained during a course or module. Here are some other key benefits:

- During a case study, students begin to internalize the critical principles being taught and retain the information for longer periods of time.
- Case studies emphasize practical or critical-thinking skills.
- The student's perspective is broadened through interaction with others.
- Case studies encourage reflection, application, and analysis.
- Case studies reinforce the value of discussion and interaction with others.

Planning, thinking about, and adhering to the instructional objectives are paramount in designing an effective case study. The key is to start at the end and work backward toward the beginning. Ask the following questions:

- What questions must be answered?
- What skills or knowledge should be exercised?
- What specific performance objectives should be measured?
- What learning objectives are to be addressed by the case study?

A case study may involve an actual situation or be fictitious. The goal of the activity is to develop group members' insight and problem-solving skills. The case study is normally presented by defining what happened in a particular incident and the events leading up to the incident. The group is then given the task of determining the actual causes or problems, the significance of each element, and acceptable solutions.

The advantage to the case study method is that it enables the trainee to develop analytical and problem-solving skills, investigate and solve complex issues, and apply learned knowledge and skills. Disadvantages include the trainees' potential inability to understand or picture the relevance to the problem because of immaturity or lack of information.

Incident Process. The *incident process* is a type of case study in which the group works with a written account of an incident. The group is allowed to ask questions about facts, clues, and details. The trainer provides the answers to the questions, and the group must assemble the information, determine what happened, and arrive at a decision. The facilitator must guide the group to prevent arguments and to prevent one or two members from dominating the discussion. This is a useful training method that encourages employee participation in the accident prevention program. Situations can be real cases in the company or potential hazards that exist.

The facilitator/moderator must be able to control the group process and progress and prevent the group from missing the true or root causes. For example, suppose an employee was struck in the eye by a foreign body, and an investigation revealed that the employee was not wearing safety glasses while operating a bench grinder. The group must seek the root cause of the accident and not settle for the common conclusion that "the worker failed to follow procedures" or "the worker failed to wear eye protection." They must specify why the supervisor or management failed to enforce the proper procedures (assuming there was an established procedure). Why did management allow this lax supervision—or did they?

Facilitated Discussion. *Facilitated discussion* or dialogue is the management of discussion about the course content so that the learning objectives are met, the discussion flows logically from topic to topic, and the applications to the learners' jobs are made clear. Facilitated discussion requires that the trainer/facilitator have the skills to accept all ideas and contributions as valid, show how they relate to the course objectives, and manage the time element and the flow of information to meet the course objectives.

The benefits of facilitated discussion include the following:

- It ensures that the learners are involved and challenged.
- It builds a bond between the trainer/facilitator and learners that encourages the free exchange of ideas and information.

Role-Playing. *Role-playing* is effective for evaluating human relations issues. Group members attempt to identify the ways people behave under various conditions. Although this technique is not an effective method of problem solving, it can uncover issues not previously considered. This method is particularly helpful in identifying and changing personnel issues such as poor morale or negative attitudes.

Advantages to role-playing include giving trainees an opportunity to assume the role of others, thereby obtaining better understanding and a different perspective on the position, task, or responsibility. This method of learning also offers an opportunity to practice skills and gain knowledge in a controlled environment. However, this method is difficult to apply effectively to large groups, and trainees may feel self-conscious and even threatened. A good facilitator is essential to making this method successful.

Lecture. Using the *lecture* method, a single person can impart information to a large group in a relatively short time. This method is normally used to communicate facts, give motivational speeches, or summarize events for trainees. There is little time or opportunity for interaction by the attendees, and follow-up for these sessions must be planned well in advance to be successful.

Advantages to this method of learning include the fact that the material is presented in a direct and logical manner. It enables the trainer to provide experiences that motivate and inspire the group, whether small or very large, effectively. The trainer must have excellent oral skills, and assessments are necessary to effectively gauge the learning.

Question-and-Answer (Q&A) Sessions. Normally, *question-and-answer sessions* follow training periods, after the trainer has summarized the material presented. Workers can use this method to clarify individual concerns or facts. However, workers often need time to prepare and organize their thoughts before they can ask questions. When workers must absorb a large amount of material, trainers should allow them time to reflect on or apply the knowledge and to formulate questions. The trainer can plan to have a follow-up session or allow workers to present their questions personally. Question-and-answer sessions are helpful in clarifying issues of policy or changes in schedules or events.

Advantages to this method include that it allows everyone to participate in an active process. The disadvantages include the fact that Q&A is not practical with large groups and can lead to a few trainees dominating the session. This type of session can also be time consuming, get off track, and yield little participation from most of the trainees if the trainer/facilitator does not work the audience for best participation.

Simulation. When actual materials or machines cannot be used, trainers can use a *simulation* device. This method is used effectively to train aircraft pilots, railroad engineers, and commercial motor vehicle drivers and in other applications in which external and internal inputs can have a varied number of possible outputs, all requiring the same outcome. Various methods are employed in management training programs as well, such as the "in-basket technique," "war games," and manufacturing-line process simulations. One simulation demonstrates the loss of eyesight to workers to encourage them to wear safety glasses on the job. The only limit to this technique is the trainer's creativity.

Simulation is most effective when workers can participate. Careful planning and attention to detail are required. The initial costs of these sessions can be high because of the equipment required and time involved in conducting training.

Individual Methods

The area of individual methods entails learning and/or training that is individualized to allow for each learner to go at his or her own pace, taking into consideration the differences in learner abilities. With individual learning, a trainer/facilitator must consider and cater to the individual needs of the learner.

Drill. Using the elements of practice and repetition, the *drill* method of instruction is valuable for developing worker skill in fundamental tasks and for performing under pressure. Workers required to perform in crisis situations should be trained under conditions that resemble the crisis as closely as possible. For example, when instructing workers in cardiopulmonary resuscitation (CPR), the trainer must try to instill the tension that workers will experience when they attempt to resuscitate a real victim. This method helps workers develop control and builds confidence; in real-life situations, workers can react competently and revert to the trained actions they have come to learn and know, rather than panicking or having knee-jerk reactions that result in the loss of critical time, energy, and—potentially—life.

Demonstration. As discussed earlier in the section on JIT, the *demonstration* method allows the trainer to perform the actual task and then have the worker repeat the performance. Trainers must be sure the job is performed exactly as required to prevent workers from developing poor habits and performance deficiencies (and supervisors must see that employees follow the designated procedure). If the conditions used in demonstrations are not similar to the actual workstation or equipment on the job, this method will yield few if any desirable results.

Testing. *Testing* is normally used to determine whether workers understand the necessary information and can apply the knowledge when required. Developing good tests is a skill that requires constant review to ensure that training objectives are being met. Poor tests can reduce workers' morale, undermine training objectives, and yield poor training assessment data, thus preventing continual improvements of the training program. For additional information on testing see the "Evaluation/Maintenance" section later in the chapter.

Video-Based Training/Podcasts. An increasing number of training programs are designed as *videotape presentations* and *podcasts*. These training formats are available on nearly any subject. This method of instruction is effective if properly applied. The use of videotapes/podcasts does not eliminate the need for professional instruction, but it can enhance a classroom presentation. Videos are available from the National Safety Council and numerous private companies as are podcasts and other similar video offerings. Trainers should screen the training to make sure the materials meet the needs of the training program.

Production companies can produce training videos on budgets ranging from hundreds to millions of dollars. The first step before selecting a production company—or, for that matter, deciding to make the video for the organization—is to determine how the video will fit into the overall training program. The major factors are the course design, the purpose of the course, and how the objectives are met. The same consideration is taken when developing podcasts. Some distinct advantages to using a video in a training class are as follows:

- Video offers the learner an opportunity to see examples of tasks and processes being performed correctly.
- The difficulty of producing training videos has been diminished. Newer formats, such as Hi8 and S-VHS, digital media, small personal

computers cameras, and now even smartphone technology offer lighter media recording devices and greater ease of use.

If the video portion is the core of the training program, a "higher-end" type of production should be used. This usually involves hiring a production company (independent producer), professional scriptwriter, director, and editor. Expect postproduction costs (editing, graphics, animation, sound design, and music) to consume two-fifths of the overall budget. However, if the video portion of the training program is supplemental or ancillary, the safety professional can tape the material and hire a professional editor to assemble the footage.

This method provides an entertaining way to introduce content and usually keeps the trainees' attention. Disadvantages of this method include raising too many issues to allow for follow-up focused discussion. This can be remedied in the design phase by limiting the focus to help in retention.

Computer-Assisted Training. Interactive computer programs, also known as *computer-based training* (CBT) or *web-based training* (WBT), are being developed for many areas of employee training. They enable workers to receive information by reading and/or watching a video presentation and then responding to situations and questions via a computer-based device. For example, if a trainee is completing a computer training session and enters the correct response to a question, the computer will advance the program to the next section; if the wrong response is entered, the program will repeat the information and retest the trainee. The system is valuable for several reasons:

- Trainees can work at their own pace.
- Records can be automatically kept of all training. The amount and type of records maintained can be modified to meet company requirements.
- Correct answers are required before a worker can proceed to the next lesson, or remediation methods can be built into the program.
- Workers receive training as time allows, rather than having to meet specified training schedules.

With computer-assisted training programs, instructions can guide workers step by step through a curriculum designed to meet individual or company goals and regulatory obligations. The company can keep records of the amount of time each worker spends in training, the type of material or information presented, and the success of the training. This type of program works extremely well for organizations with small work forces or those that cannot remove large groups of workers from their jobs at any one time.

The differences between WBT and CBT have to do more with where the information for the training is housed than differences in the actual course content. Web-based training programs use the Internet or offsite computer servers (cloud-based) to deliver content and allow for greater interactivity through live chats with an instructor and associated bulletin boards or via blogs (weblogs). Computer-based training provides multimedia instruction via CD-ROM on a desktop computer; it usually has no connection to the Internet and hence no interactivity.

Reading. Companies should provide employees with *written safety materials* such as monthly newsletters and safety magazines. In addition, organizations may establish a resource library or Internet access to allow employees to research information on subjects such as work procedures, safety, leadership, health care, and family or home safety. However, management must not assume everyone has the ability to read and comprehend all of the written material provided. Companies cannot replace instruction or training programs simply by handing an employee a training manual. Written material is meant to provide a supplement or reference for training, not replace it.

A major advantage of having a resource library for employees is that it enables motivated employees to continue learning and personal development when no other training is available. This type of training is usually accomplished at the person's own pace and on his or her own time. The cost of implementing such a program varies, but considering advancements in technology, the availability of Internet and intranet services, and the affordability of website management software, it can be readily affordable and accessible to anyone from anywhere.

Independent Study. *Independent study* methods such as home-study courses or correspondence courses are used by many companies. They can help employees advance within the organization or improve their knowledge of their jobs and the industry. A major advantage of this method of training is that the employee does not lose any time from work and can complete the course at his or her own pace. Another advantage is the low cost of implementing and maintaining home-study programs. Normally, such programs center on textbook assignments, followed by self-tests using multiple-choice, true/false, fill-in, or essay questions. Although independent study sometimes includes computer-assisted training (discussed earlier), it more commonly involves textbooks. Some independent courses also provide laboratory or performance materials as part of the curriculum. Examples include television, radio, and computer repair programs that work on actual equipment. Some home-study programs come with media presentations for workers to view and follow.

Seminars and Short Courses. *Seminars, short courses, and workshops* for safety and leadership information and skills are offered by many colleges and universities, as well as by insurance companies and private organizations. The National Safety Council offers onsite instruction for workers, supervisors, and management. Seminars, short courses, and workshops range from one-hour to several-day sessions. These types of courses, though traditionally more expensive, usually provide employees with specific, relevant, and in-depth information on the topics being discussed. These types of training programs are similar to facilitated discussions and lecture courses.

DEVELOPMENT

In this stage, the primary focus is on building the specific individual parts to the training such as presentation, handout materials, precourse work, course work, facilitator training guides, and props, to name a few. This is essentially the assembly phase of the training where all the design content is taken and organized into sections. The development stage must begin with a content outline. The content outline can be developed upon completion of the training needs analysis and the written performance analysis. The outline should be the basis for the development of the training curriculum and should contain the following:

- safety and health policy
- course objective
- statement addressing "What's in it for me?"
- introduction
- main performance objective training content
- review and summary
- assessment.

The organization of the content of the safety and health training program is achieved by outlining the content. To outline, the training developer selects an objective and identifies any actions the worker must take to achieve the objective and the related topics the worker must know to accomplish the actions or change the behavior. The training developer then sequences the content in the appropriate order, preferably with input from the safety professional, other subject matter experts as required, and management as needed. With this information, the developer can move onto the types of materials and deliverables that will be used in the delivery of the training.

The materials and deliverables used in an effective safety and health training program should include (1) an introduction; (2) presentation of the information; (3) practice and feedback; and (4) a summary, evaluation, review, or transition phase. The introduction can be an overview, a rationale, a warm-up activity, questions, or a story or analogy. The information should be presented in a manner that helps the workers organize and remember the important facts. The following types of materials can be used to achieve this goal:

- table of contents
- text
- graphics
- examples
- job aids
- checklists
- graphs
- tables
- data
- reports
- relevant articles
- glossary.

Practice and feedback should be provided to workers as an opportunity to try out the new knowledge and skills and to receive information about their performance. Materials that help guide the process of practice and feedback include the following:

- activity directions
- activity time allowance
- activity worksheets
- question-and-answer worksheets
- business scenarios
- performance checklists
- sample solutions and expert answers.

The summary, evaluation, review, or transition phase should stress important training points, answer workers' questions, and make a connection to the next training topic or the job. Supporting materials for this phase include the following:

- text
- graphics
- question-and-answer sheets
- listing of next steps
- goal sheets for implementing new knowledge and skills on the job
- duration and recurrent frequency.

Depending on operational requirements, the timing of the content of the safety and health training program is determined either before or after the outline is created. The training developer sequences the content in the appropriate order (perhaps with input from the safety professional or management) and estimates the amount of time needed for each point. If more time is needed, the trainer can either request it or narrow the scope of the objectives. In addition, regulations may require that certain content be covered and that it be covered with a certain frequency. The safety professional is responsible for knowing and understanding these requirements and for providing this information for the return-on-investment analysis and to the training developer as the training is designed.

DELIVERING TRAINING

IMPLEMENTATION

In this category, the primary focus is on the implementation of the developed training. As the threshold between development and implementation is crossed, there must be an alpha and beta rollout of the training to be implemented to test the effectiveness and validity of the training and to assess the training development's ability to meet the design and criteria (see Figure 7–1). *Alpha testing* consists of proving concepts with a team of experts who are usually part of the design team. *Beta testing* occurs when users from identified cohorts from the target testing population are involved to determine whether the test is both effective and valid. It should be noted that the trainer/facilitator (if applicable) must exhibit safety and health expertise, sound instructional skills, and flexibility. There are many cases where the trainer/facilitator does not have the necessary expertise or level of expertise, which can negatively affect the learning and performance objectives. For training that will be conducted by a trainer/facilitator, it is especially critical for the alpha and beta testing to be conducted by an individual who has expertise in both safety and health as well as a seasoned trainer/facilitator with experience delivering newly developed training. The latter is particularly important because all the participant feedback, trainer/facilitator comments, material discrepancies as related to all materials, and evaluations must all be analyzed to the original design criteria to ensure the developed training meets or exceeds the desired results.

Upon completion of the alpha and beta rollouts—and only after confirming that the developed training meets or exceeds the desired results—is the implementation stage released. Once the training has reached the implementation stage, it must be evaluated periodically as part of the continuous improvement cycle to ensure that it continues to meet the developed training needs or exceeds the desired results—for example, as maintenance. Hence, good training is never really fully developed because it should always be transitioning, either due to development improvements or because of ongoing maintenance refinements to further ensure that the learning and performance objectives are met and/or exceeded. Advantages of the alpha/beta rollout include, but are not limited to:

- course and, more specifically, module/section timing/duration verification
- verification that objectives were covered
- verification of content order
- verification that material content is best suited for media method used.

Thus, the implementation phase is much more than just rolling out the training. Rather, it affords the opportunity to prove the design stage concept, verify the development stage, ensure the selected media are appropriate for the training being conducted, verify that trainer or facilitator's skill level is appropriate, and allow for continuous improvement of the system through feedback loops back into the development stage and the analysis/identification stage.

EVALUATION/ MAINTENANCE

Evaluation Design

While the actual evaluation methodologies may be determined in the analysis/identification stage, it is in the evaluation/maintenance stage that these methodologies are expanded to incorporate best practices and potential benchmarking to enable further analysis after implementation. In their commitment to improving the knowledge, skills, and attitudes of workers, and as part of their roles and responsibilities, safety professionals must continually measure and evaluate whether workers are meeting or exceeding the learning and performance objectives. Performance testing is one way to measure whether learners have met the learning objective. Performance tests can be created only after performance objectives have been developed in the analysis/identification stage. There are three main types of performance tests: pretests, review tests, and posttests.

Pretests. A *pretest* measures how well learners can perform objectives before training. Pretests are generally optional and are often provided as a means for learners to identify how much they already know before starting the training. Trainers also use the results to customize the program to meet audience needs. In other situations, pretest and posttest results are used to assess the learning progress made by an individual or class. Pretests can be a very useful tool as a means to benchmark the learner's competency before training, after training, and at some later point in time. Comparisons can be taken and reviewed against the learning and performance objectives to determine proper recurrent training intervals, as well as to provide feedback to the organizational leadership on new, more challenging goals if they were to be adopted.

Review Tests. A *review test* measures how well learners can perform the objectives during training. Learners take review tests to determine when they are ready to move on to the next objective (topic or task). Review tests often take the form of activities or exercises. Participants' progress is informally assessed by the trainer/facilitator or by the participants themselves. While these tests are not normally collected and analyzed, they can provide good information in relation to developed training subtopics, as well as in evaluating the individual trainer/facilitator and/or the module.

Posttests. A *posttest* measures how well the learner can perform the objectives after training. Posttests often test the same information included in the pretest but may differ in complexity or format. When designing a training program, safety professionals must decide whether and when to use pretests, review tests, and posttests to measure learners' performance. In safety and health training, tests are highly recommended in the following situations:

- when the training involves a certification or qualification process
- when the organizational culture supports its use
- when the risks of not mastering the objectives may include significant financial loss, injury, or death
- when the effectiveness of training may be questioned
- when qualitative and quantitative data on training and/or safety and health issues are needed.

Postests are an effective tool in assessing trainees' competency at completion of a training program and at stated intervals after the program is complete: for instance, follow-up testing at 30, 90, and 180 days afterward. This type of follow-up, when coupled with a continuous-improvement loop that revises the training based on posttest findings, helps identify training deficiencies that require additional emphasis. This helps facilitators and ISDs focus on the identified areas of deficiency, increase trainee retention and competency, and access the trainings effectiveness in meeting the original learning and performance goals.

Additionally, it is important to have determined in the analysis/identification stage what the minimum level of acceptable performance will be. This is sometimes the goal, while other times it is a minimum competency level. This is important because knowledge retention rates fall over time, especially if the task is not performed frequently. Initial retention rates were discussed earlier in the design stage under "Adult Learning Needs," but posttesting accomplished some period of time after training completion will provide a better picture for the safety and health professional—as well as for the ISD—of what needs more emphasis during training or if there is a nontraining solution that needs to be implemented. Indiana University performed a study in which it found

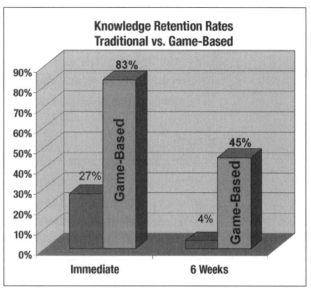

Figure 7–4. Knowledge Retention Rates: Traditional versus Game-Based

that game-based learning increased retention by more than 300% in immediate posttesting. It was further determined that the same training provided as much as 10 times the retention rate when subjects were tested 6 weeks later than traditional training (see Figure 7–4).

As it relates to safety and health, the safety and health professional will need to analyze the specific training retention rates and determine whether they are acceptable based on the business's goals and objectives. In some cases, the learning and performance goals will be achieved, yet the goal set out by the leadership may not have been obtained. In such cases, it is critical to reevaluate the whole training cycle starting with the analysis/identification stage, specifically the re-accomplishment of the training needs analysis to ensure that all training and nontraining solutions have been adequately identified and implemented for the established set of goals.

REGULATORY OBLIGATIONS

NEW EMPLOYEE TRAINING AND ORIENTATION

Many companies regard *orientation* as an excellent opportunity to begin training workers in safety policies and safe work practices. In fact, regulatory agencies state that an employer not only should provide such training but is obligated to do so. Safety and health training can be delivered through an orientation program and through written policies and procedures manuals.

Safety and health training begins when a new worker is hired. The person is usually open to ideas and information about how the company operates. From the first day, the new employee formulates opinions about management, supervisors, workers, and the organization. Some personnel managers say they have never hired a worker with a bad attitude; this may not be entirely true, but many employees' negative attitudes are developed after they have been on the job.

Timeliness of instruction is a key issue in the orientation program. For example, although statistical data differ, studies generally agree that new employees are significantly more prone to work-related accidents. This fact is attributed to the inexperience of new workers, their unfamiliarity with procedures and facilities, and their zealousness to do the work. Also, a significant number of workers are injured during the 4- to 6-year range. This is generally attributed to either a change in work duties (new or transferred employee) or worker complacency. These issues can be covered in an ongoing training program, which will help reduce the number of accidents.

The following subjects are suggested as part of the orientation program:

- company orientation: history and goals
- policy statements
- benefit packages
- organized labor agreements (if applicable)
- safety and health policy statement (if separate)
- acceptable dress code (as required)
- personnel introductions
- housekeeping standards
- communications about hazards
- personal protective equipment
- emergency response procedures: fire, spill, etc.
- incident-reporting procedures
- near-miss incident reporting
- incident investigation (supervisors)
- lockout/tagout procedures
- machine guarding
- electrical safety awareness
- ladder use and storage (if applicable)
- confined-space entry (if applicable)
- medical facility support
- first aid/CPR
- hand tool safety
- ergonomic principles

- eyewash and shower locations
- fire prevention and protection
- access to exposure and medical records.

These subjects, among many others, cover essential information that is far too important to overlook or leave to casual learning. A formal program should be developed not only to provide the worker with this information, but to create a strong link between employees and the safety and health philosophy of the organization.

Many of these subjects are left to the manager, supervisor, or team leader to cover with employees when they arrive at the worksite. This person must have time to cover these points with the employees. Unfortunately, the importance of going over these subjects with the employees is not often recognized until an accident occurs.

Managers, supervisors, and team leaders should be familiar with current information presented to new workers to avoid the age-old problem of contradicting the training material. They should also become involved in the development of training programs to keep the information current and practical in relation to work demands. When they start disregarding or contradicting the training program, the entire program—and the company's image—loses credibility with the workers.

Each manager, supervisor, or team leader should reinforce the training program content by demonstrating how it will apply to the worker's specific job assignment. For example, the new employee may have been trained how to read the warning labels on chemical containers. The manager, supervisor, or team leader can then enhance this information by conducting a tour of the department, pointing out all hazardous materials, and identifying the protection provided through personal protective equipment and control measures.

ADDITIONAL RESOURCES

All regulatory agencies publish information about employers' responsibilities to provide training and retraining to their employees. The final interpretation may still present difficulties; the best solution is to communicate with the agency involved, if necessary, and the organization's legal counsel.

The continued importance of training is evidenced by the requirements of both the Occupational Safety and Health Administration (OSHA) and the Mine Safety and Health Administration (MSHA). The major parts of the OSHA regulations (Title 29—Labor, Code of Federal Regulations) covering training requirements include the following:

- Part 1910, Safety and Health Training Requirements for General Industry

- Parts 1915–1918, Safety and Health Training Requirements for Maritime Employment
- Part 1926, Safety and Health Training Requirements for Construction
- Part 1928, Occupational Safety and Health Requirements for Agriculture.

OSHA also provides additional guidance and documents for review. The following is a short list of additional documents and resources. Additional information may also be found on the OSHA website, www.osha.gov.

- ANSI/ASSE Criteria for Accepted Practices in Safety, Health, and Environmental Training, ANSI/ASSE 2490.1-2009
- ANSI: American National Standards Institute
- ASSE: American Society of Safety Engineers
- NIEHS WETP Minimum Health and Safety Training Criteria Guidance for Hazardous Waste Operations and Emergency Response (HAZWOPER); HAZWOPER Supporting and All Hazards Prevention, Preparedness and Response
- NIEHS: National Institute of Environmental Health Sciences
- WETP: Worker Education and Training Program

The requirements for training and retraining of miners are defined by MSHA in Title 30 CFR, Part 48—Training and Retraining of Miners (see sections 48.2 and 48.22 for definitions of the terms used in Part 48). Remember that these regulatory obligations represent only the minimum requirements; therefore, a thorough evaluation as previously discussed is necessary to ensure a truly safe and health-promoting environment for employees.

SUMMARY

Training focuses mainly on behavior change, showing workers how to perform tasks properly and to apply their knowledge on the job. In some cases, however, nontraining solutions are more appropriate. In developing a quality safety and health training program, it is important to use a system that allows for full understanding and continuous improvement, such as the Training Cycle listed in Figure 7–1. This method provides the system needed to develop the best training that will provide the necessary knowledge and skills and set the appropriate behaviors to protect workers' health and lives and prevent work-related injury or illness. Effective training will help ensure that workers develop the appropriate skills and are educated and empowered to improve the working conditions in their places of employment.

One important factor that helps to ensure successful training implementation is the selection of a training facilitator who exhibits safety and health expertise, sound instructional skills, and flexibility. In developing effective training, the following are important considerations:

- Training and nontraining problems and solutions are categorized as selection and assignment, information and practice, environment, and motivation/incentive.
- Adult learners have special needs and requirements that trainers must recognize for programs to be effective. Performance-based instruction generally works well with adult learners.
- To design an effective training program, the safety professional must assess workers' needs, analyze learners' characteristics, develop specific objectives, develop materials and schedules, and design testing and evaluation methods by following the Training Cycle provided in Figure 7–1.
- Training begins with new-employee orientation. Using written policies and procedures manuals is one way to meet new-employee training needs and conform to regulatory standards.
- Training methods include on-the-job training, job instruction, group methods, and individual methods.

Maintenance of the overall training cycle is essential for training that currently meets and/or exceeds expectations, and a training program that does not degrade becomes obsolete over time.

REVIEW QUESTIONS

1. List four benefits of safety and health training.
2. Identify 7 of the 12 nontraining solutions that can be as effective as a training program.
3. Define *performance-based training*.
4. What are the five phases of the systematic approach of performance-based training?
5. Adults learn best through which of the following senses?
   a. hearing
   b. sight
   c. touch
   d. all of the above
6. Describe the four adult learning principles that should be applied to all safety and health training.

7. List the three most common types of training methods used in industry.
8. Group training encompasses which of the following techniques?
   a. brainstorming
   b. case study
   c. role-playing
   d. simulation
   e. all of the above
   f. b and c
9. Define *computer-assisted training*.
10. List the five steps in the ADDIE system or Training Cycle model.

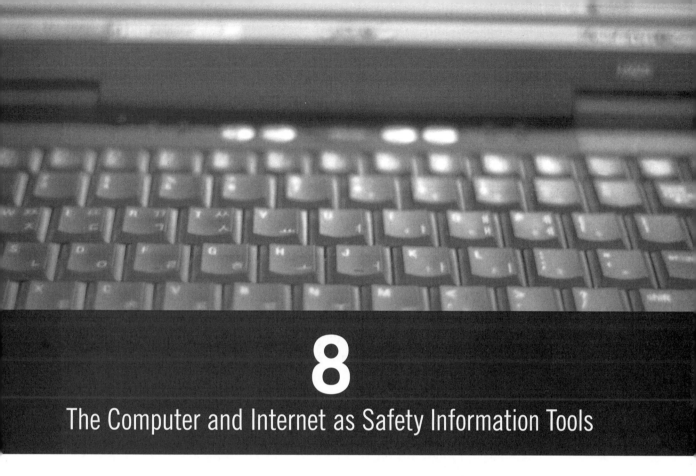

8

The Computer and Internet as Safety Information Tools

LEARNING OBJECTIVES

- ❏ Describe areas where the use of computers can enhance the safety process.

- ❏ Discuss pros and cons of using Internet-based tools for gathering safety information.

- ❏ Understand the process for conducting an effective Internet-based search for safety-related information.

- ❏ Compare and contrast the different roles list-serv participants engage in as part of an Internet-based safety discussion group.

- ❏ Discuss how the Internet can be used to support safety program management elements.

INTRODUCTION

Computers and computer networks have become increasingly important tools for safety professionals. First used to facilitate data storage, retrieval, and calculations, they have gradually emerged as core communication and educational tools throughout society. The rapid development of the Internet, particularly its powerful search engines, has increased the importance of electronic information in the daily life of professionals and organizations alike. It is difficult to imagine managing the variety and amount of information that flows through a 21st-century safety program without strong computer skills.

Another aspect of computer use by safety professionals is the collection and analysis of safety program data. This is a skill that can require significant practice to master. Many safety and health professionals have developed valuable tools for managing their work only to see these tools become obsolete as program needs, computer platforms, and organizational support change. As options for collecting, managing, and distributing electronic data proliferate, this concern is becoming an increasingly significant issue. For this reason, computer solutions proposed to serve a safety program must be carefully evaluated not only for their current functionality, but also for their scalability and long-term sustainability. The best approach to addressing this concern is developing a coherent information architecture for the data being collected; development of such architectures will benefit from partnerships with information professionals who have experience in addressing these concerns. However, the good news is that computer systems are continuing to become more powerful and easy to use; when their use is carefully planned and maintained, they can be vital assets to safety programs.

This chapter focuses on four aspects of the use of electronic information by safety professionals:

1. *As a reference tool.* Computer networks provide convenient access to a wide variety of information resources of value to the safety professional. This section describes the use of these resources at the conceptual level, and specific resources are listed in the Resources section at the end of this chapter.

2. *As a networking tool.* It is increasingly difficult for a safety professional to effectively be a "jack of all trades." The hazards and protection strategies of the 21st-century workplace are evolving rapidly as new technologies (e.g., biological tools and nanoparticles) result in new safety-related challenges and as traditional hazards are better recognized and understood. The ability to consult peers on both technical and management issues is a valuable professional tool. While professional organizations have

traditionally facilitated this aspect of professional work, the development of the Internet, particularly e-mail, has become another important way to connect with colleagues for discussions of mutual benefit. The second section discusses ways to maximize the value of this use of the Internet.

3. *As a safety culture tool.* A key aspect of a successful safety program is the ability to distribute information effectively and efficiently to stakeholders. This involves not only identifying the information that specific individuals and groups need, but also providing it in a form that is useful for that audience. This may involve providing text documents to some people while developing video forms of the same information to other people. The use of the Internet provides important opportunities and challenges for this function.

4. *As a safety program management tool.* In addition to collecting and sharing information about their workplaces, safety professionals need to fashion this information to the needs of a variety of audiences, including upper management, workers, and regulators. Often, this means restating the same information in a different way according to the question being asked. In addition, information about safety conditions in the workplace needs to be connected to other information that the organization manages, such as financial or human resource records, in order to be used effectively. The last section of this chapter considers this aspect of a safety program's use of computers and computer networks.

THE INTERNET AS A REFERENCE TOOL

One of the biggest challenges facing safety and health professionals is finding relevant information when they need it. Changing regulations, new data and emerging technologies can make paper-based resources an unreliable medium for researching occupational safety and health issues. Fortunately, the Internet now provides a legitimate alternative to an extensive library of books, manuals, and regulations. This section describes some of the tools that can be used to become familiar with the types of information available on the Internet. A strategy is then described for answering specific questions that arise in daily safety and health work.

Just as being familiar with how a library is organized makes searching a paper library for information much easier, being familiar with the Internet also makes searching for particular information easier. It is a good idea to spend some time building familiarity with a variety of websites before attempting to answer a particular question.

WEB TOOLS

While it is tempting to rely on an Internet search engine to search for whatever information is available on a particular topic as the need arises, this approach will often result in finding information that falls short of professional quality. It is a worthwhile investment of time to explore the Internet using web directories and careful search engine searches to identify reliable sources of information. There are websites that act as subject guides that list a number of Internet sites related to a specific subject. A good example of one such website for occupational safety and health audiences is that of the Canadian Centre for Occupational Health and Safety (CCOHS). This site includes a page that organizes a large number of occupational safety and health links at www.ccohs.ca/oshlinks/. By using this site as a starting point, a sense of the types of resources on the Web can be obtained. There are many other sites that can serve as starting points for this process; the references section of this chapter includes many different subject specific web-based sources that can be useful to the safety professional.

Search Engines

When interested in finding specific information on a safety subject, using a subject-based directory may not be the most efficient way of approaching the Internet. Rather, it is desirable to conduct a keyword search to find information of interest. There are several search engines available for this purpose; some search the entire Internet; others restrict their searches to specific databases on the Web. It is important to understand the scope and syntax of the search engines available for use.

In general, a large number of hits in a search indicate that the search needs to be further refined if looking for specific information. It can become quite time-consuming to check out a long list of links unless in an exploratory mode. It is also possible that the search engine's weighting of the search results is at odds with identifying the subject of one's concerns. For example, the order of results from some search engines is based on sponsorship deals with specific vendors, rather than the value of the information the site contains.

It is important to remember that general-purpose web search engines are changing rapidly and competing with each other for users, so trying more than one for a particular search is likely to find a variety of different resources. Practical experience with the various search engines will help determine which one works best for a specific search.

Refining the Search

Simply putting in the first words that one thinks to search can be rather inefficient (e.g., a simple search using the words "confined space hazards" generated more than 2,000,000 websites with those words). Fortunately, Internet search engines provide ways of refining the search so that it can be more selective and the results more useful. While the precise format of these refinements varies from search engine to search engine, the concepts they use are similar.

The first step in refining a search involves phrasing the question in a way that clarifies the needed answer. This is often rather easy (Does OSHA have any regulations that cover the use of this chemical?), but other times this can be more difficult (Is this workplace situation a confined space?).

If having trouble coming up with a question that describes the need, it may be helpful to think up the name of a magazine article that would be just what is needed. A four- or five-word phrase is a good place to start a search. It is important to think about possible other meanings for the words selected. For example, "safety" may refer to chemical concerns in one searcher's mind, while it refers to law enforcement issues in many other people's minds. An ambiguous word such as this is usually a poor choice to include as a search term unless used with connected descriptors or logical connectors: "safety in confined spaces" or "safety and confined spaces."

Subject-Specific Indexes

It is best to test out one's initial set of keywords by using it in one search engine with the idea of seeing how many useful responses are produced before using other search engines. In this phase of research, it is better to start with a more subject-focused index, such as the OSHA or NIOSH web pages.

By searching through these locations, one can see if other safety professionals use the chosen phrase to describe the situation being researched. If the results are not related to one's specific concerns, change the words used until the results are more appropriate. Once the keywords are refined in this search, they are likely to be more effective when using larger search engines.

AN INTERNET SEARCH STRATEGY

Although the preceding tips can make searching the Internet for specific information easier, it is still easy to get distracted from the original question as the Internet search proceeds. To conduct research on the Internet efficiently, it is important to have a search strategy in mind while looking. An outline of such a strategy is provided here.

Refine the Question

The first step in using the Internet successfully is to clearly state the question to be answered. While it is likely that useful information will be found that does not directly answer that question, it is important to know the end result before starting the search.

Identify What Kind of Information is Needed. Looking for a specific piece of data (e.g., the flashpoint of acetone) is different from looking for a technical interpretation of that data (e.g., whether the use of acetone requires adequate ventilation due to its flammability), which is different from looking for informal knowledge (i.e., use acetone in a fume hood if using more than 500 milliliters). These different types of information will be found in different places on the Internet.

- *Formal databases.* For specific pieces of data, formal databases are often the best places to look. Formal databases are usually maintained by public or private entities. It is important to verify that these databases contain accurate information before basing decisions on their content. There are a variety of such sources, such as Safety Data Sheet (SDS) collections and databases containing government regulations. The OSHA website is a good example of one of these formal databases. These databases are usually indexed to allow for keyword searches. As with more general search engines, selecting keywords carefully will make any search at these sites more efficient.

- *Professional interpretations.* Professional interpretations are likely to be less specific than raw data and organized in less structured ways. For technical interpretations of raw data, the best places to look are likely to be in collections of policies and procedures that are available online. Such collections are usually associated with websites that companies and institutions put online for the convenience of their employees or customers.

- *Informal knowledge.* Because informal knowledge requires technical expertise to apply appropriately in specific situations, it is unlikely to be found in the formal information sources on the Web. However, the Internet has many informal information collections available in the archives of electronic mailing lists. These are the first places to check for informal information. Even if the desired information is not found there, a reference to another Internet resource that has the needed information might be located.

Select Keywords to Use for the Search. The result of refining a question should be a set of keywords to use for the search. These keywords will be used in performing searches at various websites that are likely to contain appropriate information. For example, if simply wanting to determine the flashpoint of acetone, "flashpoint" and "acetone" are appropriate keywords. On the other hand, if concerned about ventilation requirements for using acetone, "flashpoint" is not likely to be helpful and "flammable liquid" may be a reasonable substitute for "acetone."

Keywords need to be as specific as possible while allowing for variations in terminology that are likely to arise. Using keywords such as "safety" or "health" are likely to produce too many sites for most purposes. Most website indexes allow the use of logical connectors such as "and," "or," and "not" when conducting a search. This can help refine the keyword search until there are about 20 to 40 hits. Lists of hits longer than that are probably too long to effectively search and are an indication that the keyword strategy should be refined.

Select a Website to Start the Search

Once one has a good idea of what kind of information is needed to answer the posed question and what keywords are likely to be associated with that information, it is time to start searching the file libraries on the Web. Start with familiar websites. If not familiar with any websites that would have the type of desired information, consult the website listings in the References section in this chapter.

Ask a Discussion Group

If a search of the file libraries fails to produce the desired information, or if looking for more informal information than is available at websites, it is time to post a request for information to an appropriate e-mail list or list-serv. To increase the chances of success when asking a question of a list, be sure to follow the Internet etiquette guidelines appropriate to that group.

If possible, review the archives of the group's discussions to see if it is the right group of which to ask the question and to be sure that it is not a question that has been asked and answered repeatedly. When framing the question, be as specific as possible in asking the question, so those who read it can determine what type of answers are appropriate (i.e., general pointers to the professional literature versus specific interpretations of your information).

It is most helpful, if possible, to monitor the traffic on the list for about a week before asking a question to see what sorts of questions are appropriate for the list.

Check the Information

Always be sure to assess the information obtained from the Internet before acting on it. Remember that the information available on the Internet was written based on someone else's assumptions, in ignorance of the details of one's particular situation. There may be specific, critical differences between the situations faced in this specific instance and those of the person writing the information. The effort involved in confirming Internet information may range from asking "Does this make sense?" to checking a paper reference source to consulting with a professional with more expertise. It is also important to check sources as to whether they are relevant and credible.

THE INTERNET AS A NETWORKING TOOL

In addition to the ability to access file libraries for research purposes, the Internet provides valuable opportunities for professional networking. The Internet can serve the same purposes that any other professional network does. Review of technical issues of a specific field, tips about how to approach specific problems, forewarning of new issues developing in the field, identifying prospective partners or consultants, and celebrating (or commiserating) with others in similar circumstances are just a few of the benefits of developing a professional network through the Internet.

A major advantage of using the Internet for networking activities is that it provides a convenient way to have ongoing discussions with geographically dispersed colleagues. These discussions can take place either in a group or individually. This section describes some of the considerations involved in using the Internet for this purpose.

GENERAL CONSIDERATIONS

As the Internet has grown in popularity, the time required to remain current with its content has increased as well. While the technical details of using e-mail and websites have simplified significantly since the 1990s, the task of wading through all the possibly relevant information sources has become more complex. It is important to have a clear idea of what one's goals are for using the Internet; otherwise, there is a high probability of devoting a lot of time to using it without much payback.

Using the Internet to network with other people with similar interests can minimize this learning curve. A benefit of networking on the Internet is that it is a low-budget way to be involved in a professional community. Productive professional relationships can be developed with a wide range of people without face-to-face meetings. These relationships usually start in discussion areas such as e-mail lists or newsgroups. They often develop into private correspondence that is able to be more speculative than public discussions.

The primary costs of developing a network of professional contacts over the Internet are time, patience, and a network connection. Fortunately, a powerful Internet connection is not required as most networking happens via e-mail with little graphical content and small files.

It is important to note that such electronic networking will not replace personal contacts made at professional conferences. While e-mail and other collaborative Internet tools can facilitate follow-up on ideas developed face-to-face, professional communication and brainstorming within the safety community requires a level of personal understanding and trust that cannot be generated electronically.

STYLES OF PARTICIPATION

The way in which one participates in an Internet discussion group will vary depending on many factors. There are three primary styles of participating:

- daily participation
- selective participation
- lurking.

With experience, different styles become appropriate for different lists.

Daily Participation

Some people enjoy e-mail discussions and make a daily habit of responding to many of the discussion topics that arise. These people are usually less than 10% of a list's subscribers and often account for 30% to 50% of the postings to a list. While this can be annoying if someone's e-mail style is objectionable, these people are important in keeping the list active. Not only do they provide topics of discussion, they also provide some sense of what questions are likely to be answered by the list's subscribers. It is usually easy to identify these people by following the list for a week or so.

Selective Participation

Another way to participate in a list is to read the postings regularly, but avoid responding publicly unless an issue of special interest arises. This is a more common practice than daily participation, and about 25% of a list's members fall in this category. These people provide an important "error-checking" function for the list, in that they will usually point out occasions when incorrect information is presented as fact. They also broaden the range of questions that can be answered successfully by the list.

Lurking

The most common use of e-mail lists is "lurking," or simply reading the postings of a list without responding, unless an answer is needed to a specific question. For most lists, the large majority of subscribers do this. Most people find active participation in more than one or two lists to be too time-consuming to manage. The presence of lurkers is important to a list because they provide questions and comments that normally would not come out of the general flow of discussion among more regular posters.

Finding a comfortable level of participation for a particular list will take some experience with the list and the population of participants. However, the more active one is on the list, the more likely it is that questions to that list will generate useful responses. In addition, by actively participating in discussions, a thread (a sequence of messages on the same subject) can be moved into a direction that is useful to one's particular interests.

FINDING DISCUSSION GROUPS

There are thousands of discussion groups operating on the Internet. Some are formally organized; others are simply collections of e-mail addresses being held together by someone's personal e-mail software. For this reason, finding valuable discussions can be a bit of a challenge. However, there are several good places to check.

The first place to check is professional organizations, trade magazines, and professional journals. Many sponsor e-mail lists about their technical specialties, although some are limited to members. Other sources for relevant discussions are the various "lists of lists" that exist on the Internet. One such list is available at CCOHS (www.ccohs.ca/resources/listserv.html). This site includes descriptions of a wide variety of mailing lists, organized by subject area.

Remember that formal descriptions of discussion groups can often be significantly different from the actual subjects talked about within the group. It is often possible to search the actual text of many discussions within the group's archives.

THE INTERNET AS A SAFETY CULTURE TOOL

Since 2000, the Internet has become an important form of general communication throughout society. This has led to significant cultural changes and has demonstrated the impact of information technologies on culture. System safety has become increasingly important as industrial disasters have grown in size, so the importance of organizational safety culture has been highlighted. This connection between the organization's electronic presence and safety culture must be carefully considered as web materials are developed. Developing a consistent, user-friendly tone to the interface used for safety functions will support the development of a sustainable safety culture. For this reason, it is becoming increasingly important for the safety professional to establish a useful presence within his or her organization's website so that it is clear what information applies to situations within the organization. This section briefly describes some strategies for achieving this objective.

ONLINE TRAINING

The first step in any safety program is to establish a strong educational and training presence within the organization. The style and content of this presence will vary depending on the needs of the organization, but online educational tools are increasingly being used for this purpose. Online training systems are available commercially and can also be built with relatively simple website building tools. The challenge comes in choosing the most effective approach for the population being served. For example, experience has shown that a highly educated population such as a laboratory workforce will respond quite well to online training, while use with a custodial workforce tends to be less effective.

A complete discussion of the considerations to be included in selecting an online training strategy is beyond the scope of this chapter. Issues to be considered include the type of presentations to be made (text documents versus animated sequences versus interactive games), the comfort level with computer use of the population in question, how specific the information to be provided must be, and how often refresher training must be provided. Implementation of a selected strategy should include identification of a pilot group of workers to test and evaluate the system as it is developed and a follow-up plan for determining whether the training was successful.

DEVELOPING A REFERENCE LIBRARY

In addition to introducing new employees to the safety program through training, an organization's website can serve as a reference source for both operational (procedures and specific facility information) and strategic (policies and plans) safety information. In developing such a library of information, the usability of the information posted is the key concern. This means that the information should be adapted to the applicable electronic medium.

Web pages are not well suited to delivering multiple screens of detailed information on the same page. Research has consistently shown that people using web pages browse text on the page quickly, scanning for specific details they need rather than reading carefully for comprehension. Therefore, web pages must be carefully planned and linked together in ways that allows the logic of the system to help rather than challenge the reader's use of the system.

An important source of information about usability research can be found at www.useit.com. This site describes how the design of a web page can make it more or less successful at providing information to a target audience.

MAINTAINING AWARENESS

Safety professionals face a special challenge in maintaining a successful program because there is a tendency for both individuals and the organization as a whole to take safety issues for granted over time. Maintaining an appropriate level of safety awareness is an ongoing challenge, and the organization's website, in conjunction with careful use of e-mail, can be used to meet this challenge. Accomplishing this means that the safety program's web pages must maintain a modern appearance and the content should be updated regularly. Major changes in the safety program are probably best communicated by other means (face-to-face meetings or paper manuals), but the web page should support those changes by providing a reference source for follow-up questions. Small, regular changes to the web page are useful in reminding people of the presence and value of the safety program within the organization. Since 2005, the emergence of social media platforms such as Facebook and Twitter has provided another opportunity to serve this function.

THE INTERNET AS A PROGRAM MANAGEMENT TOOL

In addition to being an important medium for professional communication, computers and the Internet can be used to collect and manage data about the activities involved in a safety program. This use of the Internet is still emerging as organizations develop a better understanding of the strengths and weaknesses of their internal information architecture, but three aspects of this use of the Internet can be briefly mentioned here.

COLLECTING DATA

The advance of electronic technologies has enabled data from specific environmental sampling instruments to be collected and organized more effectively and at lower costs than a few short years ago. Air-quality monitors, digital cameras and recorders, geographic positioning systems, bar coding, and other related techniques enable safety professionals to provide a more accurate and meaningful assessment of workplace hazards than could be previously considered. As with other forms of electronic information, using these capabilities must be carefully planned and frequently reviewed for the full potential of such capabilities to be realized. However, safety issues—including chemical exposure determinations, documentation of accidents, oversight of workplace inspections, and emergency response protocols—have all benefited from this trend.

MANAGEMENT SYSTEM DEVELOPMENT

As electronic information proliferates, it is easy to be swamped by data collected and stored. A useful tool in selecting which data are appropriate to be collected and how the data should be stored is a safety management system. Such a system, which can use a variety of models (such as the ANSI Z10 Standard for Occupational Health and Safety Management Systems, OSHA's Voluntary Protection Program, or the International Standard Organization's ISO 18000) can provide an overall architecture for the documentation necessary to manage and evaluate the safety program.

There are several Internet-based software packages commercially available for maintaining such systems for quality or environmental management aspects of an organization. It is possible that such systems can also be used for a safety management system. However, the safety professional should always be careful when choosing and implementing a proprietary software package because of potential issues with support or changes in technology. For this reason, open-source architectures for the safety data being managed should be considered as an alternative to proprietary packages. While such open-source systems may not be cheaper to implement in the short term, they tend to be more stable over time because their support is not dependent on the business viability of a single company.

CONNECTING TO OTHER MANAGEMENT INFORMATION SYSTEMS

The development of a safety management system will greatly benefit from being connected to other management systems within an organization, such as those containing facility information, financial information, and human resources data. Implementing these connections can be more challenging than first anticipated because the software involved is designed for other purposes.

For this reason, the organization's information technology (IT) professionals should be consulted on how best to succeed in this endeavor—or if it is even possible. Often times, much of this other information has significant security considerations involved, so using the data fully is not always possible. However, as the safety information management system is piloted and as it grows, attention should be given to opportunities for synergy between electronic safety information and other organizational data.

SUMMARY

- Computers have become a core professional tool for the safety community; while a comprehensive discussion of the ways in which a safety professional can use computers and computer networks may be beyond the scope of a single chapter, forethought and planning can turn the

Internet into a valuable professional asset.

- The challenge is that the power of these systems requires that a clear understanding of the safety program's role be established and careful planning and maintenance of the computer hardware and software systems being used be in place.
- The good news is that as the power of the systems increase, they enable significant increases in the effectiveness of the safety professional to serve their audiences.
- Becoming familiar with the web resources specific to the safety field, rather than simply relying on search engines, can elevate the Internet from a casual source of confusing information to a professional tool.

REVIEW QUESTIONS

1. Discuss pros and cons of using Internet-based tools for gathering safety information.
2. Describe the process for conducting an effective Internet-based search for safety-related information.
3. Compare and contrast the different roles list-serv participants engage in as part of an Internet-based safety discussion group.
4. Discuss issues related to online training.
5. Discuss areas where the Internet can be used to support safety program management elements.

RESOURCES

Agency for Toxic Substances and Disease Registry (ATSDR),
www.atsdr.cdc.gov
The ATSDR website has a variety of information about hazardous chemicals in the environment. This information includes ToxFAQs, fact sheets on the hazards associated with a variety of chemicals; a list of the Top 20 Hazardous Substances, based on Superfund experience; and a Science Corner, which includes ATSDR Special Report(s), Health and Environment Resources, Health and Environment Resources, Science Corner History, and other information.

American Biological Safety Association (ABSA), www.absa.org
The ABSA was founded in 1984 to promote biosafety as a scientific disci-

pline and serve the growing needs of biosafety professionals throughout the world. This web page provides links to information on biosafety issues.

American Conference of Government Industrial Hygienists (ACGIH), www.acgih.org

The ACGIH promotes excellence in environmental and occupational health and provides access to high-quality technical information through this website. This web page provides access to information about the ACGIH threshold limit values.

CAMEO, http://cameochemicals.noaa.gov

CAMEO Chemicals is a tool designed for people who are involved in hazardous material incident response and planning. This tool is part of the CAMEO software suite, and it is available as a website and as a downloadable desktop application that you can run on your own computer. CAMEO Chemicals contains:

- a library with thousands of datasheets containing response-related information and recommendations for hazardous materials that are commonly transported, used, or stored in the United States
- a reactivity prediction tool, which you can use to predict potential reactive hazards between chemicals.

Canadian Centre for Occupational Health and Safety (CCOHS), www.ccohs.ca

The CCOHS is a Canadian federal government agency based in Hamilton, Ontario, that serves to support the vision of eliminating all Canadian work-related illnesses and injuries. Its website includes a variety of information—some free, some available on a subscription basis.

Centers for Disease Control and Prevention (CDC), www.cdc.gov

This U.S. government site contains a large variety of health and disease information. There are numerous documents and datasets, most of which are related to public health, biosafety, occupational health and safety, and infectious diseases.

Consumer Product Safety Commission (CPSC), www.cpsc.gov

CPSC is an independent U.S. federal regulatory agency. CPSC works in a number of different ways to reduce the risk of injuries and deaths by consumer products: it develops voluntary standards with industry, issues and enforces mandatory standards or banning of consumer products, obtains the recall of products, conducts research on potential product hazards, and informs and educates consumers.

Cornell University Ergonomics website (CUErgo), http://ergo.human.cornell.edu
CUErgo presents information from research studies and classwork by students and faculty in the Cornell Human Factors and Ergonomics Research Group. CHFERG focuses on ways to enhance usability by improving the ergonomic design of hardware, software, and workplaces to enhance people's comfort, performance, and health in an approach called Ergotecture.

Environmental Protection Agency (EPA), www.epa.gov
The U.S. EPA's website contains a wide variety of information related to the environment and public health. Some of the many categories of available information include technical documents, research funding, and more; assistance for small businesses and entire industries; projects and programs; news and events; laws and regulations; databases and software; and publications.

ErgoWeb, www.ergoweb.com
Ergoweb® provides ergonomics consulting and ergonomics training services and carefully selected products, and it publishes applicable news and information. Its information is a mix of free and subscriber-only documents.

European Agency for Safety and Health at Work, http://osha.europa.eu
This site links to more than 30 national websites maintained by the agency's focal points (usually the lead occupational safety and health [OSH] organization in the EU member-states, candidate countries, and other international partners). This is a single-entry point to an overview of information that the network has to offer, from current campaigns to popular links. It is a database-driven, multilingual portal providing access to OSH information in your preferred language. Personalize the site and access the European and international network.

Haz-Map: Information on Hazardous Chemicals and Occupational Diseases from the National Institutes of Health, http://hazmap.nlm.nih.gov
Haz-Map is an occupational health database designed for health and safety professionals and for consumers seeking information about the health effects of exposure to chemicals and biologicals at work.

Haz-Map links jobs and hazardous tasks with occupational diseases and their symptoms.

Health Environment and Work, www.agius.com/hew/index.htm
This website is self-funded by the author, who is a professor of occupational and environmental medicine at the University of Manchester, in the United Kingdom. This site consists of hundreds of files about environmental and occupational health.

International Agency for Research on Cancer (IARC), www.iarc.fr
The IARC is part of the World Health Organization. IARC's mission is to coordinate and conduct research on the causes of human cancer and to develop scientific strategies for cancer control. It is involved in both epidemiological and laboratory research and disseminates scientific information through meetings, publications, courses, and fellowships.

International Centre for Genetic Engineering and Biotechnology (ICGEB), Biosafety Web Pages, www.icgeb.org/~bsafesrv
This site, based in Trieste, Italy, provides access to a variety of biosafety-related resources, including the ICGEB bibliographic database on biosafety studies, an index of selected scientific articles published on biosafety and risk assessment since 1990. Official documents on biosafety produced by international agencies as well as scientific findings, articles, proceedings, and workshops on international biosafety regulations from Europe, the United States, and other countries are available.

International Labour Organization (ILO), www.ilo.org
The ILO is the tripartite UN agency that brings together governments, employers, and workers of its member-states in common action to promote decent work throughout the world. Its website includes:
- Encyclopedia of Occupational Health and Safety (subscription fee required). The encyclopedia covers the technical fields encompassing occupational health and safety. With contributions by internationally renowned experts, this reference answers questions involving health and safety in the workplace.
- CISILO Database (subscription fee required). CISILO is a bilingual, bibliographic database that provides references to international occupational health and safety literature. The database is created by the International Occupational Safety and Health Information Centre/Centre international d'informations de sécurité et d'hygiène du travail (CIS) in Geneva.

National AgSafety Database (NASD), http://nasdonline.org/browse/1
/topic.html

The information contained in NASD was contributed by safety professionals and organizations from across the nation. Specifically, the objectives of the NASD project are (1) to provide a national resource for the
dissemination of information; (2) to educate workers and managers about
occupational hazards associated with agriculture-related injuries, deaths,
and illnesses; (3) to provide prevention information; (4) to promote the
consideration of safety and health issues in agricultural operations; and
(5) to provide a convenient way for members of the agricultural safety
and health community to share educational and research materials with
their colleagues.

National Institute of Environmental Health Sciences (NIEHS),
www.niehs.nih.gov

The NIEHS conducts basic research on environment-related diseases. Its
web pages outline the Institute's history and research highlights; it also
provides complete contact and visiting information.

National Institute for Occupational Safety and Health (NIOSH),
www.cdc.gov/niosh

This website provides access to information resources, programs, and
news from NIOSH, the federal agency responsible for conducting
research and making recommendations for the prevention of work-
related injury and illness.

North American Emergency Response Guidebook (ERG), http://hazmat.dot.
gov/pubs/erg/gydebook.htm

The Emergency Response Guidebook was developed jointly by the U.S.
Department of Transportation, Transport Canada, and the Secretariat of
Communications and Transportation of Mexico for use by firefighters,
police, and other emergency services personnel who may be the first to
arrive at the scene of a transportation incident involving a hazardous
material. It is primarily a guide to aid first responders in (1) quickly
identifying the specific or generic classification of the material(s) involved
in the incident; and (2) protecting themselves and the general public
during this initial response phase of the incident. The ERG is updated
every 3 to 4 years to accommodate new products and technology.

Occupational Safety and Health Administration (OSHA), www.osha.gov
The website for the primary workplace regulatory body in the United States includes access to its regulations, information about safe work practices for a variety of industries, and access to statistics about its enforcement programs and actions.

Public Health Agency of Canada, Pathogen Safety Data Sheets and Risk Assessment, www.phac-aspc.gc.ca/msds-ftss
These MSDSs are produced for personnel working in the life sciences as quick safety reference materials relating to infectious micro-organisms.

SafetyLine, www.safetyline.wa.gov.au
SafetyLine is an information service providing online access to the major publications issued by the WorkSafe Western Australia Commission and WorkSafe Western Australia. The objective of SafetyLine is to provide people in the workplace with access to safety and health information that can be used to help improve their working environment.

Society for Chemical Hazard Communication (SCHC), www.schc.org
SCHC is a nonprofit organization with a mission to promote the improvement of the business of hazard communication for chemicals.

Toxnet, http://toxnet.nlm.nih.gov
ToxNet, provided by the U.S. National Library of Medicine, is a collection of databases in the areas of toxicology, hazardous chemicals, environmental health, and toxic releases.

Typing Injury FAQ, www.tifaq.com
The Typing Injury FAQ (frequently asked questions) and Typing Injury Archives are sources of information for people with typing injuries, repetitive stress injuries, carpal tunnel syndrome, etc. It is targeted at computer users suffering at the hands of their equipment. You will find pointers to resources all across the Internet, general information on injuries, and detailed information on numerous adaptive products.

United Kingdom Health and Safety Executive, www.hse.gov.uk
The Health and Safety Executive ensures that risks to people's health and safety from work activities are properly controlled. As the website

says, "the law says employers have to look after the health and safety of their employees; employees and the self-employed have to look after their own health and safety; and all have to take care of the health and safety of others, for example, members of the public who may be affected by their work activity. Our job is to see that everyone does this." The site includes a variety of useful tools for the safety professional.

University of Michigan Health Physics Society Website, www.umich. edu/~radinfo
The site, maintained at the University of Michigan, contains information and links related to radiation safety issues.

University of Minnesota Environmental Health and Safety, www.dehs.umn.edu
Many colleges and universities have health and safety department websites with valuable information available on it. Larger universities have nearly every general safety or health hazard associated with some part of their operation. Thus, policies and procedures for many different situations can be found on their sites. The University of Minnesota site is typical of a well-maintained university website.

Where to Find Material Safety Data Sheets on the Internet, www.ilpi.com/msds/index.html
This commercial site provides a free list of sites useful in finding MSDSs and related software.

World Health Organization (WHO), www.who.int
This website provides descriptions of WHO's major international programs, a list of the organization's publications, the full text of the WHO *Weekly Epidemiological Record*, access to the WHO Statistical Information System, newsletters, and international travel and health information.

Young Worker Awareness, Workplace Health and Safety Agency, Ontario, Canada, www.yworker.com
This site contains health and safety information for young workers, their parents, teachers, principals, employers, and others. Although the information is specific to the province of Ontario, Canada (the Young Worker Awareness schools program is only available to Ontario high schools), many safety professionals are likely to find the information here useful.

9

Fire Protection

LEARNING OBJECTIVES

- ❏ Understand the chemistry of fire.
- ❏ List the different classifications of fires.
- ❏ Describe the objectives involved in a facility fire protection program.
- ❏ Conduct a fire risk analysis.
- ❏ Describe fire prevention methods used when constructing facilities.
- ❏ Understand the elements involved in fire detection and response.
- ❏ Compare and contrast different means of fire suppression and fire extinguishment.

INTRODUCTION

Fire protection includes (1) fire prevention; (2) detecting and responding to fires; (3) controlling, suppressing, and extinguishing fires; and (4) recovering from fires to resume normal business operations. Planning for each is essential, and a facility's fire protection program is incomplete if it does not thoroughly address each of these aspects of fire protection.

The practice of fire protection engineering is a highly developed, specialized field. Some fire protection issues require the special training and experience of a licensed fire protection engineer. Implementing efficient fire protection systems requires the involvement of the building users, other engineers, architects, interior designers, building contractors, fire detection and suppression system manufacturers, the local governmental authorities having jurisdiction, and even urban planners.

Safety professionals faced with special fire protection problems should seek professional advice from qualified fire protection consultants. The National Fire Protection Association (NFPA) and the Society of Fire Protection Engineers publish excellent texts covering all aspects of fire protection, and safety professionals involved in fire protection should consider adding some of these texts to their professional libraries.

THE CHEMISTRY OF FIRE

Fire, or the process of combustion, is extraordinarily complex. For a fire to occur, fuel, oxygen, heat, and a chemical chain reaction must join in a symbiotic relationship (see Figure 9–4 later in the chapter). In combustion, heat energy is released in a self-catalyzed reaction involving a condensed-phase fuel, a gas-phase fuel, or both. The combustion process is usually associated with rapid oxidation of a fuel by oxygen in the air. If the combustion process is confined so pressure can increase, an explosion can result. A similar process that takes place over long periods of time and at a lower temperature is called oxidation. Rusting of metal is an example of this. A fire, then, is a combustion process intense enough to emit heat and light.

In addition, a fire can be classified into two general forms or modes: flame fire and surface fire. Flame fires directly burn gaseous or vaporized fuel and include deflagrations. The rate of burning is usually high, and a high temperature is produced. The following are two types of flame fires:

- Premixed flame fires exist in a gas burner or stove and are relatively controlled.

- Diffusion flame fires refer to gases burning on mixed vapors and air. Controlling these fires is difficult.

Surface fires occur on the surfaces of a solid fuel and occur at the same temperature as do open-flame fires. A surface fire can be represented by a triangle composed of heat, fuel, and air. A flame fire includes an additional component: a chemical chain reaction. These two modes of fire are not mutually exclusive; they may occur alone or together.

Knowing how and why a fire burns suggests ways to control and extinguish it. The surface fire has three components that can be controlled, while the flame fire has four. Fires can be controlled in the following ways:

- Heat can be taken away by cooling.
- Oxygen can be taken away by excluding the air.
- Fuel can be removed to an area where there is not enough heat for ignition.
- The chemical reaction of the flame fire can be interrupted by inhibiting the rapid oxidation of the fuel and the concomitant production of free radicals, the lifeblood of the flame's reaction.

It is the vapor given off by the flammable solid or liquid that actually burns, not the solid or liquid itself.

COOLING A FIRE

To suppress and extinguish a fire by cooling, heat must be removed at a greater rate than the total heat being evolved by the fire. To do this, the cooling agent must reach the burning fuel directly. The cooling action may also stop the release of combustible vapors and gases. The most common and practical extinguishing agent is water applied in a solid stream or spray or incorporated in foam. Note that when water is the extinguishing agent, steam is generated, and in an enclosed space, the steam displaces oxygen.

LIMITING OXYGEN IN A FIRE

Most fires burn in air; therefore, it is difficult to limit a fire's access to air in the first place (it is the oxygen in the air that the fire needs to be sustained). Once a fire starts, some fires can be smothered with the use of noncombustible materials such as fire blankets, dirt, sand, inert gas flooding, or foams. Smothering is ineffective for fires that involve substances containing their own oxygen supply, such as ammonium nitrate or nitrocellulose.

REMOVING FUEL FROM A FIRE

Often, taking the fuel away from a fire is not only difficult but dangerous.

There are a few exceptions:

- Storage tanks for flammable liquids may be piped so that their contents can be pumped to an isolated, empty tank in case of fire.
- When flammable gases catch fire as they are flowing from a pipe, the fire will go out if the fuel supply can be shut off.

INTERRUPTING THE CHAIN REACTION IN A FIRE

Analyzing the anatomy of a fire reveals that the original fuel molecules appear to combine with oxygen in a series of successive intermediate stages, called branched-chain reactions. Once this happens, the end product, combustion, occurs. The intermediate stages are responsible for the evolution of flames.

As molecules break up in these branched-chain reactions, unstable intermediate products called free radicals are formed. The concentration of free radicals determines the speed of flames. The life of the free hydroxyl radical (OH^-) is very short, about 0.001 second, but long enough to be crucial in the combustion of fuel gases. The almost simultaneous formation and consumption of free radicals appear to be the lifeblood of a fire's chain reaction.

Extinguishing agents, such as dry chemicals and halogenated hydrocarbons, remove the free radicals in these branched-chain reactions from their normal function as a chain carrier. The effects that various dry chemical agents have on capturing free radicals depend on their individual molecular structure.

USING EXTINGUISHING AGENTS

Some extinguishing agents help control fire by attacking more than one of its four components. For example, both plain water fog and carbon dioxide flooding can react at flame temperatures with relatively slow-burning free carbon, producing carbon monoxide, and as a result, decreasing black-smoke production. Because this reaction absorbs heat, it lowers the heat of the fire in addition to lowering the oxygen concentration.

Matching the pace at which newer and more potent fire extinguishing agents work requires increasingly sophisticated tactics and techniques. Although a fire can be attacked from four different standpoints, attacking from any one of them does not necessarily result in the most rapid extinguishing time. Attacking from more than one, by using more than one agent, however, can produce a synergistic effect that hastens extinguishing.

CLASSIFICATION OF FIRES

Five general classifications of fires have been adopted by the NFPA. These classifications are based on types of combustibles and the extinguishing agent needed to combat fires fueled by each combustible type. Refer to the material in this chapter on portable fire extinguishers rated for these fire classifications.

CLASS A FIRES

Class A fires occur in ordinary materials, such as wood, paper, rags, and rubbish. The quenching and cooling effects of water, or of solutions containing large percentages of water, are of first importance in extinguishing these fires. Dry chemical agents (multipurpose dry chemicals) provide both rapid suppression of the flames and the formation of a coating that tends to retard further combustion. Where full extinguishment is mandatory, such fires should be completely cooled using water.

CLASS B FIRES

Class B fires occur in the vapor-air mixture over the surface of flammable and combustible liquids, such as gasoline, oil, grease, paints, and thinners. Limiting air (oxygen) to inhibit combustion is essential to stop Class B fires before they spread. Solid streams of water are likely to spread the fire as the surface area of the hot, flaming combustible liquid is disturbed, allowing additional vapors to be evolved and ignited. Under certain circumstances, water-fog nozzles are effective in the suppression of Class B fires, but not extinguishment. Generally, multipurpose dry chemicals, carbon dioxide/inert gases, and foam are effective for suppressing and extinguishing Class B fires.

CLASS C FIRES

Class C fires occur in or near energized electrical equipment where nonconducting extinguishing agents must be used. Multipurpose dry chemicals and carbon dioxide extinguishing agents are essential for such fires. Foam and water are poor choices for Class C fires because both agents can expose personnel to shock hazards. Note that when the electricity source feeding a Class C fire is deenergized, most Class C fires can be extinguished as either a Class A or Class B fire.

CLASS D FIRES

Class D fires occur in combustible metals such as magnesium, titanium, zirconium, lithium, potassium, and sodium. Specialized techniques, extinguishing agents, and extinguishing equipment have been developed to control and extinguish fires of this type. Extinguishing agents designed for Class A, Class B, and Class C fires should not be used on metal fires. In Class D fires, there is a danger of increasing the intensity of the fire because of a chemical reaction between unsuitable extinguishing agents and the burning metal. Inert dry powders are common extinguishing agents for use on Class D fires.

CLASS K FIRES

Class K fires typically involve cooking greases or cooking oils on commercial cooking appliances such as stoves and grills. Because of the special fire hazards associated with commercial cooking (large, very hot surface areas in the presence of large quantities of cooking greases and cooking oils), specialized extinguishing agents designed to saponify and form thick, long-lasting coatings over hot cooking surfaces are appropriate for use.

FACILITY FIRE PROTECTION PROGRAM

OBJECTIVES

The purpose of developing and refining a comprehensive fire protection program is to protect employees and property and to help facilitate business continuity. A comprehensive facility fire protection program has sequential objectives. The overall objectives of a comprehensive fire protection program are shown here:

1. preventing fires
2. detecting and responding to fires
   a. detecting fires early
   b. initiating appropriate alarms
   c. responding quickly to alarms
3. controlling, suppressing, and extinguishing fires
4. recovering from fires.

PREVENTING FIRES

The first overall objective in a comprehensive facility fire protection program relates to fire prevention. This involves not only building design, but also building maintenance and building use.

Fire prevention is a necessary component of building design. Using appropriate noncombustible construction materials and configuring appropriate fire area separations are essential to preventing fires, or preventing fires from spreading to other areas. Likewise, architects and engineers must understand all expected uses of the building so other facility-specific fire prevention features can be considered. It is also important to note that many fire prevention activities undertaken during design also affect one or more of the other overall objectives of a fire protection program.

DETECTING AND RESPONDING TO FIRES

The second overall objective in a comprehensive facility fire protection program is detecting fires and responding appropriately to the alarms the fire detection process initiates.

Fires may be detected several ways. Of course, fires are also detected by human observers. Electrical and mechanical detection devices are also used to detect fires. Some detectors are sensitive to the visible and invisible products of combustion (e.g., ionization and photoelectric smoke detectors). Others sense the heat energy generated by fires, while still others sense the radiated spectrum of visible and invisible light actually originating from flames. Regardless of the method of detection, the purpose of detection is straightforward: sound an alarm and sound it quickly.

When the alarm sounds, there should be a human response to the alarm. For some, the response may be as simple as heading for the nearest exit and checking in. For others, the alarm may initiate emergency response and fire-fighting activities by trained employees. Also, the alarm system may cause local fire departments to respond in planned and prescribed manners.

Detection and response processes must be planned. Building designers and building operations managers must consider the methods for detecting fires and how the facility and its occupants will respond to the ensuing alarms.

CONTROLLING, SUPPRESSING, AND EXTINGUISHING FIRES

When fire prevention activities have failed and a fire starts, the facility's fire protection program must consider how to control, suppress, and ultimately extinguish the fire. This third overall objective to a facility's comprehensive fire protection program assumes that the fire is detected and that it is desirable to extinguish it.

The methods of controlling, suppressing, and extinguishing fires cover a broad base of knowledge. Many of the fire prevention design considerations described earlier in this section are also fire control methods. Likewise, many fire detection systems are designed to engage fire control and suppression methods automatically.

For the purposes of this section, fire control includes physical barriers to the spread of fire and the products of combustion. These barriers include fire-rated walls, doors, windows, and air-handling dampers.

Fire suppression and extinguishment includes the actions of automatic sprinkler systems along with human intervention through the use of portable fire extinguishers, water-based fire fighting, and fire fighting using special chemicals and agents.

Human intervention in fire suppression may involve employees trained in fire extinguisher use, employees trained in more formal fire-fighting techniques (e.g., fire brigades), and the use of local career and volunteer fire department assets. Building designers and building operations managers must consider how a fire will be controlled, suppressed, and ultimately extinguished.

RECOVERING FROM FIRES

The facility's comprehensive fire protection program cannot omit the last overall objective. After a fire, a dedicated and planned effort is necessary to secure the scene, begin the investigation activities, and resume normal operations. Recall that the key reason for having a fire protection program is to protect employees and property and to facilitate business continuity.

Specific considerations associated with business continuity and emergency planning are covered in detail in the National Safety Council's *Administration & Programs* volume of the *Accident Prevention Manual*.

FIRE RISK

Fire protection measures can be effective only if they are based on a proper analysis and evaluation of the risk of fire. A complete evaluation is important because a wide variety of methods and equipment exist to provide protection. The optimum level of fire protection is that which minimizes both the costs and the expected fire risk. Ideally, the cost of fire protection should have a predictable effect on reducing the fire risk.

Determining fire risk can be quite complicated, and in some applications, it is necessary to engage in quantitative risk assessments involving probabilistic models and other complex approaches. The purpose of this section is to provide context on performing a qualitative fire risk assessment. A far more comprehensive treatment of the subject is contained in the NFPA *Fire Protection Handbook* (19th edition).

A simplified process for assessing fire risk is summarized in Figure 9–1. After identifying the objectives and scope of the fire risk assessment (Figure 9–1, step 1), the next step is to identify the fire hazards within the scope of the risk assessment (Figure 9–1, step 2).

FIRE HAZARD ANALYSIS

Early in the fire risk assessment process, a format and list of references for organizing a systematic, comprehensive fire hazard analysis process must be developed. The results from the fire hazard analysis will be used to identify the loss scenarios associated with the fire hazards, and ultimately, they will be used

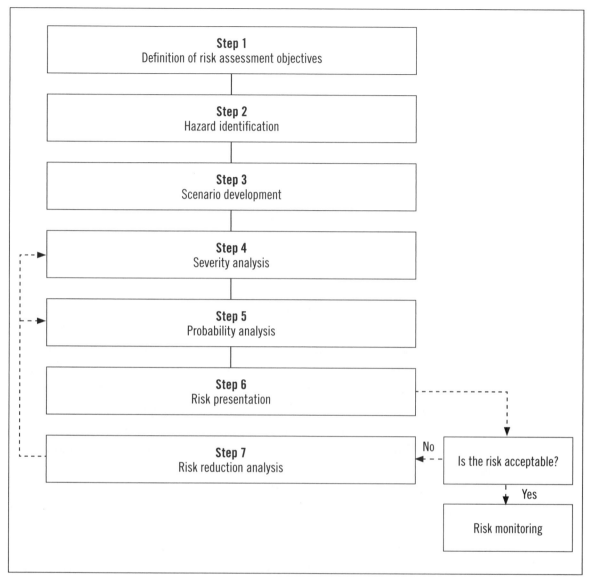

Figure 9–1. Fire Risk Assessment Steps (NFPA *Fire Protection Handbook*, 19th ed.).

Reprinted with permission from the National Fire Protection Association.

to evaluate the facility fire risk. The output from the fire hazard analysis process is also an excellent tool for developing facility fire hazard inspection points.

The following fire hazard identification structure (on the next page) is derived from the one presented in the NFPA *Fire Protection Handbook*. These are points that need to be considered and reported when identifying and characterizing the fire hazards present in a facility. The comprehensive report identifying and characterizing the fire hazards present in the facility is necessary for developing scenarios and evaluating facility fire risk.

1. property identification
2. property use
3. site information
4. construction
5. life safety
6. water supply and distribution
7. extinguishing systems and devices
8. fire alarm and detection systems
9. electrical systems
10. heating, ventilation, and air conditioning (HVAC) systems
11. fire prevention
12. special hazards and equipment
13. construction, demolition, and modifications.

IDENTIFICATION OF HAZARDOUS MATERIALS

Identifying hazardous materials used or stored in a facility and understanding the nature of hazardous materials are important parts of the fire hazard analysis. Fires often involve chemicals that have varying degrees of toxicity, flammability, and instability. Detailed information on these chemicals must be readily available to anyone in the facility as well as to personnel who may respond or who may confront emergencies involving these chemicals. Such information is conveyed via Safety Data Sheets (SDSs). When considering whether a hazardous material used in a facility is a fire hazard, consult the SDS.

In addition to consulting the SDS, the National Fire Protection Association has developed a visual system used for quickly identifying the hazardous properties of chemicals. This system is sometimes called the NFPA 704 hazardous material identification system. It uses a diamond-shaped symbol and color-coded numerals or backgrounds to indicate the degree of hazard for each hazardous property of a hazardous material in emergency conditions (e.g., fire or spill).

Three categories of hazardous properties are identified for each hazardous material: health hazard (blue), flammability hazard (red), and instability hazard (yellow). The diamond shape also provides places at the bottom of the diamond for special hazards, such as "OX" to indicate that the material possesses oxidizing properties. The order of severity in each category is indicated numerically by five divisions ranging from 0 to 4, where higher numbers indicate higher degrees of hazard for that particular hazardous property.

Figure 9–2 shows the methods of displaying the NFPA 704 hazardous material identification system. Refer to Tables 9-A, 9–B, and 9-C for qualitative definitions of the meanings of each hazardous property and their related

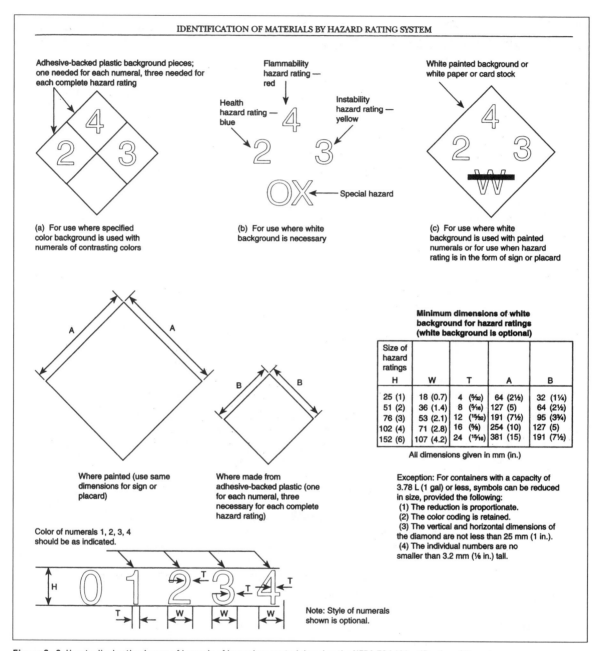

Figure 9–2. How to display the degree of hazards of hazardous materials using the NFPA 704 (*Identification of Hazards of Materials for Emergency Response*) identification system. The meanings of the numbering systems for each hazard category are shown in Tables 9–A, 9–B, and 9–C.

Reprinted with permission from the National Fire Protection Association.

degrees of hazard. This entire hazardous materials identification system is defined in the national consensus code NFPA 704, *Identification of the Hazards of Materials for Emergency Response.*

TABLE 9–A. Degrees of Health Hazards

Degree of Hazard*	Criteria
4—Materials that, under emergency conditions, can be lethal	Gases whose LC_{50} for acute inhalation toxicity is less than or equal to 1000 parts per million (ppm) Any liquid whose saturated vapor concentration at 20°C (68°F) is equal to or greater than 10 times its LC_{50} for acute inhalation toxicity, if its LC_{50} is less than or equal to 1000 ppm Dusts and mists whose LC_{50} for acute inhalation toxicity is less than or equal to 0.5 milligram per liter (mg/L) Materials whose LD_{50} for acute dermal toxicity is less than or equal to 40 milligrams per kilogram (mg/kg) Materials whose LD_{50} for acute oral toxicity is less than or equal to 5 mg/kg
3—Materials that, under emergency conditions, can cause serious or permanent injury	Gases whose LC_{50} for acute inhalation toxicity is greater than 1000 ppm but less than or equal to 3000 ppm Any liquid whose saturated vapor concentration at 20°C (68°F) is equal to or greater than its LC_{50} for acute inhalation toxicity, if its LC_{50} is less than or equal to 3000 ppm, and that does not meet the criteria for degree of hazard 4 Dusts and mists whose LC_{50} for acute inhalation toxicity is greater than 0.5 mg/L but less than or equal to 2 mg/L Materials whose LD_{50} for acute dermal toxicity is greater than 40 mg/kg but less than or equal to 200 mg/kg Materials that are corrosive to the respiratory tract Materials that are corrosive to the eye or cause irreversible corneal opacity Materials that are corrosive to the skin Cryogenic gases that cause frostbite and irreversible tissue damage Compressed liquefied gases with boiling points at or below −55°C (−66.5°F) that cause frostbite and irreversible tissue damage Materials whose LD_{50} for accurate oral toxicity is greater than 5 mg/kg but less than or equal to 50 mg/kg
2—Materials that, under emergency conditions, can cause temporary incapacitation or residual injury	Gases whose LC_{50} for acute inhalation toxicity is greater than 3000 ppm but less than or equal to 5000 ppm Any liquid whose saturated vapor concentration at 20°C (68°F) is equal to or greater than one-fifth its LC_{50} for acute inhalation toxicity, if its LC_{50} is less than or equal to 5000 ppm, and that does not meet the criteria for either degree of hazard 3 or degree of hazard 4 Dusts and mists whose LC_{50} for acute inhalation toxicity is greater than 2 mg/L but less than or equal to 10 mg/L Materials whose LD_{50} for acute dermal toxicity is greater than 200 mg/kg but less than or equal to 1000 mg/kg Compressed liquefied gases with boiling points between −30°C (−22°F) and −55°C (−66.5°F) that can cause severe tissue damage, depending on duration of exposure Materials that are respiratory irritants Materials that cause severe but reversible irritation to the eyes or lacrimators Materials that are primary skin irritants or sensitizers Materials whose LD_{50} for acute oral toxicity is greater than 50 mg/kg but less than or equal to 500 mg/kg
1—Materials that, under emergency conditions, can cause significant irritation	Gases and vapors whose LC_{50} for acute inhalation toxicity is greater than 5000 ppm but less than or equal to 10,000 ppm Dusts and mists whose LC_{50} for acute inhalation toxicity is greater than 10 mg/L but less than or equal to 200 mg/L Materials whose LD_{50} for acute dermal toxicity is greater than 1000 mg/kg but less than or equal to 2000 mg/kg Materials that cause slight to moderate irritation to the respiratory tract, eyes, and skin Materials whose LD_{50} for acute oral toxicity is greater than 500 mg/kg but less than or equal to 2000 mg/kg
0—Materials that, under emergency conditions, would offer no hazard beyond that of ordinary combustible materials	Gases and vapors whose LC_{50} for acute inhalation toxicity is greater than 10,000 ppm Dusts and mists whose LC_{50} for acute inhalation toxicity is greater than 200 mg/L Materials whose LD_{50} for acute dermal toxicity is greater than 2000 mg/kg Materials whose LD_{50} for acute oral toxicity is greater than 2000 mg/kg Materials that are essentially nonirritating to the respiratory tract, eyes, and skin

*For each degree of hazard, the criteria are listed in a priority order based on the likelihood of exposure.

TABLE 9–B. Degrees of Flammability Hazards

Degree of Hazard	Criteria
4—Materials that rapidly or completely vaporize at atmospheric pressure and normal ambient temperature or that are readily dispersed in air and burn readily	Flammable gases Flammable cryogenic materials Any liquid or gaseous material that is liquid while under pressure and has a flash point below 22.8°C (73°F) and a boiling point below 37.8°C (100°F) (i.e., Class IA liquids) Materials that ignite spontaneously when exposed to air Solids containing greater than 0.5 percent by weight of a flammable or combustible solvent are rated by the closed cup flash point of the solvent
3—Liquids and solids that can be ignited under almost all ambient temperature conditions. Materials in this degree produce hazardous atmospheres with air under almost all ambient temperatures, or though unaffected by ambient temperatures, are readily ignited under almost all conditions	Liquids having a flash point below 22.8°C (73°F) and a boiling point at or above 37.8°C (100°F) and those liquids having a flash point at or above 22.8°C (73°F) and below 37.8°C (100°F) (i.e., Class IB and Class IC liquids) Finely divided solids, typically less than 75 micrometers (200 mesh), that present an elevated risk of forming an ignitable dust cloud, such as finely divided sulfur, *National Electric Code* Group E dusts (e.g., aluminum, zirconium, and titanium), and bis-phenol A Materials that burn with extreme rapidity, usually by reason of self-contained oxygen (e.g., dry nitrocellulose and many organic peroxides) Solids containing greater than 0.5 percent by weight of a flammable or combustible solvent are rated by the closed cup flash point of the solvent
2—Materials that must be moderately heated or exposed to relatively high ambient temperatures before ignition can occur. Materials in this degree would not, under normal conditions, form hazardous atmospheres with air, but under high ambient temperatures or under moderate heating could release vapor in sufficient quantities to produce hazardous atmospheres with air	Liquids having a flash point at or above 37.8°C (100°F) and below 93.4°C (200°F) (i.e., Class II and Class IIIA liquids) Finely divided solids less than 420 micrometers (40 mesh) that present an ordinary risk of forming an ignitable dust cloud Solid materials in a flake, fibrous, or shredded form that burn rapidly and create flash fire hazards, such as cotton, sisal, and hemp Solids and semisolids that readily give off flammable vapors Solids containing greater than 0.5 percent by weight of a flammable or combustible solvent are rated by the closed cup flash point of the solvent
1—Materials that must be preheated before ignition can occur. Materials in this degree require considerable preheating, under all ambient temperature conditions, before ignition and combustion can occur	Materials that will burn in air when exposed to a temperature of 815.5°C (1500°F) for a period of 5 minutes in accordance with ASTM D 6668, *Standard Test Method for the Discrimination Between Flammability Ratings of F = 0 and F = 1* Liquids, solids, and semisolids having a flash point at or above 93.4°C (200°F) (i.e., Class IIIB liquids) Liquids with a flash point greater than 35°C (95°F) that do not sustain combustion when tested using the "Method of Testing for Sustained Combustibility," per 49 CFR 173, Appendix H, or the UN publications *Recommendations on the Transport of Dangerous Goods, Model Regulations and Manual of Tests and Criteria* Liquids with a flash point greater than 35°C (95°F) in a water-miscible solution or dispersion with a water noncombustible liquid/solid content of more than 85 percent by weight Liquids that have no fire point when tested by ASTM D 92, *Standard Test Method for Flash and Fire Points by Cleveland Open Cup*, up to the boiling point of the liquid or up to a temperature at which the sample being tested shows an obvious physical change Combustible pellets, powders, or granules greater than 420 micrometers (40 mesh) Finely divided solids less than 420 micrometers that are nonexplosible in air at ambient conditions, such as low volatile carbon black and polyvinylchloride (PVC) Most ordinary combustible materials Solids containing greater than 0.5 percent by weight of a flammable or combustible solvent are rated by the closed cup flash point of the solvent
0—Materials that will not burn under typical fire conditions, including intrinsically noncombustible materials such as concrete, stone, and sand	Materials that will not burn in air when exposed to a temperature of 816°C (1500°F) for a period of 5 minutes in accordance with ASTM D 6668, *Standard Test Method for the Discrimination Between Flammability Ratings of F = 0 and F = 1*

TABLE 9–C. Degrees of Instability Hazards

Degree of Hazard	Criteria
4—Materials that in themselves are readily capable of detonation or explosive decomposition or explosive reaction at normal temperatures and pressures	Materials that are sensitive to localized thermal or mechanical shock at normal temperatures and pressures Materials that have an instantaneous power density (product of heat of reaction and reaction rate) at 250°C (482°F) of 1000 watts per milliliter (W/mL) or greater
3—Materials that in themselves are capable of detonation or explosive decomposition or explosive reaction but that require a strong initiating source or must be heated under confinement before initiation	Materials that have an instantaneous power density (product of heat of reaction and reaction rate) at 250°C (482°F) at or above 100 W/mL and below 1000 W/mL Materials that are sensitive to thermal or mechanical shock at elevated temperatures and pressures
2—Materials that readily undergo violent chemical change at elevated temperatures and pressures	Materials that have an instantaneous power density (product of heat of reaction and reaction rate) at 250°C (482°F) at or above 10 W/mL and below 100 W/mL
1—Materials that in themselves are normally stable but that can become unstable at elevated temperatures and pressures	Materials that have an instantaneous power density (product of heat of reaction and reaction rate) at 250°C (482°F) at or above 0.01 W/mL and below 10 W/mL
0—Materials that in themselves are normally stable, even under fire conditions	Materials that have an instantaneous power density (product of heat of reaction and reaction rate) at 250°C (482°F) below 0.01 W/mL Materials that do not exhibit an exotherm at temperatures less than or equal to 500°C (932°F) when tested by differential scanning calorimetry

Tables 9–A, B, and C. The degree of hazard in each category can be assessed quickly for any hazardous material for which the NFPA 704 (*Identification of Hazards of Materials for Emergency Response*) identification system is used.

Adapted from NFPA 704, with permission from the National Fire Protection Association.

EVALUATING FIRE RISK

A simplified diagram of a fire risk assessment process is shown in Figure 9–1. After identifying and characterizing a facility's fire hazards (Figure 9–1, step 2), it is necessary to develop systematically a set of loss scenarios associated with each fire hazard (Figure 9–1, step 3). A loss scenario is the sequence of events leading to a destructive fire.

Developing loss scenarios requires understanding how fires start, how they are sustained, and the human and property effects of potential fire losses. Other factors such as the loss of a key facility or operation also are important.

It is appropriate to consider a range of consequences and frequencies for each loss scenario. A single loss scenario may reasonably have a spectrum of consequences and related frequencies of occurrence.

Once estimates of frequency and consequence for a loss scenario have been developed, a measure of uncertainty should be applied to the estimates. This uncertainty factor will be used later to prioritize risk reduction methods or to help prioritize various loss scenarios for which additional, more detailed risk analyses are warranted.

When the estimates of frequency and consequence for the developed loss scenarios are complete, the fire risk can be presented (Figure 9–1, step 6). Although there are numerous ways to present risk, a common method of presenting risk is using a risk matrix. An example risk matrix is shown in Figure 9–3.

		Consequence		
		Negligible	**Marginal**	**Critical**	**Catastrophic**
Frequency	**Frequent**	9 Scenarios	2 Scenarios		
	Probable	12 Scenarios	1 Scenario		
	Occasional	13 Scenarios	6 Scenarios	1 Scenario	1 Scenario
	Remote	65 Scenarios	21 Scenarios	7 Scenarios	3 Scenarios
	Improbable	(did not consider)	25 Scenarios	19 Scenarios	11 Scenarios

Key

Low Risk   Moderate Risk   High Risk

Figure 9–3. Example risk matrix used for presenting the risk of the loss scenarios developed from a fire risk analysis.

The number of loss scenarios evaluated in each cell in the risk matrix can be made, or a total summation of risk in each cell can be presented. In any case, it is important to identify action levels from this risk matrix so risk reduction efforts can be prioritized. These action levels are represented by the different cell background shades in the risk matrix. The darker shades represent high-risk levels; the lighter shades represent lower-risk levels. Where these action levels are set is based on the risk acceptance level of each organization and how the risk was calculated.

The final step in the fire risk evaluation process is selecting risk reduction strategies (Figure 9–1, step 7). These strategies should be well defined and researched, and an estimate of the effect of implementing each risk reduction method should be made. In many cases, a risk reduction method will have broad applications to several of the developed loss scenarios, and the aggregate risk reduction effect should be considered.

It is from this fire risk assessment process that risk reduction strategies can be developed and defended.

FIRE PREVENTION: CONSTRUCTING FACILITIES

Much of this section is adapted from *Principles of Fire Protection* published by the NFPA. Qualified fire protection engineers, local building codes and regulations, and the relevant aspects of national consensus standards such as NFPA 1 (Uniform Fire Code), NFPA 101® (Life Safety Code®), NFPA 5000 (Building Construction and Safety Code®) and the International Code Council's International Building Code® should be consulted during all aspects of facility design, construction, and renovation.

The object of fire safety is to protect life foremost and property secondly from the ravages of fire in a building. Building design and construction must take into account a wide range of fire safety features. Not only must the interiors and contents of buildings be protected from the dangers of fire, but the building site itself must have adequate water supplies and easy accessibility by the fire department. Architects, builders, and owners may assume that national, state, and local codes provide adequate protective measures; however, these codes stipulate only minimal measures for fire safety. Planning and construction based on such codes should not reduce or limit fire-safe design efforts. Codes are minimums and are not to be used as "meets code" when designing systems.

PLANNING FOR FIRE PROTECTION

Before a building designer can make effective decisions relating to fire safety design, the specific function of the building and the general and unique conditions that are to be incorporated into it must be identified clearly. Decisions regarding the fire safety design and construction of the building have the same objectives as do all fire protection measures, namely, (1) preventing fires; (2) detecting and responding to fires; (3) controlling, suppressing, and extinguishing fires; and (4) recovering from fires to resume normal business operations.

Two major categories of decisions should be made early in the design process of a building in order to provide effective fire-safe design. Early considerations should be given to both the interior building functions and exterior site planning. Building fire defenses, both active and passive, should be designed in such a way that the building itself assists in the manual suppression of fire.

The broad approach to the fire-safe design of a building requires a clear understanding of the building's function, the number and kinds of people who will be using it, and the kinds of things they will be doing. In addition, appropriate construction and protection features must be provided for the protection of the contents and, particularly for mercantile and industrial buildings, to ensure the continuity of operations if a fire should occur.

The majority of fire deaths and injuries in structural fires (70% to 80%) are caused by asphyxiation from exposure to smoke and the toxic gases that evolve as combustion products from fires. The carbon monoxide developed in most fires, particularly unventilated and smoldering fires, is probably the most common cause of death, although studies show that victims of smoke inhalation also exhibit signs of cyanide poisoning. Smoke also obscures visibility and thus can lead to panic situations when occupants cannot see and use escape routes. Direct exposure to flame, heat, or fire accounts for 20% to 30% of all fire-related deaths and injuries.

SITE PLANNING

Proper building design for fire protection includes a number of factors outside the building itself. The site on which the building is located will influence the design, especially traffic and transportation conditions, fire department accessibility, water supply, and the exposure this facility has on the public. Inadequate water mains and poor spacing of hydrants have contributed to the loss of many buildings.

Traffic and Transportation

Fire department response time is a vital factor in building design considerations. Traffic access routes, traffic congestion at certain times of the day, traffic congestion from highway entrances and exits, and limited access highways have significant effects on fire department response distances and response time and must be taken into account by building designers in selecting appropriate fire defenses.

Fire Department Access to the Site

Building designers must ask the question: Is the building easily accessible to fire apparatus? Ideal accessibility occurs where a building can be approached from all sides by existing and expected fire department apparatus. However, such ideal accessibility is not always possible. Congested areas, topography, or buildings and structures located appreciable distances away from the street make it difficult to use, or prevent effective use of, fire apparatus. When apparatus cannot come close enough to the building to be used effectively, equipment such as aerial ladders, elevating platforms, and water tower apparatus can be rendered useless.

Fire Department Access to the Facility's Interior

One of the more important considerations in facility design is access to the fire area. This includes access to the facility itself as well as access to the facility's interior. In larger and more complex facilities, serious fires over the years have brought improvements in facility design to facilitate fire department operations. The larger the facility, the more critical the issue of access for fire fighting becomes. In some facilities, fire fighters cannot function effectively. The spaces in which adequate fire-fighting access and operations are restricted because of architectural, engineering, or functional requirements should nonetheless be provided with effective protection. A complete automatic sprinkler system with a fire department connection is probably the best solution to this problem. Other methods that may be used in appropriate design situations include access panels in interior walls and floors, fixed nozzles in floors with fire department connections, and roof vents and access openings.

Water Supply to the Site

A facility designer must also ask: Are the water mains adequate? Are the hydrants properly located? Will flow (in gallons per minute) be adequate? The more congested the area in which the facility is to be located, the more important it is to plan what the fire department may face if a fire occurs on the property. An adequate water supply delivered with the necessary pressure is required to control a fire properly and adequately. The number, location, and spacing of hydrants and the size of the water mains are vital considerations when the facility designer plans fire defenses for the facility.

Exposure Protection

Still another consideration in the design of the building is the possibility of damage from a fire in an adjoining building. The building may be exposed to heat radiated horizontally by flames from the windows of the burning neighboring building. If the exposed building is taller than the burning building, flames coming from the roof of the burning building can attack and damage the exposed building.

The damage from an exposing fire can be severe. It depends on the amount of heat produced and the time of exposure, the fuel load in the exposing building, and the construction and protection of the walls and roof of the exposed building. Other factors are the distance of separation, wind direction, and accessibility of fire fighters.

FIRE PROTECTION METHODS AND CONCEPTS IN BUILDING DESIGN

National, state, and local fire codes provide explicit design guidance on the methods and features of fire protection in design. Adherence to at least the minimum code requirements is mandatory. The NFPA's National Fire Codes®, the International Code Council's *International Building Code®*, and other similar publications are excellent resources for understanding building design concepts, and in many cases, some or all of the codes are codified into law in local jurisdictions. The concepts presented in this section are general, and qualified fire protection engineers should be consulted before implementing any of these fire prevention methods in building construction.

Confining Fire

Using stair enclosures, fire walls, and fire doors and dividing a building into smaller units are ways to confine a fire. Plan them into the building's design. Regardless of the type of building construction, protected stair enclosures for multi-story buildings are necessary to provide a safe exit path for occupants. They also retard the upward spread of fire.

Under many conditions, it is necessary to divide a floor into separate fire areas with rated fire walls. Design fire walls to rigid specifications so that they can withstand the effects of a severe fire and of building collapse on one side. To prevent the passage of heat, all openings in fire walls must be protected with approved closures at the same fire rating as the fire walls or greater. This protection includes wall penetrations for electrical conduit, pipes, cables, and HVAC ducts.

Separate Units

Traditionally, dividing buildings into separate units provided functional work areas or offered occupants some degree of privacy. From the point of view of fire safety, however, dividing a building is regarded as a way to break up the total volume of a building into small cells. In such a building, fires will remain localized and can be more easily suppressed. To prevent fire from spreading from one unit to another, building codes require (1) that units be made structurally sound enough to withstand full fire exposure without major damage; and (2) that the units' boundaries be capable of acting as nonconducting heat barriers.

Fire Doors

Fire doors are the most widely used and accepted means of protecting horizontal openings. Fire doors are rated by testing laboratories as they are installed in a building and as assemblies (door frame and door as a unit). The fire doors usually have a rating of ¾ to 3 hours. They may be constructed of metal or metal-clad treated wood materials and may be hinged, rolling (sliding), or curtain doors. Single or double doors may be specified.

Exits and Evacuation

Of the many factors involved in protecting life from fire, a building's exits are the most important. Nevertheless, exits are inadequate in many buildings. Consider the design of exits in a building's total fire safety system (Figure 9–4).

Management, architects, and others entrusted with the safety of building occupants must plan for the orderly emergency evacuation of buildings. Panic is a causal factor for loss of life during a fire or other building emergency. While fire is a common cause of panic, such dangers as boiler or air receiver explosions, fumes, or structural collapse may also threaten safe and orderly evacuation.

A building's population and degree of hazard are the major factors when designing exits. Every building or structure, and every section or area in it, shall have at least two separate means of exit. Arrange them so that the possibility of any one fire blocking all exits is minimized. Designing exits involves more than a study of numbers, flow rate, and population densities. Safe exits require a safe path of escape from the fire with the least possible travel distance to the exit. The path should be arranged for ready use in case of an emergency. It should be large enough to permit all occupants to reach a place of safety before they are endangered by the fire or by smoke and toxic gases. Do not design exits and other safeguards to depend solely on any single safeguard. Provide additional safeguards in case of human or mechanical failure.

Ventilation

Ventilation is of vital importance in removing smoke, gases, and heat so that fire fighters can reach the core of a blaze. It is difficult, if not impossible, to ventilate a building unless appropriate skylights, roof hatches, emergency escape exits, and similar devices are provided when the building is constructed.

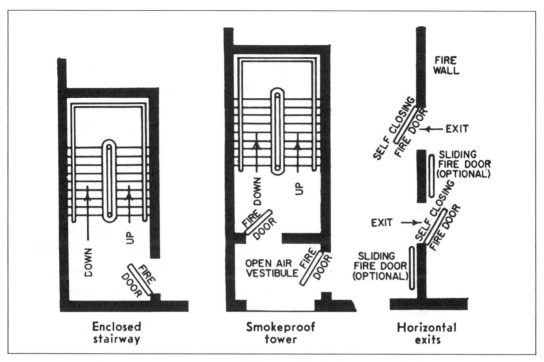

Figure 9–4. Plan views of types of exits. Stair enclosure prevents fire on any floor from trapping persons above. A smokeproof tower is better because an opening to the air at each floor largely prevents the chance of smoke on the stairway. A smokeproof tower charged with positive air pressure is more likely to prevent smoke from entering. A horizontal exit provides a quick refuge and decreases the need for a hasty flight down stairs. Horizontal sliding fire doors provided for safeguarding property values are arranged to close automatically in case of fire. Swinging doors are self-closing. Two wall openings are needed for exit in two directions.

Reprinted with permission from the National Fire Protection Association.

Controlling Smoke

Smoke control confines smoke, heat, and toxic gases to a limited area, dilutes them, or exhausts them, thus preventing their spread to other areas and minimizing fatalities. Smoke and hot gases generated by an uncontrolled fire, if confined within a building, can seriously impair fire-fighting operations, can cause illness and death, and can spread the fire under the roof for considerable distances from the point of origin. The movement of smoke within a structure is determined by many factors, including building height, ceiling heights, suspended ceilings, venting, external wind force, and the direction of the wind.

Most smoke-control systems involve a combination of methods. One method of smoke control uses a physical barrier, such as a door, wall, or damper to block the smoke's movement. Smoke-control doors may be operated manually or by some automatic detection device coupled to a door closure. An alternative method is to use a pressure differential between the smoke-filled area and the protected area.

Venting is another way of removing smoke, heat, and noxious gases from a building. Plan for smoke control during the design stage of the building by specifying vents, curtain boards, and windows. For example, use smoke- and heat-venting systems consisting of curtain boards. They protect heat-banking areas under a roof. Also, use automatic or manual roof vents to release smoke and heat through the roof.

Connections for Sprinklers and Standpipes

Connections for sprinklers and standpipes must be carefully located and clearly marked. The larger and taller the building becomes, the greater the volume and pressure of water that will be needed to fight a potential fire. Water damage can be very costly unless adequate measures, such as floor drains and scuppers have been incorporated into the building design.

FIRE DETECTION AND RESPONSE

Despite good construction, cleanliness, and modern fire-fighting methods, losses from fire nevertheless occur. Losses would be reduced if each developing fire were detected so it could be attacked and extinguished. Thus, fire detection is essential in every fire protection system. Means of detection could be a human observer; automatic sprinklers; smoke, flame, or heat detectors; or, more likely, a combination of these.

There are two tasks associated with detection:
1. Give an early warning to enable facility occupants and fire fighters to respond to the fire.
2. Begin fire control, suppression, and extinguishment processes.

Each fire detection system requires a sensor, which detects a physically measurable quantity of smoke, flame, or heat. For detection to occur, this quantity must undergo measurable variations when a fire begins in the vicinity of the sensor. A decision-making device coupled with the sensor then compares the measured quantity with a predetermined value. When the value is different, an alarm sounds. Thus a detector both detects and signals.

In general, there are three possible errors in any fire detection system:
1. activating a nuisance (false) alarm
2. not detecting a fire
3. detecting it too late.

The cause of nuisance alarms may be human interference, mechanical or electrical faults, or special environmental conditions.

HUMAN OBSERVER

A human observer is a good fire detection system for the following reason: he or she can take immediate action in a flexible way, whether calling the fire department or putting out a fire with an extinguisher. However, human observers can also respond unpredictably. For example, if a human observer detects a fire and puts it out, he or she may not report it, potentially allowing the fire to rekindle.

Early detection and notification are essential. Early notification of occupants allows time to evacuate, and early notification of the fire brigade/fire department provides a better chance of stopping the fire before extensive damage occurs.

Human observers should also report malfunctioning fire alarm systems. Fire alarm systems need to be properly maintained. Nuisance alarms have a negative effect: if an actual fire occurs, the activated alarm may be dismissed as just another "false" alarm.

AUTOMATIC FIRE DETECTION SYSTEMS

It is important to have a qualified fire protection engineer involved in the design of automatic fire detection systems. When planning the installation of fire detectors, use the following four steps:

1. Select the proper detector for each hazard area. For example, a computer area may require ionization or combination detectors. A warehouse may require infrared and ionization detectors. In low-risk areas, thermal detectors or a combination of detectors may be used.
2. Determine the spacing and locations of detectors in order to provide the earliest possible warning.
3. Select the best control system arrangement to provide fast identification of the exact source of the alarm.
4. Ensure that the system will notify the proper authorities, who can immediately respond to the alarm and take appropriate action. Every detection system must have its alarm signal transmitted to a point of human supervision.

There are many types of fire detectors to handle various scenarios and to detect various fire situations. Most manufacturers and distributors offer several or all of the commonly used types. They can also design a combination of equipment into a coordinated system to meet the special needs of a facility.

Thermal Detectors

Thermal detectors detect the heat from a fire. There are several kinds of thermal detectors, each with a specific use. Thermal detectors are reliable for what they do. However, they can only detect the heat of a fire, which usually will not build up to significant levels until the last stage of a fire. Many fires start slowly, with little heat generated at the beginning, and will be well under way by the time a thermal detector comes into operation. They are generally used where no life hazard is involved and some fire loss can be tolerated.

Bulb Detection Systems

These detectors are completely mechanical. They are especially desirable in locations in which the explosive nature of the fire hazard makes it wise or essential to avoid the use of electricity. These systems involve a number of bulbs containing air at atmospheric pressure. One or more of these bulbs are installed along the ceiling of the hazardous area, all connected to a diaphragm at the control center. When a rise in temperature strikes one or more of the bulbs, it deflects the diaphragm, and a mechanical extinguishing system can be activated. This system is used as a release mechanism for fixed carbon dioxide extinguishing systems in marine and industrial applications.

Smoke Detectors

Smoke detectors respond to the particles of combustion, both visible (smoke) and invisible. They can be triggered by either a decrease or an increase in light. When smoke enters a light beam, it either absorbs light so the receiver end of the circuit registers less light, or it scatters light so that a terminal normally bypassed by the light beam now receives part of the light.

The more sophisticated smoke detectors are responsive both to gas or products of combustion and to smoke. These products of combustion detectors are capable of detecting the beginning of a fire long before there is visible smoke or flame.

Photoelectric smoke detectors are line powered and usually include lamp supervision circuitry and an alarm in case of lamp failure. An incandescent light source may be used. Also, a high-intensity strobe lamp that generates a stronger reflection can be used so that fewer or smaller smoke particles will actuate the photocell.

Flame Detectors

Flame detectors respond to the optical radiant energy of combustibles. Flame detectors sense light from the flames. Sometimes they work at the ultraviolet end of the visible spectrum, but more often they work at the infrared end. To avoid nuisance alarms from the effects of nearby light sources, flame detectors are set to detect the typical flicker of a flame. Some operate with delay of a few seconds to eliminate nuisance alarms from transient flickering light sources, such as flashlights or headlights.

Flame detectors have some very important applications, such as in large aircraft hangars and for guarding against fires in fuel and lubricant drips. In general, however, by the time flame is visible, a fire has a good foothold. Either an infrared or an ultraviolet detector can be used to sense the flame.

Combustion Gas Detectors

These detectors are closest to being general-purpose detectors. Combustion gas detectors do not rely on heat. They measure the percentage of gas present. Also, they do not wait for the dangerous condition of flames to occur before they sound an alarm. Most fires detected by combustion gas detectors can be extinguished by workers on the site.

Combustion gas detectors can usually be set to automatically sound an alarm or to set off extinguishing equipment. Some conditions may require periodic maintenance and calibration. There are areas in which combustion gas detectors cannot be used. For example, in an area where a specific level of combustion gases may be tolerated at times because a particular process emits them, flash fires from nearby flammable liquids may be anticipated. Therefore, detection must be almost instantaneous if it is to be at all effective. In such areas, a flame detector should be used. In locations where chemicals and some plastics could generate great volumes of smoke with little combustion, a smoke detector should be used.

Extinguishing System Attachments

Some automatic detection devices are often not even thought to be detectors. These devices are extinguishing system attachments. They are, nonetheless, truly detectors. Fire detection may be handled by water-flow indicators in a sprinkler system. These indicators may operate in response to a sudden increase or decrease in pressure or by detection of the flow of water by a vane inside the piping. They are designed to detect a flow of water that exceeds a set number of gallons per minute.

A second type of device indicates that the fire-extinguishing system is jeopardized. The following are a few of these devices:

- Water-level devices warn when a self-contained water storage supply is low, or, in the case of a low differential dry pipe valve, when the level of water is too high.
- Water-temperature switches warn when the water storage supply is approaching the freezing point.

- Water supply valve position switches signal if someone unintentionally or purposely starts to turn off the water supply. These switches should give the alarm before the handle is closed two revolutions, or one-fifth the distance from the open position. However, in practice, they are often set to signal an alarm within one-half a revolution.

Sensor Systems

In smokestacks, storage tanks, or other areas in which several variables are at work at the same time, use a linear sensor system, alone or combined with other systems, for greater accuracy in detecting fires. The common heat sensors simply provide averages. Linear sensor systems, however, give continuous point-by-point readings. They pick up and monitor trouble spots instantly over an entire area.

The concept of totally integrated fire detection brings together the facility's comprehensive fire-fighting capacity. This concept demands the continuing close cooperation of all persons involved in building design and construction, as well as in safety engineering and fire protection.

A modern fire detection system should be a combination of the various types of detecting systems in one integrated system.

ALARM SYSTEMS

Alarm systems can be divided into four groups: local, auxiliary, central station, and proprietary. All types of alarm systems should be equipped with a signal system that clearly communicates to all facility occupants. Whenever an alarm is sounded in any portion of the building or area, all occupants must know what the sound means. Every fire alarm system, whether it is currently in place, newly installed, or revised, should meet the following criteria:

- When alarms are audible, the alarm sound should be clearly and immediately distinguishable from other signals that might be used in a given building. Provision for alerting hearing impaired and visually impaired occupants is necessary.
- Locate audible and visible alarm devices so they are clearly audible to all personnel. Train personnel to recognize the signal and to respond according to that location's specific response procedure.
- The fire alarm system should be composed of approved (listed) equipment and installed using methods that conform to NFPA standards.
- Maintain the alarm system in good working order. Test it at frequent intervals to ensure that it is working properly. Alarm testing protocols should conform to NFPA standards.
- All personnel should know the location of and means of contacting

external fire protection sources. Conspicuously post this information in strategic areas. Each employee should also know the proper procedures for reporting a fire if he or she is the one who detects the fire.

Protected-Premises (Local) Fire Alarm Systems

A protected-premises fire alarm system consists of bells, horns, lights, sirens, or other occupant notification and warning devices located in or on the facility. Protected-premises fire alarm systems are generally used for life protection— that is, to evacuate the occupants and limit injury or loss of life from the fire. A protected-premises fire alarm system can be tied in with other fire alarm systems to summon a fire brigade or the fire department and activate fire control and suppression systems.

Some protected-premises fire alarm systems have a presignal feature. The presignal feature alerts designated remotely supervised stations on an alarm condition before an evacuation signal is activated. The presignal feature allows an initial response and investigation to occur (in less than 1 minute, usually). There are three possible results from the initial response to an alarm presignal feature:

1. A determination is made that the fire detection system did not detect an actual fire condition for which the general alarm should be activated (a nuisance alarm). *Action*: Evacuation signal activation is cancelled.
2. A determination is made to extinguish an incipient-stage fire. *Action*: Evacuation signal activation occurs unless the incipient-stage fire is extinguished and a separate decision to cancel the ensuing activation of the evacuation signal is made.
3. A determination is made that an evacuation is warranted. *Action*: Evacuation signal activation occurs.

Protected-premises fire alarm systems are available from a wide range of suppliers and are easy to install. By themselves, however, they do not provide much protection. While they alert personnel, they do not summon the fire department or a fire brigade automatically.

Auxiliary Fire Alarm Systems

Auxiliary fire alarm systems are connected to a protected-premises fire alarm system. When the protected-premises fire alarm system activates, the auxiliary fire alarm system signals the public fire service communications center.

Supervising-Station Fire Alarm Systems

Supervising-station fire alarm systems are continually staffed and operated

Figure 9–5. This console is part of an Underwriters Laboratory-listed, continuously staffed, supervising station (central station service) that has not only fire detection and alarm annunciation, but also security and emergency facility condition indicators.

Reprinted with permission from A-1 Alarm Service, Inc., Champaign, Illinois.

by trained personnel. They monitor facilities' fire detection and alarm systems and make appropriate notification upon presignal alerts, alarms, and indications of system problems. There are three kinds of supervising-station fire alarm systems: central station service fire alarm systems; proprietary supervising-station fire alarm systems; and remote supervising-station fire alarm systems.

Central station service fire alarm systems are for-hire monitoring companies that continually monitor all aspects of the fire detection and alarm systems for a number of independent, unrelated organizations. Proprietary supervising-station fire alarm systems (Figure 9–5) are operated on behalf of facilities under one owner and continually monitor all aspects of the facilities' emergency systems (including fire detection systems) related to all of that one owner's facilities. Remote supervising-station fire alarm systems are similar to proprietary supervising-station fire alarm systems, but are limited in scope to the alarm, supervisory, or trouble, systems of one or more specific protected-premises fire alarm systems.

FIRE SUPPRESSION AND FIRE EXTINGUISHMENT

PORTABLE FIRE EXTINGUISHERS

Equipment used to extinguish and control fires is of two types: fixed and portable. Fixed systems include water equipment, such as automatic sprinklers, hydrants, and standpipe hoses, and special pipe systems for dry chemicals, carbon dioxide, and foam. Special pipe systems are used in areas of high fire potential where water may not be effective, such as where tanks for storage of flammable liquids and electrical equipment are located. Fixed systems, however, must be supplemented by portable fire extinguishers. These often can preclude the action of sprinkler systems. Not only can they prevent a small fire from spreading, but they can also rapidly extinguish a fire in its early stages, when such extinguishment is performed by a trained person.

Principles of Use

Even though a facility is equipped with automatic sprinklers or other means of fire protection, portable fire extinguishers should be available and ready for an emergency. The term portable is applied to manual equipment used on small, beginning (incipient-stage) fires immediately after discovery of a fire and before the functioning of automatic equipment or the arrival of fire fighters.

To be effective, portable extinguishers must meet all of the following criteria:
- Fire extinguishers must be approved by a recognized testing laboratory.
- Fire extinguishers must be the right type for each class of fire that may occur in the area.
- Fire extinguishers must be of sufficient size to protect against the expected exposure in the area.
- Fire extinguishers must be located where they are easy to reach for immediate use.
- Fire extinguishers must be maintained in good operating condition, inspected frequently, checked against tampering, and recharged as required.
- Fire extinguishers must be able to be operated by trained, local area personnel who can find them when needed.

Classification of Fire Extinguishers

Portable extinguishers are classified to indicate their ability to handle specific classes and sizes of fires. This classification is necessary because new and improved extinguishing agents and devices are constantly being developed and because larger portable extinguishers are available. Labels on extinguishers indicate the class and relative size of fire that they can be expected to handle.

Use the following paragraphs as a guide to the selection of portable fire extinguishers for given exposures (see NFPA 10, Portable Fire Extinguishers). Refer to the section on "Classification of Fires," earlier in this chapter. Also, observe protection and insurance recommendations, based on fire protection requirements of the authority having jurisdiction.
- Use fire extinguishers rated for use on Class A fires for ordinary combustibles, such as wood, paper, some plastics, and textiles, where a quenching-cooling effect is required.
- Use fire extinguishers rated for use on Class B fires for flammable liquid fires, such as oil, gasoline, paint, and grease fires, where oxygen exclusion or a flame-interrupting effect is essential.
- Use fire extinguishers rated for use on Class C fires for fires involving energized electrical wiring and equipment where the dielectric nonconductivity of the extinguishing agent is of first importance. These units are not

classified by a numeral, because Class C fires are essentially either Class A or Class B, but also involve energized electrical wiring and equipment. Therefore, choose the coverage of the extinguisher for the burning fuel.

- Use fire extinguishers rated for use on Class K fires on grease and cooking oil fires in a commercial kitchen environment, where hot grills and stoves are helping to maintain combustion.
- Use fire extinguishers rated for use on Class D for fires in combustible metals, such as magnesium, potassium, powdered aluminum, zinc, sodium, titanium, zirconium, and lithium. Persons working in areas where Class D fire hazards exist must be aware of the dangers in using the wrong kind of fire extinguisher on a Class D fire. These fire extinguisher units are not classified by a numerical system and are intended for special hazard protection only.

Distribution of Extinguishers

Locate extinguishers close to likely hazards, but not so close that they would be damaged or cut off by the fire. Locate them along the normal path of exit from a building, preferably at the exits. Where highly combustible material is stored in small rooms or enclosed spaces, locate the extinguishers outside the door rather than inside. Locating them outside requires potential users to exit the room and then make a conscious decision to reenter the room and fight the fire. The relative hazard of the occupancy, the nature of any anticipated fires, protection for special hazards, and requirements of local codes determine the minimum number and the type of portable extinguishers to be installed for each floor or area.

Types of Portable Extinguishers

The following types of portable extinguishers are recommended for various types of fires: water solution, dry chemical, carbon dioxide, dry powder, and wet chemical extinguishers

Water Solution Extinguishers. Fire extinguishers that use water or water solutions include pump tank, stored pressure, and AFFF. These extinguishers are effective against Class A fires because of the quenching and cooling effect of water. These units cannot be used on fires in or near electrical equipment because they can present a shock hazard to the operator.

Dry Chemical Extinguishers. The dry chemical extinguisher is one of the most versatile units available. It extinguishes by interrupting the chemical flame's chain reaction. Do not confuse it with a dry powder extinguisher.

There are four common types of base extinguishing agents used in dry chemical extinguishers: sodium bicarbonate, potassium bicarbonate (also marketed as urea potassium bicarbonate), potassium chloride, and ammonium phosphate. When recharging, use only the dry chemical agent recommended by the extinguisher's manufacturer.

On Class B and Class C fires, ammonium phosphate–based dry chemical (multipurpose) has operating characteristics similar to the other dry chemicals. When discharged into a Class A fire, its chemical reaction destroys the flames. Also, a coating formed when the extinguishing agent softens adheres to the burning surface, thereby retarding further combustion. To obtain complete extinguishment on Class A materials, thoroughly expose all burning areas to the extinguishing agent. Because any small burning ember may be a source of re-ignition, properly applying multipurpose dry chemicals on Class A fires is more critical than with water-solution extinguishers. In the presence of moisture, multipurpose dry chemicals may cause corrosion when discharged on metals.

The two basic types of dry chemical extinguishers are defined by their propellant technique: gas cartridge or stored pressure. In the gas cartridge extinguisher, pressure is supplied by a gas stored in a separate cylinder.

Carbon Dioxide Extinguishers. Carbon dioxide extinguishers put out fires by displacing the available oxygen. They do not leave a residue. The bell or nozzle from a carbon dioxide fire extinguisher can become very cold during discharge. Also, one must be quite close to the fire for a carbon dioxide fire extinguisher to be effective.

Dry Powder Extinguishers. Because the use of combustible metals—such as sodium, titanium, uranium, zirconium, lithium, magnesium, sodium-potassium alloys, and other less-common metals—has increased, dry powder extinguishers are available to fight such fires.

G-1 Powdered Agent. The oldest powdered agent is the G-l type, a graphite organic-phosphate compound. When it is applied with a scoop or shovel to a metal fire, the phosphate material generates vapors that blanket and smother the flames, and the graphite, being a good conductor of heat, cools the metal below its ignition temperature.

Met-L-X. Another dry powder is Met-L-X. It is composed of a sodium chloride base with additives to make it free flowing, to increase water repellency, and to create the property of heat caking. The heat of the fire causes the Met-L-X to cake, thus forming a crust that excludes air.

Lith-X. Lith-X is another dry powder extinguishing agent. It is composed of a special graphite base with additives that make it free flowing so it can be discharged from an extinguisher. Lith-X was developed mainly for use on lithium fires, but it is also effective on other combustible metals. Lith-X does not cake or crust when applied over a burning metal. It excludes air and conducts heat away from the burning mass, thus extinguishing the fire.

Met-L-Kyl. A problem recently developed in fire fighting involves pyrophoric liquids, such as triethylaluminum. These liquids ignite spontaneously, and the resulting fires cannot be easily extinguished by dry powder or other commonly used agents. A special material, Met-L-Kyl, has been developed, consisting of a bicarbonate-base dry chemical and an activated absorbent. The principle of extinguishment involves the combination effect of the dry chemical, which extinguishes the flames, and the absorbent, which absorbs the remaining fuel and prevents reignition.

Wet Chemical Extinguishers. The fire extinguishers can be used on Class A fires and on Class K fires. Typically, portable wet chemical fire extinguishers are available in 1.5-gal (6-L) and 2.5-gal (9.5-L) models. The chemical is a water-based solution containing one or more of the following chemicals: potassium acetate, potassium carbonate, or potassium citrate.

These fire extinguishers assist in suppressing Class K fires by creating a thick foam blanket over hot cooking surfaces and equipment while simultaneously cooling the cooking appliance and the fuel source.

Fire Blankets

In some cases, fire blankets can be used to smother a small fire. Their major purpose is to extinguish burning clothing. However, they are also useful for smothering flammable-liquid fires in small, open containers. Flame-retardant blankets are also available.

SPRINKLER AND WATER-SPRAY SYSTEMS

There are many types of sprinklers and water-spray systems for extinguishing fires. The type of building, operations performed in it, and materials used will help determine the type of sprinkler or water-spray system used.

Water Supply and Storage

Sprinkler systems need a reliable water supply of ample capacity and pressure for efficient fire extinguishment.

Automatic Sprinklers

Automatic sprinklers are the most extensively used and most effective installations of fixed fire-extinguishing systems. These systems are so basic and have proved so effective that most fire protection engineers consider them the most important fire-fighting tool.

Automatic sprinklers have an impressive lifesaving record. Loss of life by fire is rare where properly designed and maintained sprinkler systems have been installed.

However, when sprinklers do fail to operate, in perhaps 3% to 4% of the cases, the failure is caused by some readily preventable condition. More than one-third of all failures can be attributed to closed water supply valves.

There are six basic types of automatic sprinkler systems: wet-pipe; dry-pipe; pre-action; deluge; combined dry-pipe and pre-action; and limited water supply systems (see NFPA 13). The combination dry-pipe and pre-action systems are used on installations that are larger than can be accommodated by one dry-pipe valve. The limited water supply system is used for installations that do not have access to a continual or large supply of water. The other four types of sprinkler systems are discussed in the following paragraphs.

Wet-Pipe Systems. The wet-pipe system represents the greatest percentage of sprinkler installations. All parts of the system's piping are charged to the sprinkler heads with water under pressure. Then, when heat fuses the fusible link on a sprinkler head, water is immediately sprayed over the area below.

Dry-Pipe Systems. The dry-pipe system generally substitutes for a wet-pipe system in areas where piping is exposed to freezing temperatures. It is essential to locate the dry-pipe sprinkler control valve and water supply line in a heated enclosure.

In the dry-pipe system, the piping contains compressed air that holds back the water by means of a dry-pipe control valve. When a sprinkler opens, the air pressure is released, the pressure drops, and the dry-pipe valve opens to admit water into the risers and branch lines. These sequential actions delay the actual suppression process when compared with a wet-pipe system. Because of this delay, extra-hazard buildings are difficult to protect with a dry-pipe system.

Pre-action Systems. Pre-action systems are similar to dry-pipe systems. However, they react faster. The pre-action valve, which controls the water supply to the system's piping, is actuated by a separate fire detection system. These fire detectors are located in the same area as the sprinkler and operate independently of the sprinkler. Because the detection system is more heat sensitive than the sprinklers, the water supply valve opens sooner than in a dry-pipe system. The water supply valve can also be operated manually.

Deluge Systems. The deluge system wets down an entire area by admitting water to all sprinklers that are open at all times. Deluge valves that control the water supply to the system are actuated by a fire detection system located in the same area as the sprinklers. The water supply valves can also be operated manually.

This type of system is primarily designed for extra-hazard facilities where great quantities of water may have to be applied immediately over large areas.

Types of Sprinklers

There are many classifications of sprinklers, each of which is designed for specific applications. Upright sprinklers direct water upward against the deflector. Pendant sprinklers direct water downward against the deflector. Sidewall sprinklers discharge the major portion of water away from the nearby wall in a pattern resembling a quarter of a sphere. Sprinklers designated for early suppression and fast response are also available.

Temperature Rating of Sprinklers

Sprinklers are selected on the basis of temperature rating and occupancy. Sprinklers are built either with heat-actuated elements that melt (fuse) or with special devices in which chemicals fuse or expand to open the flow of water through the sprinkler. Table 9–D shows the ratings and distinguishing colors of sprinklers.

Causes of Failure of Sprinkler Systems

Sprinklers seldom fail to control fires, but when they do, failure is usually caused by not keeping all supply valves open and shutting off the supply valves prematurely during a fire.

Water-Spray Systems

Water spray may be effective on certain types of fires where there is no hazardous chemical reaction between the water and the materials that are burning. Although these systems are independent of and supplemental to other forms of protection, they are not a replacement for automatic sprinklers.

FIRE HYDRANTS

In large facilities where parts of the facility are a considerable distance from public fire hydrants or where no public hydrants are available, install hydrants at convenient locations in the facility's yard. The number needed depends on the fire exposure and the hose-laying distance to the built-up facility areas (see NFPA 24, Installation of Private Fire Service Mains and Their Appurtenances).

TABLE 9–D. Temperature Ratings, Classifications, and Color Codings

Maximum Ceiling Temperature		Temperature Rating				
°F	°C	°F	°C	Temperature Classification	Color Code	Glass Bulb Colors
100	38	135–170	57–77	Ordinary	Uncolored or black	Orange or red
150	66	175–225	79–107	Intermediate	White	Yellow or green
225	107	250–300	121–149	High	Blue	Blue
300	149	325–375	163–191	Extra high	Red	Purple
375	191	400–475	204–246	Very extra high	Green	Black
475	246	500–575	260–302	Ultra high	Orange	Black
625	329	650	343	Ultra high	Orange	Black

FIRE HOSE

Like other fire-extinguishing equipment, hose lines should be available for immediate use.

Hose Nozzles

Effective streams of water for fire fighting are controlled by the size and type of nozzle. The nozzle, in turn, must be supplied with the correct quantity of water at the discharge pressure for which it is designed. Nozzles are designed for solid streams, spray streams (frequently referred to as fog), or combination streams. Nozzles for special extinguishing agents, such as foam and dry chemical, are also available.

SPECIAL SYSTEMS AND AGENTS

Special hazards may require systems of extinguishment or control other than water. Each of the several systems available offers certain advantages and disadvantages to consider when making a selection. These systems are usually installed to supplement rather than replace the automatic sprinkler system. They should be engineered to fit the circumstances of the particular hazard. Install them so that their operation will shut down other processes, such as pumps and conveyors, that might intensify a fire.

The following special agents and systems are currently in use. The specific NFPA consensus standard related to each of these agents or systems is also shown (see also the latest edition of the NFPA *Fire Protection Handbook*).

- foam and foam systems: NFPA 11 and NFPA 16
- carbon dioxide extinguishing systems: NFPA 12

- dry chemical extinguishing systems: NFPA 17
- wet chemical extinguishing systems: NFPA 17A
- water spray and automatic sprinkler systems: NFPA 15 and NFPA 13
- explosion prevention systems: NFPA 69.

When considering the use of special extinguishing systems and agents, consulting a qualified fire protection engineer is essential.

SUMMARY

- Fire protection includes everything related to preventing fires, detecting fires, responding to fires, suppressing and extinguishing fires, and recovering from a fire to resume normal business operations. To accomplish these goals, companies must develop comprehensive fire protection programs.
- The primary purpose of a fire protection program is to prevent fires and to develop a system to help ensure that when fires occur, appropriate detection, response, and suppression activities occur. This involves a combination of facility design and engineering objectives, along with occupant objectives such as training and drills.
- Employees should know their roles in detecting a fire and in transmitting an alarm, evacuating a building, confining the fire, and extinguishing the fire. Fire protection programs should enable companies to reduce fire risk significantly.
- Fire protection engineering is a highly developed engineering specialization. Achieving the most efficient fire protection system requires the involvement of qualified fire protection engineers, as well as building users, other engineers, architects, interior designers, building contractors, fire detection and suppression system manufacturers, the local governmental authorities having jurisdiction, and even urban planners.
- Fire protection measures are effective only if they are based on a proper analysis and evaluation of the risk of fire. The best fire protection minimizes loss of life and property.
- A facility's fire risk can be evaluated, and actions to reduce the fire risk in the facility can be taken. This involves performing a comprehensive fire risk assessment, beginning with a fire hazard analysis.
- In the diamond-shaped symbol of the NFPA identification system, the three categories of hazards are identified for each material: health, flammability, and instability, with a space for special instructions. The order

of severity in each category is indicated by numbers: 4 is a severe hazard and 0 indicates relatively no hazard.

- As a first step in fire prevention, every establishment should set up a system of periodic fire inspections for every operation and ensure that proper fire-extinguishing equipment is on hand and in good working order. The person in charge of fire prevention and protection should establish the schedule, determine routing reports, maintain a complete list of inspected items, and set up regular fire drills for all personnel.

- The chemistry of fire is highly complex. Fires can be controlled by cooling burning materials, removing oxygen from the fire, inhibiting the chemical chain reaction, and removing fuel. The objective of these methods is to interrupt the chain reaction in a fire. Fire-extinguishing agents help control fires in one or more of these ways.

- The NFPA has developed five classifications of fires. Class A fires occur in ordinary materials and can be extinguished by water or dry chemical agents. Class B fires occur in the vapor-air mixture over the surface of flammable and combustible liquids and are extinguished by limiting air or applying dry chemicals. Class C fires occur in or near energized electrical equipment and can be put out by deenergizing the electricity feeding the fire, and then extinguishing the fire using dry chemical agents or carbon dioxide. Class D fires occur in combustible metals and require special techniques and extinguishing agents and equipment to put out. Class K fires occur in commercial kitchens and involve cooking oils or animal fats in the presence of hot cooking surfaces. Class K fires are extinguished by wet chemical extinguishing agents.

- Facility construction methods can help confine fires and control smoke through proper design of stairways, fire walls, fire doors, separate units, ventilation ducts, physical barriers, and fire exits.

- Standpipes, traffic and transportation routes, and fire department and water access to the site should be designed to be as fire resistant as possible and should help minimize fire hazards.

- When a fire occurs, good communication is vital to alert workers to the emergency and to mobilize fire protection forces.

- Fire detection must be part of every fire protection system. Its two main tasks involve (1) giving an early warning to enable building occupants to escape and (2) starting extinguishing procedures. Means of fire detection can be through a human observer; automatic sprinklers; smoke, flame, or heat detectors; or a combination of these.

- Facilities should be equipped with fire alarm signal systems that clearly communicate to all personnel where the fire is located and that summon appropriate fire-fighting units. Employees must be trained to respond properly to alarm signals. Spacing, location, and maintenance of fire detectors depend on the type of building, its operations, and its materials.

- Portable fire extinguishers are listed as Class A, B, C, D, K, or a combination of A, B, and C, depending on the type of fire they are designed to extinguish. This equipment must be approved by a recognized testing laboratory, located in accessible areas, clearly marked as to class and type of fire, and easily operated by workers.

- Sprinklers and water spray systems come in many varieties, depending on the type of building, the operations performed in it, and the materials used. Sprinkler systems include wet pipe, dry pipe, pre-action, deluge, combined dry pipe and pre-action, and limited water supply systems.

- All systems require a reliable water supply of ample capacity and pressure. Automatic sprinklers are the most common and effective of all fixed fire-extinguishing systems and can serve as fire alarms as well as fire protection. Sprinkler systems and their water supplies must be inspected and tested regularly to ensure they function properly.

- Fire hydrants, fire hoses, and hose nozzles should be available for immediate use. Hydrants are particularly effective in large facilities where parts of the facility are far away from public fire hydrants or when no public hydrants are available. Fire hoses and nozzles should be inspected and maintained in good repair, and workers should be trained in their proper use during emergencies.

- Special fire hazards may require special fire-extinguishing or control agents other than water. These systems are usually installed to supplement, not replace, automatic sprinklers and other fixed or portable fire protection equipment.

REVIEW QUESTIONS

1. What are the four components of a comprehensive fire protection program?
2. Name at least three nongovernmental organizations where information can be obtained on all aspects of fire protection and building codes.
3. What are the seven steps necessary in performing a comprehensive facility fire risk assessment?
4. When should a facility's fire prevention activities first occur?
5. List at least five things related to fire prevention that ought to be considered during the design of a facility.

6. What is the major cause of occupant injury and death in structural fires?

7. What are four essential fire prevention practices that must occur continually in existing buildings?

8. What are the four ways fires can be controlled?

9. When should an employee abandon his or her attempts at fighting a fire with a portable fire extinguisher?

10. Class A fires are associated with _____.

11. Class B fires are associated with _____.

12. What makes a Class C fire unique from a Class A or Class B fire? What makes it the same?

13. What are Class D fires, and what should not be done to extinguish Class D fires?

14. What are Class K fires, and how are they different from Class B fires?

15. List four comprehensive national consensus standards and codes related to general facility fire protection.

10

Electrical Safety

- ❑ Define terms related to electrical safety: current, voltage, resistance, watt, grounding and grounds, bonding.
- ❑ Describe the types of injuries that can result from electrical shock.
- ❑ Discuss criteria for selecting electrical equipment.
- ❑ Compare and contrast different types of grounding.
- ❑ Discuss safety procedures that should be used during maintenance activities to ensure worker protection.

INTRODUCTION TO ELECTRICAL SAFETY

Properly used, electricity is the most versatile form of energy. Misuse or failure to respect the danger may result in serious injuries, death, and/or fire. Safety precautions for the design, work practices, procedures, servicing, and maintenance operations for electrical equipment, however, can prevent bodily harm, including fatalities, property damage, or both. This chapter provides an overview of basic safety considerations to minimize employees' exposure to low voltages of 600 volts or less. Power-distribution systems above 600 volts (v) are not addressed here. Topics covered in this chapter include:

- definitions of common electrical energy terms
- a discussion of typical electrical injuries and emergency treatment
- safety practices for using electrical equipment
- methods of grounding power equipment
- reducing hazards through prevention and inspection
- safety procedures for maintenance and repair work
- safety training for employees working with electrical equipment.

In most cases, electrical and electronic equipment can be designed for both maximum safety and efficiency. However, potentially hazardous conditions, such as inadvertent contact with voltages, do exist. These hazards can occur during engineering analysis (commonly known as debugging), installation, servicing, testing, and maintenance of electrical and electronic equipment. Decreasing the exposure to the majority of these potential hazards is neither difficult nor expensive if safeguards and safe procedures are introduced in the design stage. If hazards are ignored, however, serious accidents may result.

DEFINITIONS

Before dealing with electrical equipment in any way, an understanding of a few basic electrical terms is needed. Three of these basic terms—current, voltage, and resistance—can be defined by using the following analogy: electricity flowing through a circuit is like the flow of water through a pipe. Keep this analogy in mind to understand these terms more easily. Although there are a few technical problems with this analogy, it serves to help provide a basic function of the parts in a standard electrical system.

CURRENT

Think of current as the total volume of water flowing past a certain point in a given length of time. Electric current is measured in amperes (amps). The measurement used in relation to electric shock or injury is the milliampere (mA, 0.001 ampere). It only takes fractions of an amp to cause serious electrical injury or death.

If current (I) is to flow through a circuit, a complete path—from the source and back—must be available. When this path is present, the circuit is said to be complete or "closed." When the path is not complete, either intentionally or by accident, the circuit is called "open."

VOLTAGE

Think of *voltage* as the pressure in a pipeline. Voltage is measured in volts (v). Low voltage can be an ambiguous term depending upon one's knowledge and application of the term. OSHA (Occupational Safety and Health Administration) and NFPA (National Fire Protection Association) use the expression "low voltage" to refer to all systems 600 volts and below. This term is often misused in casual conversation. For the purposes of this chapter, low voltage is 600 v or less. While voltage itself does not cause injury (current and resistance damage tissue), voltage is necessary to provide current flow. Potentially hazardous voltage is between 24 v and 600 v. Systems of 50 v or higher are regulated by OSHA and NFPA and considered potentially lethal. A car battery of 12 v direct current (DC) in a dead short can be hazardous.

RESISTANCE

Think of *resistance* as blockage or friction in the pipe. Resistance (R) is any condition that retards current flow; it is measured in ohms (Ω). This friction will result in heat. Most electrical circuits are protected by over-current devices that monitor the levels of heat in the circuit. When too much heat is present, the over-current device operates and stops the flow of electricity through the circuit.

WATT

A *watt* (W) is the quantity of electricity that is consumed. It is determined by multiplying volts (V) times amps (I). ($V \times I = W$).

GROUNDING AND GROUNDS

A ground is an object that connects a piece of electrical equipment to earth or some conducting body that serves in place of earth. A ground serves to redirect stray electrical currents to the earth in the event of an equipment malfunction.

Note: there should never be electrical current in the grounds unless something is damaged. The purpose of the grounding system is to draw additional current through the grounding path, direct it into the earth, and assist the over-current devices in shutting down the electrical flow.

Many people consider this a method of preventing human injury or death. This is not the purpose of electrical grounds. Grounding is designed to detect malfunctions resulting in excess heat and is considered fire protection. The over-current device will not normally respond fast enough to prevent injury. However, turning off the electrical flow to a damaged piece of equipment often prevents unexpected contact and has saved countless lives.

It is important for a safety professional to understand that the primary purpose of grounding is to protect the facility and equipment by assisting the flow of current to rapidly overload the over-current device. When protection for humans from electrical current is required, as in wet locations or explosive atmospheres, other devices are utilized (see sections on ground-fault circuit interrupters and hazardous locations later in this chapter).

BONDING

Bonding is the joining of metallic parts to form an electrically conductive path. This path ensures electrical continuity. Because electrical current will travel from a high pressure to a lower pressure, bonding is designed to keep all of the conductive materials at an equal potential. This will prevent arcing between conductive objects. Bonding is important for activities such as transferring flammable liquids from one container to another. Bonding and grounding are often combined to protect hazardous locations from stray electricity or static buildup.

ELECTRICAL INJURIES

Current flow, path, and time are the factors that cause injuries in electrical shock. The severity of electrical shock is determined by (1) the amount of current that flows though the victim (Table 10–A); (2) the path through the body; and (3) the length of time that the body receives the current.

Because current flow depends on voltage and resistance, these factors are also important. In addition to current flow and time, other factors that affect the extent of injury are the critical parts of the body involved and, if alternating current is used, the frequency of shock. Heat is a secondary effect on the body. Deadly current flow can easily be received on contact with low-voltage sources of the ordinary lighting or power circuit.

A person's main resistance to current flow is the skin's surface. Callous or dry skin has a fairly high resistance. A sharp decrease in resistance takes place, however, when the skin is moist. Once the skin's resistance is broken down,

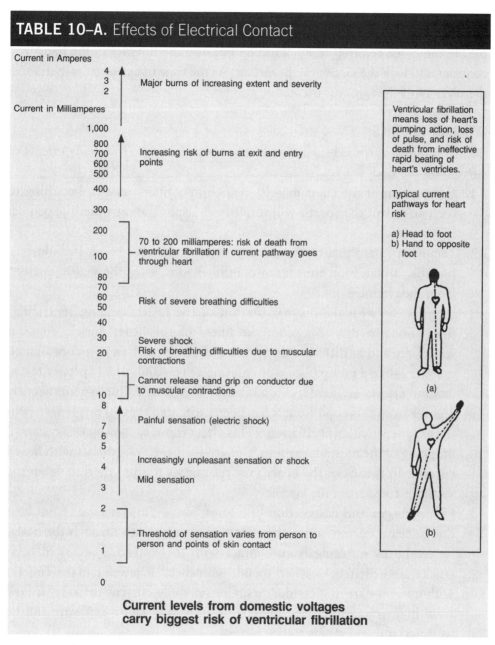

TABLE 10–A. Effects of Electrical Contact

Current in Amperes

Major burns of increasing extent and severity

Current in Milliamperes

Increasing risk of burns at exit and entry points

70 to 200 milliamperes: risk of death from ventricular fibrillation if current pathway goes through heart

Risk of severe breathing difficulties

Severe shock
Risk of breathing difficulties due to muscular contractions

Cannot release hand grip on conductor due to muscular contractions

Painful sensation (electric shock)

Increasingly unpleasant sensation or shock

Mild sensation

Threshold of sensation varies from person to person and points of skin contact

Ventricular fibrillation means loss of heart's pumping action, loss of pulse, and risk of death from ineffective rapid beating of heart's ventricles.

Typical current pathways for heart risk

a) Head to foot
b) Hand to opposite foot

(a)

(b)

Current levels from domestic voltages carry biggest risk of ventricular fibrillation

Source: Canadian Occupational Safety, January-February, 1988

the current flows readily through the nerves, blood, and the other conductive body tissues.

Whatever protection is offered by the skin's resistance decreases rapidly with increases in voltage or the presence of moisture. A high-voltage alternating current of 60 Hz causes violent muscular contraction, often so severe that the victim is thrown clear of the circuit. Although low voltage also results in muscular contraction, the effect is not so violent. Low voltage is dangerous, however, because it often prevents the victim from breaking the contact with the circuit, often referred to as "locked" because the muscles in the hand will contract and lock the victim on the circuit. As the time of exposure is increased, the severity of the injury is increased.

INTERNAL INJURIES

Death or injuries from electric shock may result from the following effects of current on the body:

1. Contraction of the chest muscles, which may interfere with breathing to such an extent that death will result from asphyxiation when the contact is prolonged.
2. Temporary paralysis of the nerve center, which may result in failure to breathe, a condition that often continues long after the victim is freed from the circuit.
3. Interference with the normal rhythm of the heart, causing ventricular fibrillation. In this condition, the fibers of the heart muscle contract separately and at different times, instead of contracting in a coordinated manner—like a pump. Blood circulation ceases and, unless proper resuscitation efforts are made, death occurs. The heart cannot spontaneously recover from this condition. It has been estimated that 50 mA is sufficient to cause ventricular fibrillation. (This effect is not caused by DC systems.)
4. Stopping of the muscular contractions of the heart, on contact with heavy current. In this case, the heart may resume its normal rhythm when the victim is freed from the circuit.
5. Hemorrhages and destruction of tissues, nerves, and muscles from heat due to heavy current along the electrical circuit's path through the body.
6. Severe burns resulting from contact with low-voltage systems in cars, trucks, and lift trucks when metal, wrenches, or jewelry make contact with current-carrying conductors. Considerable current is likely to flow from high-voltage sources. In general, only very short exposure can be tolerated if the victim is to be revived.

Injuries from electrical shock are less severe when the current does not pass through or near nerve centers and vital organs. In the majority of electrical accidents that occur in industry, however, the current flows from hand to hand or from a hand to the feet. Because such a path involves both the heart and the lungs, the results are usually serious.

SKIN AND EYE INJURIES

Electricity will follow the conductive minerals of the human body to complete the circuit. Tissue dies at current levels of about 300 mA. The tissue beneath the skin may be damaged even when the surface is apparently unharmed. These electrical burns may not be immediately detectable by the individual. Damage to organs may not result in pain. However, there have been many deaths days after electrical shock due to undetected damage to the heart, kidneys, or other organs. Qualified medical personnel should evaluate electrical shock victims immediately. Clearance distances from live conductors are set by OSHA and NFPA 70-E. These "shock protection boundaries" prevent accidental contact and arcing of energized parts.

Another type of electrical injury is thermal burns from electrical flashes or arc blasts. Temperatures from arc blasts may range between 10,000 F and 40,000 F. These burns are usually deep and slow to heal and may involve large areas of the body. Even people at a reasonable distance from the arc may receive eye burns. NFPA sets a minimum of 4 ft of clearance (at 600 v and below) whenever "live work" is performed on circuits. This "flash protection boundary" is an additional assessment that must be conducted whenever live work is performed.

Where live work is involved, flashes of explosive violence may result. This intense arcing is caused by (1) short circuits between bus bars or cables carrying heavy current; (2) failure of knife switches to completely open; (3) opening knife switches while they are carrying a heavy load; (4) pulling fuses in energized circuits; or (5) improper use of tools or electrical testing equipment.

INJURIES FROM FALLS

Other injuries from electrical shock include falls from one level to another. For example, a worker receives a shock from defective or malfunctioning equipment. The shock causes muscles to contract, causing the worker to lose his or her balance and fall. This type of accident often results from static electricity created within the workplace.

CARDIOPULMONARY RESUSCITATION

Because electrical shock can stop the heart and lungs, be sure that workers involved in working on or near live electrical systems know cardiopulmonary resuscitation (CPR) and rescue procedures. CPR training is provided by the National Safety Council First Aid Institute, the American Heart Association, the American Red Cross in the United States, and St. Johns Ambulance in Canada. Consult the telephone directory or Internet for the closest office.

Before any treatment can be attempted, ensure that the victim is clear of all electrical sources. The sooner the victim is resuscitated, the better the chances of survival; therefore, immediately apply CPR to a victim of electric shock. Continue CPR until the victim is revived, or until a physician diagnoses death.

ELECTRICAL EQUIPMENT

Most items of electrical equipment are designed and built for specific types of service. They operate with maximum efficiency and safety only when used for the purposes and under the conditions for which they are intended. OSHA regulations require electrical equipment to be listed or labeled by a nationally recognized testing laboratory and used only for the purpose approved.

SELECTING ELECTRICAL EQUIPMENT

When selecting electrical equipment, follow the recommendations of the various established codes and standards, such as the National Fire Protection Association's NFPA-70, National Electrical Code (NEC), and the American National Standards Institute's ANSI C2, National Electrical Safety Code. In addition to these codes, check state and local codes for industrial zoning requirements. Adherence to most of the provisions of the National Electrical Code is required not only by the regulators but also by many insurance companies and local governments.

Engineering consultants, manufacturers, and publications from the following groups will answer most questions concerning electrical equipment: American National Standards Institute, Canadian Standards Association, Factory Mutual System Research Organization, Illuminating Engineering Society of North America, National Fire Protection Association, and Underwriters Laboratories, Inc. (See References at the end of the chapter for addresses.) Consulting services may also be available from some of these organizations.

When ordering copies of codes or standards from publishers, give full information on the general type of equipment under consideration, the application, and the operating conditions. There is usually a charge for codes or standards.

INSTALLING ELECTRICAL EQUIPMENT

Where space and operating requirements permit, install electrical equipment in the less congested areas of the facility or, where practical, in special rooms to which only authorized persons have access. When electrical equipment is located in the production areas of the facility, build enclosures around those parts of the equipment having exposed conductors. Also post DANGER signs.

Install floor curbing or heavy steel barriers if there is even a remote danger of industrial trucks striking critical electrical equipment. Install transformers, dead-front control boards, switches, motor starters, and other electrical equipment so that the chance of accidental contact with energized conductors is at a minimum. Follow the clearance distances as described in OSHA or NFPA standards.

Interlocks

The purpose of a typical interlock is to prevent accidental contact with hazardous parts of a machine or process. They generally are not designed to provide full lockout requirements. When an interlock is used as a safety device, make sure that it is fail-safe. In other words, it must have an automatic backup in case its mechanism fails. In that way, the safety of personnel who depend on it will not be at risk. Interlocks should meet the following criteria:

- be equipped with fail-safe features because failure of the interlock mechanism, loss of power, short circuit, or malfunction of equipment will cause the circuit to be interrupted
- have a visible disconnect, or opening, in the primary power circuit
- have a locking arrangement that makes attempts to circumvent the interlock impractical.

Barriers

Barriers prevent accidental contact with electrical equipment. Make frames of wood, rolled metal shapes, angle iron, or pipe. Use wood strips, sheet metal, perforated metal, expanded metal, wire mesh, plastic, or shatterproof transparent material for filler. Dry wood and many plastics have the advantage of not conducting electricity. Unless specially treated, however, wood is combustible; with moisture, it can be conductive, and it may be hazardous. Ground all metal frames or guards.

Warning Signs

In addition, display warning signs near exposed current-carrying parts and in especially hazardous areas, such as high-voltage installations. These signs should be large enough to be read easily and should be visible from all approaches to the danger zone. The design of the warning sign should be in accordance with 29 CFR 1910.145, Specifications for Accident Prevention Signs and Tags.

Guarding

In many respects, standard machine-guarding practices can be applied to electrical equipment. Wiring, however, presents special hazards. Consider these hazards when planning the overall guarding program for the facility.

Install wiring in accordance with the NEC unless other local requirements apply. When installing new circuits or changing existing ones, observe the requirements of national and local wiring codes.

Use wires with insulation designed for the type of service and location. However, do not consider the insulation or weatherproofing alone as sufficient protection against shock, especially in high-voltage circuits. The NEC lists various types of insulation used on electrical conductors, as well as how to use them. To prevent injury, the insulation on a cable must provide at least 1,000 Ω (ohms) of resistance (R) for every volt applied. Outside power lines are normally weatherproofed, not insulated.

SWITCHES

Switches, fuses, circuit breakers, ground-fault circuit interrupters, control equipment, motors, and extension cords are needed to run electrical machines safely and efficiently. Proper use of this equipment avoids hazards and prevents accidents.

Among the several types of switches are knife switches; push-button switches; snap switches; pendant switches; and enclosed, externally operated air-break switches. Many switches are designed for a specific function, such as the enclosed switch for controlling individual motors and machine tools, and for lighting and power circuits. However, all switches, regardless of their function, must have approved voltage and ampere ratings that are compatible with their intended use.

PROTECTIVE DEVICES

The safe current-carrying capacity of conductors is determined by their size, length, material, insulation, and manner of installation. If conductors are forced to carry more than the maximum safe load or if heat dissipation is limited, overheating results. Over-current devices, such as fuses and circuit breakers, open the circuit automatically in case of excessive current flow from accidental grounds, short circuits, or overloads. Therefore, install some kind of over-current device in every circuit.

Over-current devices should interrupt the current flow when it exceeds the conductor's capacity. Selecting properly rated equipment depends not only on the current-carrying capacity of the conductor. It also depends on the rating of the power-supply transformer, or generator, and its potential short-circuit-producing capacities. Protection of this kind, both for personnel and for equipment, is one of the important features of an electrical installation. Where higher interrupting capacity is required, use special high-capacity fuses or circuit breakers.

Fuses

Among the many types of fuses are link, plug, and cartridge fuses. Use them only in the type of circuit for which they were designed. Using the wrong type or the wrong size fuse may cause injury to personnel and damage to equipment. Over-fusing is a frequent cause of overheated wiring or equipment, which can cause fires.

Before replacing fuses, lock out, tag out, and test the circuit to be sure that the voltage is turned off. Testing can save lives. Find out the cause of any short circuit or overload, and then replace a blown fuse with one of the same type and size. Never insert fuses in a live circuit.

GROUND-FAULT CIRCUIT INTERRUPTERS

A ground-fault circuit interrupter (GFCI) is a fast-acting, electrical circuit-interrupting device that is sensitive to very low levels of current flow to ground. The GFCI is designed to sense leaks of current large enough to cause serious personal injury. The unit operates only on line-to-ground fault currents, such as insulation leakage currents or currents likely to flow during accidental contact with a "hot" wire of a 120-v circuit and ground. It does not give protection in the event of line-to-line contact.

A receptacle GFCI that functions to detect this flow to ground is available. However, it protects only the associated integral receptacle, plus a limited number of additional receptacles connected downstream. GFCIs are also an integral part of some extension cords.

Use GFCIs when workers are using any electrical equipment, particularly in any work environment that is, or may become, wet; in an area that is a temporary power supply; and in other areas that are highly grounded. Per NEC 527.6, the employer shall use either a GFCI or an assured equipment ground program for branch circuits at a construction site.

Follow the manufacturer's instructions regarding the testing of the GFCI. Some recommend plugging in a load or appliance, then pushing the TEST button and resetting it monthly. Immediately replace defective units.

Remember that GFCIs do not replace a fuse or circuit breaker. Consider GFCIs as additional protection against the most common form of electrical shock and electrocution: the line-to-ground fault.

The ground fault must pass through the electronic-sensing circuit. This circuit has enough resistance to limit the current's flow to as little as 0.2 mA— well below the level where a person could feel it. Although no GFCIs protect individuals in the event of line-to-line contact, GFCIs should significantly reduce the number of electrical shock incidents, which presently account for about 1,100 deaths each year.

CONTROL EQUIPMENT

Arrange switchboards with lockout capabilities for both alternating-current (AC) and direct-current (DC) distribution circuits so the operator can easily reach the controls. Likewise, instruments should be readable and equipment adjustable from the working area. Place switchboards so the operator will not be endangered by live or moving parts of machinery. Do not use the space behind the switchboard for storage, and keep this area clear of rubbish. Place the switchboard in a special room or use screen enclosures to keep unauthorized personnel out. Keep the doors to the enclosure locked.

MOTORS

Mount motors so they do not interfere with the normal movement of personnel or materials. Motors not enclosed should be in areas free from dust, moisture, and flammable or corrosive vapors. In some instances, motors can be isolated from personnel by being mounted on overhead supports, installed below floor level, or placed in special motor rooms. If current-carrying parts of motors must be exposed and grounding is not possible, elevate them at least 8 ft (2.4 m) above the work area, or provide enclosures, barriers, or guards to prevent personnel from contacting them.

For maximum safety, each motor should be of the type and size required for the load and for the conditions under which it must operate. Avoid excessive overloading. Only use motors suitable for hazardous locations in areas that contain flammable vapors, combustibles, dusts, or fibers.

EXTENSION CORDS

Before using an extension cord, be sure it is listed by Underwriters Laboratories (UL) or other recognized testing laboratories. Inspect the extension cords regularly. To prevent the wire strands from breaking, avoid kinking or excessive bending of the cord. Broken strands may pierce the insulated covering and become a shock or short-circuit hazard.

Extension cords should be inspected before each use. Remove cords with cracked or worn insulation or with damaged plugs or sockets from service immediately. Do not permit splicing of extension cords. If a cord must be repaired, follow procedures as outlined in NEC 400.9.

Extension cords should not be connected or disconnected with an electrical load on. Store disconnected extension cords neatly coiled in a dry room at room temperature.

Extension cords are for temporary use!

TEST EQUIPMENT

Various types of electrical- and electronic-testing equipment can detect many of these conditions before they get out of control and cause damage. Qualified technicians or specially trained maintenance personnel should make these tests. The electrical test equipment should be listed by UL or another nationally recognized laboratory and used only by trained personnel.

The following types of equipment are standard and should be considered as essential testing equipment: split-core ammeter, voltmeter, ammeter, megohmmeter, ground-fault indicators and locators, wattmeter, industrial analyzer, receptacle circuit tester, receptacle tension tester, voltage detector, recording instrument, and specialized testing instruments (Figure 10–1). Specialized testing instruments, such as volt-ohm-milliammeters, oscilloscopes, and cable testers may also be used. Instruments such as these are generally fitted for detailed engineering work or for use where ordinary recording and indicating instruments are not accurate enough. Improper use of testing equipment may result in arc blast or serious injury.

SPECIALIZED PROCESSES

Among the many types of electrical equipment used in industry are the electric furnace, auxiliary heating devices, high-frequency heating equipment, electric welding equipment, x-ray laser, and ultraviolet and infrared installations. Each of these devices may introduce special operating hazards. However, protection from their electrical hazards may be secured through the same procedures recommended for use with the more common types of electrical equipment.

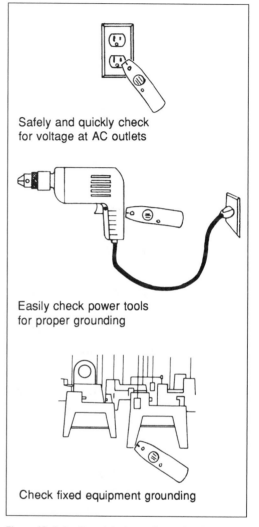

Safely and quickly check for voltage at AC outlets

Easily check power tools for proper grounding

Check fixed equipment grounding

Figure 10–1. A voltage detector can be used to check outlet voltage, equipment grounding, and circuit breaker condition.

High-frequency heating installations range in power capacity from a few hundred watts to several hundred kilowatts. Therefore, safety considerations are of prime importance.

The resistance of the body to the flow of high-frequency current is not dependent upon the skin. At frequencies of 200 kHz to several hundred megahertz, currents flow in a very thin shell on the surface of the conductor. This tendency of high-frequency current to flow on the surface is known as "skin effect" and increases as the frequency increases. Should the skin of a human being be punctured, the currents still flow on the surface and do not penetrate to the vital organs of the body.

A person coming into contact with high-frequency electrical energy will in general be burned because of the natural tendency to pull away, thereby setting up an arc. High-frequency burns can also result from radio-frequency antennae or from waveguide exposure. In many cases, the burn will occur and the person will feel nothing until after the exposure. These burns are painful and usually take longer to heal than burns from the more common thermal-heat sources.

Use the following methods to prevent high-frequency burns to operators.

GROUNDING

To understand grounding properly, note that both equipment grounding and the grounding of the electrical system itself are included under this term. (See "Definitions" at the beginning of this chapter.) The electrical system is grounded in order to prevent the occurrence of excessive voltages from such sources as lightning, line surges, or accidental contact with higher voltage lines. Both the electrical system and metallic enclosures are grounded to cause over-current devices to operate in the event of a ground fault occurring from an insulation failure. (See NFPA 70, National Electrical Code.)

According to the NEC, grounding is required for:

- refrigerators and similar equipment
- appliances using water, such as washers
- hand-held power tools
- motor-operated appliances, such as clippers
- any equipment used in damp areas
- portable hand lamps with metallic ground guards
- some parts of nonelectrical equipment, such as frames.

However, grounding is not required of these items listed if they are:

- approved and labeled double-insulated tools
- insulated transfer tools of less than 50 v.

SYSTEM GROUNDING

Alternating-current systems operating at 50 v or more must be grounded under a variety of voltage conditions. Grounding is accomplished by bonding the identified conductor to a grounding electrode by means of an unbroken wire called a grounding electrode conductor. Identification takes the form of white or neutral, gray-colored insulation.

EQUIPMENT GROUNDING

When the insulation on conductors fails within ungrounded metal enclosures, the enclosures are raised to line voltage and constitute a serious hazard for personnel. However, if the metal enclosure is attached to the main bonding jumper and to the service equipment with an equipment-grounding conductor, this voltage difference will not occur.

Moreover, if the fault itself has a low resistance, and the equipment-grounding conductor has been properly installed and well maintained, a large amount of current can flow. The over-current device that protects the circuit will then de-energize the circuit.

The NEC gives the proper sizes for equipment-grounding conductors used on various sizes of circuits.

Workmanship is one of the most overlooked aspects of good equipment grounding. The NEC states: "Connection of conductors to terminal parts shall ensure a thoroughly good connection without damaging the conductors...." Where this provision is not observed, a point of low thermal capacity will occur. Even though the resistance of the equipment-grounding circuit is measured and determined to be quite low, if the system does not have adequate thermal capacity, high-fault currents will cause these points of low thermal capacity to overheat. Arcing and fires, as well as inoperative protective equipment, could result.

MAINTENANCE OF GROUNDS

Only personnel with knowledge of electricity should install or repair electrical equipment. They should make certain that the green, insulated, equipment-grounding conductor is attached to the green-hexagonal binding screw and that the white, grounded circuit conductor is attached only to the silver-colored binding screw.

Good maintenance ensures an electrically continuous equipment-grounding path from the metal enclosure of the portable equipment through the line cord, plug, receptacle, and grounding system. This path ends at the bonding jumper at the service equipment or in the enclosure of the separately derived system.

Portable testing devices, such as a three-light neon receptacle tester, provide the most convenient means for checking polarity and other circuit connections. Other metered instruments are available to measure the actual impedance of the grounding circuit. Take precautions when using testing equipment.

Use a receptacle-tension tester to inspect receptacles for deteriorating contacts. The tester employs little pointers that indicate the amount of tension that each receptacle contact will produce on the minimum-sized, UL-listed attachment plug. By using this form of inspection, the maintenance department can replace receptacles before they produce an ineffective equipment-grounding contact or before a fire occurs in the power contacts. Tension testers can be purchased at most electrical supply houses.

THREE-WIRE ADAPTERS

Maintaining a good ground and making sure that it is used properly can be a difficult task in abusive environments. In the hands of the untrained operator, the adapter is rarely connected properly. (The NEC now requires that all adapters have a wide neutral blade. It further requires that the equipment ground be made by means of a rigid tab under the cover screw on the bottom of the adapter rather than by means of a flexible pigtail.) If the grounding pin on the attachment plug should be clipped off, the operator would be holding a potentially lethal device. While these devices are allowed for residential use, adapters are not allowed by OSHA for commercial use.

DOUBLE-INSULATED TOOLS

As an alternate to equipment grounding, the NEC recognizes the use of double-insulated appliances. Such appliances are constructed with two separate systems of insulation so that the chances of insulation failure are reduced to the lowest practical minimum.

Double-insulated appliances are of particular value in domestic situations. Many industrial users have, likewise, found them to be an effective means of reducing exposure to the hazards of electric current. In facilities that have instituted a strong safety program—where an employee looks for the grounding pin on all attachment plugs—use of double-insulated tools is now an exception to the rule. Confusion about double-insulated tools may result in the loss of some degree of safety. For example, double insulation does not protect against defects in the cord, plug, and receptacle. Continuous inspection and maintenance are required. Remember, do not use double-insulated power tools or equipment where water and a ground loop are present. Also do not use them in any situation where dampness, steam, or potential wetness can occur, unless they are protected by a GFCI.

Equipment with a dielectric housing (e.g., plastic) protects the user from shock if interior wiring contacts the housing. Exposure to water, however, can allow a leakage path that may be of either high or low resistance. Handling equipment with wet hands, in high humidity, or outdoors after a rainstorm can be hazardous.

The best indication of the safety of a double-insulated tool would be a label from either the Underwriters Laboratories or other recognized testing laboratory attached to the housing. The UL listing is evidence that the tool meets minimum standards.

For protection against electrical shock and to eliminate the need to ground the equipment, use self-contained, battery-powered tools.

POLARITY PLUGS

The use of polarity plugs has an additional safety feature for double-insulated or ungrounded tools. The two blades on the plug are of different widths, so they will only fit into a receptacle one way. The narrow blade is the "hot" side of the plug. It should always be routed through the device's switch. The wide blade is the "neutral" or return path. It is connected on the back side of the motor or appliance. Reversing these connections allows the device to be fully energized even with the switch in the "off" position. This can result in exposure to live electrical contacts even with the machine in the off position. If the system is bootlegged, the metal casing of the equipment becomes "hot."

DETERMINING HAZARDOUS LOCATIONS

Hazardous (classified) locations are areas in which explosive or flammable gases or vapors, combustible dust, or ignitable fibers are present or likely to become present. Such materials can ignite as a result of electrical causes only if the following two conditions coexist:

1. The proportion of the flammable substance to oxygen in the air must permit ignition. This mixture must be present in a large enough quantity to provide an ignitable atmosphere in the vicinity of electrical equipment.
2. An electric arc, a flame escaping from an ignited substance in an enclosure, heat from an electric heater, or another source of fire must be present at a temperature equal to or greater than the flash point of the flammable mixture.

Do not install standard electrical apparatus, considered safe for ordinary applications, in locations where flammable gases, vapors, dusts, and other easily ignitable materials are present. Sparks and electric arcs originating in such fittings have led to costly fires and explosions.

Before selecting electrical equipment and its associated wiring for a hazardous location, determine the exact nature of the flammable materials that will be present. For instance, an electrical fitting or device that is found by testing to be safe for installation in an atmosphere of combustible dust may be unsafe for operation in an atmosphere containing flammable vapors or gases.

Determining whether a hazardous situation exists in an industrial location is seldom difficult. Industries that have hazardous locations set up a formal procedure for classifying areas and for reviewing equipment and processes to determine the degree of potential hazard. Once a hazardous location has been identified and classified—and its limits defined—following NEC requirements for wiring methods and equipment compliance is relatively straightforward.

A major problem, however, is defining the limits of the hazardous location. How far above, below, and outward from the source does the hazardous location extend? For circumstances not covered by the NEC, use this general rule to determine these limits: the limits of the hazardous locations are those mutually agreed upon by the owner, the owner's insurance carrier, and the authority enforcing the code.

HAZARDOUS LOCATIONS

Hazardous locations are classified depending on the properties of the flammable vapors, liquids, or gases; combustible dusts; or fibers that may be present. Consider each room, section, or area of the facility separately.

Hazardous locations are classified as Class I, Class II, or Class III, depending on the physical properties of the combustible substance that might be present (Table 10–B). These classes are subdivided into Division 1 and Division 2, depending on the degree of likelihood that an ignitable atmosphere might be present. Combustible substances are arranged into seven groups—A through G. The grouping depends on the reaction of the substances upon contact with an ignition source—highly explosive, moderately incendiary, and so forth. Equipment installed in hazardous locations must be approved for the applicable class, division, and group. Descriptions of the three classes and two divisions in each class follow:

- Class I locations are those in which flammable gases or vapors are present or likely to become present.
- Class II applies to locations in which combustible dusts are likely to be present.
- Class III locations are those in which easily ignitable flyings, such as textile fibers, are present but not likely to be in suspensions in the air in sufficient concentrations to produce an easily ignitable atmosphere.
- In a Division 1 location, an ignitable atmosphere could occur at any time in the course of normal operations. Such an area represents a worst-case condition. One of the two requirements for ignition is likely to be present at any time, awaiting only a spark to ignite the flammable substance.
- In a Division 2 location, no ignitable atmosphere exists under normal operating conditions. However, an equipment malfunction, operator error, or other abnormal circumstance might create a hazardous environment.

Requirements for Division 2 electrical installations are less stringent than those for Division 1 locations because, in Division 2, two possible, but improbable, circumstances must coincide for ignition. In addition, any

TABLE 10–B. Hazardous Location Classifications

Class I Highly flammable gases or vapors		Class II Combustible dusts		Class III Combustible fibers or flyings	
Division 1	Division 2	Division 1	Division 2	Division 1	Division 2
Locations where hazardous concentrations are probable, or where accidental occurrence should be simultaneous with failure of electrical equipment	Locations where flammable concentrations are possible, but only in the event of process closures, rupture, ventilation failure, etc.	Locations where hazardous concentrations are probable, where their existence would be simultaneous with electrical equipment failure, or where electrically conducting dusts are involved	Locations where hazardous concentrations are not likely, but where deposits of the dust might interfere with heat dissipation from electrical equipment, or be ignited by electrical equipment	Locations in which easily ignitable fibers or materials producing combustible flyings are handled, manufactured, or used	Locations in which such fibers of flyings are stored or handled, except in the process of manufacture

Groups:
A—Atmospheres containing acetylene
B—Atmospheres containing hydrogen or gases or vapors of equivalent hazard
C—Atmospheres containing ethyl-ether vapors, ethylene, or cyclopropane
D—Atmospheres containing gasoline, hexane, naphtha, benzene, butane, propane, alcohol, acetone, benzol, or natural gas
E—Atmospheres containing metal dust, including aluminum, magnesium, and other metals of equally hazardous characteristics
F—Atmospheres containing carbon black, coke, or coal dust
G—Atmospheres containing flour, starch, or grain dusts

accidental formation of an ignitable atmosphere in a Division 2 location can usually be quickly stopped and the ignitable atmosphere dispersed. As a result, any exposure to fire and explosion is usually of short duration in a Division 2 location.

Establishing the Limits

Classifying an area as hazardous for purposes of NEC compliance is based on the possibility of flammable liquids, vapors or gases, combustible dusts, and easily ignitable fibers or flyings being present. After an area has been classified as hazardous, the next step is to determine the degree of hazard. Should the area be classified as Division 1 or Division 2? Also, the limits of the hazardous location must be defined—how far above, below, and outward from the source of the hazard does the hazardous location extend?

The safest electrical installation in a hazardous location, of course, is one that is not there at all. As much as is practical, situate electrical equipment outside the area defined as hazardous. It is, however, seldom possible or practical to locate all electrical equipment outside the hazardous area. The facility engineer is responsible for ensuring that all electrical equipment in the hazardous area, and its associated wiring, conforms to the NEC and does not significantly increase the chance of explosion.

Reducing Hazards. Two ways to reduce the chance of explosions from electrical sources are (1) remove or isolate the potential ignition source from the flammable material; and (2) control the atmosphere at the ignition source. For an explosion to occur, the following two conditions must coexist. If either of these two conditions is eliminated, the explosion hazard is reduced to zero.

1. combustible material present in a sufficient amount and the proper concentration to provide an ignitable atmosphere
2. an ignition source powerful enough to ignite the combustible materials that are present.

Planning Electrical Installations. The hardest part of planning an electrical installation to conform to NEC requirements for hazardous locations is to define the limits of the hazardous area. How far should the hazardous location be considered to extend to ensure that safety is served, without taking unnecessary and expensive precautions? No hard-and-fast rules can be applied. Experience on comparable projects and an understanding of specific conditions at the job site provide a far better basis for defining limits than any theoretical study of flammable vapors, gases, dusts, or fibers.

When establishing limits of hazardous locations, consider the area surrounding each source of hazardous material as a location and determine its individual limits.

EXPLOSION-PROOF APPARATUS

Explosion-proof apparatus is defined in the NEC, Article 100, as

> ...apparatus enclosed in a case that is capable of withstanding an explosion of a specified gas or vapor, which may occur within it, and of preventing the ignition of a specified gas or vapor surrounding the enclosure by sparks, flashes, or explosion of the gas or vapor within, and which operates at such an external temperature that a surrounding flammable atmosphere will not be ignited thereby.

Only use fittings that have undergone exhaustive tests and meet the requirements of Underwriters Laboratories for use in hazardous locations. These fittings must be of durable material, provide thorough protection, and be finished for total resistance to atmospheric conditions.

Install explosion-proof fittings not only on new work but also on old wiring systems where alterations are being made or new equipment is being installed. Observing NEC requirements minimizes dangers that might result from using ordinary fittings in hazardous locations.

Often, control equipment can be located outside a room containing hazardous materials. In these cases, conventional wiring equipment rather than explosion-proof fittings can be used. Thus, the cost and hazards of installation are reduced.

INSPECTION

Whenever possible before an inspection, the facilities electrician or other authorized person should de-energize equipment. Live circuits and equipment left in the operating mode are always a hazard. Always assume that a circuit is live until it is proved otherwise. In the inspector's presence, the facility electrician, supervisor, or operator should conduct tests to determine that the parts to be worked on are de-energized. As an additional safeguard, the inspector should have the breakers and switches locked open, grounded, and tagged so they cannot be energized until the tests have been completed. Until all testing is completed the system must be considered energized! If the electrician must leave a circuit being tested before the test is complete, he or she should use lockout procedures. Upon returning and before continuing the tests, the electrician should check all markings, breakers, and switches to be sure that they have not been altered. The OSHA standard for the Control of Hazardous Energy (Lockout/Tagout) (29 CFR 1910.147) for general industry, outlines specific action and procedures for addressing and controlling hazardous energy during servicing and maintenance of machines and equipment, and should be adhered to in all cases. All lockout and tagout procedures should safeguard workers from the release of hazardous energy.

Upon completion of the inspection, the inspector should remove any grounds and locks/lockout tags that were used. However, before the equipment is returned to service, the chief electrician, supervisor, or operator—whomever is in charge—should give it clearance.

In many electrical inspections, power must be on so that the function can be determined. In many cases, instruments are designed to test functions that way. All testing equipment needs to be checked before the inspection to test correctly. Avoid wearing metal jewelry such as rings, necklaces, and so forth.

HIGH-VOLTAGE EQUIPMENT

In general, high-voltage equipment is more carefully guarded than low-voltage equipment because of high-voltage equipment's greater inherent hazard.

Personnel

Only authorized, trained personnel should work on high-voltage equipment. In newer installations of 2,300 v or more, attempts have been made to insulate or armor apparatus to prevent casual contact with the current-carrying parts.

Protective Equipment

Persons working on high-voltage equipment should know that rubber insulating gloves are not a good substitute for safety devices or proper procedures. Such gloves should be worn only as a supplementary measure. Before each use, check the gloves for punctures, tears, or abrasions. A glove inflator should be used to perform daily checks on rubber gloves. If the glove inflator is not available, roll up the cuffs and force air into the fingers and palms of the gloves. If there is an air leak, do not use the gloves. Electrical gloves must be laboratory tested at least every 6 months. (See Chapter 13, Personal Protective Equipment; National Safety Council (NSC) Occupational Safety and Health Data Sheet 12304–0598, Flexible Insulating Protective Equipment for Electrical Workers; and OSHA 29 CFR 1910.132 and 1910.137, General Equipment PPE and Electrical Protective Equipment, for further discussion of gloves.)

MAINTENANCE

For safety and service, electric equipment must be well maintained. Motors, circuit breakers, moving parts of switches, and similar current-carrying devices wear out, break down, and need adjustment. Only have trained and experienced electricians make repairs on electrical circuits and electrical apparatus. Refer to NFPA 70-E for complete requirements for electrical maintenance requirements.

Good safety practices lie not only in using the proper protective equipment, but in taking care of that equipment as well. Protective equipment should be inspected before it is used and should be checked at frequent intervals.

To prevent accidental grounding and possible severe injuries, maintenance personnel must constantly be on guard when working around electrical equipment and circuits. Grounding can easily occur if an energized loose wire contacts a water pipe, conduit, metal fixture, another wire, or anything metallic that is connected in some way to the earth.

EMPLOYEE TRAINING

Deviating from safe usage and installation practices with electrical and electronic equipment often results in unnecessary hazards that can cause injuries or death.

Consequently, a facility's safety program must thoroughly train all employees who work with electrical and electronic equipment or who operate electrical and electronic systems. In addition to instructions on the hazards of electricity, train employees in CPR; the use of warning signs, guards, and other protective devices; and safe operational procedures. Each employee must be trained to handle emergency situations. Be sure that they are instructed never to work alone with potentially hazardous electrical equipment.

In developing appropriate safety programs, management should base them on the layout of the facility's electrical system and its use of electronic equipment. The program can then be applied to the specific operations and changes that may occur within the systems.

Supervisors should be kept informed about existing and possible electrical hazards. Management should require them to maintain close supervision over all operations that involve the use of electrical or electronic equipment. Supervisors must encourage employees to report any electrical defect or problem immediately. The supervisor must then have the tool or equipment repaired or replaced at once. (See Chapter 7, Safety and Health Training, for more information about training programs.)

SUMMARY

- Failure to establish or use safety practices for electrical equipment can result in property damage and serious injuries or fatalities. Workers must understand clearly the need to learn and follow safe work practices.
- Severity of electrical shock is determined by (1) the amount of current that flows through the victim; (2) the length of time the body receives current; and (3) parts of the body involved.
- Electrical equipment should be installed in controlled areas and have fail-safe devices and guarding to protect workers and others nearby. All electrical equipment should be properly wired, grounded, and connected to circuit breakers, ground-fault circuit interrupters, or other control equipment installed for emergency shut-off.
- Extension cords must be inspected frequently to detect any wear, fraying, or breakage in the line.
- Make sure that workers are thoroughly trained to check their electrical equipment for safe operation, to report any abnormal conditions, to have equipment tested regularly, and to observe all safety regulations and practices to operate specialized equipment.
- Grounding includes both equipment grounding and grounding of the electrical system itself. Only trained personnel should install, test, and

repair grounds.

- Standard electrical equipment should not be installed in locations where flammable gases, vapors, dusts, or other easily ignitable materials are present.
- Management should determine the specific hazards in any particular location before selecting and installing electrical equipment. Management should also reduce the hazards by removing or isolating sources of possible ignition and by controlling the atmosphere at the ignition source.
- Before inspections, electrical equipment should be de-energized whenever possible and the systems locked and tagged to prevent accidental reenergizing while tests are being conducted. Inspectors should be thoroughly trained and properly protected before inspecting high-voltage equipment.
- All components of electrical equipment must be well maintained. Only trained and experienced electricians should make repairs on electrical circuits and apparatus.
- A facility's safety program should include thorough training for all employees who work with electrical and electronic equipment or who operate electrical systems. Supervisors should know about existing and possible hazards and all employees know CPR, rescue, and other emergency procedures.

REVIEW QUESTIONS

1. What is a person's main resistance to current flow?
2. Why is low voltage considered dangerous in regards to electrical shock?
3. Describe the relationship between current, voltage, and resistance.
4. What is measured in ohms?
5. Name two factors that cause injuries in electrical shock.
6. List the different types of fuses.
7. Why is an electrical system "grounded?"
8. What is the procedure for grounding equipment?
9. What is the difference between low- and high-voltage equipment?
10. Describe OSHA required procedures to ensure the safety of personnel working on devices that could release hazardous energy.

11

Construction Safety

SAFETY IN CONSTRUCTION

INTRODUCTION

This chapter addresses the management of construction and demolition operations carried out in an industrial environment. It has been developed for those looking for an overview of the safety and health process that should be in place for construction operations performed on their property. The term *construction* as used throughout this chapter includes demolition operations.

SAFETY PROGRAMS

Given the technical resources and safety information available today, the goal of every project should be zero incidences resulting in injury, illness, or damage to equipment or property. Unfortunately, high-profile stories such as the collapse of tower cranes in New York continue to provide headline news. Less newsworthy, but just as devastating, are the avoidable construction-related injuries and fatalities that continue to occur with alarming frequency.

Responsibility for construction site safety has been the focus of heated debate for some time. Plaintiff and defense attorneys argue the subject regularly. Architects, engineers, and clients often contend safety is the responsibility of the construction manager or general contractor. The construction manager is the single entity that will be responsible for providing controls over contracts awarded, seeing that they are within the estimated budget, and administering construction without having to engage any field employees or tradesmen.

Construction managers attempt to skirt the issue of responsibility for safety by arguing limited contractual authority. General contractors point out that their contracts place responsibility on the subcontractors to follow OSHA regulations and safe work practices. In turn, subcontractors and craftsmen point back up the line to both the owner and the general contractor as being the ones controlling—and therefore responsible for providing—a safe job site. To further complicate the issue of safety responsibility, many contracts contain indemnification clauses requiring the contractor doing the work to defend the party letting the contract against third-party claims.

Responsibility for safety on construction sites tends to be confusing because lines of responsibility are often blurred by the attempts of those involved to transfer responsibility and accountability for safety to others. The issue of who is responsible for safety is becoming more contentious as the costs of accidents/incidents, insurance, litigation, workers' compensation, and other associated expenditures escalate.

The primary factor in the success of an effective safety program is management and its involvement in the safety program. Although a dollar value cannot be placed on the humanitarian aspects of a safety program, it is also impossible to place a dollar value on the negative effects personal injuries and fatalities have on labor relations and publicity. Merely incorporating safety clauses in contracts and printing a safety program will not yield the desired results without a serious and persistent management commitment to make the program work. It is human nature to place emphasis on the program (or programs) that will be evaluated. Thus, safety will receive attention proportional to the importance placed on it by management.

The safety of all employees, engineers, managers, subcontractors, visitors, and bystanders in the vicinity of contracted work should be of significant concern to everyone involved in the construction process. Only through the clear definition of responsibility and accountability for safety can personal injuries and other related losses be minimized in a continually changing environment such as that on a construction site.

Owners ultimately pay the cost of the safety program on a job site. The effectiveness of the implementation of a safety program will have a direct bearing on the losses sustained by the project. Therefore, it is in the interest of owners to establish an environment within which contractors are required to follow safe work practices. Fear of incurring liability by becoming involved in establishing safety requirements should not be a reason for failing to take a proactive role in defining expectations of an effective construction safety program. All incidents and personal injuries can be prevented. This has been demonstrated by the organizations that have implemented world-class safety programs. A useful reference in this regard is *Construction Site Safety: A Guide for Managing Contractors* (Hilsop, 1999).

ESTABLISHING A SAFETY PROGRAM

A safe work environment does not just materialize. To establish a safe worksite, roles and responsibilities of each project participant must be clearly and unambiguously defined. This is particularly the case where one party assumes multiple roles in the construction process, such as an owner who designs and chooses to oversee the execution of the work by multiple prime contractors.

What is the role of the owner? How much of the safety program is the owner responsible for? Who will be responsible for planning and coordinating the project safety plan? Who is responsible for safety audits and inspections? Whose job is it to mitigate identified safety hazards? Frequently, the task of assigning responsibilities for safety is overlooked by the owner in the initial enthusiasm and accelerating momentum of a new project.

Construction projects that had extended periods with no lost-time injuries and projects without OSHA recordable injuries have the common safety management approaches and practices:

- demonstrated management commitment to safety, as shown by regular field presence and tracking project safety indices
- management and supervisor accountability for safety performance
- adequate safety staff, who report directly to senior management
- project-site-specific safety plan and a requirement that subcontractors submit project-specific safety plans
- worker involvement and participation in work planning
- task preplanning meetings held by foreman with his or her crew before starting each task
- structured safety observation program
- accident/incident reporting and investigation, which includes top management participation
- safety orientations and safety training
- drug and alcohol testing
- safety recognition and rewards
- imposition of sanctions on work crews that do not comply with safety requirements.

RISKS OF USING CONTRACTED SERVICES

An owner has two options with regard to establishing a construction safety program: develop and manage the safety program directly or have it developed and managed by a second party such as a construction manager (CM). In the first case, where the owner has the technical expertise and resources to do so, the owner might manage the safety program directly. Typically, owners do not have professionals on staff with the technical expertise to direct or manage construction safety programs in a contracted work environment. Where owners do not have the technical resources in-house, they generally opt to retain a CM. The CM acts as the owners' agent and manages the work, including safety. In this scenario, the owner must clearly communicate its expectations regarding safety responsibilities and how performance will be measured. The owner might go so far as to define specific program elements that are important to its particular culture or require that technical criteria be applied to the selection of contractors.

Regardless of the type of approach chosen, the owner/client must adopt and support certain basic tenets, such as:

- supporting the safety program, including adequate budget
- defining minimum expectations of the project safety program
- recognizing that construction safety is part of a dynamic process where decisions must be made in a timely manner

- addressing problems as they occur
- monitoring and verifying that the safety program and site-specific plan are being effectively implemented.

The establishment of a safe worksite requires that those in control commit to the importance of having a well-defined safety program during early project conceptual development. It requires them to carry and communicate this commitment through contractual negotiations, work implementation, and finally project completion, never wavering in their commitment to safe work planning and practices.

MANAGING SAFETY ON A PROJECT

Monitoring day-to-day activities of construction trades and contract compliance is an essential function of the owner. Usually, it is only after a tragic personal injury or a serious safety-related loss that the employer begins to take an interest in safety. At this stage, it is difficult and often very expensive to implement an effective safety program.

We often mistakenly assume that individuals who have been assigned supervisory and management positions, and contractors who bid to perform work, have all been anointed with safety awareness and insight. This is not so. Safety awareness—the ability to recognize hazards—and the technical background to be able to eliminate or control identified hazards are learned.

The project owner must define the expected outcome of the safety program and assign responsibility for managing it even before developing the contract language. Safety is just as important as schedule, quality, material control, or any other facet of construction. Like schedule and quality, safety does not just happen. There must be a clear and unambiguous description of the safety program criteria, as in any other aspect of business. Most important, perhaps, is the assignment of responsibility for safety; because generally there is not a contractual relationship between subcontractors or even between prime contractors, it is the role of the owner to clearly establish responsibility for safety down through the organizational hierarchy.

ELEMENTS OF A SAFETY PLAN

Owner requirements, government regulations, and industry standards for safety contain the basic elements of the overall *construction safety program.* Extracting the provisions from the program that apply to a specific project results in the *project safety plan* that identifies the entities and individuals responsible and accountable for implementing the safety plan. The safety program describes what must be included in the safety plan, and the safety plan describes how and by whom the program elements will be implemented. A successful safety plan must address site-specific hazards, define safety expectations with regard to safe work practices, and clearly define safety roles and responsibilities. Federal, state, and local safety regulations and standards define the minimum expectations that should be in place for a given project. Safety plan requirements and their emphasis will differ for each project. A project that involves significant work with buried utilities will have very different safety plan requirements and emphases than that of a project with extensive work at heights. To ensure a clear understanding of the owner's safety expectations, they should be documented in the project safety plan.

MANAGEMENT COMMITMENT AND EXPECTATIONS

To promote the integration of safety into regular work practices, an owner must define its expectation to the individuals controlling the work that "safety is important." Safety begins with the attitude that incidents are preventable through the commitment of management and the requirement that planning and safe work practices must be followed. The owner should establish that safety be included as the first item of discussion at all meetings, including those dealing with cost, schedule, sales and training. Once again, a safety program will only be as good as the owner's commitment to safety and its visible support of it. The importance of safety, over expediency, must be regularly emphasized so that supervisors and the workforce understand that although schedule and production are important, above all else, work must be performed safely.

Management must clearly define its commitment to safety and its expectations in that regard on a regular basis. To document its safety expectations, the owner must commit the safety requirements to writing in the contract, including all entities performing work on the project and clearly identifying responsibility and accountability for safety.

Policy Statement

The cornerstone of the safety program is the owner's affirmation of its position on safety (i.e., its safety policy). This is a written statement of the principles and general rules embodying the company's commitment to workplace safety and health. The policy statement can be brief, but should address:

- management's commitment to employee safety
- the organization's safety philosophy
- who is accountable for the occupational health and safety program

- acknowledgement of the organization's responsibilities for the safety of all employees
- that safety shall not be sacrificed for expediency
- that the work and the work environment must be evaluated for potential hazards before any work is initiated and all potential hazards be eliminated or controlled.

The policy should be stated in clear and unambiguous terms, and it should convey that management is sincerely committed to safety.

This is particularly important in an environment where the safety message is different than safety practices in the past. Each organization must determine how best to communicate its safety policy and safety rules to its contractors and workforce.

Safety Procedures

Safety procedures are needed to simply and concisely define accepted work practices. Poorly defined procedures, or those procedures with little relevance to the work being performed, may be interpreted as an indication that safety is not important. The following are some guidelines for establishing safety procedures.

Procedures should be:

- available to all employees in written form
- specific to safety concerns in the workplace
- stated positively and in understandable terms
- explained
- enforceable
- reviewed periodically to evaluate their effectiveness and to make changes for improved effectiveness.

One approach to initially establish safety procedures is to address the most frequent causes of injuries on construction sites or those that have occurred with most regularity at the owner's facility.

Safe Job Work Procedures

Many job-related injuries occur because employees are not aware of existing or potential hazards and how to control the hazards related to their work. This may be because they were never trained to perform the work safely in the first place, or they may not have received training to help them identify hazards, or they do not have the background to develop appropriate controls to deal with those hazards once they have been identified. Prior to starting work, each work task should be evaluated to identify the most efficient way of performing it safely. The agreed-upon safe work practices defined as the result of this evaluation should then be communicated to the individuals required to perform the work by those responsible for supervising it at the pre-task meeting.

Job Safety Analysis

A means of systematically identifying and evaluating safety issues associated with a work task is a job safety analysis (JSA). Each step of a task is evaluated to identify the hazards associated with the work. Where issues are identified, an effective means of performing the work in a safe manner is agreed to. This process should involve the participation of several individuals, including supervisors, individuals who perform the work, and technical specialists with an awareness of safety-related considerations to help recommend safe procedures to execute the work.

A JSA should be developed for all critical tasks with priority given to addressing tasks:
- where frequent accidents/incidents and injuries occur
- where severe accidents/incidents and injuries occur
- with a potential for severe injuries
- that are new or that are a modification to a previous procedure
- that are infrequently performed.

A job safety analysis generally consists of the following steps:
1. Select the job.
2. Break down the job into a sequence of steps.
3. Identify the hazards associated with each step.
4. Define preventive measures.

Where a job consists of more than one specific task, each separate task should be analyzed.

After workers have been briefed on the manner in which work is to be performed, supervisors should monitor their subordinates' work to ensure the procedures have been understood and are being followed.

RESPONSIBILITY AND ACCOUNTABILITY

For a safety program to be successful, management, supervisors, and workers must recognize that they each have a role in the safety process. Management has a responsibility to provide its employees with a safe and healthful work environment. Management must also ensure that employees have the tools, personal protective equipment (PPE), and other resources needed to execute their work safely. Supervisors have the responsibility to ensure that each of their subordinates clearly understands how to perform their work safely and that they follow safe work practices. It is the responsibility of workers, prior to starting a task, to make sure they understand how they are expected to perform the work safely and to have the tools and protective equipment they require to perform the work following approved safe work procedures.

Documented safety programs/plans should define the safety responsibilities of individuals at each level of the project organization—from management to the subcontractor's craftsmen. This information will enable everyone on the project to understand what his or her respective responsibilities are and who is responsible for what in the project safety program.

Worker responsibilities:
- knowing and complying with safety regulations
- following safe work procedures
- using PPE appropriate for the work being performed
- correcting or reporting unsafe work practices and unsafe conditions
- helping new employees recognize job site hazards and follow proper work procedures
- reporting injuries or illnesses immediately.

First-line supervisors are responsible for:
- instructing workers on how to identify unsafe conditions
- requiring subordinates to follow safe work practices
- ensuring that individuals assigned to operate equipment are adequately trained and authorized to operate equipment
- correcting unsafe acts and unsafe conditions
- enforcing health and safety regulations
- promoting safety awareness among workers
- ensuring required PPE is worn by workers and that workers understand the reason for its use
- inspecting their own and surrounding work areas and taking action to control or eliminate hazards
- ensuring injuries are treated and reported
- investigating all accidents/incidents.

Management responsibilities:
- providing a safe and healthy workplace
- establishing and maintaining a health and safety program
- ensuring workers are trained or certified, as required

- providing workers with safety and health information
- ensuring PPE is available
- supporting supervisors in their safety and health activities
- providing medical and first-aid facilities
- evaluating safety performance of supervisors
- reporting accidents/incidents and occupational illnesses to appropriate authorities.

DESIGNATED SAFETY REPRESENTATIVE

Although the project manager is ultimately responsible for ensuring that an effective job site safety program is in place, it may be necessary to appoint a knowledgeable individual to provide the project manager with technical support and assist in the responsibility of overseeing the implementation of the safety program. This individual is the *designated safety representative* (project safety manager). Supervisors, including foremen, must understand that even though a project safety manager is included in the project staff, the supervisor will still be held accountable for his or her own safety-related decisions and the performance of his or her respective subordinates. Workers must also be made to understand that they are expected to look out for their own safety and adhere to the safety rules.

It is the role of the designated safety representative to bring safety issues and concerns to management's attention and to guide supervisors and workers in the implementation of their respective safety responsibilities. The designated safety representative is not the safety program but is the technical safety support for the project.

Competence Commensurate with Responsibilities

We often mistakenly assume that individuals who have been conferred the status of craftsman, supervisor, or manager—by virtue of the excellence of their technical knowledge—should also be able to recognize safety hazards associated with their work.

Our second mistake is to assume that those individuals who are able to recognize hazards will include safety considerations to mitigate those hazards in their work planning, thereby eliminating or controlling the hazards associated with their work. Although some aspects of safety are intuitive, the ability to recognize hazards and to develop means by which to control the hazards must be learned by most individuals. They must also understand that the owner is willing to pay them for the additional time the supervisor perceives that it will take to incorporate the necessary safety controls into the performance of their work.

We must make sure that supervisors to whom we delegate work understand their safety responsibility and are competent and have the technical background and experience to fulfill this responsibility. We must also make sure that they make similar assurances regarding the training and safety awareness of the individuals to whom they, in turn, assign work. Even when owners contract with general contractors with national name recognition, they must make a concerted effort to ensure that the specific individuals who will be working on the project can demonstrate that they are committed to safety and that this is reflected in their past track record.

Competent Person

A *competent person* is defined as an individual, who, as the result of training and/or experience:
- is capable of identifying or predicting hazardous situations
- has the authority and responsibility to take prompt corrective measures to eliminate them
- takes action to implement corrective measures that have been determined to be necessary to control a recognized hazard.

The fact that regulators have felt the need to define a requirement for a competent person classification suggests that in many cases, individuals assigned supervisory and oversight responsibility do not effectively identify and control known hazards. *Competence* in this context is about action, not certification. The following is a listing of some activities, operations, and health areas in which 29 CFR 1926 and various ANSI standards require that competent persons be designated.

Competent person categories:
- excavation
- scaffolds
- fall protection
- cranes and derricks
- hazardous chemicals
- underground construction
- ionizing radiation
- flammable liquids
- painting
- lead
- slings
- ladders

- material handling
- hearing protection
- powder-activated devices
- helicopters
- respiratory protection
- shipyards
- telecommunication systems
- blasting agents.

REINFORCEMENT (DISCIPLINE)

Consequences control behavior and behavior is based on work direction and work conditions. A mechanism must be in place to address situations where the violations of safety principles occur. It is accepted practice in construction that once training, guidance, and encouragement have been exhausted, discipline is the remaining recourse to reinforce the application of safe work practices. The expectation of safety compliance should be defined in the contract, as should the repercussions of failing to do so.

INSPECTIONS

When work is in progress, a regular evaluation of the job site conditions must be conducted to verify that workplace hazards are being identified and controlled and that safe work practices are being followed. Traditionally, safety representatives and supervisors conduct safety inspections.

Current safety legislation requires workplace inspections be conducted on a "frequent and regular basis" by a competent person to ensure workplace safety. The frequency of planned formal inspections must be defined by each organization, based on the rate of change of physical conditions on the job site, their record of compliance with safe work practices, and the frequency of accidents/incidents and injuries. Participation in formal inspections should be part of every supervisor's and manager's job description. They should include contracted work activities during their inspections.

The safety program and plan should answer these questions:
- Who should conduct inspections?
- When should inspections be conducted?
- What is the focus of the inspections?
- Who should receive the reports?
- How should deficiencies be addressed?
- What records should be kept?

A process should be established to collect the results of all these observations, electronically if possible, because this allows for rapid analysis of the information in order to identify if there are any areas of greater-than-expected incidents.

TRAINING

Training should be an integral part of all safety programs. Only through regular communication of hazards, control measures, and safe work practices can the incidence rate of work injuries be systematically reduced. The most frequent incident root cause and most frequently issued OSHA citation following workplace accident/incident investigations involves deficiencies in employer training programs. To perform their work safely, workers must be trained. For the training to be effective, each task must be thoroughly analyzed and safe work procedures developed and communicated to the workforce.

According to the Business Round Table, approximately 250,000 new workers join the construction workforce each year. About 80% are nonunion and do not have the benefit of formal construction trade training or safety training. This is a significant concern given the increasing sophistication and complexity in construction. The unfortunate result is the very high fatality and injury rate being experienced by construction workers. There must be a process in place to ensure that individuals coming to the job site are aware of project-specific safety issues and are trained to handle them.

As a point of reference between 29 CFR 1910 and 29 CFR 1926, there are 192 nonoverlapping requirements for the provision of training. A single employer will not perform all the activities that require training. However, there are a significant number of requirements for training, and employers should be aware of this and have a process in place to address the needs of the workers. OSHA has placed the burden on employers to provide their employees with safety training. There is no guidance regarding the frequency of training other than when employees are observed not following established procedures; then training or retraining is required.

The host employer should ensure that individuals coming to its facility to perform work are familiar with, at the very least, site-specific safety issues and their controls. Owners should include in their contract specifications that contractors only employ trained and qualified tradesmen on the projects. The host employer should also define an expectation that each subcontractor employee be briefed by the respective supervisors on the work to be performed that day and be given the opportunity to address specific safety issues that may surface as the work evolves.

Safety Orientations

Job site safety orientations provide a forum for the host employer to convey its commitment to providing a safe working environment. The orientation is an opportunity to point out site-specific information regarding the facility safety hazards, and it is an opportunity to remind workers of their responsibility to give due consideration to safety while performing their work. Even the most seasoned workers and supervisors need to become familiar with job site layouts, project management personnel, company policies, and other information related to an unfamiliar project. It is an opportunity to remind workers to bring hazards they might create to the attention of their supervisors so other individuals who might be affected by them can be advised.

Safety awareness and hazard communication training should be conducted before any individual is permitted to begin work on or visit an unfamiliar site. Statistically, the majority of injuries occur to employees who are not familiar with site-specific safety expectations and those individuals who are not familiar with the job-related hazards. Approximately 50% of construction industry deaths occur to individuals who have been on a job site less than 30 days. Accident/incident frequency decreases with increased experience and greater safety awareness. The awareness of safety issues can be accelerated through safety and health training.

Orientations must be conducted with sufficient frequency to enable contractors to get their personnel trained and onto the job site; otherwise, they may find a way to circumvent the process. Visitors and contractors delivering materials do not necessarily need the same course detail required by a specialty contractor as long as they are accompanied by a qualified person while on the job site.

The contents of site orientations should include, as a minimum:

- introduction to the job site
- site rules and regulations
- site-specific hazards
- requirements for PPE
- fire protection system and emergency procedures
- first-aid and treatment program
- immediate reporting of injuries
- permit requirements
- disciplinary program
- introduction to key project personnel.

The message that must be reinforced is the fact that working safely is the corporate objective. *No one has authority or permission to work unsafely or to take shortcuts that place him or her or the project at risk.*

Generally, a single safety training session is not sufficient to convey all the requisite information needed in construction and to maintain a heightened sense of safety awareness. To reinforce what has been addressed at the site, regularly scheduled safety orientation follow-up training is required.

Pre-Work Meeting

A pre-work meeting provides an opportunity for the supervisor to speak with each employee to determine if he or she is prepared to work that day. The supervisor has the opportunity to observe each worker's behavior and to judge if alcohol, drugs, or some preoccupation impairs him or her. Workers who are unfit for work are a danger to themselves and to the rest of the work crew. The supervisor should document the main points addressed at the pre-work meeting in the daily log. Work practices will improve to the extent individuals are provided with feedback on what is expected of them.

Weekly Toolbox Talks

Weekly toolbox talks provide the opportunity to reinforce the company's safety policy, note changes in safety procedures, review lessons learned from accidents/incidents that may have occurred within the company at other sites, address safety topics of a general nature, or discuss the development of JSAs for upcoming work.

INCIDENT REPORTING AND INVESTIGATIONS

Accidents and incidents must be investigated so that measures can be identified to prevent a recurrence of similar events. Although investigations represent an "after-the-fact" response, a thorough investigation may uncover hazards or problems that can be eliminated to prevent the occurrence of future incidents.

HOUSEKEEPING

Slips, trips, and falls are the leading cause of injuries on construction work sites. Litter and debris conceal tripping hazards and increase the possibility of other injuries. As a general rule, a site with poor housekeeping practices also has a poor safety record. Debris on a site also creates extra work because it frequently needs to be relocated for worksite access. However, as with any other objective, there must be regular reinforcement of the importance of this requirement.

SUBSTANCE ABUSE PROGRAM

The Center for the Protection of Worker's Rights has determined that in some regions of the United States, up to 30% of construction workers report to work under the influence of some behavior-modifying substance.

Substance abuse is widespread throughout the United Sates. A study conducted by the Institute for Health Policy at Brandeis University found substance abuse to be the foremost health problem in the United States, resulting in more deaths, illnesses, and disabilities than any other preventable health condition. Companies that screen job applicants report that a high percentage of candidates initially test positively; as word spreads of the company's requirements, this number reduces to between 5% and 8% of applicants. In many cases (and sometimes, mandated by law), workplace drug and alcohol testing programs are used to identify at risk individuals.

Workplace Drug Testing

There are several approaches to workplace testing:

- preemployment testing (from the site owner's perspective, this is following the site safety orientation and before the individual begins to perform work on behalf of a subcontractor)
- postaccident or for-cause testing
- scheduled testing (during employee medicals)
- random testing.

It is imperative that organizations implementing a drug-free workplace program have written policies and procedures in place. A lawyer experienced in labor and contract matters should review the procedures and help design a program that complies with state laws and meets the specific needs of the employer.

EMERGENCY PROCEDURES

Emergency procedures are plans for dealing with emergencies such as major injuries, fires, explosions, releases of hazardous materials, violent occurrences, or natural hazards. When such events occur, the urgent need for rapid decisions in a short time can lead to chaos if there is a lack of resources and trained personnel to deal with the situation. At a minimum, procedures for prompt medical response must be established. OSHA expects that any employee should receive medical response within 3 to 4 minutes. This requires that at a minimum, there must be someone on each work crew or shift with first-aid and CPR training.

The objective of the emergency plan is to prevent or minimize fatalities, injuries, and damage. The organization and procedures for handling these sudden and unexpected situations must be clearly defined. The process of establishing an emergency plan is not all that complex and is strongly advocated by individuals and organizations that have been caught without one. However, few organizations have established emergency procedures or a crisis management plan.

To develop a set of emergency procedures, compile a list of the hazards (e.g., fires, explosions, earthquakes, and floods). Identify the possible major consequences of each (casualties, damage to equipment, or impact on the public). Determine the required countermeasures (which might include evacuation, rescue, fire fighting, etc.). Inventory the resources needed to carry out the planned actions (e.g., medical supplies, rescue equipment, and trained personnel). Based on these considerations, establish the necessary emergency organization and procedures. Communication, training, and periodic drills are required to ensure adequate performance when the plan must be implemented in response to an emergency situation.

INTEGRATING SAFETY INTO THE CONSTRUCTION PROCESS

WORK—CONSTRUCTION PHASE

When the contractor's employees initially report to work at the job site, they should be briefed on the site rules and regulations, the general hazards, and any special emergency response requirements specific to that worksite before they begin work. Workers need to be aware of the hazards peculiar to the site. Increasingly, site hosts are communicating this information to contractors themselves to ensure it is done to their satisfaction.

Specific Worksite Safety Briefing

Where appropriate, contractors should be briefed on facility-specific work practices and requirements such as lockout/tagout or work entry permit requirements. At this time, the contractor should inform the workers of the specific individuals who will approve permitted work and how they should be contacted. They should be briefed on all site-specific safety hazards and applicable emergency response requirements.

Job-Specific Training

Contractors review the job safety analysis they prepared for their specific job with their respective employees prior to the start of work. Specific training must be provided to address hazards identified in the JSA. Contractor employees should sign the JSA to indicate they have read or been briefed on the information contained in the JSA and understand it. The JSA should be available for the field engineer's review and for the reference of the workers.

Inspections and Audits

Both the contractor and the host employer should conduct regular inspections of the work place to ensure that housekeeping is being kept up and that no new hazards are being created by the work in progress. Audits to evaluate how effective the safety program and plan are being implemented should be conducted by a third party, with reports being provided to the owner and contractors. Specific actions and a timetable should be established for correction of hazards identified during inspections and audits.

ROLES AND RESPONSIBILITIES

THE CLIENT

Clients must clearly define their safety expectations to the project designers and construction manager, just as required quality standards and the scheduled date of completion of the project are defined. The client must regularly reinforce its commitment to safety by addressing the subject at meetings and when following up on design issues so everyone involved in the project realizes the client is serious about its commitment to safety.

CONSTRUCTION MANAGER

The construction manager retained to act on the owner's behalf to manage the development and construction of a project is also responsible for the safe execution of the work. The owner should unambiguously define the construction manager's responsibility and authority for safety. The owner should hold the construction manager accountable for developing requisite protocols and monitoring the safety program implementation.

GENERAL CONTRACTOR

General contractors are responsible for defining the safety practices for the means and methods to be implemented in the execution of the work for which they are responsible and to ensure that their subcontractors implement those practices.

The general contractor must ensure that his or her subcontractors are aware of the site safety requirements and the standards against which their performance will be measured. The general contractor should review and agree to the manner in which the subcontractors will perform their work as defined in the subcontractors' site-specific safety plan and the job safety analysis produced by the subcontractors for each phase of the work they are expected to perform.

Neither the client nor the construction manager should delegate the decision regarding the standards to be met to the general contractors. Doing so will result in a broad disparity in the implementation of the safety program, eventual discord, and circumvention of safe work practices.

SUBCONTRACTORS

Subcontractors are expected to supply the labor and tools to complete the work as scheduled and within defined specifications. They are responsible for ensuring that the individuals they bring to work are technically and physically capable of performing the work assigned to them. They are also responsible for ensuring that the individuals they bring to work have the required equipment and personal protective equipment to perform their work safely.

To be assured that this is the case, subcontractors should be required to produce a safety plan that includes JSAs for each phase of their work. Where their work creates hazards (such as the release of toxic fumes, excessive noise, radiation, etc.), these will be documented and be apparent to the general contractor reviewing the JSA. The JSA will define how employees will be protected from the hazards and the means by which the subcontractor proposes to alert others who might be exposed to those hazards.

CRAFTSMEN

Last in the hierarchical chain are the craftsmen. They are expected to apply themselves and the tools of their trade to produce work of a defined standard. They are expected to perform their work in an informed and safe manner by complying with accepted safe work practices as defined and communicated by the owner, construction manager, general contractor, and their immediate employer.

Craftsmen are responsible for their own safety in regard to the work they are performing. They must understand that it is their responsibility to ensure that their tools are in safe working condition and that they have the knowledge to perform the work safely. The craftsmen must inspect their own equipment (such as ladders and scaffolds) regularly for obvious defects. They must be aware of site-specific requirements, such as work entry permits or whether the site host insists on placing the first lock on lockouts/tagouts. This information will be included in the subcontractor safety plan and will be available through review of the JSA specific to the work that the craftsmen are to perform.

INSURANCE

Construction insurance is a major project-related cost, following materials and labor. A study conducted by Stanford University, on behalf of the Business Round Table, concluded that insurance premiums on typical industrial projects cost 7% of direct labor costs for workers' compensation insurance and another 1% for builders' risk and liability insurance. Because labor can represent about one-third of the total project cost, insurance represents a measurable portion of total project cost (Samelson and Levitt, 1982). Owners or contractors who are able to transfer responsibility for loss exposures to another and have that other entity pay for the insurance to cover that responsibility are able to substantially reduce their own loss-related costs.

While some risk managers would advocate the transfer of risk and support insurance as the sole solution to loss control, this does not of itself eliminate the hazards or moderate unsafe work practices that are the source of the majority of losses. The transfer of risk does not eliminate the potential of being involved in litigation or having to defend a third-party lawsuit. The selection of insurance coverage and determination of limits should be a risk-based decision to protect the project and project-related assets from losses that could disrupt the project schedule and its timely completion or, more fundamentally, the operational viability of the enterprise. Insurance should not be considered to be an alternative to a safety program. Insurance provides risk financing support both for project-related issues and impacts to workers (workers' compensation).

EXPERIENCE MODIFICATION RATE

The National Council on Compensation Insurance (NCCI) formulates the experience modification rate (EMR). This organization compiles workers' compensation payroll and injury data from approximately 600 insurance carriers. Contractors that have reached a minimum premium threshold size in their particular state are rated and receive a new experience modification rate each year. The calculation of this rate is based on each contractor's payroll and injury data, actuarial factors, weights, and ballasts. The resulting EMR for each contractor is sent to the contractor's insurance carrier by the NCCI. This information is used by the carrier to calculate the contractor's annual workers' compensation insurance premiums. Therefore, the EMR is an unbiased means of judging the relative effectiveness of a contractor's safety program and the rate at which it experiences injuries.

The EMR is a reflection of an employer's safety performance as compared with the average contractor in a specific specialty. An experience modifier of 1.00 is average. The EMR is the value by which an insurance carrier's base rate is multiplied to determine the insurance premiums paid by its client, the contractor. An employer with above-average losses is assessed a modifier higher than 1.00; conversely, employers with fewer than average losses will have an EMR of less than 1.00.

The EMR formula is designed to account for statistical variations in the size of employers. An employer with a large number of employees will usually have accident/incident claims that result in a fairly even distribution of both the number and severity of claims. In the case of small employers, frequency and severity are adjusted to minimize the unpredictability. With smaller employers, primary weight is given to frequency and secondary emphasis to severity. As the size of the employer increases, statistical variations decrease and the experience modification formula reduces to the simple ratio of actual to expected losses.

EMRs generally vary between 0.20 and 2.60. A contractor with an EMR of 2.60 pays 2.6 times more in workers' compensation insurance premiums than does the contractor with an EMR of 1.00. The greater the contractor's EMR, the greater the proportion of the contractor's bid that is being allocated to cover insurance costs. It should be obvious who has the competitive advantage. Logically, when a contractor's EMR is higher, proportionally less is being paid for the quality of material and labor to complete the work than would be paid by a contractor with a low EMR. The additional benefit to owners of using contractors with low experience modification rates is the proportional reduction in the number of accidents/incidents that will occur on the job site and the lower probability of being involved in litigation.

CONTRACTOR SELECTION

Construction is an industry that, by its very nature, contains danger if potentially hazardous conditions are not aggressively addressed. Owners can protect workers and themselves—if they are willing to lead the way and confront the risks head-on. Dynamic leadership by individual owners can help reduce injuries, disabilities, and deaths caused by construction accidents/incidents. Project safety will only be as good as that of the poorest performer on the job site. Selecting contractors with a demonstrated record of safe performance is perhaps the most effective means of improving the odds of having a safe job site. Both project managers and owners are becoming increasingly aware—as they experience the ever-increasing rise in injury claims and accident/incident costs—of the need to be more selective in their choice of contractors. Safety practitioners, owners, and general contractors who regularly use contracted services now advocate the consideration of contractors' past safety performance in their selection criteria.

SELECTION CRITERIA

It has generally been the practice in construction to base the selection of contractors solely on the lowest bid. Consideration of safety in the selection process tends to be the exception rather than the rule. Why this continues to be so is difficult to understand.

OSHA Citation History

Criteria: Absence of a negative trend of OSHA citations.

Another source of information regarding a contractor's past safety performance is the evaluation of his or her OSHA citation history. This information is often neglected out of concern about requesting confidential information. In fact, OSHA inspection records are public record and can be obtained directly from OSHA through the Freedom of Information Act if the prospective bidder is reluctant to provide this information.

Just as the absence of citations does not indicate outstanding safety performance, the presence of citations should not be an automatic basis for rejection. Where there are repeated citations for the same type of violation or regularly occurring citations that span some extended period of time, there may be cause for concern.

If a contractor has been the subject of regular OSHA scrutiny and citations, he or she may not be the right contractor for the job site. The presence of that contractor may motivate OSHA representatives to consider visiting the site more frequently than they might have in the past.

References from Previous Employers

Criteria: Were previous employers satisfied with the contractor's safety performance?

Ask for references. Was the contractor responsive? What problems did he or she experience that might occur if that contractor should come to work with the host employer?

Integration of Safety on Current Jobs

Criteria: Demonstrated effectiveness of integrating safety into current work practices on current jobs.

The most effective means of evaluating a contractor's ability to work safely is to visit a job site where he or she is working to see how he or she performs work. The condition of the work area and how the contractor manages the work will provide some insight into the corporate culture regarding the standard of care a contractor applies to his or her work.

Interview the prospective contractor. Does he or she have a documented safety program? If so, does the program address the hazards to which workers will be exposed, and does the program comply with applicable regulations? Can the contractor/manager produce his or her documented safety program?

Therefore, these criteria should be applied to both the contractor and the performance of the contractor's key personnel, project manager, superintendent, and designated safety representative, who will directly influence the work on the job site. What better means of improving the odds of good safety performance on a project than the selection of organizations and individuals with proven track records?

WORK TO BE DONE

Having established selection criteria and developed the request for bid (RFB) documentation, prospective bidders should be invited to a pre-bid meeting. Prospective bidders should be provided with an opportunity to review the RFB requirements, ask questions, and obtain clarifications as directly as possible. The work to be done should be described in sufficient detail to enable prospective contractors to understand the content of the work required as well as the work environment.

Identified Hazards and Work Restrictions

Unusual hazards and potential restrictions should be brought to the contractor's attention in the RFB and repeated during the pre-bid meeting. It may sometimes be difficult for prospective contractors to get an accurate picture of the scope of work in a particular project by just reading the contract documents. A good way of communicating this information is to include a worksite visit in the "pre-bid meeting" agenda. This provides the prospective bidders with an opportunity to see the job site and ask questions relevant to their bid development. Make sure that all requests for clarification are also submitted in writing. Then provide written answers to all the prospective bidders.

Work Permits and License Requirements

Work permits and licenses required by the site or by local code should be identified. The methods by which they will be issued and controlled should also be addressed. Some areas to be considered are:
- onsite entry and security
- vehicle passes
- confined-space entry
- excavation
- lockout/tagout requirements
- working hot (electrical)
- explosive devices
- hazardous materials handling and transportation
- hazardous-waste disposal
- radiation source management
- environmental permits.

The RFB document should indicate that the successful bidder and his or her subcontractors will be responsible for the enforcement of safe work practices outlined in the permits and licenses, as well as all other site or local code requirements that apply to the work under his or her control.

Contractor Safety Qualification Requirements

Contractor qualifications are those criteria the selection team will use to evaluate the prospective contractors and their bids.

Special Job Site Safety Program Requirements

The job site manager must define all site-specific safety requirements, which might include specific types of tools, restrictions on certain work practices, special lockout procedures, or site-specific fall protection requirements. The contractor and his or her subcontractors should provide detailed documentation that demonstrates that their safety programs meet the job site manager's requirements.

Contract Management Arrangements

The RFB document should define the job site organization hierarchy and the key contact points. Critical questions that should be addressed include the following:

- What is the job site organization structure?
- Who within the host's organization is responsible for contract coordination and administration?
- Who will address safety and health issues?
- What technical support, if any, will be provided?
- How will work delays, challenges, accidents/incidents, and similar events be reported to the job site coordinator?
- What information must the contractor report to the job site coordinator during the life of the contract, and to whom should the reports be made?
- What anticipated hazards will be present on the job site, and how will the host control them?

Orientation and Training Requirements

The RFB should identify specific training requirements that the job site manager feels are necessary for successful completion of the work. The contractor should be required to demonstrate, to the satisfaction of the job site manager, that his or her employees and subcontractors have completed the site orientation and job specific training, as well as any other qualifications specified by the job site manager.

Some host organizations prefer to provide and manage certain orientation and training requirements they feel are particularly important prior to granting contractor employees permission to be on the worksite, rather than relying on the contractor to communicate this information.

Audits of Contractor Performance

The RFB should specify that the job site manager will conduct periodic assessments of the contractor's safety and health program implementation during the contract period. A copy of the audit protocol and performance requirements should be available if the contractor would like to see what would be evaluated. The job site manager should carefully consider the practicality of each type of measurement in consideration of the length and risk level of each individual contract.

Onsite Control of Work

Contractors should be expected to have a process in place to monitor for unsafe work practices. Appropriately trained individuals must do this. Specific requirements are now in place to recognize the individuals who are able to competently inspect specialized work such as excavations and scaffolding. The contractor should be asked to explain the basis upon which these individuals have been determined to be competent to inspect the work. The contractors should also be aware that they will be expected to provide for direct supervision of employees at all times. Ideally, the contractor should provide senior managers, supervisors, and onsite safety coordinators with training in hazard recognition and safety and health management.

Code Compliance Requirements

The RFB documents should identify specific code requirements and relevant regulations, including licensing of individuals and certification of equipment.

Record-Keeping and Reporting Requirements

All records and reports required by the job site manager pertaining to the contractor's safety program should be identified. Such records generally should include:

- weekly personal injury reports and man-hour reports
- records of personnel training
- documentation and follow-up of identified safety problems
- inspection reports
- accident/incident investigation reports
- equipment inspections
- safety meetings.

Standard forms to be used for records and reports may be specified in the RFB; however, the major concern of the job site manager should not be whose form is to be used, but that the critical information on each issue is provided.

Contract Termination/Completion Criteria

The RFB documents should clearly define contract penalties and termination procedures in case of substandard safety performance. The documents should also specify when and how disciplinary measures will be imposed. Consideration should also be given to defining what will be required to make the determination that the contract has been satisfactorily completed.

Preference for contractors with good safety experience will improve the probability of completing a project with a low injury incidence rate and the absence of major mishaps. If the selection of preferred bidders is not an option, then safety should be an integral aspect of the contract technical selection criteria.

ACCIDENT/INCIDENT INVESTIGATION AND REPORTING

Investigations are generally relegated to the contractor to perform. However, the field engineer should participate in the investigation process, even if it is in the role of an observer. This will provide insight into why the incident occurred, help prevent a similar incident from happening again, and ensure that proper documentation is collected for the safety file. The investigation of occurrences (accidents/incidents) is the only way the source of the incident can be determined. Investigations should not be a hunt for the guilty perpetrator, but a determination of why the incident occurred in the first place.

SAFETY PROGRAM DOCUMENTATION AND RETENTION

In today's litigious society, there is little need of a discussion regarding why an organization would wish to retain project-related safety records. The challenge is to determine what should be retained. The corporation may already have guidelines in this regard; otherwise, corporate legal counsel will surely have an opinion. The following are questions to ask:

- What information should be retained?
- Where should it be stored?
- How long should it be retained?
- Who will know where to find it?

Information that will be requested first, in the event that an injury claim is filed against the firm, will be a request for documentation of the safety program and its structure (i.e., program documentation, permit and inspection forms, training syllabuses, safety posters, etc.).

The historical information that relates to the implementation of the program should include information such as the following, which are evidence of the execution of the safety program:

- inspection reports
- weekly site safety audits and progress photos
- safety meeting minutes
- job safety assessments (JSAs)
- toolbox talks and sign-off sheets
- employee orientation outline and attendance records
- approved safety variances
- enforcement/reinforcement documentation
- safety notices.

SAFETY STATISTICS

At the conclusion of a project, there are always close-out meetings and presentations to advise the client how its money was spent and the virtues of the product it is receiving. Safety statistics and related project experience should be an integral part of that information:

- man-hour reports and summaries
- log of summary and occupational illness and injuries
- commendations and citations
- copies of articles that reported on the project's successes.

ACCIDENT/INCIDENT REPORTS AND PERSONAL INJURY INFORMATION

Is there a complete file of all accidents/incidents reported and investigated? These can be filed either by contract or chronologically:

- employer's first report of injury
- supervisor's accident/incident investigation report
- project accident/incident investigation reports
- all other claim-supporting documentation.

SUMMARY

- This chapter addresses how to plan and manage contractor safety in order to improve the odds of having an injury-free workplace. Managing safety can be learned. While some people seem to intuitively know how to motivate people to work safely, most effective managers learn this skill. Skillful safety management involves knowing what is to be done, who is to do it, and when and how it should be done. This chapter addresses many of these factors and provides a description of how to implement an effective safety program.

- The program elements addressed in this chapter apply to both large and small projects, from conceptual design to completion of the work. Large or complicated projects offer more opportunity to overlook critical aspects than do small projects, but small projects still require the application of the same fundamental safety tenants. In either case, the individuals planning and coordinating contracted work must pay attention to the factors discussed in this chapter, if they are to have a project free of injuries.

- In many cases, the consequences of inept safety management are not terribly significant. The workforce on a small project may experience scraped knuckles or perhaps a lost day of work. It may be the assumption of the project manager that things just happen and "after all, people do get hurt in construction." But if the circumstances leading up to a potentially minor incident are complicated with a few more factors, the occurrence may result in significant consequences. Instead of a scraped knuckle, the worker could lose fingers. Instead of a simple slip and fall near a leading edge, the worker might go over the edge if adequate physical controls and safe work procedures are not in place.

REVIEW QUESTIONS

1. The primary factor in the success of an effective safety program depends on _____ and its involvement in the safety program.
   a. the union
   b. insurance agent
   c. management
   d. craft steward

2. _____ ultimately pay(s) the cost of the safety program on a job site.
   a. Owners
   b. Insurance companies
   c. Government
   d. Employees

3. Monitoring day-to-day activities of construction trades and contract compliance is an essential function of the _____.
   a. union
   b. government
   c. owner
   d. insurance company

4. It is the role of the _____ to clearly establish responsibility for safety down through the organizational hierarchy.
   a. owner
   b. union
   c. contractor
   d. government

5. A successful safety plan must address the following:
   a. site-specific hazards
   b. safety expectations
   c. safety roles and responsibilities
   d. all of the above

6. To ensure a clear understanding of the owner's safety expectations, they should be documented in the _____.
   a. project safety plan
   b. insurance policy
   c. union contract
   d. subcontracts

7. A means of systematically identifying and evaluating safety issues associated with a work task is a _____.
   a. site audit
   b. daily inspection
   c. job safety analysis
   d. crew briefing

8. A JSA should be developed for all critical tasks with priority given to addressing tasks:
   a. where frequent accidents/incidents and injuries occur
   b. where severe accidents/incidents and injuries occur
   c. that are infrequently performed
   d. all of the above

9. For a safety program to be successful, who must recognize that they each have a role in the safety process?
   a. management
   b. supervisors
   c. workers
   d. all of the above

10. Workers are responsible for which of the following?
    a. knowing and complying with safety regulations
    b. following safe work procedures
    c. correcting or reporting unsafe work practices and unsafe conditions
    d. all of the above

11. It is the role of the designated safety representative to:
    a. bring safety issues and concerns to management's attention
    b. guide workers in the implementation of their respective safety responsibilities
    c. guide supervisors in the implementation of their respective safety responsibilities
    d. all of the above

12. A *competent person* is defined as an individual, who, as the result of training and/or experience:
    a. is capable of identifying or predicting hazardous situations
    b. has the authority and responsibility to take prompt corrective measures to eliminate them
    c. takes action to implement corrective measures that have been determined to be necessary to control a recognized hazard
    d. all of the above

12

Basics of Industrial Hygiene

LEARNING OBJECTIVES

- ❏ List and discuss the four definitive elements of industrial hygiene.

- ❏ Compare and contrast chemical, physical, biological, and ergonomic hazards based on potential adverse effects to an exposed individual.

- ❏ Identify the different routes of exposure for toxic materials based on industrial hygiene assessments.

- ❏ Understand the hierarchy of controls and how it applies to industrial hygiene exposures.

- ❏ Compare and contrast the use of in-house industrial hygiene services and use of a consultant to do the same work.

INTRODUCTION

Industrial hygiene, as defined by the American Industrial Hygiene Association (AIHA), is a science and art devoted to the anticipation, recognition, evaluation, prevention, and control of those environmental factors or stresses arising in or from the workplace that may cause sickness, impaired health and well-being, or significant discomfort among workers or among citizens of the community.

Industrial hygienists are occupational safety and health professionals concerned with the control of environmental stresses or occupational health hazards that arise as a result of or during the course of work. The industrial hygienist recognizes that occupational health hazards may endanger life and health, accelerate the aging process, or cause significant discomfort. Working with management, medical, safety, and engineering personnel, the industrial hygienist can help to eliminate or safeguard against environmental conditions caused by chemical, physical, biological, or ergonomic stresses. This chapter covers the following topics:

- the nature, purpose, and scope of industrial hygiene
- the role of the industrial hygienist in recognizing and controlling environmental hazards
- four general categories of environmental conditions or stresses
- three definitive elements of industrial hygiene practices
- health and psychological problems associated with altered environments
- the inherent medical and physiological issues involved in shiftwork
- toxicity and hazards in the workplace.

Industrial hygiene includes the development of corrective measures to control health hazards by either reducing or eliminating the exposure. These control measures may include substituting safer materials for harmful or toxic ones, changing work processes to eliminate or minimize work exposure, installing exhaust ventilation systems, practicing good housekeeping (including appropriate waste disposal methods), and providing proper personal protective equipment.

The five factors necessary to ensure an effective industrial hygiene program are (1) anticipation and recognition of health hazards arising from work operations and processes; (2) evaluation and measurement of the magnitude of the hazard (based on past experience and study); (3) control of the hazard; (4) commitment and support of management because effective controls can be expensive and the need for these controls must be made clear within company management; and, perhaps most important, (5) recognition of the industrial hygienist—by the workers within the facility—as reliable, believable, and honest, so that recommendations for changes in work practices are diligently implemented and assurances that conditions are acceptable are indeed believed.

Various reporting structures are used for entities with an in-house industrial hygiene function. Depending on the company, the industrial hygiene function can be found reporting through human resources, risk management, medical, environmental, engineering/facilities maintenance, safety, or security. In today's world of complex regulatory requirements and the need to minimize costs, the industrial hygienist is often found with collateral responsibilities and spends part of his or her time dealing with environmental and/or safety issues.

For many small and mid-sized companies, a full-time industrial hygienist cannot be justified economically. In these cases, a consulting agreement with a qualified local consulting firm or individual consultant can be the most appropriate way for the company to obtain essential services. Ordinarily, the consultant reports to the safety director of the company. There are numerous qualified industrial hygienists who act as consultants, and many companies are taking this approach, as described in the following section. Also, insurance companies and the consulting services offered by OSHA should not be overlooked. Insurance companies (usually the workers' compensation carrier) have a vested interest in improving the workplace environment and reducing the potential for occupational illness.

INDUSTRIAL HYGIENIST ON THE OCCUPATIONAL HEALTH AND SAFETY TEAM

The commitment to the protection of employee health and the industrial hygiene program should be incorporated into the overall safety policy from the company's management. The industrial hygienist specializes in anticipating, recognizing, evaluating, and controlling health hazards. The industrial hygienist is principally responsible for control of chemical, physical, biological, or ergonomic stresses. In larger and more complex organizations, the control of radiation rests with the radiation specialist or the health physicist. As the need for control of biological stresses (especially for indoor air quality—such as prevention of Legionnaires' disease or mold-related disorders) has become more widely recognized, many industrial hygienists have this responsibility as well. Depending on their expertise, industrial hygienists may also be responsible for ergonomics. Industrial hygienists maintain lists of chemical, physical, and biological agents found within the facility; evaluate exposures to those agents; and institute controls to ensure that exposures to those agents are within acceptable limits.

IN-HOUSE INDUSTRIAL HYGIENE SERVICES

The industrial hygienist must have a good working relationship with the engineering department. Many of the most effective exposure controls involve the industrial hygienist providing input during the design phase of planned construction or renovation projects. Additionally, any hazards identified by the industrial hygienist requiring engineering controls or process modifications to existing facilities will require working collaboratively with the engineering department. Two of the most important departments for the industrial hygienist are the safety and medical departments. The environmental staff—those responsible for control of emissions outside the facility—should also be part of the industrial hygienist's internal network. Controls to reduce exposures within the facility can lead to increased emissions; a unified approach to reducing exposures is essential.

OCCUPATIONAL HEALTH AND SAFETY TEAM

The chief goal of a facility's occupational health and safety program is to prevent occupational injury and illness by anticipating, recognizing, evaluating, and controlling occupational health and safety hazards. The medical, industrial hygiene, and safety programs may have distinct program goals, but all programs must interact with all components of the overall health and safety program. The occupational health and safety team consists of the industrial hygienist, the safety professional, the occupational health nurse, the occupational physician, the employees, senior and line management, and others depending on the size and character of the particular facility. Frequently, information provided by the medical component on possible causes of symptoms can be important in developing effective evaluation and sampling strategies. Support of senior management can demonstrate to workers that healthy and safe environments are company priorities. Line management and workers can provide valuable information on details of production processes that can be examined during industrial hygiene evaluation. All team members must act in harmony to provide information and activities, supporting the other parts to achieve the overall goal of a safe and healthy work environment. Therefore, the separate functions must be administratively linked in order to create a successful and effective program.

Serious commitment to the protection of employee health and the industrial hygiene program is demonstrated when management is visibly involved in the program and all personnel are in compliance with health and safety practices. Equally critical is the assignment of authority, as well as responsibility, to carry out the health and safety program. The health and safety function must be given the same level of importance and accountability as the production function.

PRACTICING INDUSTRIAL HYGIENE

The four definitive elements of industrial hygiene are anticipating, recognizing, evaluating, and controlling occupational hazards. Anticipating health hazards before they occur allows a more efficient use of resources by minimizing costly retrofits and renovations needed to protect the health of workers. An unrecognized health hazard cannot be evaluated or controlled. Upon recognizing a health hazard, the industrial hygienist should be able to identify the set of measures necessary for proper evaluation. When the evaluation is complete, the industrial hygienist, in consultation with other members of the occupational health team, can implement controls needed to reduce exposures to tolerable limits. Reduction of exposures should follow the following hierarchy of control:

- elimination or substitution of the hazard
- engineering controls to reduce exposure
- administrative controls to minimize exposure
- personal protective equipment (PPE).

ANTICIPATING AND RECOGNIZING OCCUPATIONAL HEALTH HAZARDS

The first steps in the process leading to the evaluation and control of exposure to harmful materials and processes are anticipating and recognizing potential occupational hazards. Such identification can be based on general knowledge of the characteristics of materials and processes, on clinical findings that disease or discomfort is present in the exposed population, on reports from others in scientific literature, on bulletins from trade associations or governmental agencies, on conversations with peers, or on reports by workers.

Very important to the process of anticipating and recognizing occupational health hazards is the ability to identify and analyze the impacts of the individual parts of a multifaceted process. To achieve this goal, a competent industrial hygienist uses a trained power of observation coupled with a fundamental knowledge of communication processes, sciences, statistics, mathematics, engineering and industrial processes, business, and psychology. This process can include the following:

- review of plans for new facilities and renovations
- conversations with workers on perceived problems
- review of historical records
- discussions with medical personnel
- observation of work practices
- review use of chemical, physical, and biological agents
- apparent effectiveness of control measures
- production and process review.

The outcome or final product of the recognition phase should be a written industrial hygiene assessment or preliminary survey that identifies the variables observed, such as the occupations, number of employees working the various occupations, raw materials, products, by-products/washes, potential contaminants/hazards, representative production levels, worst-case scenarios, and controls available. In addition to the assessment, process flow diagrams and general arrangement drawings/sketches of the workplace should be obtained.

Based on the initial assessment, the industrial hygiene exposure monitoring/ sampling plan for the workplace should be developed and implemented. The initial or baseline exposure results will, in turn, dictate the frequency of future periodic evaluations and the types of controls necessary.

A health hazard does not exist in isolation from the workplace. A chemical, physical, biological, or ergonomic stress is necessarily a concern only if workers can be exposed. The industrial hygienist must use all of his or her knowledge, experience, and resources to evaluate the workplace. In addition, discussions with workers and managers are extremely helpful in evaluating the potential for exposure.

EVALUATING AND CONTROLLING ENVIRONMENTAL HAZARDS

The various environmental factors or stresses that can cause sickness, impaired health, or significant discomfort in workers can generally be classified as chemical, physical, biological, or ergonomic in nature.

Chemical Hazards

Exposure to a variety of chemical substances occurs both on and off the job, and most do not present a hazard under ordinary conditions; all, however, have the potential for being harmful at some concentration and level of exposure. Chemicals pose a wide range of potential health hazards (such as irritation, disease, sensitization, and carcinogenicity) and physical hazards (such as flammability, corrosion, and reactivity).

Chemical hazards can be found in the following basic forms:

- *Dusts*—particles generated from solid organic or inorganic materials by reducing their size through either mechanical or natural processes
- *Liquids*—aqueous substances that flow freely, like water
- *Fumes*—aerosolized particles formed when a volatilized solid, such as a metal, condenses in cool air
- *Mists*—finely dispersed liquids suspended in the air
- *Gases*—formless fluids that can be changed to the liquid or solid state only by the combined effect of increased pressure and decreased temperature
- *Vapors*—the gaseous form of substances that are normally in the solid or

liquid state at standard temperature and pressure

- *Smoke*—carbon or soot particles produced from the incomplete breakdown of carbon-containing materials.

When chemical stresses are encountered in the workplace, a hazard evaluation should be conducted to identify potential health impacts. The most effective worksite evaluation includes all pertinent operations and work activities. The industrial hygienist inspects, researches, or analyzes how the particular chemical hazards at a worksite could affect the worker. To determine the extent of a worker's exposure, the industrial hygienists may review Safety Data Sheets (SDSs), formerly known as Material Safety Data Sheets (MSDSs), and/or conduct environmental monitoring and use applicable analytical methods. Airborne concentration, type and length of exposure, and regulatory and consensus exposure limits (both short- and long-term limits) may be some of the issues affecting the evaluation.

If the chemical exposure evaluation indicates potentially hazardous conditions affecting employee health, the industrial hygienist then recommends appropriate corrective actions. Substitution with less hazardous materials is one of the most effective ways of eliminating or reducing exposure to chemicals that are toxic or pose other hazards. If substitution is used, one should be careful not to generate a more hazardous situation with the substitute. Engineering controls (ventilation, isolation, enclosure), work practices (procedures, good housekeeping), administrative controls (worker rotation), and other methods (personal protective equipment) can also be used to control potential health hazards.

Physical Hazards

Physical hazards include excessive levels of ionizing and nonionizing radiation, noise, vibration, and extremes of temperature.

Ionizing and Nonionizing Radiation. Evaluation and recommendation of controls for ionizing and nonionizing radiation require an industrial hygienist with specialized training and education. These areas are covered extensively in Chapter 14, Laboratory Safety, and in the sixth edition of *NSC's Fundamentals of Industrial Hygiene* (Plog, 2012).

Noise. Noise is one of the most commonly encountered occupational health hazards. If a noise problem is suspected, then a noise assessment or survey should be performed to determine source(s) of noise, amount, exposure population, and duration of exposure. With proper instrumentation, monitoring noise levels is a relatively straightforward operation for an experienced industrial hygienist.

To prevent adverse outcomes from excessive noise exposure, noise levels should be reduced to acceptable levels. After evaluating the workplace, an industrial hygienist can help develop a hearing-protection strategy by recommending engineering and administrative controls and the use of personal protective equipment (PPE) where needed.

A variety of control techniques are documented in the literature to reduce overall worker exposure to noise. Controls to reduce the amount of sound energy released by the noise source, divert the flow of sound energy away from the receiver, or protect the receiver from the sound energy reaching him or her are frequently used. Types of noise controls include proper maintenance of equipment, revised operating procedures, equipment replacements, acoustical shields and barriers, equipment redesign, enclosures, and administrative controls (NIOSH No. 79-117, 1979). In cases where engineering and administrative controls cannot adequately control the problem, personal hearing protection can be used (see Chapter 13, Personal Protective Equipment (PPE)). As always, personal protection should be considered as an interim measure while other means of reducing workplace noise to within acceptable limits are explored and implemented.

Vibration. Vibration exposure occurs in many occupations where a worker comes in contact with vibrating machinery or equipment. Significant exposure to vibration could occur from either stationary or portable equipment. The industrial hygiene evaluation should look at the following risk factors: intensity and frequency of the vibration, the duration (time) of exposure, and the part(s) of the body receiving the vibration energy. The evaluation is typically described in terms of frequency, amplitude, and acceleration.

- *Frequency*—The number of cycles that a vibrating object completes in one second. The unit of frequency is hertz (Hz). One hertz equals one cycle per second.
- *Amplitude*—The distance from the stationary position to the extreme position of oscillation. The intensity of vibration depends on amplitude.
- *Acceleration*—A measure of how quickly the speed of a vibrating object changes with time.

Vibration exposure occurs through contact with a vibrating mechanism that transfers vibration energy to a person's body. The effect of vibration exposure also depends on the frequency of vibration. Each organ of the body has its own resonant frequency (tendency to vibrate at one particular frequency depending on the makeup, size, and structure of the organ). If exposure occurs at or near any of these resonant frequencies, the resulting effect is greatly increased.

Adverse effects from vibration exposure can be reduced through engineering controls (isolate the vibrating source), appropriate tool selection (antivibration and/or vibration-damped), use of appropriate vibration-absorbing materials (gloves and shoes), good work practices, administrative controls (limited contact time), and education programs.

Temperature. Both very cold and very hot temperatures can be encountered in numerous occupational settings and are frequently evaluated by industrial hygienists. Excessive exposure to heat is referred to as *heat stress*, and excessive exposure to cold is referred to as *cold stress*. An evaluation of temperature extremes includes an examination of environmental conditions, worker behavior, medical records, and body indices.

An industrial hygienist conducts temperature-stress evaluations on operations involving high and low air temperatures, radiant heat sources, high humidity, or direct physical contact with hot and cold objects. Strenuous physical activities or outdoor operations conducted in hot or cold weather extremes may also require evaluations.

Two types of exposure limits are often used as guidelines for an evaluation: occupational exposure and thermal comfort. *Occupational exposure limits* are designed to protect industrial workers from temperature-related illness. *Thermal comfort limits* are used to ensure productivity and quality of work for office workers. An industrial hygienist uses portable heat-stress instruments to measure thermal conditions (temperature, humidity, air velocity). These measurements are used to calculate the wet-bulb globe temperature (WBGT) and effective temperature (ET) indexes, two common heat-stress indices.

Protective measures to control exposure to temperature extremes include training (knowledge of the hazards of thermal stress), fluid replacement when warranted, medical surveillance, engineering controls (ventilation, air cooling or heating, fans, shielding, and insulation), administrative controls (acclimation, scheduling, and reducing time of exposure via work/rest regimens), and specialized personal protection. Each method of control should be specific to the type and degree of hazard.

It is possible to acclimate workers to heat stress. Short leaves of absence from a job where acclimation has occurred for heat stress can result in a complete loss of that acclimation. Workers do not acclimate to cold stress conditions.

Biological Hazards

Biological agents include, but are not limited to, bacteria, fungi, and viruses. These agents can present a hazard resulting in health effects ranging from skin irritation and allergies, to infections and life-threatening diseases. One of the more recognized categories of these agents is bloodborne pathogens. Examples of these agents include hepatitis B (HBV), hepatitis C (HCV) and the human immunodeficiency virus (HIV). Biological agents can affect workers in a wide variety of settings that would include microbiology, public health, clinical, and molecular biology laboratories; hospital and health care facilities; biotechnology facilities; animal facilities and veterinary practices; and agriculture operations. The agent may be introduced into the work environment as a result of a source (vector) such as plants, birds, animals, insects, or humans. In laboratory settings, exposure can be associated with the direct handling and manipulation of these agents related to the clinical or research operation.

An industrial hygienist completing a biosafety risk assessment examines epidemiology, pathogenicity, susceptible populations, and routes of transmission. Recommended control measures may include education and training in good handling practices, engineering controls (ventilation, biological safety cabinets, isolation), medical intervention and surveillance (immunizations), and use of PPE (see Chapter 13, Personal Protective Equipment (PPE)). An effective biosafety control measure has been the development and use of the concept of *universal precautions*. Originally developed for health care settings, the concept has been adapted to a wide range of workplaces. Universal precautions are an approach to infection control that treats all human blood and certain human body fluids as though known to be infectious for bloodborne pathogens. The identification, risk assessment, classification, and control of biological agents are covered extensively in *Fundamentals of Industrial Hygiene* (Plog, 2012).

Ergonomic Factors

Ergonomics is the science of fitting the job to the worker. A mismatch between the physical requirements of the job and the physical capacity of the worker can result in injuries and disorders affecting cartilage, joints, ligaments, muscles, nerves, spinal discs, and tendons. These would be generally classified as musculoskeletal disorders (MSDs). Although evaluation and treatment of these impairments should be conducted by a qualified health care practitioner, the workplace factors leading to MSDs can be evaluated by an industrial hygienist and corrective actions implemented based on the evaluation.

In analyzing a potential ergonomics problem, an industrial hygienist could perform a job safety analysis (see Chapter 5, Identifying Hazards). Risk factors that are frequently identified during ergonomic evaluations include repetitive motions, awkward work positions, excessive amounts of force used to perform jobs, repeated or improper lifting of heavy objects, cold temperatures, and vibration. Good engineering and biomechanical principles must be applied to eliminate hazards of this kind.

Ergonomic interventions may include training and education, adjusting the height of working surfaces, providing the right tool for the job, encouraging short rest breaks, reducing repetitive motions, eliminating forceful or awkward hand exertions, or using equipment for heavy or repetitive lifting.

TOXICITY

Toxicity is the capacity of a chemical to harm or injure a living organism by other than mechanical means. Toxicity entails a definite dimension (quantity or amount); the toxicity of a chemical often depends on the degree of exposure. A toxic effect is any reversible or irreversible noxious effect on the body, including any chemically induced tumor or any mutagenic or teratogenic effect or death as a result of contact with a substance via the respiratory tract, skin, eye, mouth, or any other route into the body. Toxic effects are undesirable disturbances of physiological function caused by an overexposure to chemical or physical stresses. These effects can also arise as side effects in response to medication and vaccines.

The responsibility of the industrial hygienist is to quantify levels of exposure to chemical agents and to prescribe cautionary measures and limitations to prevent overexposures. From a toxicological viewpoint, the industrial hygienist must consider all types of exposure and the subsequent effects on the living organism. An industrial hygienist should work closely with occupational health practitioners to ensure that recommendations for exposure levels are low enough to prevent adverse impacts on the working population.

TOXICITY VERSUS HAZARD

A distinction must be made between toxicity and hazard. Toxicologists generally consider *toxicity* to be the ability of a substance to produce an unwanted effect when that material has reached a sufficient concentration at a certain site in the body. *Hazard* is the practical likelihood that exposure to the toxic material will cause harm. Many factors contribute to determining the degree of hazard—route of entry, dosage, physiological state, environmental variables, and other factors. Assessing a hazard involves estimating the probability that a substance will cause harm. Toxicity, along with the chemical and physical properties of a substance, determines the level of hazard. Two liquids can possess the same degree of toxicity but present different degrees of hazard.

A chemical stimulus can be considered to have produced a toxic effect when it satisfies the following criteria:

- An observable or measurable physiological deviation has been produced in any organ or organ system. The change can be anatomic in character and may accelerate or inhibit a normal physiological process, or the deviation can be a specific biochemical change.
- The observed change can be duplicated from animal to animal even though the dose-effect relationships vary.
- The stimulus has changed normal physiological processes in such a way that a protective mechanism is impaired in its defense against other adverse stimuli.
- The effect does not occur without a stimulus or occurs so infrequently that it indicates a generalized or nonspecific response. When high degrees of susceptibility are noted, equally significant degrees of resistance should be apparent.
- The observation must be noted and be reproducible by other investigators.
- The physiological change reduces the efficiency of an organ or function and impairs physiological reserve in such a way as to interfere with the ability to resist or adapt to other normal stimuli, either permanently or temporarily.

ENTRY INTO THE BODY

For an adverse effect to occur, the toxic substance must first reach the organ or bodily site where it can cause damage. Common routes of entry are inhalation, skin absorption, ingestion, and injection. Depending on the substance and its specific properties, however, entry and absorption can occur by more than one route, such as inhaling a solvent that can also penetrate the skin. When absorption into the bloodstream occurs, a substance may elicit general effects, or, most likely, the critical injury will be localized in specific tissues or organs. It is important for an industrial hygienist to determine the routes of entry during any exposure evaluation. It is also important to remember that an exposure could occur through several different routes.

Inhalation

For industrial exposures to chemicals, the most common route of entry is inhalation. Nearly all materials that are airborne can be inhaled.

The respiratory system is composed of two main areas: the upper respiratory tract airways (the nose, throat, trachea, and major bronchial tubes leading to the lobes of the lungs) and the alveoli, where the actual transfer of gases across thin cell walls takes place. Only particles smaller than about 5 μm in diameter are likely to enter the alveolar sac.

The total amount of a toxic compound absorbed via the respiratory pathways depends on its concentration in the air, the duration of exposure, and the pulmonary ventilation volumes, which increase with higher work loads. If the toxic substance is present in the form of an aerosol, deposition and absorption occur in the respiratory tract. For more details, see *Fundamentals of Industrial Hygiene* (Plog, 2012).

Gases and vapors of low water solubility but high fat solubility pass through the alveolar lining into the bloodstream and are distributed to organ sites for which they have special affinity. During inhalation exposure at a uniform level, the absorption of the compound into the blood reaches equilibrium with metabolism and elimination.

Skin Absorption

An important route of entry is absorption through either intact or abraded skin. Contact of a substance with skin results in four possible actions: the skin can act as an effective barrier; the substance can react with the skin and cause local irritation or tissue destruction; the substance can produce skin sensitization; or the substance can penetrate into the blood vessels under the skin and enter the bloodstream.

The cutaneous absorption rate of some organic compounds rises when temperature or perspiration increases. Therefore, absorption can be higher in warm climates or seasons. The absorption of liquid organic compounds may follow surface contamination of the skin or clothes; for other compounds, it may directly follow the vapor phase, in which case the rate of absorption is roughly proportional to the air concentration of the vapors. The process may be a combination of deposition of the substances on the skin surface followed by absorption through the skin.

Ingestion

Anything swallowed moves into the intestine and can be absorbed into the bloodstream and thereafter prove toxic. The problem of ingesting chemicals is not widespread in the industry; most workers do not deliberately swallow materials they handle.

Workers can ingest toxic materials as a result of eating in contaminated work areas; contaminated fingers and hands can lead to accidental oral intake when a worker eats or smokes on the job. They can also ingest materials when contaminants deposited in the respiratory tract are carried out to the throat by the action of the ciliated lining of the respiratory tract. These contaminants are then swallowed, and significant absorption of the material may occur through the gastrointestinal tract.

Injection

Material can be injected into some part of the body. This can be done directly into the bloodstream, the peritoneal cavity, or the pleural cavity. The material can also be injected into the skin, muscle, or any other place a needle can be inserted. The effects produced vary with the location of administration. In industrial settings, injection is an infrequent route of worker chemical exposure.

INDUSTRIAL HYGIENE CONSULTING SERVICES

The ideal circumstance for most companies is to have a full-time industrial hygienist on staff. However, because of economic factors and the lack of fully qualified personnel, industrial hygienists can be employed in a consulting capacity. There are drawbacks to this approach. The industrial hygienist consultant is ordinarily called in only when problems arise. The person may not be as familiar with the facility and company personnel as a full-time industrial hygienist would be. The extent of this problem can be lessened by scheduling regular industrial hygiene consulting visits to discuss policy issues and inspect the facility during normal conditions. Some of these routine visits should coincide with visits of the medical consultant. Many companies with industrial hygiene consulting services also have medical consulting services.

Several sources are available to assist in the quest for a competent and qualified industrial hygiene consultant. First is the listing of industrial hygiene consultants published by the AIHA. Presence of a name on the list does not guarantee competence, however. For an industrial hygiene consultant to be considered, the minimum requirements should be certification (i.e., designation as CIH) and familiarity with the industry or other occupational setting of interest. As with other professional services, personal recommendations from satisfied users of consulting services are often the best source for information. This allows for the differentiation between otherwise apparently equivalently qualified consultants.

In addition to the qualifications of the person being considered as a consultant, resources of his or her firm can also be important. When quick turnaround of analytical results from air monitoring or other workplace monitoring is required, the availability of an in-house laboratory can be important. In any case, the laboratory considered for use should be accredited by the AIHA. (This accreditation should be required regardless of whether the analysis required is one for which specific accreditation is offered. The AIHA accreditation includes evaluation of such general areas as quality control and record keeping, in addition to performance on specific analytes.)

In some cases, trade associations have experience with consulting firms and can recommend those that are familiar with the industry of interest. Formal consulting agreements with the industrial hygiene consultant should include adequate time to discuss problems of mutual interest with the medical director and engineering staff, as well as operations.

CERTIFICATION AND LICENSURE

Certification of industrial hygienists began in 1960, when the AIHA and American Conference of Governmental Industrial Hygienists (ACGIH) established the American Board of Industrial Hygiene (ABIH) to set up certification requirements. Figure 12–1 shows the industrial hygiene code of ethics. Two classes of certification are currently recognized: (1) diplomates (permitted to use the designation Certified Industrial Hygienist—CIH); and (2) the Certified Associate Industrial Hygienist (CAIH), which was discontinued in 2006.

Certification is currently offered in comprehensive practice. Beginning in 1993, specialized competence of diplomates in the two subspecialties of indoor air quality and hazardous materials management and remediation were formally recognized by ABIH. Before 1992, certification in the specialized fields of acoustical, air pollution, engineering, radiological, and toxicological aspects of industrial hygiene was offered. Certification in the specialized field of chemical practice was discontinued after 2000. Those certifications remain valid, although no new certificates will be offered.

Applicants for the Certified Industrial Hygienist (CIH) credential are required to meet educational and experience requirements as well as demonstrate their knowledge and skills through examination. Qualifications are as follows:

1. Graduation from a regionally accredited college or university, or other college acceptable to the ABIH, with at least a four-year degree in biology, chemistry, physics, engineering, or a program accredited by the Accreditation Board for Engineering and Technology Inc. (ABET) in industrial hygiene or safety. The ABIH may consider and accept any other bachelor's degree from an acceptable college or university provided the degree is based upon appropriate coursework and represents at least 60 semester hours in undergraduate or graduate level courses in science, math, engineering, and science-based technology, with at least 15 of those hours at the upper (junior, senior, or graduate) level.

2. Four years of broad-based professional industrial hygiene experience.

3. 180 academic contact hours or 240 continuing education contact hours

CODE OF ETHICS FOR THE PRACTICE OF INDUSTRIAL HYGIENE

OBJECTIVE

These canons provide standards of ethical conduct for Industrial Hygienists as they practice their profession and exercise their primary mission: to protect the health and well-being of working people and the public from chemical, microbiological, and physical health hazards present at, or emanating from, the workplace.

CANONS OF ETHICAL CONDUCT

Canon 1

Industrial Hygienists shall practice their profession following recognized scientific principles with the realization that the lives, health, and well-being of people may depend upon their professional judgment and that they are obligated to protect the health and well-being of people.

Interpretive Guidelines
- Industrial Hygienists should base their professional opinions, judgments, interpretations of findings, and recommendations upon recognized scientific principles and practices which preserve and protect the health and well-being of people.
- Industrial Hygienists shall not distort, alter, or hide facts in rendering professional opinions or recommendations.
- Industrial Hygienists shall not knowingly make statements that misrepresent or omit facts.

Canon 2

Industrial Hygienists shall counsel affected parties factually regarding potential health risks and precautions necessary to avoid adverse health effects.

Interpretive Guidelines
- Industrial Hygienists should obtain information regarding potential health risks from reliable sources.
- Industrial Hygienists should review the pertinent, readily available information to factually inform the affected parties.
- Industrial Hygienists should initiate appropriate measures to see that the health risks are effectively communicated to the affected parties.
- Parties may include management, clients, employees, contractor employees, or others, dependent on circumstances at the time.

Canon 3

Industrial Hygienists shall keep confidential personal and business information obtained during the exercise of industrial hygiene activities, except when required by law or overriding health and safety considerations.

Interpretive Guidelines
- Industrial Hygienists should report and communicate information which is necessary to protect the health and safety of workers and the community.
- If their professional judgment is overruled under circumstances where the health and lives of people are endangered, Industrial Hygienists shall notify their employer, client, or other such authority, as may be appropriate.
- Industrial Hygienists should release confidential personal or business information only with the information owner's express authorization, except when there is a duty to disclose information as required by law or regulation.

Figure 12–1. The American Board of Industrial Hygiene Code of Ethics, May 2007.

Reprinted with permission of the American Board of Industrial Hygiene.

Canon 4

Industrial Hygienists shall avoid circumstances where a compromise of professional judgment or conflict of interest may arise.

Interpretive Guidelines

- Industrial Hygienists should promptly disclose known or potential conflicts of interest to parties that may be affected.
- Industrial Hygienists shall not solicit or accept financial or other valuable consideration from any party, directly or indirectly, which is intended to influence professional judgment.
- Industrial Hygienists shall not offer any substantial gift, or other valuable consideration, in order to secure work.
- Industrial Hygienists should advise their clients or employer when they initially believe a project to improve industrial hygiene conditions will not be successful.
- Industrial Hygienists should not accept work that negatively impacts the ability to fulfill existing commitments.
- In the event that this Code of Ethics appears to conflict with another professional code to which Industrial Hygienists are bound, they will resolve the conflict in the manner that protects the health of affected parties.

Canon 5

Industrial Hygienists shall perform services only in the areas of their competence.

Interpretive Guidelines

- Industrial Hygienists should undertake to perform services only when qualified by education, training, or experience in the specific technical fields involved, unless sufficient assistance is provided by qualified associates, consultants, or employees.
- Industrial Hygienists shall obtain appropriate certifications, registrations, and/or licenses as required by federal, state, and/or local regulatory agencies prior to providing industrial hygiene services, where such credentials are required.

Canon 6

Industrial Hygienists shall act responsibly to uphold the integrity of the profession.

Interpretive Guidelines

- Industrial Hygienists shall avoid conduct or practice which is likely to discredit the profession or deceive the public.
- Industrial Hygienists shall not permit use of their name or firm name by any person or firm which they have reason to believe is engaging in fraudulent or dishonest industrial hygiene practices.
- Industrial Hygienists shall not use statements in advertising their expertise or services containing a material misrepresentation of fact or omitting a material fact necessary to keep statements from being misleading.
- Industrial Hygienists shall not knowingly permit their employees, employers, or others to misrepresent the individuals' professional background, expertise, or services which are misrepresentations of fact.
- Industrial Hygienists shall not misrepresent their professional education, experience, or credentials.

of industrial hygiene coursework. At a minimum, half of those hours must include coursework in the areas of industrial hygiene fundamentals, measurements, controls, and toxicology.

4. An additional 2 hours of coursework/training is required in the area of ethics.

After certification is achieved via examination, active practice, technical committee work, publications, education, meetings, teaching, retest, or other approved methods must be documented to ensure that the certification remains current. Maintaining certification requires documenting continued activity in certain defined professional activities and continuing education.

Although many industrial hygienists are becoming interested in seeking some form of government licensure, no federal licensure requirements were established by the end of 2013. However, the CIH designation is often required for industrial hygiene practice on projects or jobs supported by government funds. The CIH is increasingly recognized as a minimum requirement to ensure that industrial hygiene work is being performed according to professional standards, especially when litigation is anticipated or feared. As of 2013, 17 states (Alaska, California, Connecticut, Florida, Georgia, Indiana, Minnesota, Nebraska, Nevada, New Jersey, North Carolina, Ohio, Oregon, South Carolina, Tennessee, Texas, and Virginia) had enacted title protection that prohibits use of the CIH designation without ABIH certification.

PROFESSIONAL ORGANIZATIONS

The AIHA is the predominant U.S. industrial hygiene organization. The AIHA was formed in 1939 by a small group of industrial hygienists and has grown in the intervening years to more than 10,000 members. The only restrictions on membership are those of educational qualifications and practice of industrial hygiene. A full member must have an appropriate degree (usually in one of the physical or biological sciences) and must have practiced industrial hygiene full-time for three years. The AIHA provides many services to the profession, including accreditation of laboratories offering analytical services. There are local (regional) sections of the AIHA in all areas of the United States, and many foreign occupational health professionals are members as well.

The American Conference of Governmental Industrial Hygienists previously limited full membership to health and safety professionals practicing in government agencies and educational institutions. Today, the ACGIH offers membership to all practitioners in industrial hygiene, occupational health, environmental health, and safety domestically and abroad. Two publications offered by the ACGIH are of particular value to the profession. One of these is the manual *Industrial Ventilation—A Manual of Recommended Practice* by the Industrial Ventilation Committee of ACGIH. This manual gives guidance in design of ventilation systems for the control of airborne health hazards and is a standard reference source. The other is the annual publication of the *Threshold Limit Values (TLVs) and Biological Exposure Indices (BEIs)*. The TLVs and BEIs are widely used as measures of allowable exposure limits; in fact, the 1968 TLVs were adopted into law as the permissible exposure limits in the OSH Act.

Many industrial hygienists are also members of organizations representing major and minor industries. The American Petroleum Institute, the Chemical Manufacturers Association, and the National Agricultural Chemical Association are examples of industry organizations with active committees on various aspects of occupational health on which industrial hygienists can serve. Some industrial hygienists also maintain membership in organizations representing the disciplines of their original training. The American Chemical Society and the American Institute of Chemical Engineers are examples of societies claiming many industrial hygienists among their members. Industrial hygienists also belong to organizations with peripheral interests in industrial hygiene or representing fields within which industrial hygienists have responsibilities. The American Biological Safety Association (ABSA), the Air & Waste Management Association (A&WMA), the American Management Association (AMA), the American Public Health Association (APHA), the American Society of Safety Engineers (ASSE), the Genetic Toxicology Association (GTA), the National Environmental Health Association (NEHA), and the Society for Epidemiological Research (SER) are a few examples of these organizations.

SUMMARY

- Industrial hygiene is the science and art devoted to anticipating, recognizing, evaluating, and controlling environmental hazards or stresses arising in or from the workplace.
- The industrial hygienist works with management, medical, safety, and engineering personnel to help eliminate or guard against environmental pollution and other conditions that can endanger human health.
- The four definitive elements of industrial hygiene are anticipating, recognizing, evaluating, and controlling occupational hazards. These include chemical, physical (excessive noise, radiation, etc.), biological, and ergonomic hazards.

- Toxic effects are undesirable disturbances of physiological function caused by an exposure to chemical or physical stresses. Toxicity is the capacity of a chemical to harm or injure a living organism by other than mechanical means. Hazard is the practical likelihood that exposure to the toxic material will cause harm.
- The responsibility of the industrial hygienist is to quantify levels of exposure to hazardous conditions and to prescribe cautionary measures and limitations to protect workers' health. These professionals can be either full-time or part-time consultants.

REVIEW QUESTIONS

1. Define *industrial hygiene*.
2. Whom does the industrial hygienist work with to control environmental stresses or occupational health hazards in the workplace?
   a. management
   b. medical personnel
   c. safety personnel
   d. engineering personnel
   e. all of the above
3. List five control procedures that are used to reduce or eliminate exposure.
4. List five factors of an effective industrial hygiene program.
5. The industrial hygienist is responsible for monitoring what types of environmental factors or stresses that can cause sickness, impaired health, or significant discomfort?
6. Which department is the most important to the industrial hygienist?
7. Who, at minimum, should be members of the occupational health and safety team?

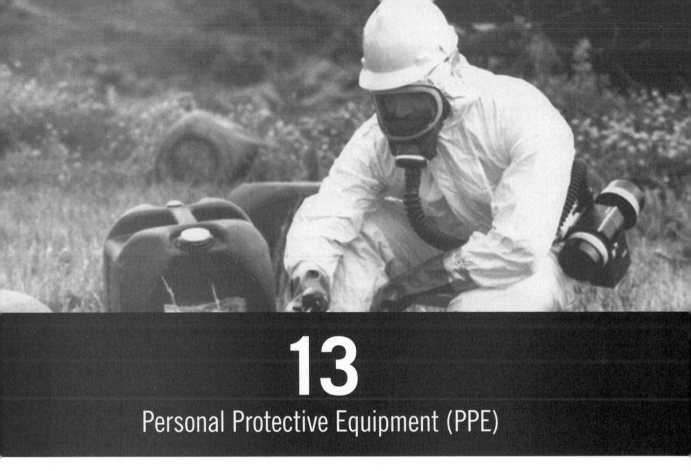

13

Personal Protective Equipment (PPE)

LEARNING OBJECTIVES

❑ Understand the elements needed to develop an effective personal protective equipment program.

❑ Describe the different types of head protection used in the workplace.

❑ Describe the criteria for eye and face protection and how to select appropriate eye and face protection.

❑ Discuss the requirements for developing a hearing conservation program.

❑ Identify the type of fall protection needed for working at heights.

❑ Understand the requirements for respiratory protection and which respirators should be used to protect workers in hazardous environments.

❑ Describe various types of hand, arm, and foot protection used to protect workers from workplace hazards.

❑ Understand the special requirements for working in extreme environments.

INTRODUCTION

Methods of controlling potentially harmful exposures to hazardous substances or forms of energy found in the workplace environment are typically classified into four broad, occasionally overlapping, categories: elimination/substitution, engineering controls, administrative controls, and personal protective equipment (PPE). *Elimination/substitution* is self-explanatory. *Engineering controls* are passive measures designed into the work environment to prevent contact with a harmful substance or other hazard. Common examples of engineering controls are eliminating toxic materials or using less toxic substitutes, changing process design, using barriers or guards, isolating or enclosing hazards, and using local exhaust ventilation. *Administrative controls* include such measures as worker rotation to minimize exposure, implementing proper housekeeping practices, and devising appropriate worker training.

This chapter covers the following topics:
- developing a program to introduce PPE in a company
- types of protective head, face and eye, and hearing protection and how to use them
- types of fall arrest systems and their use and care
- major respiratory protection equipment, including care and maintenance
- major types of footwear and hand and arm protective gear
- protective clothing for special work situations.

Personal protective equipment (PPE) refers to the use of respirators, special clothing, safety glasses, hard hats, or similar devices whose proper use reduces the risk of personal injury or illness resulting from occupational hazards. Generally speaking, use of PPE is the least desirable method of controlling exposure to harmful substances in the workplace environment.

Properly implemented engineering and administrative controls can greatly reduce or eliminate the hazard at the source. In contrast, when PPE is the primary control measure, the hazard is still present in the environment. The particular protective device merely provides a barrier between the hazard and the worker. Improper use or failure of the device means the worker is exposed to a direct threat to health and safety.

In some instances, PPE may be the only recourse. However, against such risks as chemical hazards, good industrial hygiene practice dictates that PPE be used only when the more desirable engineering and administrative controls are not feasible, when PPE is an interim control method while the "higher" controls are being implemented as a supplement, or as added protection.

Clearly, management must design a safe working environment by evaluating all hazards in the work environment, assessing the need for controls, and controlling or eliminating hazards to protect workers. Such a policy means considering the worst-case analysis of conditions. For those work environment hazards that cannot be eliminated through engineering or administrative controls, PPE becomes the best protection method. It is important for management to take a strong, positive attitude toward the proper use of PPE.

A PROGRAM TO INTRODUCE PPE

Companies should conduct an assessment of hazards in the workplace, as recommended by the Occupational Safety and Health Administration (OSHA), to determine their needs for PPE to protect workers. Once management decides on the use of PPE, the following steps should be taken:
1. Write a policy on usage of the PPE, and communicate it to employees and visitors as needed.
2. Select the proper type of equipment.
3. Implement a thorough training program to make certain employees know the correct use and maintenance of their equipment.
4. Enforce the use of PPE.

POLICY
A written PPE program should include a policy, hazard assessment or PPE needs assessment, selection of PPE to be used, worker training and motivation in the use of PPE, and enforcement of company rules. The policy should clearly state the need for and use of PPE. It also may contain exceptions or limitations on use of PPE. Some policies or safety rules may include such details as the specific work conditions expected. Management staff must follow the same safety rules.

The following is an example of a policy on the wearing of PPE devices:

For safe use of any personal protective device, it is essential the user be properly instructed in its selection, use, and maintenance. Both supervisors and workers shall be so instructed by competent persons.

SELECTION OF PROPER EQUIPMENT
After the need for PPE has been established, the next step is to select the proper type. The most important criterion is the degree of protection that a particular piece of equipment affords under various conditions.

Except for respiratory protective devices, few items of PPE available commercially are tested according to published and generally accepted performance specifications and approved by an impartial examiner. Although satisfactory performance specifications exist for certain types of PPE (notably protective helmets, devices to protect the eyes from impact and from harmful radiation, and rubber insulating gloves), there are no approving laboratories to test equipment regularly according to these specifications. (See the latest National Institute for Occupational Safety and Health [NIOSH] Certified Equipment List, which can be obtained from the U.S. Superintendent of Documents, Washington DC.)

The Safety Equipment Institute (SEI) has formulated objective policies for third-party certification of safety equipment. SEI voluntary certification programs involve both product testing and an ongoing program of quality assurance audits. Participating manufacturers are required to submit a specific number of product models to undergo demanding performance tests in SEI-authorized independent laboratories. When the laboratory has completed the test, SEI receives a pass or fail notification. For the quality assurance program, SEI conducts an audit at a manufacturer's production facilities to ensure that products coming off the assembly line are made to the same exacting specifications as the product model actually tested for certification.

The Safety Equipment Institute's existing certification programs include (1) eye and face protection, such as goggles, face shields, spectacles, and welding helmets; (2) emergency eyewash and shower equipment; (3) fire-fighter's helmets; (4) protective headwear, such as helmets; (5) protective footwear; and (6) personal fall protection.

PROPER TRAINING

The next step is to obtain worker compliance with company requirements to wear the PPE. Several factors influence compliance, including (a) how well workers understand the need for the equipment; (b) how easy, comfortable, and convenient the equipment is to wear; (c) how effectively economic, social, and disciplinary sanctions can be used to influence the attitudes of workers; and (d) employee involvement in the decision-making process.

For organizations in which workers are accustomed to wearing PPE as a condition of employment, compliance may be only a minor problem. People are issued equipment meeting the requirements of the job and are taught how and why it must be used. Thereafter, periodic checks are made until use of the issued equipment has become a matter of habit.

A good deal of the resistance to change can be overcome if the persons who are going to use the PPE are allowed to choose their equipment from among several styles preselected to meet job requirements. In some situations, it may be advisable to have a committee from the work force help select suitable devices. Management may not be able to purchase one standard type of equipment right away and may need to stock several types. In the latter case, the cost, though higher than the cost of stocking only one style, will be small compared with the potential expense of injuries resulting from failure to use the equipment. For the convenience of their employees, some companies maintain equipment stores on the facility premises.

Employees required to use PPE should be given proper training. The training program routinely should cover the following topics:
- describing what hazard and/or condition is in the work environment
- telling what has been, can be, or cannot be done about it
- explaining why a certain type of PPE has been selected
- discussing the capabilities and/or limitations of the PPE
- demonstrating how to use, adjust, or fit the PPE
- practicing PPE use
- explaining company policy and its enforcement
- discussing how to deal with emergencies
- discussing how PPE will be paid for, maintained, repaired, cleaned, and so on.

USE AND MAINTENANCE

All equipment must be inspected before and after each use. The company should keep records of all inspections by date, with the results tabulated. Supervisors and workers should follow the recommendations of the manufacturer for inspection, maintenance, repair, removal from service, and replacement of parts supplied by the manufacturer.

ENFORCEMENT

Employees need to know how the use of PPE will be enforced. Many companies have some type of progressive disciplinary action ranging from unpaid time off to termination. Management enforcement of the PPE program is critical to success.

WHO PAYS FOR PPE?

Employers must provide and pay for PPE required by the company for the worker to do his or her job safely and in compliance with OSHA standards. Examples would include welding gloves, respirators, hard hats, specialty glasses, specialty foot protection, and face shields. General work clothes (e.g., uniforms, pants, shirts, or blouses) not intended to function as protection against a hazard are not considered to be PPE.

For those cases in which equipment is personal in nature and usable by workers away from the job, the matter of payment may be decided by labor–management negotiations. Examples would include nonspecialty safety glasses, safety shoes, and cold-weather outerwear of the type worn by construction workers. On the other hand, shoes or outerwear subject to contamination by hazardous substances that cannot be safely worn off site must be paid for by the employer.

OSHA's 29 CFR 1910.132–138 establishes the employer's obligation to provide personal protective equipment to employees as follows:

> Protective equipment, including personal protective equipment for eyes, face, head and extremities, protective clothing, respiratory devices and protective shields and barriers, shall be provided, used and maintained in a sanitary and reliable condition wherever it is necessary by reasons of hazards of processes or environment, chemical hazards, radiological hazards or mechanical irritants encountered in a manner capable of causing injury or impairment in the function of any part of the body through absorption, inhalation, or physical contact.

Although there are some circumstances in which workers in a particular trade would provide their own PPE, it is still the employer's obligation to ensure that such equipment is adequate and properly maintained.

In cases where a union contract does not include payment for time putting on PPE, then anyone covered under that contract will not be compensated for that time.

The next few sections discuss seven major categories of PPE—protection for the head, eyes and face, ears, respiratory system, hands, feet, and trunk. Each section provides information on the standards available or proposed, some details about the equipment available, and suggestions for selecting equipment to meet the job hazard.

HEAD PROTECTION

Employees exposed to head injury hazards must be given protective headwear. It is very important that workers wear hard hats as they are intended to be worn and not put on backward or without the safety harness. Some operations requiring head protection include tree trimming, construction work, shipbuilding, logging, mining, electric and communication line construction or maintenance, and basic metal or chemical production.

PROTECTIVE HEADWEAR

Protective headwear is designed to absorb the shock of a blow and shield the wearer's head from the impact and penetration of falling objects. In some cases, protective headwear is required to prevent electric shock and burns. Protective headwear can also prevent the head and hair from becoming entangled in machinery or exposed to hazardous environments. Safety and health professionals should be alert to any changes in operations that may create a need for protective headwear.

The American National Standards Institute (ANSI) has established standards recognized by OSHA for protective hats. The standard is intended to be used in its entirety on a product. Identification inside the helmet shell must list the manufacturer's name and ANSI standard designation (Z89.1), and it should include the designation for both Type and Class. Type and Class designation is a requirement of the standard and all protective devices meeting the standard (as per OSHA) must bear these markings:

- type I—helmets intended to reduce the force of impact from a blow to the top of the head
- type II—helmets intended to reduce the force of impact from a blow to the sides or top of the head
- class G (general)—general service, limited voltage protection
- class E (electrical)—utility service, high-voltage protection
- class C (conductive)—special service, no voltage protection.

Class G helmets are intended for protection against impact hazards and are typically used in heavy industrial settings, such as manufacturing or construction.

Class E helmets protect the wearer's head from impact, from penetration by falling or flying objects, and from high-voltage shock and burn. Generally, this type of helmet is constructed of insulated materials and is used by the utility services industry.

Class C helmets are used for comfort and impact protection, usually when there is a possibility of bumping a head against a fixed object and in settings where there is no danger from electrical hazards or corrosion.

MAINTENANCE

Before each use, helmets should be inspected for cracks, no matter how small; signs of impact or rough treatment; and wear that might reduce the degree of safety originally provided. Prolonged exposure to ultraviolet (UV) radiation from sunlight or other sources, like welding and chemicals, can shorten the life expectancy of thermoplastic helmets. Discard all helmets that show signs of chalking, cracking, or reduced surface gloss or those with broken or damaged harnesses. Any helmet that has received an impact should be removed from service. Additionally, users should consult manufacturer's product literature for guidance on product service life.

COLOR-CODED PROTECTIVE HELMETS

Many companies use color-coded protective helmets to identify different working crews. Some colors are painted on during manufacture, and others have the color molded in. It is not recommended that paint be applied after manufacture because paint solvents may reduce the helmet's dielectric properties or affect the shell. Alterations of any sort can affect the performance of the gear. However, if painting is necessary, manufacturers should be consulted with regard to the type of paint that would be compatible with the construction of the protective helmet. Lighter-colored hats are cooler to wear in the sun or under infrared energy sources.

EYE AND FACE PROTECTION

Protection of the eyes and face from injury by physical and chemical agents or by radiation is vital in any occupational health and safety program. In fact, this type of protection has the widest application and the broadest range of styles, models, and types.

The cost of acquiring and fitting eye protective devices is small when measured against the expense of eye injuries. Some 70% of all eye injuries resulted from flying or falling objects. Contact with harmful substances, chemicals, and so forth, caused more than 20% of injuries. Foreign bodies in the eye occurred in about 60% of the cases.

The eye and face protection standard, ANSI Z87.1, American National Standard Practice for Occupational and Educational Eye and Face Protection, sets fairly comprehensive standards to be used for protective eye and face devices. In lieu of complying specifically with an applicable ANSI standard, the employer could demonstrate that alternative protective equipment would be equally effective. These standards set performance standards, including detailed tests, for a broad range of hazards—excluding only x-ray, gamma, and high-energy particulate radiation; lasers; and masers.

Besides general requirements applying to "all occupations and educational processes," the standard provides requirements and limitations on the following:
- welding helmets

- welding hand shields
- protector selection and fitting
- flammability
- face shields
- goggles—eye cup (chipper's), dust and splash, welder's and cutter's
- spectacles—metal, plastic, and combination
- attachments and auxiliary equipment—lift fronts, chin rests, snoods, aprons, magnifiers, etc.

CONTACT LENSES—RUMOR VERSUS FACTS

For more than 25 years, a rumor has persisted that welding or other electric flashes make contact lenses stick to the eyeball. This rumor has been proved false.

Incident data and studies suggest that contact lens wearers do not appear to have problems when their eyes are properly protected in the workplace. Prevent Blindness America (formerly known as The National Society to Prevent Blindness) publishes the latest research findings as a service to both business and safety and health professionals. Their purpose is to help contact lens wearers keep their eyes in good condition

Recommendations

Prevent Blindness America makes the following recommendations as a service to managers who must direct contact lens use and employees who must wear them:

- A specific written management policy on contact lens use should be developed with employee consultation and involvement.
- Occupational safety eyewear meeting or exceeding ANSI Z87.1 standards should be worn at all times by individuals in designated areas.
- Employees and visitors should be advised of defined areas where contacts are allowed.
- At workstations where contacts are allowed, the type of eye protection required should be specified.
- Restrictions on contact lens wear do not apply to usual office or administrative assistants (unless they must enter hazardous areas where exposure is significant).
- A directory should be developed that lists all employees who wear contacts. This list should be maintained in the medical facility for easy access by trained first-aid personnel. Foremen or supervisors should be informed of individual employees who wear contact lenses.
- Medical and first-aid personnel should be trained in the proper procedures and equipment for removing both hard and soft contacts from conscious and unconscious workers.

- Employees should be required to keep a spare pair of contacts and/or a pair of up-to-date prescription spectacles in their possession. They will then be able to continue their job functions should they damage or lose a lens while working.
- Employees who wear contact lenses should be instructed to remove their contacts immediately if redness of the eyes, blurred vision, or pain in the eyes associated with contact lens use occurs.

Guidelines for the Use of Contact Lenses in Industrial Environments

The American Optometric Association has adopted the following policy statement concerning the use of contact lenses in industrial environments (Anthony P. Cullen, MSc, OD, PhD, DSc, FCOptom, FAAO):

> Contact lenses may be worn in some hazardous environments with appropriate covering safety eyewear. Contact lenses of themselves do not provide eye protection in the industrial sense.

Most successful contact lens wearers wish to wear their contact lenses in all aspects of their lives, including the workplace. This may conflict with government- or industry-imposed restrictions on the use of contact lenses in a given industrial environment. These restrictions, in turn, may be unreasonable and discriminatory.

In risk management it is necessary to balance risk with benefits and to differentiate perceived risk from actual risk. Because both contact lenses and certain environments may produce adverse ocular effects, it is tempting to assume that there may be additive or synergistic effects when contact lenses are worn in that environment.

COMFORT AND FIT

To be comfortable and effective, eye-protective equipment must be properly fitted. Corrective spectacles should be fitted only by optometrists or ophthalmologists. An employee can be trained to adjust and maintain eye-protection equipment, however, and each employee can be taught the proper care of the device used. To give the widest possible field of vision, goggles should be fitted as close to the eyes as possible, without bringing the eyelashes in contact with the lenses.

In areas where goggles or other types of eye protection are used extensively, goggle-cleaning stations should be conveniently located. The stations should provide defogging materials and wiping tissues, along with a receptacle for discarding them. Before choosing a defogging material, test to determine the most effective type for a specific application.

FACE PROTECTION

As a general rule, face shields should be worn over suitable basic eye protection. A variety of face shields protect the face and neck from flying particles, sprays of hazardous liquids, splashes of molten metal, and hot solutions. In addition, they provide antiglare protection where required.

The materials used in face shields should combine mechanical strength, light weight, nonirritation to skin, and the ability to withstand frequent disinfecting operations. The shield should be made of noncorrosive metals and slow-burning plastics. Only optical-grade (clear or tinted) plastic, which is free from flaws or distortions, should be inserted for the windows. However, plastic windows should not be used in welding operations unless they conform to the standards on transmittance of absorptive lenses, filter lenses, and plates.

ACID HOODS AND CHEMICAL GOGGLES

The company can provide head and face protection from splashes of acids, alkalis, or other hazardous liquids or chemicals in several ways, depending on the hazard. A hood made of chemical-resistant material with a glass or plastic window can give good protection. Some manufacturers provide a hood with replaceable inner and outer windows. In all cases, there should be a secure joint between windows and hood materials.

Although hoods are extremely hot to wear, they can be made with air lines for the wearer's comfort. If so, the wearer should have a harness or belt like that on an airline respirator to support the hose.

LASER BEAM PROTECTION

Lasers produce monochromatic, high-intensity light beams, frequently capable of causing significant eye damage. A laser beam of sufficient power can theoretically produce retinal intensities at magnitudes even larger than those produced when directly viewing the sun. Exposures to this type of laser beam have the potential for causing permanent blindness.

No one type of glass or plastic offers protection from all laser wavelengths. Consequently, most laser-using firms do not depend on safety glasses to protect an employee's eyes from laser burns. Some point out that laser goggles or glasses might give a false sense of security, tempting the wearer to unnecessary exposures.

EYE PROTECTION FOR WELDING

In addition to damage from physical and chemical agents, the eyes are subject to the effects of radiant energies. Ultraviolet, visible, and infrared bands of the spectrum can all damage the eyes and, therefore, require special protective measures to eliminate the hazard.

Ultraviolet radiation can produce cumulative destructive changes in the structure of the cornea and lens of the eye. Short exposures to intense UV radiation or prolonged exposures to UV radiation of low intensity will produce painful but ordinarily self-repairing corneal damage.

For welding, cutting, brazing, or soldering operations, use the guide for the selection of proper shade numbers of filter lenses or windows in the current ANSI Z87.1–, Standard for Occupational and Educational Personal Eye and Face Protection Devices. To protect the filter lenses against pitting, they should be worn with a replaceable plastic or glass cover plate.

HEARING PROTECTION

Medical professionals have long been aware of the problem of noise-induced hearing loss (NIHL) in industry. Noise, or unwanted sound, is a by-product of many industrial processes. Sound is created by pressure changes in a medium (usually air), originating from a source of vibration or turbulence. Exposure to high levels of noise can cause hearing loss. The extent of damage depends primarily on the intensity of the noise and the duration of the exposure. NIHL can be temporary or permanent. Temporary hearing loss results from short-term noise exposures, while prolonged exposure to high noise levels over a period of time gradually causes permanent damage.

OCCUPATIONAL NOISE-INDUCED HEARING LOSS

Occupational noise-induced hearing loss, as opposed to occupational acoustic trauma, is a slowly developing hearing loss over a long period (several years) as the result of exposure to continuous or intermittent loud noise. Occupational acoustic trauma is a sudden change in hearing as a result of a single exposure to a sudden burst of sound, such as an explosive blast. The diagnosis of noise-induced hearing loss is made clinically by a physician and should include a study of the noise exposure history.

HEARING CONSERVATION PROGRAM

The OSHA hearing conservation standard (29 CFR 1910.95, Occupational Noise Exposure) requires a hearing conservation program for employees exposed to excessive noise. U.S. agencies and firms must develop and maintain an audiometric testing program for all employees who are exposed to noise levels in excess of 85 dB for an 8-hour time-weighted average. With the increasingly frequent use of extended-hour shifts (i.e., 10 or 12 hours), the 85-dB exposures level must be recalculated to reflect the new shift length.

OSHA currently enforces a 90-dBA permissible exposure limit. Exposure to 115 dBA is permitted for a maximum of 15 minutes for an 8-hour workday. No exposure above 115 dBA is permitted (29 CFR 1926.52).

The hearing conservation program may also require the use of hearing protection devices. Before requiring any employee to wear hearing protection, management should measure and evaluate the noise in the workplace. This step serves several purposes: (1) provides the physical evidence of individual exposures; (2) identifies areas where controls need to be established; (3) helps prioritize noise-control and noise-reduction efforts, including administrative controls; (4) documents exposures in the work environment for medical-legal purposes; (5) establishes documentation for state, federal, or insurance compliance requirements; (6) provides a basis for analyzing cause–effect relationships between noise exposure and hearing status; and (7) provides insights for improving education and compliance among workers, supervisors, and managers.

When noise measurement is completed, and other possible noise-control efforts are unsuccessful, then the need for hearing protection is clearly established. For explanation of noise measurement, evaluation, and control, see the National Safety Council's *Fundamentals of Industrial Hygiene*, 6th ed.

To develop an effective hearing protection program, companies need to have an accurate knowledge of the noise levels (and frequencies) that pose a hazard to workers. From the data obtained in the noise survey described earlier, management can select the proper hearing protection devices.

To help management choose the right devices, firms can use the U.S. Environmental Protection Act (EPA) requirement that calls for all protectors to carry a label that indicates their noise reduction rating (NRR). The number provides an estimate of a device's degree of protection and generally can be subtracted from the decibel value of noise in the workplace. This value indicates the noise level theoretically being received in the worker's ear.

However, companies should exercise some caution in applying the full NRR when using hearing protection devices to reduce occupational exposures. Because the NRR is derived under laboratory conditions, wearing conditions of the device on the job will be less than ideal, and noise frequencies and sound levels will not be equal across the spectrum. When evaluating occupational noise exposure, OSHA de-rates the NRR by one-half for all types of hearing protection. On the other hand, NIOSH considers the performance of different types of hearing protectors and recommends subtracting from the NRR 25% for earmuffs, 50% for formable earplugs, and 70% for all other earplugs.

TYPES OF HEARING PROTECTION DEVICES

In general, hearing protectors can be categorized as four types: enclosure (helmets), aural (ear insert), superaural (canal caps), and circumaural (earmuffs).

Before a company issues any ear insert, management should take certain measures: (1) each employee's ear canals should be examined for any abnormalities or irregularities; for example, certain diseases may not allow use of earplugs; (2) employees must be taught proper insertion techniques; and (3) employees must be taught proper sanitation and checking techniques.

Enclosure

The enclosure hearing protector completely surrounds the head, such as an astronaut's helmet. Sound is reduced through the acoustical properties of the helmet. Additional attenuation can be achieved by wearing inserts with the enclosure helmet. Expense, temperature inside the helmet, and its bulk normally rule out general use of the enclosure hearing protector, but certain firms or industries may have specific needs for it.

Aural Insert

Commonly called inserts or earplugs, the aural insert is generally inexpensive and has a limited service life. The plug or insert falls into three broad categories: (1) formable; (2) custom molded; and (3) molded.

1. Formable aural inserts fit all ears. Many of the formable types are designed to be used once, then thrown away.
2. As the name indicates, custom-molded hearing protectors are made for a specific individual. A prepared mixture is carefully placed in the person's outer ear, with a small portion extending into the ear canal. As the material sets, it conforms to the shape of the individual's ear and external ear canal.
3. Molded (or premolded) aural inserts are usually made from a soft silicone rubber or plastic. The most important aspect of this protector is a snug fit to provide adequate protection.

Superaural

The superaural, or canal cap, hearing protector depends on sealing the external edge of the ear canal to achieve sound reduction.

Circumaural

Cup (or earmuff) devices cover the external ear to provide an acoustical barrier between external sound and the inner ear. The attenuation provided by earmuffs varies widely due to differences in size, shape, seal material, shell mass, and type of suspension. Head size and shape also influence the attenuation characteristics of these protectors.

When selecting a hearing-protection device, also consider the work area in which the employee must use it. Another consideration when selecting a hearing-protective device is how often employees are exposed to excess noise (once a day, once a week, or infrequently). For such cases, an insert or plug device may satisfy legal requirements. If the noise exposure is relatively frequent and the employee must wear the protective device for an extended time, a muff protector might be the best choice. If noise exposures are intermittent, muff protectors are probably more desirable because it is somewhat more difficult to remove and reinsert earplugs than earmuffs.

FALL ARREST SYSTEMS

Many employees in today's work force are tasked with duties that require work at heights above ground level. The tasks can be as simple as changing a light bulb or as difficult as painting a chimney. Both of these work situations require fall protection for the employee while the job is being done. At greater heights, as in construction or utility work, fall protection becomes mandatory under most safety regulations.

The impact from even a 4-ft (1.2-m) fall can be enough to cause serious injury. Companies can use many methods to prevent employees from falling. This section will deal only with fall protection systems and not with mobile elevated access equipment, ladders, aerial buckets, rescue equipment, and so on.

WHAT IS FALL ARREST?

Fall arrest is defined as a means of preventing workers from experiencing disastrous falls from elevations. Fall arrest systems are usually classified as passive or active.

Passive Fall Arrest

This system consists of components and systems, such as nets, that do not require any action on the worker's part. A properly designed passive fall arrest system, installed correctly, will protect the individual 100% of the time.

Active Fall Arrest

This system is made up of components and systems that require some manipulation by the workers to make the protection effective. These systems include harnesses; lanyards and their attachments; and component parts such as rope-grabbing devices, lifelines, self-retracting lanyards (SRLs), and so on. Active equipment will not work by itself and must be connected or employed by the individual to be protective.

WHEN ARE FALL ARREST SYSTEMS NEEDED?

The first factor to consider in selecting a fall arrest system is the height at which the worker will be performing the job.

Second, the safety and health professional should analyze the job site and specific task to be done. If the job requires working vertically, a different or modified system will be needed than if the worker must move laterally.

Third, other factors should be addressed including rescue methods, backup systems, length of time at workstations, dry or wet conditions, number of workers needed on the job site, and environmental factors.

This complete analysis, along with a review of regulations, helps determine the fall arrest system needed. Modern fall protection encompasses a variety of technical, medical, ergonomic, and legal issues and has become a multidisciplinary science of its own. In most cases, the introduction of a fall arrest system involves much more than simply selecting and purchasing one. Quite often, a system has to be specially designed for a particular application by a design engineer, or other competent person.

ELEMENTS OF A SUCCESSFUL FALL ARREST PROGRAM

Some criteria need to be established for designing a fall arrest program. First, the employer must set a policy, which is clearly communicated to employees and enforced during applicable operations, that addresses these points:

- Worker qualification—Is the employee qualified to perform work at elevated conditions?
- Training—Are workers who are placed in the elevated work positions trained in the arrest system to be used?
- Selection of equipment—Is equipment being used as required to perform the job safely? Equipment purchased for the job must meet appropriate standards and, if required, be certified.
- Installation of equipment—Has equipment been installed according to acceptable standards, regulations, and manufacturer's recommendations?
- Equipment maintenance and inspection—Can equipment be maintained as recommended, and will employees inspect their personal system components daily before each use?
- Rescue procedures—Has a plan been developed to rescue any employee who has fallen while using a fall protection system?
- Job survey analysis—Has a job procedure been developed and implemented for every job in an elevated situation?

WHICH FALL ARREST SYSTEM TO USE?

Many different kinds of passive and active fall arrest systems are available.

Choosing the one best suited to a particular task requires planning, forethought, and a thorough understanding of the systems on the market today. When falling hazards are identified and cannot be eliminated, management must adopt some means of control to minimize the risk of personal injury.

Next, the appropriate system and its components must be selected. A variety of equipment is available to help employers set up an effective fall arrest program. Generally, this includes nets, body support mechanisms, climbing arrest systems, vertical lifeline systems, horizontal lifeline systems, confined entry and retrieval systems, and controlled descent–emergency escape systems.

PASSIVE FALL ARREST SYSTEMS

Passive fall arrest systems include general all-purpose nets, personnel nets, and debris nets. These devices are easy to use and have a wide range of applications.

Nets

Properly installed, nets can be a vital part of a passive fall arrest system. Nets are designed to provide protection under and around an elevated work area where fall hazards exist. The worker is not directly involved by "wearing" fall arrest equipment; rather, the net is there to catch a falling worker before she or he hits the ground or obstructions.

Personnel Nets

Personnel nets can be used for large work crews, such as those employed on bridge construction or repair or on long-term structural projects. The advantage of nets is that individual worker training is not required. Once installed, nets are always in place and ready for use. However, other personnel fall arrest systems must be available during net installation and removal.

Debris Nets

Debris nets are designed to catch falling debris (i.e., tools, foreign objects, falling concrete, and other construction debris) and to protect workers and pedestrians below. The strength and size of the mesh must be sufficient to catch and contain the size, weight, and impact of the objects that are likely to fall.

These net systems can also be used to catch personnel as well as debris. In these cases, personnel nets are deployed in conjunction with debris nets. The nets must be kept clear of debris to help ensure a falling worker's safety.

NOTE: A means of rescuing a fallen worker must be available.

ACTIVE FALL ARREST SYSTEMS

Active fall arrest systems include components such as fall arresters and shock absorbers, harnesses, lifelines, and SRLs. All active systems begin with an anchorage point and have some connecting components to the worker.

Anchor/Anchorage Points

The critical problem in all active fall protection—the anchorage point—is the position on an independent structure to which the fall arrest device or lanyard is securely attached. Supervisors and workers must also analyze all hazards below and to the side of the anchoring point to ensure that the worker does not strike or swing into any obstacles should he or she fall.

Lanyard

A lanyard is a short, flexible rope, strap, or webbing connecting the worker to the anchor. A lanyard permits limited lateral movement on the job. Its length (and placement of the anchor) determines the amount of free fall a worker experiences before the protective device stops the fall.

Body Belts

Body belts are not acceptable as part of a personnel fall arrest system. However, the use of a body belt in a positioning device system is acceptable.

- Positioning devices shall be inspected prior to each use for wear, damage, and other deterioration, and defective components shall be removed from service.

Harnesses

Full-body harnesses encompass the torso and are attached to other parts of the fall arrest system. A full-body harness distributes the fall arrest force over the shoulder-to-thigh body areas.

Retracting Lifeline Devices

Retracting lifeline devices are portable, self-contained devices fixed to an anchorage point above the work area. They act as an automatic taut lanyard. The lifeline rope, webbing, or cable is attached directly to the worker's body harness. The line extends out of the device as distance increases and retracts as the worker moves closer. At the moment a fall occurs, a centrifugal locking mechanism is activated to arrest the movement, thereby reducing the potential free-fall distance shock load. This device is ideal for use on sloping roofs and angular structures, because the rope is never slack and does not interfere with the surface work.

Lifelines

A horizontal lifeline is an anchoring cable rigged between two fixed anchorage points on the same level. The line may serve as a mobile fixture to attach lanyards, lifelines, or retracting lifelines. The purpose is to limit swing injuries by providing a continuously overhead fixture point as the worker moves horizontally. Lightweight, low-stretch synthetic cables serve as a practical alternative to steel cable.

Extremely careful engineering is required for all horizontal lifelines. When used with retracting lifelines, the horizontal lifeline should be arranged overhead with little sag. The worker may not be able to travel down the horizontal lifeline slope after a fall. Slack in the line during and after a fall should be considered to determine proper clearance in relation to other obstacles and the ground.

Lifeline ("Dropline")

A dropline is a vertical lifeline that extends from an independent anchorage point and to which a lanyard is attached using a grabbing device. Ropes always must be protected from abrasive or cutting edges, which may weaken the fibers.

Weather-protected nylon and polyester lifelines with neoprene jackets are available. Polypropylene ropes are popular with utilities because of the low moisture absorption and high dielectric constant. Ultraviolet-stabilized polypropylene is popular for many suspended scaffold operations because of its light weight and low cost; however, unstabilized ropes could be hazardous after short exposures to sunlight.

Hardware Connectors

Hardware connectors consist of bolts, shackles, D-rings, snaphooks, and metal links that connect parts of the lifeline. Snaphooks should be attached to compatible hardware and never to each other. These hooks must always be tested during inspection and maintenance to see if they fully close and if they will do so on the anchorage point without stress to the gate.

Fall Arresters and Shock Absorbers

Many types of fall arresters are available in various sizes and types of lifeline. These devices slow a worker's fall or break the fall to prevent injury. Nearly all fall arresters use friction in the rope to disperse fall energy. Often, there is a gradual delay action so the body does not experience a severe jolt or shock when the fall is arrested.

Fall Arresting System

A fall arresting system (FAS) is engineered from components and designed for a work positioning system. The purpose of an FAS is not only to stop the fall, but also to ensure that the energy gained by the body during the fall is distributed so as to prevent the wearer from being injured.

It is usually easier to slowly arrest a fall and to prevent injury to the worker during and after the fall. Injuries generally occur as a result of forces acting on the body at the instant a fall is stopped or through collision with obstacles.

Work Positioning System

This is a system that permits users of harnesses and lanyards to lean to do work. Fall arrest is a separate system that does not involve the parts of a work positioning system during fall arrest.

Restraint System

This is a system that permits users of harnesses and lifelines to move up to a fall-hazard zone but restricts movements. The system must meet fall arrest requirements because of the likelihood of a free fall under some configurations of use.

RESCUE SYSTEMS

The moments following a fall can be critical in preventing worker injuries. Organizations should develop, implement, and regularly practice rescue procedures. The following section discusses rescues for aboveground and belowground or confined spaces rescues.

Aboveground

Descent devices permanently installed or immediately available at such workstations as overhead crane cabs and grain elevator workhouses can be used effectively for lowering an injured member of the crew quickly and safely to ground level. Devices with no inherent speed control require the presence of a trained rescue team or trained co-workers to supervise the rescue operation. Automatic speed-limiting descent devices reduce or eliminate the need for trained rescue personnel; the machine itself controls the injured worker's rate of descent.

Belowground Tanks or Confined Spaces

Confined spaces are those enclosed spaces that have limited openings for entry and exit, have poor ventilation, and are not designed for continuous worker occupancy. Examples of confined spaces include storage tanks, process vessels, ship compartments, pits, silos, vats, sewers, boilers, tunnels, vaults, and pipelines.

Rescue workers can be lowered into tanks or confined spaces by means of lifelines to locate workers or to determine if they need assistance.

EQUIPMENT INSPECTION AND MAINTENANCE

The fall arrest equipment manufacturer's instructions must be incorporated into a company's inspection and preventive maintenance procedures. Workers need to be trained to inspect equipment, understand the basics of static loading of fall equipment for test purposes, and check equipment for damage before each use. Equipment should be removed from service after exposure to the forces of arresting a fall or equivalent forces.

FALL PROTECTION STANDARDS

The newly approved fall protection code, ANSI/ASSE Z359, incorporates basic fall safety principles, including hazard survey, hazard elimination and control, and education and training. These standards also offer guidance on design considerations for new buildings and facilities, recognizing that design deficiencies often increase the risk for employees who may be exposed to fall hazards. For more detailed information on the ANSI/ASSE Z359 Fall Protection Code, visit asse.org.

RESPIRATORY PROTECTION

A longstanding hierarchy of controls requires employers to use engineering and work practice controls as the primary means to protect an employee's health from contaminated or oxygen-deficient air. However, if such controls are not technologically or economically feasible (or otherwise inappropriate), an employer may rely on a respiratory protection program to protect employees.

The respiratory protection program must consist of worksite-specific procedures specifying the selection, use, and care of respirators. The program must be updated as often as necessary to reflect changes in workplace conditions and respirator use.

The respiratory protection program must cover basic elements from 29 CFR 1910.134.

NOTE: If an employee is voluntarily using a filtering facepiece, then an employer is only required to provide a copy of Appendix D, 29 CFR 1910.134 to each respective user. For cases in which employers allow the voluntary use of respirators other than filtering facepieces, the costs associated with ensuring use of the respirator itself does not create a hazard, such as medical evaluations and maintenance, must be provided at no cost to the employee.

SELECTING RESPIRATORY PROTECTION

Given the hundreds of toxic substances workers may encounter and the wide variety of respiratory protection equipment available, making the right choice of breathing equipment can be a difficult task.

The proper selection of respiratory protective equipment involves three steps: (1) identifying the hazard; (2) evaluating the hazard; and (3) selecting the appropriate, approved respiratory equipment based on the first two considerations.

IDENTIFICATION OF THE HAZARD

Airborne hazards that could require respiratory protection generally fall into the following basic categories (taken from the OSHA Technical Manual, Chapter 2, Section VIII:

Dusts

Particles that are formed or generated from solid organic or inorganic materials by reducing their size through mechanical processes such as crushing, grinding, drilling, abrading, or blasting.

Fumes

Particles formed when a volatilized solid, such as a metal, condenses in cool air. This physical change is often accompanied by a chemical reaction, such as oxidation. Examples are lead oxide fumes from smelting and iron oxide fumes from arc welding. A fume can also be formed when a material such as magnesium metal is burned or when welding or gas cutting is done on galvanized metal.

Mists

A mist is formed when a finely divided liquid is suspended in the air. These suspended liquid droplets can be generated by condensation from the gaseous to the liquid state or by breaking up a liquid into a dispersed state, such as by splashing, foaming, or atomizing. Examples are the oil mist produced during cutting and grinding operations, acid mists from electroplating, acid or alkali mists from pickling operations, paint spray mist from spraying operations, and the condensation of water vapor to form a fog or rain.

Gases

Gases are formless fluids that occupy the space or enclosure and that can be changed to the liquid or solid state only by the combined effect of increased pressure and decreased temperature. Examples are welding gases (such as acetylene, nitrogen, helium, and argon); carbon monoxide generated from the operation of internal combustion engines; and hydrogen sulfide, which is formed wherever there is decomposition of materials containing sulfur under reducing conditions.

Vapors

Vapors are the gaseous form of substances that are normally in the solid or liquid state at room temperature and pressure. They are formed by evaporation from a liquid or solid and can be found where parts-cleaning and painting take place and where solvents are used.

Smoke

Smoke consists of carbon or soot particles resulting from the incomplete combustion of carbonaceous materials such as coal or oil. Smoke generally contains droplets as well as dry particles.

Oxygen Deficiency

An oxygen-deficient atmosphere has an oxygen content below 0.5% by volume. Oxygen deficiency may occur in confined spaces, which include, but are not limited to, storage tanks, process vessels, towers, drums, tank cars, bins, sewers, septic tanks, underground utility tunnels, manholes, and pits.

Biological Agents

Some biological agents are pathogenic microorganisms or infectious agents that could cause disease in a susceptible population. Tuberculosis is spread by airborne droplets when a person coughs, sneezes, or speaks, and use of respiratory protection can be an effective response measure. Other biological agents, such as the bacterium *Chlamydia psittaci* and *Histoplasma capsulatum* spores, are examples of health hazards for which respiratory protection could be helpful in reducing potential exposures.

EVALUATION OF THE HAZARD

The next step in a respirator selection process is a walkthrough survey of the facility to identify employee groups, processes, or worker environments where the use of respiratory protective equipment may be required. The physical and chemical nature of the identified hazard(s) must be evaluated, potential exposures quantified (concentrations, length and nature of exposure), the surrounding environment assessed, and other potential stressors identified (physical and psychological, if present).

There will be one of two outcomes from the hazard evaluation. Either (1) respiratory protection is needed; or (2) engineering and administrative controls are sufficient to protect the health of the workers. If the hazard evaluation indicates the need for a respiratory program, then it is important to know which respirator to select for use.

NIOSH recommends that the hazard evaluation include examining the nature and extent of the hazard, work requirements and conditions, and the characteristics and limitations of the respirators available.

For atmospheres that are immediately dangerous to life and health (IDLH), the highest level of respiratory protection and reliability is required. Only the following respirators must be provided for use in an IDLH atmosphere: either a full-facepiece pressure demand self-contained breathing apparatus (SCBA) certified for a minimum service life of 30 min, or a combination full-facepiece, pressure-demand, supplied-air respirator (SAR) with an auxiliary self-contained air supply.

PROTECTION FACTORS

Assigned protection factors (APFs) are used to indicate the level of effectiveness a respirator provides to the wearer. An employer should ensure that the APF for an assigned respirator is adequate to provide protection from the identified hazardous contaminant. In August 2006, OSHA published its final rule, Assigned Protection Factors, 29 CFR Parts 1910, 1915, and 1926, that mandates the use of specified APFs by employers when selecting respiratory protection for workers.

AIR-SUPPLYING RESPIRATORS

Air-supplying respirators provide a breathing gas (usually air) to the worker. The different types are classified according to (1) the method used to supply breathing gas; and (2) the method used to regulate the gas supply.

Self-Contained Breathing Apparatus

An SCBA provides a transportable supply of breathing air and affords protection against both toxic chemicals and oxygen deficiency. The wearer carries enough air or oxygen for up to 4 hours, depending on the design.

COMBINATION SUPPLIED-AIR SCBA RESPIRATORS

Combination respirators have an auxiliary air supply to protect workers against potential failure of the compressor. An air tank of 3-, 5- or 10-minute service time is typically used, mainly for emergency and escape for IDLH. The SCBA part is used only when the air line fails and the wearer must escape, or when the worker disconnects the line temporarily to change locations.

AIR-PURIFYING RESPIRATORS

Air-purifying respirators can purify the air of gases, vapors, and particulates but do not supply clean breathing air. They must never be used in oxygen-deficient atmospheres. The useful life of the air-purifying device is limited by (1) the concentration of the air contaminant; (2) breathing demand of the wearer; and (3) removal capacity of the air-purifying medium (cartridge or filter).

The second type of air-purifying respirator, the particulate respirator, is also known as a mechanical filter respirator. Depending on the design, the filters can screen out dust, fog, fumes, mist, spray, or smoke by passing the contaminated air through a pad or filter. (They do not provide protection against gases, vapors, or oxygen deficiency.) These respirators consist of a facepiece with an attached mechanical filter, papers, or similar filter substance. The classes of nonpowered particulate respirators require following a decision logic for selection of the proper respirator. A synopsis of the selection process for using the new particulate classification is outlined as follows:

- If no oil particles are present, use a filter of any series (i.e., N-, R-, or P-series).
- If oil particles (e.g., lubricants, cutting fluids, etc.) are present, use an R- or P-series filter.
- If oil particles are present and the filter is to be used for more than one work shift, use only a P-series filter.

Selection of filter efficiency (i.e., 95, 99, or 99.97%) depends on how much filter leakage can be accepted. Higher filter efficiency means lower filter leakage and a higher degree of protection. The choice of facepiece depends on the level of protection needed—that is, the assigned protection factor (APF) discussed earlier.

Gas Masks

Gas masks have been used effectively for many years for respiratory protection against certain gases, vapors, and particulate matter that otherwise might be harmful to life or health. Gas masks are air-purifying devices designed solely to remove specific contaminants from the air; therefore, it is essential that their use be restricted to atmospheres that contain sufficient oxygen to support life.

FITTING RESPIRATORS

Required fit tests must be performed before an employee uses a respirator in the workplace. Fit-testing is required for all employees fulfilling any of the following criteria:

- using negative or positive pressure tight-fitting respirators
- where such respirators are required by OSHA
- where the employer requires the use of such a respirator.

Fit tests must be repeated under the following guidelines:

- at least annually
- whenever a different respirator facepiece is used
- whenever a change in the employee's physical condition could affect respirator fit.

A fit test is not required for voluntary users or for escape-only respirators.

Facial hair, jewelry, corrective glasses or goggles, or other personal protective equipment must not interfere with the seal of the facepiece of tight-fitting respirators.

1. The tight-fitting respirator is designed to form a seal with the face of the wearer. It is available in three types: quarter-mask, half-mask, and full facepiece.
2. The loose-fitting respirator has a respiratory inlet covering that is designed to form a partial seal with the face. These include loose-fitting facepieces, as well as hoods, helmets, blouses, or full suits, all of which cover the head completely. Because the hood is not tight-fitting, it is important that sufficient air is provided to maintain a slight positive pressure inside the hood relative to the environment immediately outside the hood. In this way, an outward flow of air from the respirator will prevent contaminants from entering the hood.

Qualitative Tests

In the irritant or odorous chemical agent test, the wearer is exposed to an irritant smoke (isoamyl acetate vapor) or other suitable test agent easily detectable by irritation, odor, or taste. An air-purifying respirator must be equipped with the appropriate air-purifying element. If the wearer cannot detect any penetration of the test agent, the respirator is probably tight enough.

The advantages of a qualitative test are speed, convenience, and ease of performing the test. However, these tests rely on the wearer's subjective response, so they may not be entirely reliable.

Quantitative Tests

In quantitative testing, the employee, wearing a specially designed probed respirator, stands in a test chamber and is exposed to a test atmosphere of a nontoxic, easily detectable aerosol, vapor, or gaseous test agent. Instrumentation is used to measure the leakage into the respirator.

Protection factors can be determined from quantitative fit tests by dividing the ambient airborne concentration of the challenge contaminant by the concentration inside the facepiece. For example, if the concentration outside the facepiece is 500 parts per million (ppm), and the concentration inside the respirator is 10 ppm, the protection factor would be 50. Protection factors are used in the selection process to determine the maximum use concentration (muc), which is determined by multiplying the Threshold Limit Value (TLV) or permissible exposure level (PEL) by the protection factor.

The greatest advantage of a quantitative test is that it does not rely on a subjective response. The quantitative test is recommended when facepiece leakage must be minimized for work in highly toxic or IDLH atmospheres.

Quantitative fitting tests require expensive equipment that can be operated only by trained personnel.

Daily Fit Test

Employees who wear respirators should check the fit of their respirator each time they don it, with both negative- and positive-pressure tests.

STORAGE OF RESPIRATORS

Respirators should be stored to protect them from dust, sunlight, heat, extreme cold, excessive moisture, and damaging chemicals. Unprotected respirators can sustain damaged parts or facepiece distortion that make them ineffective.

Before storing the respirator, clean or wash the device according to the manufacturer's instructions. Wiping a respirator with a cloth is not acceptable practice because fibers from the cloth can be deposited on the respirator's surface. Workers should never store the respirator with folds or creases and should never hang it by the elastic headband or place it in a position that will stretch the facepiece.

MAINTENANCE OF RESPIRATORS

The ongoing maintenance of the respirators themselves is an essential part of the respiratory protection program. If the equipment malfunctions because of poor maintenance, the employee may be exposed to a potentially fatal hazard.

The maintenance program should incorporate the manufacturer's instructions and should include provisions for disassembly, including the removal of the respirator's purifying elements, cleaning, sanitizing, inspecting for defects, repairing parts (if necessary), installing purifying elements, reassembling, packaging, and storing equipment.

CLEANING AND SANITIZING

Make sure that each time an employee uses a respirator it is clean and sanitized.

The respiratory protection equipment should be dismantled and washed with whatever cleaner the manufacturer recommends in warm water using a brush, thoroughly rinsed in clean water, and then air dried in a clean place.

Workers should follow the manufacturer's instructions regarding which cleaners to use. Check with the manufacturer for disinfectants that will not damage the respirators.

INSPECTION OF RESPIRATORS

After cleaning and sanitizing, each respirator should be reassembled and inspected for proper working condition and repair or replacement of parts. The respirator should also be inspected routinely by the user immediately before each use to ensure that it is in proper working condition.

TRAINING

Once the right respirator has been selected, the wearer must be trained in its proper use and care. This step is important for every type of respirator. Each user should not only be trained when first acquiring the equipment but also be retrained periodically.

The instructor should be a qualified person, such as an industrial hygienist, safety professional, nurse, or the respirator manufacturer's representative.

MEDICAL SURVEILLANCE

Employers must provide a medical evaluation to determine each employee's fitness to wear a respirator before initial fit-testing and prior to using a respirator for the first time. Medical evaluations consist of the administration of a medical questionnaire that can be found in the mandatory Appendix C of 29 CFR 1910.134, or provision of a physical examination that elicits the same information as the questionnaire for the employee.

HAND AND ARM PROTECTION

No one type of PPE for the extremities is suitable for the many different work situations involved in any business or industrial operation, from the laboratory to the loading dock. Thus, management and workers must select proper protection for the hands, fingers, arms, and skin based on potential exposure to identified hazards. The specific type of protection and its material depend on the type of material being handled and the work atmosphere.

GLOVES

The material to be used for gloves largely depends on what is being handled. For most light work not involving exposure to hazardous materials or microbial contamination, a cotton glove is satisfactory and inexpensive. Rough or abrasive material requires leather gloves or leather reinforced with metal stitching for safe handling. Leather reinforced by metal stitching or metal mesh or highly cut-resistant plastic gloves also provide good protection from edged tools, as in butchering and similar occupations. Double gloving affords added protection. If the outer glove starts to degrade or tears, the inner glove may offer protection until the gloves are removed and replaced. It is a good idea to check the outer glove frequently, watching for signs of deterioration (color, texture change, holes, etc.) and re-glove as necessary.

Many plastic and plastic-coated gloves are available in materials such as neoprene, latex, and nitrile. They are designed to protect workers from a variety of hazards. Management must give careful consideration to actual permeation tests of these gloves against hazardous chemicals. Some plastic models surpass leather in durability and effective shielding. Other types have granules or rough materials incorporated into the plastic for better gripping ability, while still others are disposable. Computer software is now available to help select the appropriate glove material. Most manufacturers can provide information regarding the rate and degree of chemical permeation through their glove materials.

Exposure to proteins from the use of natural rubber latex (NRL) products may result in adverse responses in susceptible workers. These could include irritation and several types of allergic reactions. Recommended strategies for risk reduction include reducing unnecessary exposure to NRL proteins for all workers. For example, workers in food service or landscaping industries do not need to use NRL gloves for food-handling or gardening purposes.

When workers do not need complete gloves, they can wear finger stalls or cots. These are available in combinations of one or more fingers and are usually made of rubber, duck, leather, plastic, and metal mesh. The construction of the cot depends on the degree or type of hazard to which the worker is exposed. Employees should not use gloves while working on moving machinery such as drills, saws, grinders, or other rotating and moving equipment. Machine parts might catch the glove and pull it and the worker's hand into hazardous areas.

In addition to gloves, workers also can wear mittens (including one-finger and reversible types), pads, thumb guards, finger cots, wrist and forearm protectors, elbow guards, sleeves, and capes. These protective devices are made in a wide range of materials and lengths.

Gloves or mittens having metal parts or reinforcements should never be used around electrical apparatus. Work on energized or high-voltage electric equipment requires specially made and tested rubber gloves. Workers should wear overgloves of leather to protect the rubber gloves against wire punctures and cuts and to protect the rubber in the event of electrical flashes. Conduct frequent tests and inspections of line workers' rubber gloves and discard those that fail to meet original specifications.

HAND LEATHERS AND ARM PROTECTORS

For jobs requiring protection from heat or from extremely abrasive or splintery material (such as rough lumber), hand leathers or hand pads are likely to be more satisfactory than gloves. This is primarily because they can be made heavier and less flexible without discomfort.

Because hand leathers or pads are used mainly for handling heavy materials, they should not be used around moving machinery. They must always be sufficiently loose to allow workers to slip their hands and fingers out of the device if it is caught on a rough edge or nail.

For protection against heat, hand and arm protectors should be made of wool, terry, or glass fiber. Although leather can be used, it will not withstand temperatures over 150 F (65 C). Wristlets or arm protectors may be obtained in any of the materials of which gloves are made.

IMPERVIOUS CLOTHING

For protection against dusts, vapors, and moisture of hazardous substances and corrosive liquids, the safety and health professional can choose from among many types of impervious or impermeable materials. These are fabricated into clothing of all descriptions, depending on the hazards involved. They range from aprons and bibs of sheet plastic to suits that enclose the body from head to foot and contain their own air supply.

Gloves coated with synthetic rubber, synthetic elastomers, polyvinyl chloride, or other plastics offer protection against all types of petroleum products, caustic soda, tannic acid, muriatic and hydrochloric acid, and even sulfuric acid. These gloves are available in varying degrees of strength to meet individual conditions.

Where acid may splash, rubber boots or rubber shoes also should be worn. Never tuck trousers into boots when working with corrosive materials. If workers wear safety shoes inside their boots, the legs of impervious trousers should cover the tops of the shoes. These precautions keep the liquid from draining off aprons or trousers into the footwear.

PROCEDURAL STEPS

After PPE is used in a corrosive atmosphere, management must establish a strict procedure for disposing of the equipment to prevent workers from coming into contact with contaminated parts. Before the equipment is removed, it should be thoroughly washed with a hose stream whether or not it has come in contact with the corrosive chemical. Boots, coats, aprons, and hats should then be taken off, followed by removal of the gloves. This is the logical order of removal if the coat has been properly put on with the sleeves outside the cuffs of the gloves.

PROTECTIVE FOOTWEAR

Specifications for protective footwear are contained in ASTM F2413-05, Standard Specification for Performance Requirements for Foot Protection. Protective footwear is classified according to its ability to meet both the requirements for compression resistance and impact resistance. All protective footwear meeting the ASTM F2413 standard contains a protective toe box. Steel, reinforced plastic, and hard rubber are materials commonly used to make protective toe boxes. For protection in wet conditions, rubber footwear is also available with toe protection. Five other types of protection are available in addition to the basic toe protection.

Regulations such as OSHA standards 29 CFR 1910.132, General Requirements for Personal Protective Equipment, and 29 CFR 1910.136, Foot Protection, contain hazard assessment and foot protection requirements for employees whose work presents hazards to their feet. These hazards include objects falling onto or placed on the foot, objects rolling over the foot, sharp objects penetrating the sole of the footwear, static electricity buildup, and contact with energized electrical conductors.

Although comfort and proper fit are important factors for any footwear, it is particularly essential for protective footwear in order to encourage employee use. Management should carefully select foot protection to match the specific hazards faced by the wearer; educate employees on the need for such protection; and train workers in the proper use, care, and replacement of footwear.

METATARSAL FOOTWEAR
Metatarsal footwear is designed to prevent or reduce the severity of injury to the metatarsal bones and toe areas of the foot.

CONDUCTIVE FOOTWEAR
Conductive, protective-toe footwear is intended to protect employees from the hazards of static electricity buildup and help equalize the electrical potential between the wearer and energized high-voltage power lines in the wearer's immediate area.

ELECTRICAL HAZARD FOOTWEAR
Protective-toe electrical hazard footwear is intended to protect workers against contact with exposed circuits of up to 100 v AC/750 v DC under dry condi-

tions. This type of footwear is not intended for use in explosive or hazardous locations where conductive footwear is required. Electrical hazard footwear is intended to provide secondary electrical hazard protection on surfaces that are substantially insulated. Because the electrical insulative quality of the heel and sole provides the protection in this footwear, no metal parts should be used in these parts of the shoes.

STATIC DISSIPATIVE FOOTWEAR

Protective-toe static dissipative footwear is designed to reduce the accumulation of excess static electricity in the body by conducting the charge to ground while maintaining a sufficiently high level of resistance to protect the wearer from electrical hazards.

SOLE-PUNCTURE-RESISTANT FOOTWEAR

Protective-toe footwear with sole-puncture resistance reduces the risk of puncture wounds caused by sharp objects penetrating the sole of the footwear. A protective shield inserted in the sole of the footwear covers an area from the toes to overlap the crest of the heel.

FOUNDRY FOOTWEAR

Specialty types of footwear are available to protect workers in the smelting and foundry industries, where employees' feet can be exposed to molten metals. Such footwear often has no fasteners so they can be removed quickly in an emergency. Some NSC members in the foundry and smelting business have reported instances in which workers have suffered serious burns to their feet when unable to quickly remove ordinary footwear that came in contact with molten metal. In these occupations, the tops of the footwear should be covered by protective spats, leggings, and other devices that will prevent the entry of molten metal.

OTHER FEATURES OF PROTECTIVE FOOTWEAR

Other protective footwear features not covered by standards are made available by various manufacturers. They include waterproofing, chemical resistance, and insulation against thermal extremes. Nearly all footwear manufacturers offer some variation on materials used in the soles and upper parts of the footwear for purposes of lengthening the life of the footwear and providing sole slip resistance under various field conditions. Manufacturers of protective footwear should be consulted about the products they offer that will best protect against the hazards that the wearer will encounter on the job.

SPECIAL WORK CLOTHING

In the modern industrial environment, exposure to fire, extreme heat, molten metal, corrosive chemicals, cold temperature, body impact, cuts from handling materials, and other specialized hazards is often part of what is known as "job exposure." Special protective clothing helps to minimize the effects of these hazards, and manufacturers will usually supply sample swatches of protective materials for testing by individual firms.

PROTECTION AGAINST HEAT AND HOT METAL

Leather clothing is one of the more common forms of body protection against heat and splashes of hot metal. It also provides protection against limited impact forces and infrared and UV radiation.

Garments should be made of good-quality leather, solidly constructed, and provided with fastenings to prevent gaping during body movement. Fastenings should be so designed that the wearer can remove the garment rapidly and easily. Workers should not wear turned-up cuffs or other items of clothing that can catch and hold hot metal. Garments should either have no pockets or have pockets with flaps that can be fastened shut.

For ordinary protection against hot metal, radiant heat, or flame hazards somewhat stronger than those in welding operations, wool and leather clothing is used. Specially treated clothing has been developed that is impervious to splashes of metal up to 3,000 F (1,650 C). Wool garment requirements are, in general, the same as those for leather, except that metal fastenings should be covered with flaps to keep them from becoming dangerously hot.

Asbestos substitutes, including fiberglass or other special high-temperature-resistant materials, are available. These materials are effective when made into leggings and aprons usually worn by foundry personnel working with molten metal. Such leggings should completely encircle the leg from knee to ankle, with a flare at the bottom to cover the instep. The design of the leggings should permit rapid removal in emergencies.

If the front part of the legging is reinforced, it can provide impact protection when required. Fiberboard is the most common material used for reinforcement.

When people must work in extremely high temperatures up to 2,000 F (1,090 C)—as in furnace and oven repair, coking, slagging, fire fighting, and fire rescue work—aluminized fabrics are essential. Aluminized heat-resistant clothing generally falls into two classes: emergency and fire proximity suits.

Emergency suits are used when temperatures exceed 1,000 F (540 C), as in a kiln or furnace, or when workers must move through burning areas for fire-fighting or rescue operations. These suits are made of aluminized glass fiber with layers of quilted glass fibers and a wool lining on the inside.

Fire proximity suits are used in areas near high-temperature operations, such as slagging, coking, furnace repair work with hot ingots, and fire fighting where workers do not enter the flame area. These suits are seldom one-piece construction. They depend primarily on the reflective ability of an aluminized coating on a base cloth of glass fiber or synthetic fiber. Remember, never use fire proximity clothing for situations in which workers are required to enter a fire.

FLAME-RETARDANT WORK CLOTHES

Cotton work clothing can be protected against flame or small sparks by flame-proofing. One available commercial flame-retardant preparation can be applied to work clothing in ordinary laundry machinery after the garment is washed. Treating the material has two advantages: it makes the cloth highly flame resistant and adds little to the material's weight or stiffness.

PROTECTION AGAINST IMPACT AND CUTS

A worker's body needs protection from cuts, bruises, and abrasions on most jobs where heavy, sharp, or rough material is handled. Special protectors have been developed for almost all parts of the body and are available from suppliers of safety equipment. (See also the section "Hand and Arm Protection" earlier in this chapter.)

For example, pads made of cushioned or padded duck will protect the shoulders and back from bruises when workers carry heavy loads or objects with rough edges. Aprons of padded leather, fabric, plastic, hard fiber, or metal can protect the abdomen against blows. Similar devices of metal, hard fiber, or leather with metal reinforcements shield the worker against sharp blows with edged tools. Leg protection is required on many jobs. Guards of hard fiber or metal are widely used to protect the shins against impact. Knee pads should be worn by mold loftsmen and others whose task requires continual kneeling.

HEAT STRESS

When selecting PPE, management must keep in mind that some types of equipment may contribute to the potential for heat stress. (See Chapter 12, Thermal Stress, in the National Safety Council's *Fundamentals of Industrial Hygiene*, 6th ed., for further information about heat stress.) Workers who wear SCBAs in combination with full-body impervious suits, such as those worn on hazardous-waste sites, are particularly vulnerable to heat stress. Such workers must be allowed adequate rest breaks. The employer should ensure employees are adequately hydrated and acclimatized to the heat. If necessary, cooling vortexes or vests should be supplied.

COLD-WEATHER CLOTHING

In recent years, thermal insulating underwear has become popular among outdoor workers because of its lightweight protection against the cold. Thermal knit cotton patterned after regular underwear, quilted materials, or synthetic polyester fabric-quilted between layers of nylon are common types of construction.

Although polyester- and nylon-quilted material does not catch fire any more easily than does cotton, once the synthetic material starts burning, it melts, forming a hot plastic mass, not unlike hot pitch, that adheres to skin and causes serious burns. Fire-retardant quilted insulating underwear is now available to combat this danger. Other special fabrics available include a nylon material that chars at a relatively high temperature and does not melt, a glass fiber material for special uses, and a breathable fabric used with a sandwich of cotton or similar material to offer excellent cold-weather protection.

When teaching workers how to dress warmly in cold weather, make sure they check not only the thermometer but wind velocity as well. The temperature may read 35°F (1.7°C), but if there is also a wind of 45 mph (72.4 km/h) it will feel like –35°F (–37°C). A high wind chill factor, as it is known, means workers must wear more layers against the cold and protect all exposed skin surfaces from frostbite and windburn.

HIGH-VISIBILITY CLOTHING

High-visibility clothing provides dramatically enhanced visibility for workers through the use of fluorescent and retroreflective materials. ANSI/ISEA 107, American National Standard for High-Visibility Safety Apparel, identifies three performance classes of apparel and headwear, based on specified amounts of materials and worker hazards and tasks, complexity of the work environment or background, and vehicular traffic and speed considerations.

- Performance class I provides a minimum specified amount of material to differentiate the wearer from the work environment and is appropriate for occupational activities that permit full and undivided attention to approaching traffic, provide ample separation of workers from traffic, and in which the vehicle and moving equipment speeds do not exceed 25 mph.
- Performance class 2 is defined as apparel for use in activities where greater visibility is needed during inclement weather conditions or in work environments with risks that exceed those for performance class 1. As such, the specified amount of high-visibility background and retroreflective materials exceeds that of performance class 1. Workers likely to utilize these garments include airport baggage handlers, crossing guards, and survey crews.
- Performance class 3 apparel provides the highest level of visibility and is designed to provide enhanced visibility to more of the body,

including arms and legs, so that the wearer can be seen through a full range of motions and be identifiable as a person. These are appropriate for employees involved in high task load projects or who are exposed to significantly higher vehicle speeds and/or reduced-sight distances, such as emergency response personnel and roadway construction workers.

When selecting the appropriate high-visibility garment, consideration should be given to the background environment to allow for contrast between the background and the wearer. For example, roadway construction workers should consider colors other than orange to differentiate themselves from barriers, traffic cones, and heavy equipment.

SPECIAL CLOTHING

Safety experts have developed many ingenious, highly specialized types of clothing for protection against special hazards. A partial list includes such items as:

- disposable clothing made of plastic or reinforced paper for exposure to low-level nuclear radiation, for use in the drug and electronic industries, or for hazardous materials work, where contamination may be a problem
- leaded clothing made of lead glass fiber cloth, leaded rubber, or leaded plastic, for laboratory workers and other personnel exposed to x-rays or gamma radiation
- electromagnetic radiation suits, which provide protection from the harmful biologic effects of electromagnetic radiation found in high-level radar fields and similar hazardous areas
- conductive clothing, made of a conductive cloth, for use by lineworkers doing bare-hand work on extra-high-voltage conductors; such clothing keeps the worker at the proper potential.

For special applications, manufacturers have a vast number of materials they can draw upon to meet specific hazards.

SUMMARY

- Once a company decides on the use of PPE, it should develop a company policy on PPE usage for employees and visitors, select the proper equipment for the existing hazards, implement a training program, and enforce the use of PPE.
- Companies can encourage workers to use PPE by enlisting the aid of line supervisors and managers, letting employees have some choice in the

type of equipment purchased, and establishing a sound training program with consistent enforcement of all rules and regulations.

- All workers exposed to head injury hazards must wear protective headwear to shield them from falling objects, blows, electric shock and burns.

- Protective devices for the eyes and face include safety glasses, goggles, and face shields. Face shields alone generally do not provide adequate protection against eye injuries and must be combined with basic eye protective glasses or goggles.

- Management must evaluate the workplace for hearing hazards and determine the need for hearing protection devices. Daily work in steady noise of more than 85 dB for 8-hour shifts is considered hazardous noise exposure. Hearing protectors are categorized as enclosure, aural, superaural, and circumaural.

- Fall arrest protection, either active or passive, is defined as a means of preventing workers from experiencing disastrous falls from elevations. In selecting the right fall protection system, management should conduct a thorough job survey analysis and establish a fall protection program. Companies must also develop rescue procedures for retrieving a fallen worker from aboveground, belowground, or confined-space operations.

- To protect workers from airborne health hazards, management must provide respiratory protection equipment against gaseous, particulate, and combination contaminants and oxygen-deficient environments. Respirators are classified as air-supplying or air-purifying devices. All respirators must be routinely inspected, cleaned, and properly stored to ensure their protective effectiveness.

- Safety footwear includes steel, reinforced plastic, and hard rubber models, depending on the shoe design protective level required. Some jobs require conductive, nonconductive, foundry, or special-design safety shoes to protect workers' feet from injury.

- Special protective clothing is used to shield workers from such workplace hazards as heat, hot metal, chemical splashes, weather extremes, and electrical shock or burns.

REVIEW QUESTIONS

1. What are the three broad categories of methods used to control harmful exposures to hazardous substances?
2. Define personal protective equipment (PPE).

3. Information on certified equipment is available through which of the following?
   a. Environmental Protection Agency (EPA)
   b. Safety Equipment Institute (SEI)
   c. National Institute for Occupational Safety and Health (NIOSH)
   d. all of the above
   e. only b and c
4. Which of the following adds considerably to the protection offered by a helmet?
   a. chin strap
   b. bump cap
   c. paint applied after manufacture of helmet
   d. all of the above
5. Name the standard established by the American National Standards Institute (ANSI) for eye and face protection.
6. The aspect of protective eye lenses that provides the filtering effect against infrared and UV radiation is:
   a. color
   b. chemical composition
   c. cost
   d. all of the above
7. Briefly describe the four types of hearing protection devices.
8. Name the two classifications of fall protection systems.
9. List three devices used in passive fall arrest systems.
10. How often should audiometric testing be done on employees?
    a. when new employees are hired
    b. when new employees are hired and annually thereafter
    c. annually
    d. every 2 years
11. Name five components of active fall arrest systems.
12. What are the three steps in selecting respiratory protective equipment?
13. The two main categories of respirators are:_____and_____.
14. Gloves or mittens having metal parts or reinforcements should never be used around _____.
15. Protective footwear is classified according to its ability to meet what two requirements?

14

Lab Safety

LABORATORY SAFETY

Laboratories are typically small (one- or two-room), general-use workplaces designed to provide as much flexibility as possible to manage potentially hazardous operations. These operations can vary frequently (often from week to week) and are generally managed on a case-by-case basis by many different individuals. Laboratories can be found in clinical, industrial, and academic settings. They also have varied purposes, such as teaching, research, and routine quality control testing of industrial products.

The hazards associated with laboratory settings vary widely, but they share some common characteristics. Hazardous materials are present in small quantities. For example, according to the OSHA laboratory standard (29 CFR 1910.1450), *laboratory scale* refers to hazardous chemicals in quantities that are easily and safely manipulated by one person. Engineering controls are usually limited to general ventilation of the room, some generic local ventilation units (e.g., fume hoods and biological safety cabinets), and chemical storage cabinets. This means that laboratory safety depends to a large extent on the professional expertise of the workers and the administrative controls this expertise supports.

Regulatory requirements and consensus guidelines, when properly implemented, can help ensure that these operations are conducted in a manner safe to the worker and environment. Unfortunately, many regulations that apply to the materials used in laboratories are written with industrial-scale use of chemicals in mind. In many cases, this leaves significant ambiguity as to how these regulations apply in laboratory settings. For this reason, each laboratory process should be assessed for potential risks, and appropriate safeguards should be put into place. These safeguards will often go beyond regulatory requirements.

Some of the more common hazards encountered in laboratories that should be evaluated include chemical hazards, biohazards, ionizing and nonionizing radiation, and physical hazards. To provide an overview of identification and control of these hazards, this chapter discusses the following topics:
- laboratory safety management
- chemical safety practices and applicable regulations
- biological safety, biosafety levels, and appropriate containment measures
- the nature and hazards of ionizing, nonionizing, and laser radiation and how these hazards are controlled
- special considerations for working in altered environments and other unusual laboratory hazards.

LABORATORY SAFETY MANAGEMENT

Laboratories are general-purpose workplaces designed to permit the safe use of a wide variety of hazardous materials and processes using generic safety equipment such as fume hoods and flammable storage cabinets. In general, safe laboratory practice uses few engineering controls and relies heavily on the technical training of laboratory staff to develop and follow administrative controls specific to the work at hand. The OSHA laboratory standard (29 CFR 1910.1450) addresses the importance of these administrative controls when it requires the development and implementation of a chemical hygiene plan (CHP) and the appointment of a chemical hygiene officer (CHO) for laboratories. To understand why administrative controls are the preferred approach to laboratory hazards, it is helpful to first discuss the nature and magnitude of these hazards.

SCALE OF LABORATORY HAZARDS

Chemical Hazards

Laboratories use a wide variety of chemicals in varying amounts and ways. The hazards associated with these chemicals vary similarly. For example, in biomedical laboratories, flammable liquids in gallon quantities and other auxiliary chemicals with a range of physical and health hazards in similar and smaller quantities are likely to be found. However, which specific chemicals will be used on a day-to-day basis is quite unpredictable. On the other hand, chemistry and engineering research laboratories may routinely work with highly reactive materials in quantities that present explosion or other reactivity hazards.

Generally, laboratory chemicals include flammable chemicals, corrosive chemicals (acids and bases), reactive chemicals (which can be water reactive or explosive under certain conditions), and acutely toxic chemicals. Many of these chemicals are in weak concentrations that present a much lower hazard than those described on Safety Data Sheets (SDSs) for those chemicals. In many laboratories, unnamed chemicals are produced. Although, generally, the flammability or corrosivity of these new chemicals may be predictable, their toxicity is not.

Biological Hazards

Biological laboratories work with specific biological agents in the course of their research. These laboratories are proliferating rapidly as biotechnology applications expand. The risk of exposure to these biological agents is rated as biosafety levels on a scale of 1 to 4 by the scientific community, with 1 representing biological agents not known to cause illness in healthy humans, and 4 representing a biological agent that presents a high individual risk of aerosol transmitted laboratory infection for which there is no cure. For example, human blood is a Biosafety Level 2 agent, which means it can cause illness in healthy people if the person comes into mucous membrane or injection contact with the material and a disease is present. *Biosafety levels* refer not only to the biological agent, but to the laboratory facility and to the practices to be implemented.

Radiation Hazards

Many laboratories use radioactive isotopes and/or electrically powered sources of radiation of various kinds in their work. The strength of unsealed chemicals marked with radioactive isotopes is barely above natural background levels in the environment. The primary health concern associated with such unsealed sources is the ingestion of these materials, in which case they could cause health concerns for exposed individuals. Radiation from x-ray devices and other electrically powered radiation sources is a concern when these units are turned on. These devices are marked with radiation hazard signs similar to those for radioactive chemicals.

Physical Hazards

Laboratories also include many physical hazards, such as strong magnets, lasers of all classes, gas cylinders, and high-voltage electricity. Many of these are permanently located in specific rooms designed to control these hazards. Other hazards are mobile depending on the needs of particular processes, so some rooms may not be designed for them.

THE CHALLENGES OF LABORATORY SAFETY MANAGEMENT

Laboratory safety management involves many different aspects. The safety manager not only must master a significant amount of technical, scientific, and safety information, but also must understand government regulations and how they are enforced. He or she must be comfortable with management information (such as budgets and deadlines) that helps him or her to understand how decisions are made within the organization. The safety manager must use communication and leadership skills to develop a set of safety recommendations and present this information in an effective way. This section provides a brief review of these different issues.

Scientific Information

Understanding the safety implications of work under way in a laboratory requires at least a general understanding of the work itself. For example, identifying the hazards associated with the chemicals in use requires looking at specific physical properties such as flash point, pH, and known incompatibilities with other chemicals. It is also important to understand how the use of this information is affected by the concentrations and amounts of the chemicals and how the hazards associated with these properties will change as the process proceeds. The laboratory safety program must also address situations in which this information is unavailable. One way is by including provisions in the safety program to ensure that scientists will discuss the properties of the chemicals they are using to elicit whatever information is available to make reasonable predictions of these factors.

Regulatory Information

Although the OSHA lab standard is a reasonable and flexible approach to the laboratory work setting, the same cannot be said of all government regulations that apply to laboratories. For example, the lab standard acknowledges that the chemical hygiene plan must address issues such as proper disposal of the chemicals involved in laboratory processes. This issue will be determined by EPA's Resource Conservation and Recovery Act (RCRA) regulations (40 CFR 239–299) and state variants of these regulations. A chemical waste disposal plan must address the Department of Transportation's requirements for shipment of hazardous materials (49 CFR 100–185) and the transport of threshold quantities of certain waste chemicals is covered by Department of Homeland Security requirements for security plans (6 CFR 27).

Combining all of these requirements, with their varying jargon and expectations, requires understanding not only the text of the appropriate regulations, but also the enforcement policies of the relevant agencies. These factors must be connected with each other to develop a coherent plan that answers the question, "What do I do with this stuff now that I'm finished with it?" Similar chains of regulatory responsibility can be developed for many other laboratory safety questions.

Management Information

Laboratory safety is significantly affected by the nature of the work to be carried out, the facilities available in which to conduct the work, and the people available to do the work. These choices are made by the management of the organization that oversees the laboratory. The laboratory safety program must consider any such factors that may compete with its recommendations for prudent laboratory practice. Such factors can include budget limitations, deadline requirements, available facilities and equipment, and the level of training of laboratory workers. For example, requiring the use of a fume hood for all chemicals may not be achievable if not enough fume hoods are available. The laboratory safety program's resources may be better spent delineating which materials require the use of a fume hood and which may be used with appropriate precautions in areas served by the laboratory's general ventilation, while advocating for addition of more hoods in the laboratory facility over time.

Communication and Leadership Skills

The appropriate guidelines for conducting safe work in the laboratory are established by the controlling entity and must be communicated to the affected stakeholders. This often requires translating the regulatory requirements to the scientist while describing the requirements of the laboratory process in the terms of the regulatory standard. In effect, both the regulatory parties and the laboratory parties must have confidence in the abilities of the laboratory safety program manager's competence for them to accept his or her guidance related to regulatory issues.

To successfully transmit their recommendations, laboratory safety managers must use good communication skills, both oral and written, and the ability to provide leadership around laboratory safety issues for groups with multiple competing priorities.

The Unexpected

Laboratory safety would not be an issue if all work went according to plan. No one plans to create situations that risk their own or others' health or put their work in danger of being lost. However, laboratory safety issues inevitably arise when an adopted procedure is inadequate to meet events that transpire. These events can become emergencies that involve assistance from outside agencies such as fire departments and emergency medical services. The laboratory safety program must address these issues, not only in terms of emergency planning and response, but also by using these events as opportunities for developing information from "lessons learned" that can be incorporated into future work practices. Again, this role requires not only technical knowledge, but also effective use of communication supported by leadership skills, both during and after the emergency.

LABORATORY SAFETY MANAGEMENT TOOLS

The challenges just described may seem daunting. However, important tools are available for use in laboratory safety programs. The safety manager has the opportunity to connect with workers' self-interest when developing and implementing safety guidelines. Not only are laboratory workers' health and safety involved, but following safety protocols significantly enhances the protection of their work and its validity. Laboratory safety programs can take advantage of two other key assets: peer sharing and support and development of a management system approach to the work.

Peer Sharing and Support

Safety professionals often lack the resources they need to meet the challenges and opportunities presented by their role and the variety of skills required to succeed in their goals. Fortunately, they are not alone; many other safety professionals face similar challenges every day. These professionals form an important peer-to-peer support network for both technical and management advice. In particular, the Internet has developed into a professional communication medium that provides many low-cost opportunities to learn and elicit advice from peers in other organizations. Sharing information resources such as training materials, forms, and experiences with similar situations via websites and e-mail lists is a common and often critical strategy to support a laboratory safety program as new technologies and related hazards arise.

A Management System Approach

Because there is no "bright line" between safe and unsafe conditions in the laboratory, developing laboratory safety guidelines quickly leads to larger questions such as, "How does an organization as a whole effectively manage laboratory safety?" and "What tools are available to make this process easier and more effective?" The answers often revolve around the amount of resources an organization is willing (or able) to put into safety response efforts. For this reason, these questions fall into the management category, not only for the laboratory safety manager, but also for the upper management of the organization.

A key strategy for approaching these questions is to set goals for continuous improvement of the safety program by establishing indicators of the program's success that can be tracked over time. Fortunately, significant research into how to implement this approach has taken place over the last few decades. For an example of such work, see OSHA's Voluntary Protection Programs.

This research has led to a focus on the "Plan, Do, Check, Act" management system approach to health and safety issues based on Dr. Edward Deming's theories of quality control. More specifically, occupational safety management systems (SMSs) have come to the forefront as an important organizational tool in identifying ways to continuously improve the safety program. Figure 14–1 provides a conceptual outline of how this approach works. In the case of the laboratory safety program, the laboratory safety plan and its associated procedures and documentation fill the "standardization" role of the "chock" that maintains safety program improvements over time.

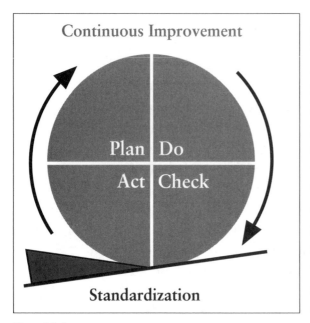

Figure 14–1.

A SAMPLE SAFETY MANAGEMENT SYSTEM FOR LABORATORIES

A safety management system (SMS) does not provide a cookie-cutter approach to laboratory safety. The specifics of the safety program developed will depend on the specific resources and needs of the organization involved. The SMS model is best used to assess whether the safety program is complete and balanced from both a management and a compliance point of view. This means expressing the program activities in terms of performance indicators and goals for those indicators. These indicators may be qualitative or quantitative, but quantitative indicators are usually easier to work with and provide a better framework for developing a safety program, particularly in a scientific setting.

As an example, a generic chemical hygiene management system based on the Plan, Do, Check, Act framework can be outlined with this goal in mind. This system could be one of several that works together to manage overall laboratory safety for a particular organization. Such a plan could consist of the following components.

Hazard Identification (Plan)

The rapidly changing nature of work in laboratory settings often makes the hazard identification step a significant challenge. Regular reviews of the work being conducted to ensure that hazard evaluations are still appropriate would be an important sign of a healthy chemical hygiene program. A numerical indicator of the health of this step could be the frequency at which these evaluations are reviewed for completeness. OSHA's requirement of an annual review of the chemical hygiene plan may not be adequate in many research laboratories.

Training and Consultations (Do)

After hazards are identified, specific precautions to control those hazards must be established and disseminated to laboratory workers. In many organizations, counting the number of training sessions and safety consultations that the laboratory safety program conducts is one convenient way to monitor this aspect of the program. Another way is to track contact hours.

Laboratory Audits (Check)

Training and consultations are not likely to be effective without follow-up to determine whether recommendations are implemented. The most common approach to determining the strength of this part of the program is development of a safety checklist specific to each laboratory that tracks conditions and habits that affect safety conditions. This checklist gives each laboratory a numerical grade that can be tracked over time to measure improvement in safety practices. The checklist must be used regularly and also routinely modified to reflect changes noted during the hazard evaluations conducted in the plan stage of this system.

Incident Review and Waste Quantities (Act)

Two potential indicators for the Act stage of the system present themselves: review of safety incidents in the laboratory (not only accidents, but near misses as well) and tracking of the laboratory wastes generated in the course of the laboratory work. Clearly, over time the first of these indicators should drop in number as the review of safety incidents results in implemented recommendations. For this reason, the waste analysis information should be thought of as a complement to the incident review indicator. For example, if the degree of hazard associated with the waste decreases with time (e.g., less waste is generated, less-hazardous materials are substituted), this can indicate the success of the safety program, not only for improving the safety conditions in the laboratory but also for pollution prevention.

SAFETY MANAGEMENT AND SAFETY CULTURE

Laboratory safety management must be done in the context of the culture and priorities of the organization that hosts the laboratory. The SMS approach requires a significant allocation of resources and continued attention over time. As described in *Prudent Practices in the Laboratory* (National Research Council, 2011), the ultimate goal of the management system is to foster the development of a "safety culture" throughout the laboratory organization. The key purpose of this culture is to support laboratory workers' ongoing efforts to understand and manage the hazards of their work. These hazards can be expected to change continuously, and the development of an effective safety culture is critical to maintaining a safe workplace as these changes occur.

CHEMICAL SAFETY

Nearly all laboratories use chemicals in one form or another. And nearly all chemicals are considered hazardous by one regulatory agency or another. And often chemicals present the most significant hazards associated with laboratory work. Therefore, chemical safety is a leading issue in laboratory safety management.

In this context, *chemicals* are materials whose use does not depend on their shape. Thus, chemicals include gases, liquids, powders, and dusts. Clearly, a wide variety of materials fall into this category, so developing blanket chemical safety rules to cover all chemical processes is a significant challenge. This section describes the overall process of chemical safety management in the laboratory setting. Specific details of chemical safety hazards can be found in the References at the end of this chapter.

CHEMICAL SAFETY INFORMATION

A primary challenge in dealing with chemical safety questions is gathering relevant information. Once this information is gathered, it must be interpreted in light of the specific situation in which it will be used. Two sources of information for chemical safety are labels and Safety Data Sheets (SDSs). OSHA's hazard communication standard (29 CFR 1910.1200) requires manufacturers, distributors, and importers of chemicals to provide extensive safety information that can be used to train end users on how to use the chemical safely.

However, OSHA's hazard communication requirements for laboratory workplaces are simpler: They require only that labels on incoming containers of hazardous chemicals shall not be removed or defaced, and that employers shall maintain any SDSs that are received with incoming shipments of hazardous chemicals, ensuring that they are readily available and accessible during each work shift to laboratory employees when they are in their work areas.

Safety Data Sheets (SDS)

The hazard communication standard (HCS) requires chemical manufacturers, distributors, or importers to provide SDSs (formerly known as Material Safety Data Sheets or MSDSs) to communicate the hazards of hazardous chemical products. As of June 1, 2015, the HCS will require new SDSs to be in a uniform format. This format includes 16 sections that cover topics such as hazard identification, storage and handling, required personal protective equipment, chemical and physical characteristics, disposal considerations, and the like. These changes respond to the adoption of the Global Harmonization System (GHS), which has been adopted by OSHA and EPA.

- Globally Harmonized System (GHS) for Classification and Labeling of Chemicals and Environmental Protection Agency (EPA)
- www.osha.gov/dsg/hazcom/index.html
- www.osha.gov/dsg/hazcom/HCSFinalRegTxt.html

Laboratory Chemical Safety Summaries

The National Research Council committee that wrote *Prudent Practices in the Laboratory* recognized the problem of using SDSs in laboratories. In response, it developed a format for safety information that is more appropriate for the laboratory setting. This format described Laboratory Chemical Safety Summaries (LCSSs) that can be used to highlight the most pertinent information for the safe laboratory use of chemicals. The committee also provided 88 sample LCSSs for the most commonly used chemicals. In contrast to SDSs, which may be longer than 10 pages, LCSSs are no more than 2 pages long. The LCSS identifies the major hazards associated with the chemical in the laboratory setting in straightforward language and is intended to be used in the context of an effective chemical hygiene plan by workers well trained in chemical terminology.

Other Sources

In addition to SDSs and LCSSs, which are specific to certain chemicals, safety information about chemical processes commonly used in laboratories should be reviewed. Sometimes these processes create hazards that cannot be predicted by simple review of the hazards of the various chemicals involved. Fortunately, in the 21st century, Internet search engines provide a convenient way to find such information. All such safety information is written for circumstances that may not match those in a specific laboratory. Therefore, any information collected from other sources must be reviewed with this limitation in mind.

Unfortunately, adequate health and safety information is not available for many laboratory chemicals. This may be because the chemicals have not been tested yet or because the chemical has not been produced anywhere else. In these cases, the laboratory workers using the chemical must work closely with safety professionals to develop appropriate operating procedures for its use. The goal of these procedures should be similar to the core principle of radiation safety, which is to keep exposures to new chemicals as low as reasonably achievable (ALARA).

Training and Documentation

The OSHA lab standard recognizes that laboratory workers generally have more education in chemistry than typical workers. This is one reason a separate regulation was written for the laboratory workplace. However, OSHA recognizes that this education does not necessarily directly translate into a familiarity with good chemical practice. Therefore, OSHA requires that laboratory workers be provided with specific safety training for the chemical procedures they are using. Because of the changing use of chemicals inherent in the laboratory environment, this training should be conducted on an ongoing basis.

Training should both provide general information about chemical hazards, such as might be found on an LCSS or SDS, and information about how these hazards are affected by the specific chemical process conducted in the laboratory. An explanation of what safety equipment, such as fume hoods, and personal protective equipment, such as gloves and eye protection, should be used—as well as the limitations of these safety precautions—should be provided to laboratory workers before they begin work. This training should be documented so that it is clear who is authorized to conduct what work within the laboratory.

CHEMICAL SAFETY PRACTICES

Although chemical hazards vary widely, certain generic practices that are common to the safe use of hazardous chemicals in laboratories can often be identified.

Housekeeping

Housekeeping is the daily practice of maintaining an organized and neat workplace. Housekeeping protects not only the workers in the laboratory, but also the wide variety of people who provide support services to the laboratory, including facility maintenance people, chemical waste technicians, cleaning staff, and emergency response personnel, such as firefighters and emergency medical technicians. Any of these people can be put at risk by bad housekeeping when they are required to enter the laboratory in the course of their duties.

In this context, *good housekeeping* means that chemical work surfaces are routinely cleaned. Sharp instruments are stored in puncture-resistant containers. All chemical containers must be stored in the correct storage cabinets and/or shelves. Aisles are kept clear of equipment and chemicals to allow easy access to all parts of the laboratory.

In larger laboratory organizations, housekeeping becomes a significant challenge in shared areas. When specialized laboratory spaces and equipment are shared among several laboratory groups, a conscious commitment to maintaining a group approach to housekeeping is necessary to maintain a safe workplace.

Labeling

Clear, accurate labeling of chemicals is a critical safety step for both laboratory workers and others who work in or pass through their work area. All containers must have the appropriate labels at all times. Chemical labels should include the name of the chemical written in English (rather than scientific notation or abbreviations) with a description of the hazards associated with that chemical. In general, common words such as *Flammable, Corrosive, Acutely Toxic,* or *Reactive* are appropriate for these hazard warnings. Ideally, the label should also include the date the chemical was received and the date it was opened.

When transferring chemicals from an original container into a laboratory container, all relevant information regarding the chemical must be reflected in the new label.

In addition to enabling laboratory workers to identify the contents of a chemical container, this information is also critical to ensure correct disposal of the chemicals and to enable emergency responders to assess the risks associated with responding to an emergency in the laboratory. Emergency responders may appropriately refuse to respond to rooms in which unlabeled, potentially hazardous materials are present. Appropriate warning labels should be attached to the entry door to a laboratory. This gives emergency responders ample warning of possible laboratory hazards that could be encountered during a response.

Storage of Chemicals

Chemicals can present significant hazards if good storage practices are not followed. Incompatible chemicals must not be stored in a way that they will interact with each other. In addition, hazardous liquids should be stored in secondary containment in case their containers are broken or leak.

Many segregation schemes for chemical storage have been developed over the years. Each should be evaluated on a case-by-case basis for use in a particular laboratory. The best arrangement will depend on the specific chemicals included in a laboratory's inventory. The following guidelines present the most important considerations involved:

- *Flammables*—Materials with a flash point of less than 100 F must be stored in a flammable liquid storage cabinet; organic materials must be kept separate from oxidizing materials; if they mix, a fire is likely to result (examples: acetone, ethanol, xylene).
- *Nonflammable solvents*—Organic materials with flash points of more than 100 F can be stored with flammable liquids, still separate from oxidizing materials (examples: carbon tetrachloride, ethylene glycol, mineral oil).
- *Inorganic acids*—Keep separate from other acids; store in a cabinet of acid-resistant material; keep separate from caustics, cyanides, sulfides (example: hydrochloric acid).
- *Oxidizing acids*—Keep separate from other acids and flammables (examples: nitric acid, sulfuric acid, perchloric acid).

- *Organic acids*—Keep separate from oxidizing acids, caustics, cyanides and sulfides (examples: acetic acid, formic acid).
- *Bases*—Store in a dry area, separately from acids (examples: ammonium hydroxide, sodium hydroxide, amines).
- *Poisons*—Keep separate from all other chemicals and secure from unauthorized access.
- *Water-reactive chemicals*—Store in a cool, dry location, separate from aqueous solutions; protect from fire sprinkler water (examples: sodium, calcium hydride, lithium).
- *Oxidizers*—Store in a cabinet of noncombustible material, separate from flammable and combustible materials (examples: potassium permanganate, sodium nitrate, sodium hypochlorite).
- *Nonvolatile, nonreactive solids*—May be stored in general-use cabinets or open shelves (examples: agar, sodium chloride, sodium bicarbonate).

A more detailed consideration of chemical storage schemes can be found in *Prudent Practices in the Laboratory* (National Research Council, 2011). It is also important to review SDSs concerning specific reactivity information for chemicals being stored together.

In addition to appropriate segregation of stored chemicals, a well-maintained chemical inventory can be an important safety tool. Many chemicals degrade over time and can create serious hazards if they undergo spontaneous reactions such as polymerization or dehydration (e.g., peroxide crystals should be marked with a date the moment the package is opened), which occurs over time. All chemical containers should have shelf lives marked or coded on their labels; routine culling of aging chemicals is an important safety practice.

Chemical Waste Management

Most chemical wastes are considered regulated hazardous wastes by federal or local regulations. For this reason, their disposal must be considered carefully and managed appropriately. EPA regulations form the basis for the hazardous waste disposal system in the United States. A full discussion of how these regulations apply to laboratory chemicals is beyond the scope of this chapter. However, many laboratories, both academic and industrial, have been fined by EPA and state agencies for improper management of hazardous wastes within the laboratory. If laboratory workers do not have a good understanding of how these regulations work, they should seek professional guidance in addressing this issue.

If a laboratory uses chemicals, it has to produce chemical waste. Chemical waste must be treated as the original chemicals, considering the chemical hazard class, whether flammables, corrosives, and so forth. All laboratories generating chemical waste must select a satellite accumulation area (SAA) in accordance with applicable regulatory requirements to store and manage the waste following basic principles such as:

- Label all chemical waste containers properly.
- Do not leave the funnel on the waste container, always cap it.
- Dispose properly of empty chemical containers.
- Remember, nothing goes down the drain!

LABORATORY DESIGN

The design of the laboratory has a direct impact on the safety practices necessary to work effectively with laboratory chemicals. As mentioned earlier, many safety design considerations for laboratories are quite generic; some of the key elements are discussed here.

Ventilation

Heating, ventilation, and air conditioning (HVAC) systems are designed to maintain temperature control in the laboratory. They are also used as an engineering control measure to protect laboratory workers by providing dilution air to the space and removing airborne contaminants. Laboratories should be designed so that the HVAC system maintains a negative air pressure inside the lab relative to the surrounding environment. This pressure relationship ensures that air moves from nonlaboratory spaces into the laboratory, thus preventing laboratory processes from contaminating adjacent spaces. Air moved by laboratory HVAC systems should be entirely exhausted from the building to reduce the possibility of a buildup of contaminated air.

Fume Hoods

In general, most work with chemicals in the laboratory has to be done in a chemical fume hood. Ventilation of specific processes that require more control than the general HVAC system can provide is managed by laboratory fume hoods. For a hood to be effective at containing chemical vapors, the hood must be used carefully. Variables that affect the effectiveness of a hood include the height of the sash opening, the amount of equipment in the hood, chemical storage within the hood, velocity of the air moving through the hood, and hood location. These factors should be evaluated routinely to ensure that the hood is performing as expected. Chemical fume hoods are designed to work with toxic chemicals, not to store chemicals.

Traditionally, the optimum performance of a fume hood is considered to be at a face velocity of between 80 and 120 feet per minute (fpm). In most situations, the target average face velocity is 100 fpm. However, in recent years, this target face velocity has been more carefully examined because of the expenses associated with heating and cooling the air exhausted by the fume hood. Because laboratory HVAC systems are designed to exhaust and not recirculate air because of potential contamination issues, a large cost is usually associated with conditioning the air. This cost can be reduced when a low-flow fume hood system is used. Fume hoods can be operated over a range of lower face velocities and still achieve effective containment when properly designed and installed. Containment of contaminants in a low-flow hood is demonstrated by the ASHRAE 110 tracer gas test. Experienced ventilation engineers should be involved in the placement and installation of low-flow fume hoods to ensure that they meet the requirements of this test. In addition, strict work practices may have to be implemented to take advantage of these types of fume hood systems.

Emergency Eyewashes and Showers

OSHA regulations [29 CFR 1910.151(c)] require employers to provide suitable facilities for quick drenching or flushing of the eyes and body when employees are potentially exposed to corrosive materials. Minimum performance and use requirements for emergency eyewashes and showers are provided by ANSI Z358.1-2009. In summary, emergency eyewashes and showers shall be in accessible locations that require no more than 10 seconds to reach. A shower or eyewash station should be capable of providing a flow of tepid water for at least 15 min. Eyewashes may be located at sinks or at other readily accessible areas. Eyewashes must be capable of hands-free use after starting the water flow, so that the hands can be used to keep eyes open while flushing.

Stagnant water in both safety showers and eyewashes can be breeding grounds for environmental microbes such as *Legionella* and *Acantha amoeba*. Both of these can present serious health concerns to exposed people; therefore, showers and eyewashes must be routinely flushed. The general recommendation is to flush them weekly. This flushing also ensures that the equipment is ready for use if needed.

Equipment Hazards

Regular inspections and preventive maintenance should be performed on equipment. Whenever preventive maintenance or repairs are conducted on equipment, lockout/tagout procedures should be practiced in accordance with 29 CFR 1910.147 to prevent inadvertent start-up.

Heating Devices

Uncontrolled heat sources (e.g., Bunsen burners) should not be used near flammable substances and must not be left unattended. Hot plates, heating mantles, and other heaters should have enclosed elements and controls should have a thermal shutoff safety device. Heating devices should have cut-off points to preclude overheating.

Electrical Safety Considerations

All electrical equipment used in the laboratory should be grounded. Ground-fault circuit interrupters must be used whenever equipment is exposed to a wet environment (e.g., near a sink or in a cold room). The use of extension cords should be avoided when possible. When absolutely necessary, extension cords should be used only temporarily (less than a workshift). Electrical cords should be placed in such a way to minimize the risk of tripping. Frayed or damaged electrical cords should not be used. Equipment with electrical plugs and cords should be kept in good repair.

Compressed-Gas Cylinders

Compressed-gas cylinders present hazards in a variety of ways:

- They are heavy, clumsy containers that can be awkward to handle without the correct equipment.
- Gases contained inside cylinders are stored at high pressure; if the cylinder is ruptured, it can become a high-speed projectile.
- Some stored gases can create toxic atmospheres, either by the nature of the gas itself or by displacing oxygen from associated spaces.

For these reasons, gas cylinders must be carefully managed. Cylinders transported by truck must be fastened securely in an upright position so that they will not fall or strike each other. Always secure gas cylinders upright to a wall, cylinder truck, or cylinder rack. A clamp and belt or chains are used for this purpose and should be attached around the body of the cylinder, not around the valves or caps.

Caps used for valve protection should be kept on cylinders at all times, except when the cylinder is in use. Cylinders should not be transported without safety caps in place and screwed all the way down on the cylinder's neck ring. Cylinder valves should be opened slowly. Always use a cylinder wrench or another tightly fitting wrench to tighten the regulator nut and hose connections unless the cylinder is a handwheel type.

A handwheel-type cylinder valve should be operated only by hand. Before attaching a cylinder to a connection, be sure that the threads on the cylinder and the connection are compatible. If the connections do not fit together readily, then the wrong regulator is being used. Do not permit oil or grease to come in contact with cylinders or their valves. The threads and mating surfaces of the regulator and hose connections should be cleaned before the regulator is attached. Ensure that the regulator is attached securely before opening the valve wide.

If using cylinders containing toxic gases, use the smallest size possible. Appropriate monitoring devices, soapy water, or solutions recommended by the gas supplier should be used to check for leaks. Emergency procedures should be in place for each type of cylinder so if a leak does occur, there will be minimal impact to laboratory personnel and the surrounding environment.

Portable Fire Extinguishers

Fire extinguishers should be available, unobstructed, and inspected on a schedule that complies with NFPA 10, Standard for Portable Fire Extinguishers. This should include a monthly "quick check," verifying that the fire extinguisher is available and will operate (fully charged) and that no obvious physical damage or condition to prevent operation is noted. The inspection needs to be documented with the date and initials of the person performing the inspection. This documentation can be either through the use of a tag attached to the fire extinguisher or in an electronic system (e.g., bar coding) that provides a permanent record.

LABORATORY CHEMICAL SAFETY REGULATIONS

As mentioned earlier, a variety of federal regulations address chemical hazards in the laboratory. The most important of these is the OSHA laboratory standard, which covers workplace laboratories where relatively small quantities of hazardous chemicals are used on a nonproduction basis.

The OSHA Laboratory Standard (29 CFR 1910.1450)

All facilities engaged in the "laboratory use of hazardous chemicals" must comply with the provisions of the standard. "Laboratory use of hazardous chemicals" means use of chemicals in which all of the following conditions are met:

- Chemical manipulations are carried out on a "laboratory scale," which means work in which the containers used are easily and safely manipulated by one person.
- Multiple chemical procedures or chemicals are used.
- The procedures involved are not part of a production process and do not in any way simulate a production process.
- "Protective laboratory practices and equipment" are available and in common use to minimize the potential for employee exposure to hazardous chemicals.

Chemical Hygiene Plan

To comply with the laboratory standard, the employer must implement a chemical hygiene plan (CHP). The CHP documents the work practices, procedures, and policies to ensure that employees are protected from hazardous chemicals in their work area. Thus, this plan provides a context for the standard operating procedures associated with specific chemical processes. The CHP must be available to employees, employee representatives, and OSHA inspectors.

The employer must provide employees with information and training to ensure that they are aware of the hazards of the chemicals present in their work area and how to protect themselves from those hazards. The training must cover the following issues:

- the location and contents of the employer's chemical hygiene plan
- the physical and health hazards of chemicals in the work area
- the location and availability of reference materials on the hazards
- methods and observations that may be used to detect the presence or release of a hazardous chemical
- signs and symptoms associated with exposures to hazardous chemicals used in the laboratory
- OSHA's permissible exposure limits (PELs) for chemicals that have such limits established
- the measures employees can take to protect themselves from these hazards.

Training should be conducted at the time of an employee's initial assignment to a work area where hazardous chemicals are present and before assignments involving new exposure situations.

Employee Monitoring

The employer must determine which hazardous chemicals are present in the laboratory. This includes both chemicals delivered to the laboratory and chemicals produced in the laboratory. Based on this inventory, the employer must evaluate employees' potential exposure periodically and monitor for exposure to any regulated substance if there is reason to believe that exposure levels for that substance routinely exceed the action level (or in the absence of an action level, the PEL). The employer must notify the employee of the results within 15 working days after receipt of the monitoring results.

All employees who work with hazardous chemicals must be given the opportunity to receive medical attention when they develop symptoms associated with the chemicals they work with or after a chemical release in the laboratory. Medical examinations and consultations must be provided without cost to the employee, without loss of pay, and at a reasonable time and place.

The employer must provide the physician with the identity of the hazardous chemicals, a description of the conditions under which the exposure occurred, and a description of the signs and symptoms of exposure that the employee is experiencing.

A system must be in place for informing employees of the hazards associated with chemicals they use in the laboratory. At a minimum, labels on incoming containers of hazardous chemicals must not be removed or defaced. SDSs received with shipments of incoming hazardous chemicals must be retained and made available to lab employees.

BIOLOGICAL SAFETY

Biological hazards, or biohazards, are pathogenic (disease-causing) micro-organisms that pose a risk to the health of humans, animals, or other biological organisms. In the past, this definition has focused on infectious pathogenic micro-organisms responsible for common communicable diseases. However, the realm of biohazards has now expanded to include other agents with the potential for causing disease, including cancer-causing viruses, recombinant DNA molecules, animals and plants and their by-products, and microorganisms (including fungi, bacteria, yeasts, and algae) and some proteins causing disease, such as prions.

Biosafety can be described in lay terms as a set of principles designed to work with infectious and potentially infectious biological agents in a safe manner and avoiding exposure to laboratory employees. The principal mechanisms to safely handle a biological agent are based on a risk assessment process. This process will necessarily result in a risk management plan, which translates into the following basic elements of containment:
- laboratory design
- safety equipment
- good laboratory practices
- personal protective equipment.

Laboratory-acquired infections (LAIs) have been documented since the late 1800s. However, with the emergence of new and reemergent diseases, and growing interest in applying biotechnologies in a variety of settings, an increasing percentage of the laboratory community is working with materials that present a risk of infection.

BIOSAFETY GUIDELINES
The Centers for Disease Control and Prevention (CDC) and the National

Institutes of Health (NIH) have developed and published guidelines for different levels of protective measures appropriate when working with biohazards. *Biosafety in Microbiological and Biomedical Laboratories*, currently in its fifth edition, is commonly known as the BMBL (CDC/NIH, 2009). These guidelines outline four biosafety levels (BSLs) that consist of combinations of laboratory practices and techniques, safety equipment, and laboratory facilities that combine to provide appropriate containment for the agents being used. Each level is appropriate for the use of specific procedures with specific agents, based on the risk presented by the operations performed, the documented or suspected routes of transmission of the infectious agents, and the laboratory activity. These levels of protection are designated Biosafety Levels 1, 2, 3, and 4. Biosafety Level 4 practices and engineering controls offer the highest level of protection to a lab worker and the surrounding environment.

These guidelines describe special handling techniques, personal protective equipment, and facility design that should prevent the occurrence of LAI or the release of biological agents to the environment.

Biosafety Level 1 (BSL-1)

Biosafety Level 1 represents a basic level of containment that relies on standard microbiological practices with no special primary or secondary barriers recommended, other than a sink for hand washing. Biohazards that are managed at this level are not known to cause disease in healthy humans.

Biosafety Level 2 (BSL-2)

Biosafety Level 2 practices, equipment, and facility design and construction are applicable to clinical, diagnostic, teaching, and other laboratories in which work is done with a broad spectrum of moderate risk agents that are present in the environment and associated with human disease of varying severity. The primary hazards to personnel working with BSL-2 agents are accidental percutaneous or mucous membrane exposures or ingestion of infectious materials. With good microbiological techniques, these agents can be used safely in activities conducted on the open bench, provided that the potential for producing splashes or aerosols is low. Hepatitis B virus, HIV, and *Toxoplasma* spp. are representative of microorganisms assigned to this containment level.

Biosafety Level 2 is also appropriate when work is done with any human blood, body fluids, tissues, or primary human cell lines in which the presence of an infectious agent may be unknown. Laboratory personnel working with human-derived materials should also follow the OSHA Bloodborne Pathogen Standard, 29 CFR 1450, for specific required precautions required by this regulation.

Caution should be taken with needles or sharp instruments contaminated with these agents. Other elements of personal primary protective equipment, such as splash shields for face protection, gowns, and gloves should also be used as appropriate. Even though organisms manipulated at BSL-2 are not known to be transmissible by the aerosol route, work that presents aerosol or high splash potential must be conducted in primary containment equipment or in devices such as a biological safety cabinet or safety centrifuge cups. A risk assessment of the procedure being conducted will determine which of these forms of containment are necessary.

In addition to these steps for worker protection, secondary barriers, such as hand-washing sinks and waste decontamination facilities, must be available for BSL-2 work in order to reduce potential environmental contamination.

Biosafety Level 3 (BSL-3)

Biosafety Level 3 practices, safety equipment, and facility design and construction are applicable to clinical, diagnostic, teaching, research, or production facilities in which work is done with "indigenous or exotic agents that may cause serious or potentially lethal disease through the inhalation route of exposure" agents with a potential for respiratory transmission. *Mycobacterium tuberculosis*, St. Louis encephalitis virus, and *Coxiella burnetii* are representative of the microorganisms assigned to this level. The primary hazards to personnel working with these agents are exposure to infectious aerosols.

BSL-3 requirements place more emphasis than BSL-2 on secondary barriers to protect personnel in contiguous areas, the community, and the environment from release of potentially infectious aerosols. All manipulations of infectious agents at this level must be done in the biosafety cabinet or other enclosed equipment, such as a gas-tight aerosol generation chamber. Secondary barriers for this level include controlled access to the laboratory and ventilation design that prevents the release of infectious aerosols from the laboratory.

Biosafety Level 4 (BSL-4)

Biosafety Level 4 practices, safety equipment, and facility design and construction are applicable for work with dangerous and exotic agents that pose a high individual risk of life-threatening disease, which may be transmitted via the aerosol route and for which there is no available vaccine or therapy. Agents with a close or identical antigenic relationship to Biosafety Level 4 agents also should be handled at this level. Viruses such as Marburg or Crimean-Congo hemorrhagic fever are manipulated at BSL-4.

The primary hazards to personnel working with BSL-4 agents are respiratory exposure to infectious aerosols, mucous membrane or broken skin exposure to infectious droplets, and autoinoculation. All manipulations of

potentially infectious diagnostic materials, isolates, and naturally or experimentally infected animals pose a high risk of exposure and infection to laboratory personnel, the community, and the environment.

Complete isolation from aerosolized infectious materials is accomplished
by working in a Class III biological safety cabinet or in a full-body, air-supplied,
positive-pressure personnel suit. The BSL-4 facility itself is generally a separate
building or completely isolated zone with complex, specialized ventilation
requirements and waste management systems to prevent release of viable
agents to the environment.

At all of the biosafety levels, the laboratory director has primary responsibility for the safe operation of the laboratory. His or her knowledge and
judgment are critical in assessing risks and appropriately applying these
recommendations. Many institutions supplement this judgment by appointing
a biosafety officer, who assists the supervisor in assessing risk levels and
implementing the appropriate procedures. Appointment of such an officer is
required to oversee BSL-3 and BSL-4 work.

Four biosafety levels are also described for activities involving infectious
disease work with experimental animals. These four combinations of practices,
safety equipment, and facilities are similar to, but distinct from, those just
discussed, and are designated Animal Biosafety Levels 1, 2, 3, and 4 in order
of increasing levels of protection to personnel and the environment.

CONTAINMENT PRACTICES

The general term *containment* describes methods for controlling the location
of infectious materials in the laboratory environment. The goal of containment is to reduce or eliminate exposure of laboratory workers, other persons,
and the outside environment to potentially hazardous biological agents. The
three key elements of containment are facility design, safety equipment, and
laboratory practices and techniques.

Primary containment (i.e., primary barriers) focuses on the protection of
workers and the immediate laboratory environment from exposure to infectious
agents. Good microbiological technique and the use of appropriate safety
equipment are associated with primary containment. Agent-specific vaccines can
be used to provide an increased level of personal protection in some cases.

Secondary containment (i.e., secondary barriers) protects the environment
outside the laboratory from contamination with infectious materials. It is
achieved by a combination of facility design and operational practices.

A person experienced in biosafety should conduct a risk assessment of
planned work before work begins with a new biohazard to determine the
appropriate combination of these elements necessary to achieve containment.

Standard Microbiological Technique

The most important element of containment is adherence to standard micro-biological practices and techniques. These are outlined in the BMBL (CDC/NIH, 2009). This publication defines four different biosafety levels (1 to 4) as discussed in the preceding section. *Biosafety levels* refer not only to the biological agent, but to the laboratory facility and to the practices to be implemented.

The essential elements of the four biosafety levels (BSLs) for activities involving infectious microorganisms and laboratory animals are summarized in Tables 14–A and 14–B. The levels are designated in ascending order, by degree of protection provided to personnel, the environment, and the community. In summary, these practices require that persons working with infectious agents or potentially infected materials must be aware of the hazards and must be trained and proficient in the practices and techniques required in handling such material safely. The person in charge of the laboratory is responsible for arranging the appropriate training of personnel.

In addition, each laboratory should develop a biosafety manual that documents potential hazards that may be encountered and control methods to be used. A scientist trained and knowledgeable in appropriate laboratory techniques, safety procedures, and hazards associated with handling infectious agents must be responsible for the development of this manual and oversight of affected work. This individual should consult with biosafety or other health and safety professionals with regard to risk assessment for new procedures. Institutions receiving NIH funds are required to have this risk assessment process overseen by an Institutional Biosafety Committee (IBC).

PRIMARY BARRIERS

Safety Equipment

Safety equipment includes biological safety cabinets (BSCs), enclosed containers, and other engineering controls designed to remove or minimize exposures to hazardous biological materials. The biological safety cabinet is the principal device used to contain infectious splashes or aerosols generated during microbiological procedures. High-efficiency particulate air (HEPA) filters are incorporated by design into BSCs to filter and control the movement of aerosolized particles outside of the cabinet. BSCs do not provide any containment of chemical vapors; in fact, because the air in the cabinet is recirculated, chemical vapors can be released outside the cabinet into the laboratory air.

Three types of biological safety cabinets are used in microbiological laboratories (Figures 14–2a, 14–2b, and 14–2c). Class I biological safety cabinets are primary barriers that protect laboratory personnel and the environment when used with good microbiological techniques. The Class II biological safety cabinet also protects biological materials from external contamination. The gas-tight Class III biological safety cabinet provides the highest attainable level of protection to personnel and the environment. Tables 14–A and 14–B provide information to assist in selection of a safety cabinet.

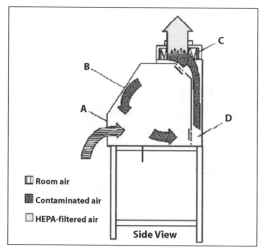

Figure 14–2a. Suitable for handling low-to-moderate-risk biohazardous aerosols when product protection is not essential, Class I cabinets provide partial personnel protection and no product protection.

Courtesy CDC/National Institutes of Health. Biosafety in Microbiological and Biomedical Laboratories. 4th Edition. Atlanta, GA: U.S. Department of Health and Human Services, Public Health Service, CDC and NIH, 1999.

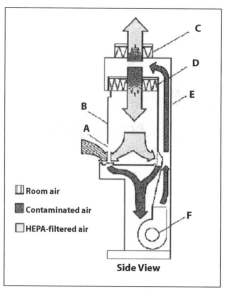

Figure 14–2b. Designed for the handling of low- and moderate-risk biohazards, Class II cabinets provide both product and partial personnel protection. Type B-2 cabinets do not recirculate air and are more suitable for handling carcinogens and other hazardous chemicals than either Type A or Type B-1 cabinets.

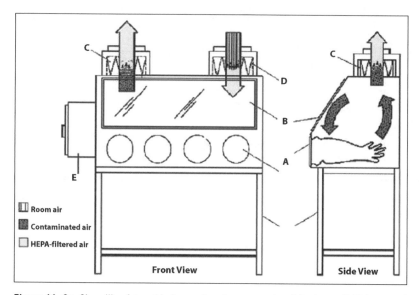

Figure 14–2c. Class III safety cabinets, or glove boxes, are closed-front, gas-tight boxes and provide the highest degree of personnel protection and a clean work environment.

Table 14–A. Selection of a Safety Cabinet through Risk Assessment (Adapted from the Office of Health and Safety, Centers for Disease Control and Prevention)

Biological Risk Assessed	Protection Provided			BSC Class
	Personnel	Product	Environmental	
BSL 1,2,3	YES	NO	YES	I
BSL 1,2,3	YES	YES	YES	II (A, B1, B2, B3)
BSL 4	YES	YES	YES	III (B1, B2)

Table 14–B. Comparison of Biosafety Cabinet Characteristics (Adapted from the Office of Health and Safety, Centers for Disease Control and Prevention)

BCS Class	Characteristics		Applications	
	Face Velocity	Airflow Pattern	Nonvolatile Toxic Chemicals and Radionuclides	Volatile Toxic Chemicals and Radionuclides
I	75	In at front; exhausted through HEPA to the outside or into the room through HEPA (see Figure 14-2b)	YES	YES[1]
II, A	75	70% recirculated to the cabinet work area through HEPA; 30% balance can be exhausted through HEPA back into the room or to the outside through a thimble unit	YES	NO
II, B1	100	Exhaust cabinet air must pass through a dedicated duct to the outside through a HEPA filter	YES	YES (minute amounts[2])
II, B2	100	No recirculation; total exhaust to the outside through hard-duct and HEPA filter	YES	YES (small amounts)
II, B3	100	Same as II, A, but plenums are under negative pressure to room; exhaust air is thimble-ducted to the outside through a HEPA filter	YES	YES (minute amounts[2])
III	N/A	Supply air inlets and hard-duct exhausted to outside through two HEPA filters in series	YES	YES (small amounts)

[1] Installation may require a special duct to the outside, an in-line charcoal filter, and a spark-proof (explosion-proof) motor and other electrical components in the cabinet. Discharge of a Class I cabinet into a room should not occur if volatile chemicals are used.

[2] In no circumstances should the chemical concentration approach the lower explosion limits of the compound.

Personal Protective Equipment

Personal protective equipment (PPE) may include clothing for personal protection, such as gloves, coats, and face shields. Personal protective equipment is often used in combination with BSCs and other devices that contain the agents, animals, or materials being handled to protect both the worker and the experimental material. In some situations in which it is impractical to work in biological safety cabinets, PPE may form the barrier between personnel and the infectious materials.

Autoclaves

Autoclaves are important pieces of biosafety equipment because they are used to steam-sterilize equipment and materials that are potentially contaminated with either environmental or experimental biohazards. However, they can present significant hazards to the worker and/or the environment if they are not used correctly.

Autoclaves should be operated in accordance with the manufacturer's instructions. Personal protective equipment such as eye protection, heat-resistant gloves, and aprons should be worn when loading and unloading a hot autoclave. To minimize exposure to hot fluids and noxious vapors, the operator should not open autoclave doors too soon after a run is finished (20 min is commonly required for the autoclave to cool down).

An autoclave should have an easily accessible manual control that can run a complete cycle in the event of a power failure. Each autoclave should have alarms that indicate when the chamber is flooded and that the steam and pressure parameters were within acceptable ranges during the cycle. Common safety interlocks include control lockout switches that prevent cycles from starting if the door is not closed and locked, and mechanical steam pressure locks to prevent operators from opening a door while the chamber is under positive pressure. Before installation of an autoclave, availability of adequate ventilation, electrical, and plumbing services should be assessed.

Ultraviolet Lights

Ultraviolet (UV) lights are often found in biological safety cabinets and other biomedical laboratory equipment. UV light may be used to kill certain types of microorganisms; however, its effectiveness depends on the radiation intensity and exposure time. UV light should not be considered a sterilizing agent except in certain exceptional circumstances. Typically, UV light is intended only to reduce the number of microorganisms on surfaces and in the air.

UV light presents hazards to laboratory workers. The eyes and skin should not be exposed to direct or strongly reflected UV radiation. Some individuals are more susceptible to UV injury than others. Overexposure of the eyes and/or skin will result in symptoms (redness, irritation) developing up to 9 or so hours following exposure. The symptoms usually disappear in a day or two. A hazard warning sign should be displayed prominently on the doors of laboratories with UV light installations. Adequate eye and skin protection must be worn when working in an irradiated area. Safety glasses with side shields or goggles with solid sidepieces must be worn. Skin protection can be afforded by face shields, caps, lab coats, gloves, aprons, and gowns.

SECONDARY BARRIERS

Facility Design

The design and construction of the facility contribute to laboratory workers' protection, provide a barrier to protect persons outside the laboratory, and protect persons or animals in the community from infectious agents that may be accidentally released from the laboratory. Laboratory management is responsible for providing facilities commensurate with the laboratory's function and the recommended biosafety level for the agents being manipulated.

The recommended secondary barrier(s) will depend on the risk of transmission of specific agents. For example, the exposure risks for most laboratory work in Biosafety Level 1 and 2 facilities (discussed earlier) will be direct contact with the agents or inadvertent contact exposures through contaminated work environments (Tables 14–C and 14–D). Secondary barriers in these laboratories may include separation of the laboratory work area from public access, availability of a decontamination facility (e.g., autoclave), and hand-washing facilities.

When the risk of infection by exposure to an infectious aerosol is present, higher levels of primary containment and multiple secondary barriers may become necessary to prevent infectious agents from escaping into the environment. Such design features include specialized ventilation systems to ensure directional airflow, air treatment systems to decontaminate or remove agents from exhaust air, controlled-access zones, airlocks as laboratory entrances, or separate buildings or modules to isolate the laboratory.

BLOODBORNE PATHOGENS

Biomedical laboratories, especially those in health care facilities, commonly work with human specimens for a variety of research, diagnostic, and clinical support services. Typically, the infectious nature of these clinical materials is unknown.

Table 14–C. Summary of Recommended Biosafety Levels for Infectious Agents

BSL	Agents	Practices	Safety Equipment (Primary Barriers)	Facilities (Secondary Barriers)
1	Not known to consistently cause disease in healthy adults	Standard Microbiological Practices	None required	Open bench top sink required
2	Associated with human disease; hazard = percutaneous injury, ingestion, mucous membrane exposure	BSL-1 practice plus: • Limited access • Biohazard warning signs • "Sharps" precautions • Biosafety manual defining any needed waste decontamination or medical surveillance policies	Primary barriers = Class I or II BSCs or other physical containment devices used for all manipulations of agents that cause splashes or aerosols of infectious materials; PPEs: laboratory coats; gloves; face protection as needed	BSL-1 plus: Autoclave available
3	Indigenous or exotic agents with potential for aerosol transmission; disease may have serious or lethal consequences	BSL-2 practice plus: • Controlled access • Decontamination of all waste • Decontamination of lab clothing before laundering • Baseline serum	Primary barriers = Class I or II BCSs or other physical containment devices used for all open manipulations of agents; PPEs: protective lab clothing; gloves; respiratory protection as needed	BSL-2 plus: • Physical separation from access corridors • Self-closing, double-door access • Exhausted air not recirculated • Negative airflow into laboratory
4	Dangerous/exotic agents which pose high risk of life-threatening disease; aerosol-transmitted lab infections; or related agents with unknown risk of transmission	BSL-3 practices plus: • Clothing change before entering • Shower on exit • All material decontaminated on exit from facility	Primary barriers = All procedures conducted in Class III BSCs or Class I or II BSCs in combination with full-body, air-supplied, positive pressure personnel suit	BSL-3 plus: • Separate building or isolated zone • Dedicated supply and exhaust, vacuum, and decon systems • Other requirements outlined in the text

Courtesy CDC/National Institutes of Health. *Biosafety in Microbiological and Biomedical Laboratories.* 4th Edition. Atlanta, GA: U.S. Department of Health and Human Services, Public Health Service, CDC and NIH, 1999.

For this reason, human specimens can be handled safely at BSL-2, the recommended level for work with bloodborne pathogens such as hepatitis B, hepatitis C, and HIV.

BSL-2 recommendations and OSHA requirements focus on the prevention of percutaneous and mucous membrane exposures to clinical material. Primary barriers such as biological safety cabinets (Class I or II) should be

Table 14–D. Summary of Recommended Biosafety Levels for Activities in Which Experimentally or Naturally Infected Vertebrate Animals Are Used

BSL	Agents	Practices	Safety Equipment (Primary Barriers)	Facilities (Secondary Barriers)
1	Not known to consistently cause disease in healthy human adults.	Standard animal care and management practices, including appropriate medical surveillance programs	As required for normal care of each species.	Standard animal facility No recirculation of exhaust air Directional airflow recommended Hand-washing sink recommended
2	Associated with human disease. Hazard: percutaneous exposure, ingestion, mucous membrane exposure.	ABSL-1 practices plus: Limited access Biohazard warning signs Sharps precautions Biosafety manual Decontamination of all infectious wastes and of animal cages prior to washing	ABSL-1 equipment plus primary barriers: containment equipment appropriate for animal species; PPE: laboratory coats, gloves, face and respiratory protection as needed.	ABSL-1 facility plus: Autoclave available Hand-washing sink available in the animal room Mechanical cage washer used
3	Indigenous or exotic agents with potential for aerosol transmission; disease may have serious health effects.	ABSL-2 practices plus: Controlled access Decontamination of clothing before laundering Cages decontaminated before bedding removed Disinfectant foot bath as needed	ABSL-2 equipment plus: Containment equipment for housing animals and cage-dumping activities Class I or II BSCs available for manipulative procedures (inoculation, necropsy) that may create infectious aerosols. PPEs: appropriate respiratory protection	ABSL-2 facility plus: Physical separation from access corridors Self-closing, double-door access Sealed penetrations Sealed windows Autoclave available in facility
4	Dangerous/exotic agents that pose high risk of life-threatening disease; aerosol transmission, or related agents with unknown risk of transmission.	ABSL-3 practices plus: Entrance through change room where personal clothing is removed and laboratory clothing is put on; shower on exiting All wastes are decontaminated before removal from the facility	ABSL-3 equipment plus: Maximum containment equipment (i.e., Class III BSC or partial containment equipment in combination with full-body, air-supplied positive-pressure personnel suit) used for all procedures and activities	ABSL-3 facility plus: Separate building or isolated zone Dedicated supply and exhaust, vacuum, and decontamination systems Other requirements outlined in the text

Courtesy CDC/National Institutes of Health. *Biosafety in Microbiological and Biomedical Laboratories.* 4th Edition. Atlanta, GA: U.S. Department of Health and Human Services, Public Health Service, CDC and NIH, 1999.

used when performing procedures that might cause splashing, spraying, or splattering of droplets.

The segregation of clinical laboratory functions and limited access to such areas is the responsibility of the laboratory director. It is also the director's responsibility to establish standard, written procedures that address the potential hazards of clinical specimens and the required precautions to be implemented.

THE BLOODBORNE PATHOGENS STANDARD—INFECTION CONTROL PLAN

OSHA's bloodborne pathogens standard (29 CFR 1910.1030) limits occupational exposure for all employees who, as the result of performing their job duties, could be "reasonably anticipated" to face contact with blood and other potentially infectious materials. "Good Samaritan" acts such as assisting a co-worker with a nosebleed would probably not be considered occupational exposure.

Other potentially infectious materials include semen, vaginal secretions, cerebrospinal fluid, synovial fluid, pleural fluid, pericardial fluid, peritoneal fluid, amniotic fluid, cell lines, saliva in dental procedures, any body fluid visibly contaminated with blood, and all body fluids in situations in which it is difficult or impossible to differentiate between body fluids.

The standard requires employers to develop a written *occupational exposure control plan* that identifies tasks and procedures as well as job classifications in which the potential for occupational exposure to blood occurs (without regard to personal protective clothing and equipment). The plan must specify the procedure for evaluating circumstances surrounding exposure incidents and be accessible to employees and available to OSHA.

Training must be conducted initially upon assignment and annually thereafter. Employees who have received appropriate training within the past year need only receive additional training in items not previously covered. The standard requires that warning labels—including the orange or orange-red biohazard symbol—be affixed to containers of regulated waste, refrigerators and freezers, and other containers that are used to store or transport blood or other potentially infectious materials. Red bags or containers may be used instead of labeling. When a facility uses universal precautions in its handling of all specimens, labeling is not required within the facility. Likewise, when all laundry is handled with universal precautions, the laundry need not be labeled. Decontaminated regulated waste and blood that has been tested and found free of HIV or HBV and released for clinical use need not be labeled. Nevertheless, identification, labeling and disposal of biomedical waste must be done according to the respective state regulations. Employers must provide (at no cost), and require employees to use, appropriate personal protective equipment such as gloves, gowns, masks, mouthpieces, and resuscitation bags and must clean, repair, and replace these when necessary.

Hepatitis B vaccinations must be made available to all employees who have occupational exposure to blood within 10 working days of assignment. These vaccinations should be made available according to the latest recommendations of the U.S. Public Health Service. Employees must sign a declination form if they choose not to be vaccinated, although they may later decide to receive the vaccine.

The standard specifies procedures after an employee has been exposed to materials potentially infected with bloodborne pathogens. Follow-up must include a confidential medical evaluation documenting the circumstances of exposure, identifying and testing the source individual if feasible, testing the exposed employee's blood if he or she consents, post-exposure prophylaxis, counseling, and evaluation of reported illnesses. This work will be conducted at no cost to the employee.

RADIATION SAFETY

PRINCIPLES OF RADIATION

There are two basic kinds of radiation:

- *Particle radiation* consists of tiny fast-moving particles that have both energy and mass (weight).
- *Electromagnetic waves* or *electromagnetic radiation* consists of pure energy with no weight. This kind of radiation is like vibrating or pulsating waves of electrical and magnetic energy.

Radioactive materials and radiation-producing machines are commonly found in laboratories. The types of radiation used vary widely. Providing a safe and healthy workplace that uses radiation sources requires an understanding of the hazards and the regulations that apply.

In this section, the term *radiation* refers to the process in which energy is emitted by a source, transmitted through an intervening medium, and absorbed by another body. The energy transfer occurs in the form of subatomic particles (charged particles) or electromagnetic waves (photons). *Ionizing radiation* is any radiation consisting of particles or electromagnetic waves with sufficient energy to produce ions.

Ionization is the process of removing electrons from atoms, leaving two electrically charged particles (ions) behind. Ionization occurs when enough energy is transferred to displace an electron from an atom. Some forms of radiation, such as visible light, microwaves, and radio waves, do not have sufficient energy to remove electrons from atoms and, hence, are called *nonionizing radiation*. The negatively charged electrons and positively charged nuclei may cause changes in living tissue.

Ionization can be caused by alpha-particles, beta-particles, gamma-rays, neutrons, and x-rays. The first three types are emitted from the nucleus of a radioactive atom. Neutrons are created from nuclear fission and are not normally found in a laboratory setting. Radioactive materials are present in our natural environment, and they can also be artificially produced. For example, x-rays are produced when high-speed electrons are decelerated; some of the electrons' kinetic energy is converted into x-rays. Because x-rays are produced by high voltage, turning the x-ray–producing machine off stops the x-rays.

Alpha-, beta-, and gamma-radiation cannot be turned off like x-rays. The emitted radiation is produced from the decay of a radioactive atom. Radioactive isotopes decay with a specific *half-life*. This half-life is the length of time it takes for half of the original radioactive atoms to decay to another nuclear configuration. The duration of a half-life ranges from fractions of a second to billions of years. Each radioactive material has a unique half-life. After a radioactive material goes through seven half-lives, less than 1% of the radioactive material is left:

Number of Half-Lives Elapsed	Percentage of Radioactivity Remaining
0	100%
1	50%
2	25%
3	12.55%
4	6.25%
5	3.13%
6	1.56%
7	0.78%

RADIATION HAZARDS

As radiation passes through a substance (such as air, water, tissue, or bone), a transfer of energy can result in ionization. In tissue or bone, this ionization can produce damage related to the amount of transferred energy. Unless high exposures occur, the affected individual will notice no immediate effects. The deposited or absorbed energy can produce damage, generally assumed to be proportional to the energy absorbed (dose). At high dose levels, this relationship can be shown. At low dose levels, the exact relationship of energy and damage is still being debated. As a conservative approach, the dose–response relationship is assumed to be constant (linear) regardless of dose or dose rate (Table 14–E).

Table 14–E. Effect versus Dose for a Full-Body Exposure Received in a Few Days or Less

Dose	Effect
1 Rem (0.01 Sv)	No detectable change
10 Rem (0.1 Sv)	Some blood changes may be detectable
100 Rem (1 Sv)	Some injury, no disability
200 Rem (2 Sv)	Injury and some disability
400 Rem (4 Sv)	50% mortality within 30 days*
600 Rem (6 Sv)	100% mortality within 30 days*
10,000 Rem (100 Sv)	50% mortality within four days*
Rem:	(Roentgen equivalent man) is a radiation dose unit that equals the dose in rads multiplied by the appropriate value of relative biological effect or Quality Factor for the particular radiation.

*Deaths at four days are due to intestinal damage; deaths at 30 days are due to blood cell damage.

Radioactive contamination is different from radiation. *Contamination* is the unwanted presence of radioactive material, which emits energy in the form of alpha-, beta-, and gamma-rays. When unwanted radioactive materials are in the body, the body is considered internally contaminated. There will always be some radioactivity in the body because of the natural radioactivity in our environment. When the radioactive contamination is on the skin of the body or the surface of an object, it is called *skin* or *surface contamination*.

Equal doses of different types of ionizing radiation are not equally damaging. For a given absorbed dose, alpha-particles produce greater harm than do beta-particles, gamma-rays, and x-rays. Radiation dose is expressed as equivalent dose in units of roentgen equivalent man (rem) or sievert (Sv), discussed shortly, to account for this difference.

Alpha-Radiation

Alpha-radiation is not an external hazard. Alpha-particles on the skin deposit most of their energy in the dead layer of epidermal tissue that covers the body, resulting in little damage or harm. But once inside the body, there is no dead layer of cells to protect the living tissues, and alpha-particles then deposit all of their energy within a few cell layers. Alpha-radiation potentially can cause greater damage to the cells in the immediate vicinity of the source than do other types of radiation. A few sheets of paper can stop alpha-particles.

Beta-Radiation

Beta-radiation is an external and internal hazard. A highly energetic beta-particle can penetrate a centimeter in tissue, about 500 times farther than an alpha-particle. This radiation can deposit energy in the base layers of the skin, but not the internal organs. The lens of the eye is particularly vulnerable to beta-radiation. Beta-particles deposited in the lens may cause cataracts. Though beta-particles are not as energetic as alpha-particles, the potential damage area for beta-radiation extends beyond the immediate vicinity to adjacent tissues, including nearby internal organs.

Gamma- and X-Ray Radiation

Gamma- and x-ray radiation are external and internal hazards. The properties of these two types of radiation are identical. Gamma- and x-ray radiation can pass completely through the human body, including the internal organs and bones. Because of their ability to penetrate tissue, gamma-rays and x-rays are whole-body radiation hazards. Gamma-radiation does not lose energy continuously as do alpha- and beta-radiation. As a result, gamma-rays are capable of causing less damage but inflict the damage over a wider area.

RADIATION PROTECTION METHODS

The guiding principle or goal in radiation safety is to keep radiation exposures *as low as reasonably achievable* (ALARA). Exposure is the potential of a radiation field to deposit energy in an individual. The basic radiation protection methods use the concepts of time, distance, shielding, quantity, and signs and labels.

- *Time*—Reducing the length of time the individual is exposed to a radiation field reduces the individual's radiation exposure.
- *Distance*—If the distance to the source is doubled, the radiation exposure is reduced by the square (a factor of 4 in this case). This is referred to as the *inverse-square law*.
- *Shielding*—Placing radiation-absorbing materials between the source and the potentially exposed individual will reduce radiation exposure. The effectiveness of the shielding will depend on type of material and thickness used, as well as the strength of the source and type of radiation present. Beta-radiation can be shielded by relatively thin pieces of material. Gamma- and x-rays are effectively shielded by materials with a

higher atomic number (e.g., lead and concrete).

- *Quantity*—Limiting the amount of radioactive material will limit the potential for external and internal exposure (Table 14–F).
- *Signs and labels*—Proper identification and labeling of radioactive materials and radiation-producing devices alert persons to the presence of a radiation hazard.

Table 14–F. Exposure Limits for Workers in Radiation Areas (10 CFR 20,101)

Body Area	Rems/Calendar/Quarter
Whole body; head and trunk; active blood-forming organs, lens of eyes; or gonads	1¼
Hands and forearms; feet and ankles	18¾
Skin of whole body	7½

Source: 29 CFR 1910.1096 (b) (1), Table G-18.

RADIATION STANDARDS

Radiation standards provide dose limits to ionizing radiation. The occupational limit in the United States for whole-body radiation dose is 5 rem (0.05 Sv) per year. Another common unit of measure of dose is the millirem, or 0.001 rem.

The U.S. Nuclear Regulatory Commission (NRC) standard for units of radiation dose (10 CFR 20.1004) defines units as follows:

- The *gray* (Gy) is the SI unit of absorbed dose. One gray is equal to an absorbed dose of 1 joule/kilogram (100 rads).
- The *rad* is the special unit of absorbed dose. One rad is equal to an absorbed dose of 100 ergs/gram or 0.01 joule/kilogram (0.01 Gy).
- The *rem* is the special unit of any of the quantities expressed as dose equivalent. The dose equivalent in rems is equal to the absorbed dose in rads multiplied by the quality factor (1 rem = 0.01 sievert).
- The *sievert* is the SI unit of any of the quantities expressed as dose equivalent. The dose equivalent in sieverts is equal to the absorbed dose in grays multiplied by the quality factor (1 Sv = 100 rem).

The quality factors for converting absorbed dose to dose equivalent are shown in Table 14–G. There are different limits for different organs, including the extremities, the eyes, and the skin.

Table 14–G. Quality Factors and Absorbed Dose Equivalencies

Type of Radiation	Quality Factor (Q)	Absorbed Dose Equal to a Unit Dose Equivalent[a]
X-, gamma-, or beta-radiation	1	1
Alpha-particles, multiple-charged particles, fission fragments, and heavy particles of unknown charge	20	0.05
Neutrons of unknown energy	10	0.1
High-energy protons	10	0.1

[a]Absorbed dose in rads equal to 1 rem or the absorbed dose in grays equal to 1 sievert.

The basic standards for protection against ionizing radiation, such as those for the extremities and skin or for pregnant women, are written into NRC regulations. The NRC regulates the use of radioactive materials through 10 CFR 20, Standards for Protection against Radiation. Part 20 includes agency requirements for the following:

- dose limits for radiation workers and members of the public
- monitoring and labeling radioactive materials
- posting radiation areas
- reporting the theft or loss of radioactive material.

Although the NRC sets radiation protection standards and rules for radioactive materials, it does not govern x-rays because x-rays are not produced by radioactive materials or by x-ray machine design or use. The Food and Drug Administration provides x-ray machine manufacturers with performance standards for x-ray machine design.

The NRC has agreements with most states that these states will regulate radiation protection at least as strictly as the NRC does. In addition to radioactive materials usage, most states (nonagreement states included) regulate the use of x-rays because this type of radiation is not covered by the NRC. Some states now have regulations that also cover a hazard known as the use of naturally occurring radioactive materials.

NONIONIZING RADIATION SAFETY

In terms of overall workplace exposures to the electromagnetic spectrum, nonionizing radiation sources have become extremely common. Examples of nonionizing radiation—such as visible light, microwaves, and radio waves—

do not have sufficient energy to remove electrons from atoms.

Electric and magnetic fields are present whenever electricity is generated, transmitted, or used. *Electric fields* represent the forces that electric charges exert on charges at a distance, whereas *magnetic fields* are produced by the motion of the charge. These fields vary as a function of the frequency, or the number of times that the field oscillates per second. Power systems produce an electromagnetic field (EMF) that oscillates 50–60 times per second, or at 50–60 hertz (Hz). At frequencies between 3 and 3,000 Hz, the electric and magnetic fields are essentially independent of each other.

Health regulations applying to electric fields tend to fall into two categories: *exposure criteria*, which describe how much of an electrical field a person can be exposed to, and *emission criteria*, which describe how much can be released into or present in the environment near a source. The International Commission on Non-Ionizing Radiation Protection (ICNIRP) has issued general public and occupational exposure criteria based on induced current flow considerations. The American Conference of Governmental Industrial Hygienists (ACGIH) also established Threshold Limit Values (TLVs). A number of states have established emission criteria for transmission power lines by stating the maximum fields that can exist along the edges of the right-of-way occupied by a power transmission line.

The demand for guidelines to protect workers on the job has resulted in several ideas, two of which deserve mention. The first is *prudent avoidance*, which relies on reducing magnetic fields when and wherever possible. The second approach is a *specific limit of 2 mG*, which represents an averaged exposure level used to describe scenarios from epidemiological studies. However, this value does not define the field strengths that actually might cause harmful effects. Much work remains to be done in this area of worker protection and accident prevention from magnetic fields, and it is important to manage the risk from this potential hazard in settings where strong magnets are used.

RADIATION SAFETY PROGRAM

Companies that use radiation sources are required to institute a radiation safety program to protect workers and to comply with safety standards and regulations. The basic objective of any effective radiation control program is to reduce unnecessary exposure to ionizing radiation. A radiation safety program should use some or all of the elements discussed next. The exact mix of these elements will depend on the size and number of the radiation sources and the exposure potentials during their use.

RADIATION SAFETY OFFICER

A radiation safety officer (RSO) should administer the radiation safety program. RSOs should be well trained and educated to meet the radiation needs of the program as well as the managerial requirements. The RSO should provide advice and assistance to the users and the radiation safety committee, if a committee is needed. The RSO is the individual authorized by a company to officially communicate with state and federal regulatory agencies. This person should have the authority to act on behalf of the organization when addressing radiation-related matters.

The RSO is also the individual specifically named on a license to receive communications from nuclear regulatory agencies. An RSO should act as a resource to help users comply with applicable regulations.

EXPOSURE CONTROL

Limiting worker exposure to radiation is an essential element of a radiation program, whether the radiation comes from radioactive sources or x-ray producing equipment. Reducing exposure supports the philosophy of keeping radiation exposures as low as reasonably achievable (ALARA), which is now a regulatory requirement. The control of radiation exposure includes minimizing both external and internal sources of radiation exposure (dose). Methods of controlling radiation exposures (doses) include posting signs marking radiation areas, restricting access to these areas or to radiation-emitting equipment, and training users in safe procedures and practices. Workers can also be separated from radiation hazards by distance or shielding with appropriate materials to reduce the radiation received to below the maximum permissible dose.

CONTAMINATION CONTROL

Loose radioactive material is the primary source of internal contamination. Radioactive materials can enter the body via four basic paths: ingestion, inhalation, injection, and absorption. In most cases, the potential for ingestion and inhalation is higher than the potential for injection or absorption. Preventing radioactive materials from gaining access to these paths helps prevent internal contamination and subsequent exposure. Control methods and practices to protect individuals from internal radioactive contamination can include wearing gloves; prohibiting smoking, eating, or drinking in work areas; and providing respiratory protection and adequate ventilation.

RADIATION DETECTION INSTRUMENTATION

There are two common types of portable survey equipment: gas-filled detectors and scintillation detectors. Gas-filled detectors are the most popular and versatile. Within this category are two types of meters: ionization chambers and Geiger-Mueller (G-M) detectors. Each type of meter has strengths and weaknesses. G-M detectors respond much faster and can be designed to measure radiation or contamination levels. Ionization chambers measure radiation dose independent of the radiation energy. Both instruments are useful and belong in a sound radiation program.

Scintillation detectors are generally more sensitive than gas-filled detectors. Scintillation detectors are normally designed to measure a single radiation type, such as alpha-particles. An alpha detector is designed to measure surface contamination levels. If the radioactive materials program uses alpha-emitting materials, an alpha detector helps locate contamination so it can be removed. However, the information obtained from such survey meters is only as good as the instrument calibration. Survey instrument calibrations should be based on standards set by the National Institute of Standards and Technology (NIST). The survey instruments should be calibrated to within 10% of the dose rate standard. These calibrations should be performed at least annually but can be required as often as once a quarter. Recalibration helps ensure the accuracy and consistency of radiation survey measurements. In addition, each time a portable survey meter is used, a pre-survey test should be done that includes checking the battery level, taking a background reading, and using a radioactive check source.

Dosimetry is used to measure the dose received by individual workers. Commercial dosimetry processors use either film or thermoluminescent dosimeters as the radiation detector. These dosimetry processors have tested their dosimeters' accuracy through the National Voluntary Laboratory Accreditation Program (NVLAP). This program tests the dosimetry in eight radiation categories. Any dosimetry processor used by a radiation safety program should be accredited through the NVLAP process.

Bioassay involves determining the extent of a worker's internal contamination by radioactive materials. This process can be accomplished by direct measurement or analyzing the individual's urine or feces. The method of bioassay will depend greatly on the type of material suspected in the contamination. The bioassay process should be performed only by well-qualified experts who have the equipment and protocols to provide accurate results.

OTHER PROGRAM ELEMENTS

Safety training programs and course content will depend on a company's use of radiation machines or radioactive materials. At a minimum, users should be trained in radiation protection methods and regulatory requirements for relevant operations. Users should also be trained in the operations they will perform before starting work. The qualifications of principal users should be specified by a knowledgeable radiation safety officer or a radiation safety committee. Principal users will manage the use of the radiation source and employees who work with that source.

Transport of radioactive materials either as sources or as waste on a public road is controlled by the U.S. Department of Transportation (DOT). The DOT specifies the packaging, marking, and labeling of these and other hazardous materials offered for transport. The specifics for radioactive materials are found in 49 CFR 400–478. The NRC uses 10 CFR 71 to determine acceptability of transport packaging.

Since the enactment of the Low-Level Radioactive Waste Policy Act (LLRWPA) in 1980, the disposal of radioactive waste and materials has become an expensive but necessary part of doing business. Waste reduction methods, perceived as too costly 10 years ago, are now routinely used to reduce current volumes and disposal charges. Waste minimization and effective contamination control will help reduce the amount and thereby the cost of waste disposal. The amount of radioactive waste generated has been drastically reduced since the passage of the LLRWPA.

LASER SAFETY

The term *laser* is an acronym for *light amplification by stimulated emission of radiation*. Laser radiation is a form of electromagnetic radiation characterized by its wavelength. The wavelengths typically associated with laser radiation range from 180 nm to 1 mm. This range of wavelengths encompasses several regions of the electromagnetic spectrum: ultraviolet, visible, and infrared. Although laser radiation is often referred to as "light," many lasers produce radiation in the ultraviolet and infrared regions, which cannot be seen by the human eye.

PRINCIPLES OF LASERS

As a specific type of radiation, lasers are versatile and beneficial when used properly but potentially hazardous when used unwisely. Lasers produce a beam that is coherent and directional. Lasers are also monochromatic, meaning that the output of energy of a laser is a single wavelength.

Probably the most important quality of laser radiation is *coherence*—that is, all the photons act in unison. Coherent radiation is an efficient way of delivering energy because there is no destructive interference. A coherent beam produces a concentrated and powerful effect when striking a surface.

Lasers are also directional. Directional beams keep their shape for long distances and retain these properties even after reflecting off a mirror-like surface. This directionality allows the laser to be guided but can also present a hazardous condition at a distance from the laser itself.

Although lasers may take various forms, they are all constructed with an *optical cavity* and a source of excitation. An optical cavity contains the active medium—a solid, liquid, or gas—and two mirrors. The medium is excited by high-voltage electricity until it begins to emit radiation in all directions. Mirrors placed in parallel at each end of the medium reflect the laser radiation between them until standing electromagnetic waves form in the cavity. One type of mirror is totally reflective and the other is partially reflective to allow the release or emission of the laser radiation. Although the active medium generally dictates the type of laser wavelength emitted, the length of the optical cavity plays a substantial role as well. Figure 14–3 shows a schematic diagram of a simple laser system.

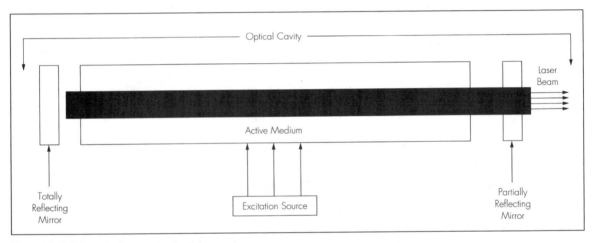

Figure 14–3. Schematic diagram of a simple laser system.

HAZARDS OF LASER RADIATION

Hazards associated with laser equipment can be divided into beam hazards and nonbeam hazards. *Beam hazards*, from direct or scattered laser radiation, affect primarily two organs: the eyes and the skin.

The skin is the less susceptible of the organs because it can repair itself when injured. The main hazard to the skin is thermal burns produced from the extreme heat of a laser beam. Some lasers emitting UV laser radiation add a photochemical effect, which produces the equivalent of sunburn on exposed skin. Workers burned by lasers should seek immediate medical attention.

Compared to the skin, eyes have less ability for repair and so are more vulnerable to injury. The eyes have three basic structures that can be affected by laser radiation: the cornea, the lens, and the retina. The cornea, which is the outer covering of the eye, helps focus visible-light radiation used in normal vision and absorbs the energy of deep UV and far infrared laser radiation. The hazard for the cornea is both thermal and photochemical laser burns.

The retina is the most sensitive structure in the eye. Visible and near-infrared light passes through the cornea and lens to the retina. The light receptors in this structure focus the laser beam and can intensify the thermal and photochemical damage to the retina. Lasers can also damage the retina through thermoacoustic effects. This occurs when the highly focused beam forms a steam bubble near the retina. When the bubble pops, it sends out shock waves that damage retinal tissue and blood vessels. The degree of permanent damage caused by thermoacoustic injury is determined by what part of the retina was struck and whether blood reached nerve tissue. In general, brief pulses of laser light lasting only millionths of a second can produce more damage to the eye than can longer pulses because shorter bursts retain more heat.

Nonbeam hazards associated with lasers are numerous and potentially more dangerous than beam hazards. Lasers generally use high-voltage electrical power as a source of excitation for the active medium. As a result, electric shock is by far the greatest hazard associated with lasers. In addition, because of the inefficiency of many lasers, the power supply provides much more power than the laser can convert, and the remaining energy is given off as heat. This heat must be safely dissipated to minimize risk of personal injury, equipment damage, and property damage.

Chemical hazards are associated with the use of some lasers. Potential chemical hazards include asphyxiant gases such as carbon dioxide. Acid gases such as hydrogen chloride and potentially toxic by-products from the laser action on a surface are also chemical hazards of concern.

Other nonbeam hazards requiring evaluation in the laser workplace are noise, dust, hot surfaces, cryogenic gases, explosion of high-pressure flash lamps, toxic laser dyes, electrocution or shock, fire, and laser-generated airborne contaminants (LGACs). High-powered lasers also have the potential to ignite combustible materials. Workers should keep flammable materials out of areas where Class 4 and some focused Class 3 lasers are used.

Hazard Classification

Laser products are classified by manufacturers according to the requirements of 21 CFR 1040.10, the U.S. federal performance standards. The classification scheme, which designates hazards as Classes 1–4, is based on the hazard level the laser presents (Table 14–H). These classifications are based on normal operation of the laser product. Maintenance and service procedures may expose the individual to levels of laser radiation far above those encountered during normal operation. Before work begins, the company should evaluate the hazards that workers will encounter under actual working conditions.

Table 14–H. Laser Classification Scheme	
Class 1:	Levels of laser radiation are not considered to be hazardous.
Class 2a:	Levels of laser radiation are not considered to be hazardous if viewed for any period of time less than or equal to 1000 seconds, but are considered to be a chronic viewing hazard for any period of time greater than 1000 seconds.
Class 2:	Levels of laser radiation are considered to be a chronic viewing hazard.
Class 3a:	Levels of laser radiation are considered to be, depending upon the irradiance, either an acute intrabeam viewing hazard or chronic viewing hazard, and an acute viewing hazard if viewed directly with optical instruments.
Class 3b:	Levels of laser radiation are considered to be an acute hazard to the skin and eyes from direct radiation.
Class 4:	Levels of laser radiation are considered to be an acute hazard to the skin and eyes from direct and scattered radiation.

HAZARD CONTROLS

Engineering Controls

In general, engineering controls, such as protective housings, interlocked enclosures, ventilation systems, and beam enclosures, should be the primary method used to control exposure to laser hazards. Ideally, these controls require no action by the individual worker to be effective.

Interlocked laser beam enclosures include plastic panels on a framework and metal boxes with doors large enough to accommodate a person or vehicles. Laser beams can also be routed over or below walkways by the use of mirrors or elevated enclosures or tunnels. Interlocked laser beams either shut off the electrical power or drop a shutter into the beam, cutting it off. Interlocks can also be operated remotely and are used for laser systems that cover large areas.

For Class 4 lasers, viewing portals, viewing screens, and optical instruments must be connected to interlocks to reduce beam intensity to acceptable levels. Status lights, loudspeakers, and buzzers can be installed to protect employees working inside and outside the area of laser operations.

Although engineering controls are effective when lasers are installed, they are less useful when workers set up the device or carry out maintenance work. As a result, management should make sure that workers use special caution during these times, including the use of administrative controls and warning signs. For example, nearly 37% of laser accidents occur during the process of aligning the beam. Workers should use special protective equipment, such as laser alignment goggles, so that the laser beam will not go into the eyes. ANSI Z136.1 specifies the types of special warning signs that workers should use during setup. Finally, workers and management should remove all unnecessary reflecting surfaces, such as chrome chairs, mirrors, or highly polished floors or furnishings. Even painted walls and stipple-polished tools can serve as highly reflective surfaces for gas laser beams.

The personal protective equipment used for lasers, such as safety eyewear, must meet the provisions of the latest edition of ANSI Z87.1. Workers should select laser eyewear that is tailored to the specific laser wavelength used and severity of exposure. This eyewear can be color-coded to indicate the specific use.

Administrative Controls

Maintenance and service operations may require more stringent safety controls than during operation of a laser. The Laser Institute of America's LIA/ANSI standard Z136.1-2014 specifies calculating the nominal hazard zone (NHZ) (where people could be exposed to laser beam levels) above the maximum permissible exposures (MPEs) and blocking people from entering this zone by barrier signs, flashing lights, and warning signs. Specifications for these items can be found in the ANSI Z535 series of standards, which specify colors, warning words, standard symbols, and warning sign layout.

Because administrative controls require the individual to take some proactive action, they should not be used in place of engineering controls. Instead, they should serve as backup in case engineering controls fail. When engineering controls are determined ineffective or impractical, administrative controls can assume a primary role. Examples of administrative laser safety controls are adherence to written standard operating procedures, observing warning signs and labels, establishing a nominal hazard zone for a laser product, training laser users and maintenance personnel, and any other procedures that will enhance the laser safety process.

Personal Protective Equipment

The use of personal protective equipment is the third type of control measure. PPE is used to minimize a worker's exposure to a hazard when engineering or administrative controls have not been fully implemented or are infeasible. The most recognizable type of laser PPE is laser goggles or glasses, which provide a defined amount of eye protection at specific wavelengths. However, companies must make sure that the correct laser PPE is specifically chosen for each laser. Eye protection is determined by reducing the exposure to less than the MPE. The required protection value is called the optical density (OD). The OD calculation can be found in the ANSI Z136.1 standard. The ODs for specific wavelengths must be provided on the laser glasses to help management select the proper eye protection (Table 14–I).

Table 14–I. Selecting Laser Safety Glass

Intensity, CW Maximum Power Density (watts/cm³)	Optical Density (OD)	Attenuation Factor
10^2	5	10^5
10^4	6	10^6
1	7	10^7
10	8	10^8

Source: 29 CFR 1926.102(b)(2)(I)

RECOMMENDATIONS FOR LASER SAFETY PROGRAMS

Laser safety programs developed by companies should be based on laser hazard classifications and hazard evaluations. Although no two laser safety programs will be identical, an effective laser safety program should follow the requirements of the applicable ANSI and FDA standards.

Safety Regulations

The main U.S. standard for laser safety is the Laser Institute of America's LIA/ANSI Z136.1, American National Standard for Safe Use of Lasers, revised in 2014. The Laser Institute of America (LIA) is the international society for laser applications and safety information (www.laserinstitute.org). The Center for Devices and Radiological Health (CDRH) of the Food and Drug Administration has promulgated regulations for safety in the use of commercial laser devices (21 CFR 1040). These standards focus on the hazard control class of regulation, which requires classifying the severity of the hazard posed by a laser device. The two main measures of severity are wavelength and power or energy output; other measures include pulse duration and size or spread of reflection of the beam. The LIA/ANSI and CDRH standards set accessible emission limits (AELs) for each class of laser. Safety precautions become more stringent as the output of the laser increases from Class 1 to Class 4.

The LIA also specifies maximum permissible exposures (MPEs) for lasers, which are similar to OSHA PELs set for chemicals or the MPEs set for radiofrequency/microwave radiation by ANSI/IEEE C95.1-2005. The standard also gives protocols for evaluating the risks of exposure to pulsed lasers, although the protocols are complicated and difficult to apply. Managers and other employees working with pulsed lasers should read paragraph 8.2.2 of the LIA/

ANSI standard carefully.

The Food and Drug Administration publishes regulations that contain the performance standards that laser manufacturers must meet to sell lasers in the United States. The laser product standard is found in 21 CFR 1040, Performance Standards for Light-Emitting Products. These standards provide the requirements for the construction, classification, and labeling of laser products. Laser manufacturers and importers must certify that their laser products comply with the performance standards according to the requirements in 21 CFR 1000–1010.

Currently, OSHA does not have an all-encompassing and comprehensive laser standard. In the construction industry, there is an OSHA standard that covers the use of lasers (29 CFR 1926). However, OSHA has issued citations associated with laser use under the "general duty clause" of Public Law 91-596, the Occupational Safety and Health Act of 1970. In these cases, employers are asked to revise their reportedly unsafe workplace using the recommendations and requirements of such industry consensus standards as the ANSI Z136.1 standard.

The Written Program

The program document should describe the overall purpose of the organization's laser safety program, with responsibilities and authorities assigned. The document should reference ANSI Z136.1 or a similar standard as the basis for the company's laser safety practices.

The appointment of a laser safety officer (LSO) is critical, with a duty to manage the laser safety program. Training for the LSO is very important. Because hazard recognition and control methods form the basis of a successful laser safety program, the LSO should be viewed as the company resource for information and regulatory requirements for laser use.

Medical surveillance monitors employees' health to determine whether they have the physical capabilities needed to perform a task and whether they have experienced symptoms that indicate overexposure to the hazard. In the case of lasers, the practice deals specifically with evaluation of the eyes or skin for laser damage. The examination (generally done by an ophthalmologist) helps identify any preexisting conditions and the extent of injury from exposures. The ANSI standard recommends that users of Class 3b and Class 4 lasers receive examinations before starting laser work and following any suspected laser injury.

The type and content of laser training depend on the particular hazards. Important ideas to communicate are the recognition of hazards and methods of protection from laser hazards. Service and maintenance personnel should be trained to protect themselves against the highest hazard level of accessible laser radiation because many laser products have lower hazard classifications based on enclosure of the beam. Repair and maintenance technicians should also be trained in high-voltage safety and cardiopulmonary resuscitation. Sometimes, these workers must remove or circumvent safety interlocks to perform a maintenance or service task. With safety interlocks defeated, the accessible laser radiation can be far in excess of the laser hazard indicated by the classification. Companies should prepare specific procedures and checklists to help protect employees properly during and after such service.

Several types of inspections should be included in an effective laser safety program. These would include installation, post-service, and annual inspections. The inspections should focus on engineering controls (e.g., enclosures, interlocks) and administrative controls (e.g., labels, signs, procedures). Personal protection equipment use and applicability should be an important part of these inspections. Users should demonstrate the proper selection, care, and maintenance of their safety equipment.

PHYSICAL HAZARDS AND OTHER CONSIDERATIONS

CRYOGENIC LIQUIDS

Cryogenic liquids are extremely cold refrigerated liquids (below –130 F/–90 C) normally stored at low pressures in specially constructed, multi-walled, vacuum-insulated containers. Potential hazards include the following:

- exposure to extreme cold that can freeze human tissue on contact
- extreme pressure as a result of rapid vaporization of the refrigerated liquid when leakage occurs
- asphyxiation due to displacement of air by escaping liquid that changes to gas/vapor when released to the ambient surroundings.

Transfer operations involving open containers (Dewars) must be conducted slowly to minimize boiling and splashing of the cryogenic liquid and must be conducted only in well-ventilated areas to prevent accumulation of inert gas that can lead to asphyxiation. All personnel handling cryogenic liquids should be trained in the use of specialized equipment designed for the storage, transfer, and handling of these products. PPE that must be worn while handling these materials include heavy leather protective gloves, safety shoes, aprons, and eye protection.

FIBER-OPTIC CABLES

Fiber-optic technology has revolutionized communications, improving fidelity, distance of transmission, and safety. The cables are made of fiberglass. Fiber-optic cable is basically a cylindrical mirror that reflects light internally. In fiber-optic cable, photons flow, not electrons, as in electrical transmission. These photons originate from a laser.

Laser energy is the principal hazard of fiber-optic devices. The signal is transmitted through the fiber by means of lasers, so anyone working with fiber-optic cables should also be familiar with basic laser safety. Fortunately, the energy spreads rapidly from the end of a fiber-optic cable, unlike many laser devices in which the energy remains concentrated over distance. But fiber-optic devices can still be hazardous when in close proximity. Fiber optics may need to be covered by a lockout/tagout-type program to protect individuals from inadvertent exposure to laser energy if the cable is connected to the laser source.

Further information on laser and fiber-optic safety can be found in ANSI standards Z136.1; Z136.2, Safe Use of Optical Fiber Communication Systems Utilizing Laser Diode and LED Sources; Z136.3, Safe Use of Lasers in Health Care Facilities; Z136.4, Recommended Practice for Laser Safety Measurements for Hazard Evaluation; Z136.5, Safe Use of Lasers in Educational Institutions; and Z136.6, Safe Use of Lasers Outdoors. In addition, there are International Organization for Standardization (ISO) counterparts to these American standards.

Caution should be used when handling fiber-optic cables to prevent splinters. Also, scraps should be collected in a container for disposal to minimize the chance of exposure to splinters. Safety glasses should be worn when working with fiber.

ALTERED ENVIRONMENTS

Altered environments are special-purpose workplaces that require special conditions in order to carry out the work they host. These are often associated with laboratories and can include clean rooms, animal quarters, dark rooms, warm rooms, and cold rooms. Traditionally, safety issues surrounding altered environments have focused on exposure to physical hazards such as heat, cold, humidity, and altitude. Over the past 25 years, workers have found that they now are confronting new physical and psychological exposures and stresses. The solutions to the problems raised by these environments require specialized information and expertise from medical, safety, hygiene, ergonomics, engineering, and human resources personnel.

CLEAN ROOMS

Clean rooms are designed and built to control dust and particulates in order to protect work materials from contamination by airborne particles. This is important in a number of settings, including electronic chip manufacturing. Dust control at this level requires a series of engineering controls that can also create potential hazards for the work force. For example, clean-room ventilation hoods typically push air away from the product and toward the worker, thereby increasing employees' potential exposure to chemical vapors from the work zone.

An additional problem that can increase worker exposure to air contaminants is the recycling of internal air within the clean-room environment. This means that any chemical vapors in the room are also rapidly redistributed into the work area. Safety professionals must be prepared to understand the mechanical engineering aspects of clean-room ventilation so that they can successfully address worker questions and problems.

The clean room is typically a semi-arid environment: hot (74°F), dry (35% relative humidity), and drafty because of the rapid number of air changes per hour. This environment creates a number of potential medical problems for workers, including dermatologic, allergic, and respiratory aliments. Chronic skin problems are one of the most frequent causes of medical transfer from the clean room.

Upper respiratory problems, such as sinus, throat, and lung complaints, have also been attributed to working in a clean-room environment. Because these problems are usually attributed to the environmental conditions required by the manufacturing process, it is often unlikely that anything short of medical transfer will be a satisfactory treatment. A similar but less difficult problem is eye irritation, which can usually be treated with simple over-the-counter drops or lubricating fluids.

An additional problem associated with protective garments is the development and aggravation of facial acne due to constant use of headgear or respiratory protection. This has been attributed to the combination of relatively hot ambient air temperatures and the constant rubbing and irritation that can be produced by full facial garments. Similarly, health problems, primarily dermatologic, have been associated with the polyvinyl chloride gloves that are usually used in the clean-room environment. Any individual experiencing health issues should be examined by an occupational health physician or health care practitioner experienced in dealing with occupational health exposures.

ANIMAL FACILITIES

Animal facilities, which house laboratory animals, face many of the same health and safety challenges as described for clean rooms. An additional hazard in these workplaces is exposure to dander from experimental mice and rats. Some individuals are allergic to this dander, or develop allergies with time, which is likely to require them to cease working in this environment. Thus, animal care workers must be monitored and provided with careful oversight of this concern by occupational doctors, and good use of personal protective equipment is important in controlling this problem. Other potential issues include the sensitivity of animals to environmental conditions such as temperature, noise, and vibration.

WARM AND COLD ROOMS

Many biological procedures require specific temperature and humidity conditions to proceed. These conditions are often provided by environmental rooms that are kept at specific temperature and humidity. The temperature control required for this is sometimes achieved by eliminating fresh air into the room; air is simply recirculated in the room on an ongoing basis. Therefore, if laboratory workers use hazardous chemicals or store liquid nitrogen or dry ice in such rooms, hazardous concentrations of the chemicals can build up, or decreased levels of oxygen can result. Workers in these rooms must be educated as to potential hazards, and the rooms must have signs pointing this concern out to laboratory workers working in them.

POTENTIAL PSYCHOLOGICAL PROBLEMS

Given the conditions that are required in these specialized rooms, it should not be surprising that workers who work in them on a regular basis report a myriad of psychological problems. Large amounts of time are spent in a constant, unchanging environment. The use of protective equipment further accentuates the sense of isolation and dehumanization. Overall, these conditions can make the clean room a relatively harsh workplace environment. To date, no large-scale psychological studies of workers in this environment have been conducted. However, it would not be surprising to find somewhat increased rates of alienation, depression, or other mood disorders. Clearly, this environment presents both an opportunity and a challenge for specialists in occupational health, safety, hygiene, and human resources.

LABORATORY ERGONOMICS

The Centers for Disease Control and Prevention (CDC) conducts a significant amount of biomedical laboratory research, which has led the agency to recognize that laboratory work presents significant ergonomic challenges to its workers. The information on this subject that follows is adapted from the CDC website.

Laboratory workers are at risk for repetitive-motion injuries during routine laboratory procedures such as pipetting, working at microscopes, operating microtomes, and using cell counters and video-display terminals. Repetitive-motion injuries develop over time and occur when muscles and joints are stressed, tendons are inflamed, nerves are pinched, and the flow of blood is restricted. Standing and working in awkward positions in laboratory hoods and biological safety cabinets can also present ergonomic problems.

General solutions include providing fully adjustable seating and encouraging workers to take short breaks of 3–5 min for every 20–30 min of intense awkward work. These breaks can be spent doing mild hand exercises or stretches. The following are further suggestions specific to certain kinds of equipment.

BIOSAFETY CABINETS, FUME HOODS, AND LABORATORY WORKBENCHES

Biosafety cabinets, fume hoods, and laboratory workbenches present similar ergonomic challenges—largely because of the lack of adjustability and leg room associated with use of the equipment. To manage this hazard, cabinets should be removed from under the workbenches when possible in order to provide leg room. Use a turntable to store equipment near the worker. This reduces excessive reaching and twisting, which places an increased load on the lower back. Position materials in the cabinet and on the bench top as close as possible to avoid extended reaching without compromising containment of the cabinet.

COMPUTER WORKSTATIONS

Many laboratory workers spend 50% or more of their day entering data with their keyboard and mouse resting on a lab bench. Because of the nature of laboratory furniture, many of these lab benches are too high and require users to elevate their arms and excessively stretch their wrists while inputting data. In addition to standard computer ergonomic considerations, laboratory personnel should not go from keyboarding to pipetting activities (or vice versa) without an adequate break to allow hand washing and a recovery period.

MICROSCOPY

The following practices are recommended for control of ergonomic hazards associated with the use of microscopes:

- Don't use a microscope for more than 5 h/day. Spread the use out over the entire workday, avoiding long uninterrupted periods of microscope work.
- Use a cut-out microscope table. This puts the worker close to the scope and gives an area for supporting forearms.

- Maintain a neutral spine posture. A neutral spine is neither rounded forward nor arched back too much.

REPETITIVE PIPETTING

Pipetting is one of the most common tasks performed in the research laboratory. It involves several ergonomic stressors: thumb force, repetitive motions, and awkward postures, especially of the wrists, arms, and shoulders. The following are recommendations for addressing ergonomics hazards associated with the use of pipettes:

- Use pipettes with newer trigger mechanisms requiring less force to activate; use the pointer finger to aspirate and the thumb to dispense.
- Use pipettes that fit comfortably in the user's hand.
- Use shorter pipettes. This decreases hand elevation and consequent awkward postures.
- Rotate pipetting activities among laboratory tasks, hands, and people.

MICROTOME AND CRYOSTAT WORK

The following are recommended for control of ergonomic hazards associated with the use of a microtome or cryostat:

- Lower the workstation to keep the arms closer to the body.
- Apply padding to the front edge of the work surface to eliminate sharp edges and increase the amount of blood flow to the hands.
- Retrofit the existing handle with an adapter that will allow the operator to use the handwheel in a pistol grip position. This will help alleviate repetitive wrist flexion and extension.
- Consider the use of an automatic foot-operated cryostat when frequent cryosectioning is performed.

GLOVE BOXES

Working in glove boxes or anaerobic chambers requires extended static loading on the shoulders. Extending the arms for more than a couple of minutes can be exhausting. In addition to static loading and frequent side reaching, the thick gloves also make the user overcompensate on grip strength. Where possible, the following controls are recommended for ergonomic hazards associated with using a glove box:

- Move all needed materials for the experiment from the side chamber to the main chamber at one time to reduce the amount of side reaching.
- Use highly absorbent hand powder for glove comfort.
- Utilize job enlargement (periodically performing other activities) to avoid long, continuous use of glove boxes.

CENTRIFUGES

Centrifuge rotors present a unique lifting hazard in the laboratory. Centrifuge rotors can weigh up to 35 lb and are awkward in shape. For this reason, if possible, use a second person to assist with lifting and removing the rotors. It is also a good idea to use a cart to transport rotors.

EMERGENCY PLANNING

Laboratory emergencies occur infrequently, but because of the variety of hazards found in laboratories, planning for effective response can be a challenge. Although emergency responders such as police, fire fighters, and emergency medical technicians are trained in how to assess the risk associated with entering the scene of an emergency, they are usually not familiar with the combinations of chemicals, biological agents, radiation sources, and other hazards found in the laboratory setting. Further, the training they receive in managing hazardous materials is typically built around industrial settings, where the nature of the hazard is very different from that found in laboratories.

This means that there is no standard way to plan for emergencies in laboratory settings. However, it is imprudent to wait until the emergency is occurring to address these issues. The laboratory safety program must proactively undertake an emergency-planning effort that involves the agencies that are expected to respond to fire, medical, or security emergencies. This usually involves touring the laboratory facilities and discussing the oversight programs in place to maintain a safe workplace.

The nature of the emergency plan developed through this interaction will depend on the resources available to both the laboratory organization and the local responders. In some settings, local response agencies may have specific requirements for laboratories. In other settings, they may be completely unfamiliar with laboratories and their special hazards. On the other hand, laboratory workers should have received specific training about how to effectively work with emergency responders in explaining the hazards associated with the laboratory. For the safety of all parties and to avoid undue disruption of laboratory work, an ongoing emergency-planning and preparedness effort should be maintained.

LABORATORY WASTE AND CLOSING PROCEDURES

As mentioned earlier, disposal of hazardous chemical waste is heavily regulated by federal and local agencies. This is also true of biological and radioactive wastes. Although the development of a complete laboratory waste management program is beyond the scope of this chapter, significant management advantages can be realized by connecting this waste program with the rest of the laboratory safety effort. A common element of these programs is that a risk assessment should be performed before work begins to ensure that proper practices are implemented and that the use of hazardous materials is minimized as much as possible.

In addition to routine waste disposal protocols, each organization should have a documented protocol in place for laboratory closures or moves. This protocol should be developed into a formalized procedure involving input and participation from laboratory administration, facilities management, housekeeping, and the safety staff. The following issues should be addressed in this procedure:

- evaluation of chemicals and equipment for continued usefulness
- proper disposal of chemical, biohazardous, and medical waste
- clear labeling of all materials in the laboratory, whether to be disposed of or transferred to another laboratory
- use of appropriate cleaning solutions for cleaning and decontaminating equipment
- packaging unused chemicals for transfer to another location
- radiological safety decommissioning through contamination surveys
- removal and proper disposal of refrigerant and mercury switches in scientific equipment.

SUMMARY

- Laboratory safety management presents special challenges because of the wide variety of activities that occur in laboratories, which change frequently. Development of a proactive safety culture among laboratory workers is necessary to manage laboratory hazards successfully.
- Laboratory risks include chemical, biological, radiation, and physical hazards that vary widely in magnitude. In general, hazardous materials are small in quantity, but can be high in hazards that must be managed carefully.
- An ongoing laboratory safety inspection program is necessary to provide adequate oversight of laboratory operations as conditions and processes change.
- A successful chemical safety program requires ongoing evaluation of the risks of the chemical processes being used; careful housekeeping,

handling, storage, and disposal of hazardous chemicals; proper use and maintenance of equipment and PPE; and training and compliance appropriate to the hazards involved.

- A biological safety program involves training in and compliance with CDC biosafety guidelines, containment principles, and bloodborne pathogen issues. Risk assessments of biological practices in laboratories should be conducted to ensure that the correct biosafety level practices are used for the work being performed.

- An effective radiation safety program includes the following elements: appointment of a radiation safety officer, exposure and contamination control, use of radiation detection instrumentation, inventory control, guidelines for transporting radioactive materials, and guidelines for complying with radioactive waste disposal.

- The basic radiation protection methods are limiting workers' time of exposure, keeping the source of radiation at a distance, shielding workers, careful labeling of all radiation sources, and limiting the amount of radioactive material used.

- Nonionizing radiation potentially presents some acute hazards, but the long-term health effects of this radiation are not well understood.

- Lasers produce high-energy beams that are coherent, directional, and monochromatic. Hazards associated with laser equipment are classified as Classes 1–4 (least hazardous to most hazardous) and involve beam and nonbeam hazards. Beam hazards affect primarily the skin and eyes, subjecting these organs to varying degrees of thermal and photochemical burns. Nonbeam hazards include electric shock, heat, toxic by-products, noise, dust, and explosion of high-pressure flash lamps.

- The FDA and OSHA have established specific guidelines and regulations for the use of lasers that require manufacturers and employers to comply with performance standards and safe practices.

- Altered environments, such as clean rooms, animal facilities, and temperature-controlled environments, also pose threats to human health. Hazards associated with clean rooms include arid environmental conditions, air pollution, health problems such as dermatitis, and psychological isolation. Animal facilities present exposures to allergenic animal dander. Temperature-controlled environments such as warm rooms and cold rooms generally do not have ventilation; therefore, hazardous atmospheres can develop in them.

- Laboratory workers are at risk for repetitive-motion injuries during routine laboratory procedures such as pipetting, working at microscopes, operating microtomes, and using cell counters and video display terminals. Careful planning of workstations to minimize these hazards and frequent breaks from repetitive tasks are key to minimizing this hazard.

- Emergency planning for laboratories is a significant challenge that requires ongoing proactive attention to be successful.
- Waste disposal regulations require that laboratory wastes be minimized as much as possible. Extra attention should be paid to the transition of laboratories from one occupant to another to ensure that hazards are not passed from one to the other.

REVIEW QUESTIONS

1. How close should emergency showers and eyewashes be located to areas where hazardous chemicals are used?
2. What are the four stages of the management system approach to safety?
3. Name three key sources of chemical safety information.
4. Which of the following is a key piece of chemical safety information in assessing the risk of a particular chemical?
   a. molecular weight
   b. number of electron shells
   c. concentration of the chemical solution
   d. electronegativity
5. Distinguish between primary and secondary containment in biosafety.
6. List and describe the different levels of biosafety.
7. At what biosafety level is human blood appropriately handled?
8. The role of a radiation safety officer (RSO) includes
   a. performing medical evaluations of employees' eyes or skin for laser damage
   b. managing the laser safety program
   c. communicating with regulatory agencies on behalf of the company
   d. all of the above
9. What are the four basic radiation protection methods?
10. The term *laser* is an acronym for what words?
11. Lasers use which of the following as the active medium?
    a. liquid
    b. gas
    c. solid
    d. all of the above
12. What wavelengths of light are lasers used at?
    a. visible

      b. infrared

      c. ultraviolet

      d. all of the above

13. List the broad types of health problems that are associated with clean rooms.

14. Which of the following is not an important strategy for dealing with laboratory ergonomic issues?

      a. taking frequent short breaks

      b. stretching exercises for limbs that are placed in awkward postures

      c. providing background music in the laboratory

      d. providing adjustable seating at workstations

15. Which emergency responders should be consulted in planning for laboratory emergencies?

      a. fire fighters

      b. emergency medical technicians

      c. hazard materials technicians

      d. police

      e. all of the above

References

CHAPTER 1: SAFETY CULTURE

Arden, P. "Create a Corporate Safety Culture." *Safety and Health* 147(2), 1993.

Ashforth, B.E. "Climate Formation: Issues and Extensions." *Academy of Management Review*, 10:837–847, 1985.

Bigoes, S., "Back Injuries in Industry: A Retrospective Study; Employee Related Factors." *Spine* 11(1), 1986.

Bodley, J.H. *Cultural Anthropology: Tribes, States and the Global System*. New York: McGraw-Hill, 1994.

Burns, C. "The Role of Trust in Safety Culture." Unpublished PhD thesis. University of Aberdeen, Aberdeen, 2004.

Chaudron, D. "Building a Framework: Begin at the Beginning in Organizational Change," 2003. www.organizedchange.com/decide.htm. Accessed Aug. 22 2014.

Cooke, R.A. and Rousseau, D.M. "Behavioral Norms and Expectations: A Quantitative Approach to the Assessment of Organizational Culture." *Group and Organizational Studies* 13, 1988.

Creek, R.N. "Organizational Behavior and Safety Management: Evolution of Safety." *Professional Safety* 40, 1995.

Denison, D. and Mishra, A. "Toward a Theory of Organizational Culture and Effectiveness," *Organizational Science* 6(2):204–233, 1995.

Downey, H.K., Hellriegel, D., Phelps, M., and Slocum, J.W. "Organizational Climate and Job Satisfaction: A Comparative Analysis." *Journal of Business Research* 2, 1974.

Fleming, M. 2000. "Safety Culture Maturity Model." The Keil Centre for the Health and Safety Executive (HSE). www.hse.gov.uk/research/otopdf/2000/oto00049.pdf. Accessed Aug. 22 2014.

Geller, E.S. "Ten Principles for Achieving a Total Safety Culture." *Professional Safety* 39(9), 1994.

Greenwood, J., and Wolf, H. "Job Satisfaction Affects Rates of Occupational Accidents." *West Virginia News Digest,* November 1987.

Hale, A. "Organizational Culture and Safety." In *International Encyclopedia of Ergonomics and Human Factors*, 2nd ed., vol. 3. Boca Raton, FL: Taylor & Francis Group, 2006.

Hansen, L. "Safety Management: A Call for (R)evolution." *Professional Safety* 38, 1993.

———. " 'Re-braining' Corporate Safety and Health." *Professional Safety* 40(10), 1995.

Hellriegel, D., and Slocum, J.W. *Organizational Behavior,* 10th ed. Mason, OH: Southwestern College Publishing, 2004.

Helmreich, R., and Merritt, A. *Culture at Work in Aviation and Medicine*. Aldershot: Ashgate, 1998.

Hirschhorn, L. *The Workplace Within*. Cambridge, MA: MIT Press, 1987.

Hudson, P. "Safety Management and Safety Culture—The Long, Hard and Winding Road." *Proceedings of the First National Conference,* Occupational Health and Safety Management Systems, Crown Content, Work Cover NSW, 2001.

———. "Applying the Lessons of High Risk Industries to Health Care." *Quality and Safety in Health Care* 12(Suppl 1), 2003.

Hudson, P., and van der Graaf, G.C. "Hearts and Minds: The Status After 15 Years Research." *International Conference on HSE in Oil and Gas Exploration and Production.* Society of Petroleum Engineers (SPE 73941), Kuala Lumpur, 2002.

INSAG. "Basic Safety Principles for Nuclear Power Plants." *Safety Culture Safety Series No. 76-INSAG-3.* Vienna, Austria: International Atomic Energy Agency, 1988.

James, L.R., and James, L.A. "Psychological Climate and Affect: Test of a Hierarchical Dynamic Model." In Cranny CJ, Smith PC, and Stone EF, eds. *Job Satisfaction: How People Feel about Their Jobs, and How It Affects Their Performance.* New York: Lexington Books, 1992.

Kilmann, R.H., Saxton, M.J, Serpa, R., and Associates. *Gaining Control of the Corporate Culture.* San Francisco: Jossey-Bass, 1985.

Lewin, K. *Field Theory in Social Science; Selected Theoretical Papers.* Cartwright D, ed. New York: Harper & Row, 1951.

Martin, J., and Meyerson, D. "Organizational Cultures and the Denial, Channeling, and Acknowledgement of Ambiguity." In Pondy LR, Boland RJ, and Thomas H, eds, *Managing Ambiguity and Change.* New York: Wiley, 1988.

Mayer, R.C., and Davis, J.H. "The Effect of the Performance Appraisal System on Trust of Management: A Field Quasi-Experiment." *Journal of Applied Psychology* 84, 1999.

Mayer, R.C., Davis, J.H., and Schoorman, F.D. "An Integrative Model of Organizational Trust." *Academy of Management Review* 20, 1995.

McLain, D.L. "Responses to Health and Safety Risk in the Work Environment." *Academy of Management Journal* 38, 1995.

Mead, M. *Mind, Self and Society.* Chicago: University of Chicago Press, 1934.

Mearns, K.J., and Flin, R. "Assessing the State of Organizational Safety: Culture or Climate?" *Current Psychology* 18, 1999.

Menzies, I.E.P. "A Case Study in the Functioning of Social Systems as a Defense against Anxiety." *Human Relations* 13, 1960.

Petersen, D. *Techniques of Safety Management: A Systems Approach.* New York: Aloray Inc., 1989.

Reason, J. *Managing the Risks of Organizational Accidents.* Aldershot: Ashgate, 1997.

Roethlisberger, F.J., and Dickson, W.J. *Management and the Worker.* Cambridge, MA: Harvard University Press, 1946.

Rousseau. *On the Social Contract,* Paperback, Revised. Hackett Publishing Company, Inc., 1988.

Sarkus, D.J. "Safety and Psychology." *Professional Safety,* January 2001.

Schein, E.H. "Coming to a New Awareness of Organizational Culture." *Sloan Management Review.* 25, 1984.

———. "Organizational Culture: Skill, Defense Mechanism or Addiction?" In Brush, F.R, and Overmier, J.B., eds. *Affect Conditioning, and Cognition.* Hillsdale, NJ: Erlbaum, 1985.

———. *Organizational Culture and Leadership: A Dynamic View,* 2nd ed. San

Francisco: Jossey-Bass, 1990.

———. *Organizational Culture and Leadership,* 2nd ed. San Francisco: Jossey-Bass, 1992.

Schneider, B. *Organizational Climate and Culture.* Oxford, UK: Jossey-Bass, 1990.

Schneider and Gunnarson. *Evaluating Safety Culture and Climate: Key Measurement,* 1996.

Simon, S.I., and Leik, M. "Breaking the Safety Barrier: Implementing Culture Change." *Professional Safety,* March 1999.

Skinner, B.F. *Science and Human Behavior.* New York: Macmillan, 1953.

Turner, J.C. "A Self Categorization Theory." *The Blackwell Encyclopedia of Social Psychology,* 1987.

Westrum, R., "Cultures with Requisite Imagination." In Wise, Hopkin, and Stager, eds. *Verification and Validation of Complex Systems: Human Factors Issues.* NATO ASI Series. New York: Springer-Verlag, 1993.

———. "Organizational Dynamics and Safety." In McDonald, N., Johnston, N., and Fuller, R., eds. *Applications of Psychology to the Aviation System.* Aldershot: Avebury, 1995.

Williams, J.C. "Safety Cultures: Their Impact on Quality, Reliability, Competitiveness and Profitability." In Matthews RH, ed. *Reliability '91,* London: Elsevier Applied Science, 1991.

CHAPTER 2: REGULATORY FRAMEWORK FOR SAFETY

Bureau of National Affairs, 1801 South Bell Street, Alexandria, VA 22202.

Occupational Safety and Health Reporter.

Balge, M.Z., and Krieger, G.R., eds. *Occupational Health and Safety,* 3rd ed. Itasca, IL: National Safety Council, 2000.

National Institute for Occupational Safety and Health, 5600 Fisher Lane, Rockville, MD 20857.

OSHA Compliance Advisor. Issued twice monthly.

Occupational Safety and Health Directory.

National Safety Council, 1121 Spring Lake Drive, Itasca, IL 60143.

Fundamentals of Industrial Hygiene, 6th ed., 2012.

Safety and Health. Issued monthly.

OSHA Up to Date. Issued monthly.

Price, M.O., and Bitner, H. *Effective Legal Research,* 4th ed. Boston: Little, Brown, 1979.

Rothstein, M. *Occupational Safety and Health Law,* 4th ed. St. Paul, MN: West, 1998. Updated annually.

Superintendent of Documents, U.S. Government Printing Office, Washington, DC 20402.

Annual List of Toxic Substances.

Directory of Federal Agencies.

Federal Register.

Field Operations Manual.

Industrial Hygiene Technical Manual.

Occupational Safety and Health Act of 1970 (Public Law 91-596).

Occupational Safety and Health Administration, OSHA 3302-01R (2013).

Occupational Safety and Health Regulations, Title 29.

Code of Federal Regulations (CFR):

Part 11—Department of Labor, National Environmental Policy Act (NEPA)

Compliance Procedures.

Part 1901—Procedures for State Agreements.

Part 1902—State Plans for the Development and Enforcement of State Standards.

Part 1903—Inspections, Citations and Proposed Penalties.

Part 1904—Recording and Reporting Occupational Injuries and Illnesses.

Part 1905—Rules of Practice for Variances, Limitations, Variations, Tolerances, and Exemptions.

Part 1906—Administration Witnesses and Documents in Private Litigation.

Part 1907—Accreditation of Testing Laboratories.

Part 1908—Consultation Agreements.

Part 1910—Occupational Safety and Health Standards.

Part 1911—Rules of Procedure for Promulgating, Modifying, or Revoking Occupational Safety or Health Standards.

Part 1912—Advisory Committees on Standards.

Part 1912a—National Advisory Committee on Occupational Safety and Health.

Part 1913—Rules of Agency Practice and Procedure Concerning OSHA Access to Employee Medical Records.

Part 1915—Occupational Safety and Health Standards for Shipyard Employment.

Part 1917—Marine Terminals.

Part 1918—Safety and Health Regulations for Longshoring.

Part 1919—Gear Certification.

Part 1920—Procedure for Variations from Safety and Health Regulations under the Longshoremen's and Harbor Workers' Compensation Act.

Part 1921—Rules of Practice in Enforcement Proceedings under Section 41 of the Longshoremen's and Harbor Workers' Compensation Act.

Part 1922—Investigational Hearings under Section 41 of the Longshoremen's and Harbor Workers' Compensation Act.

Part 1924—Safety Standards Applicable to Workshops and Rehabilitation Facilities Assisted by Grants.

Part 1925—Safety and Health Standards for Federal Service Contracts.

Part 1926—Safety and Health Regulations for Construction.

Part 1928—Occupational Safety and Health Standards for Agriculture.

Part 1949—Office of Training and Education, Occupational Safety and Health Administration.

Part 1950—Development and Planning Grants for Occupational Safety and Health.

Part 1951—Grants for Implementing Approved State Plans.

Part 1952—Approved State Plans for Enforcement of State Standards.

Part 1953—Changes to State Plans for the Development and Enforcement of State Standards.

Part 1954—Procedures for the Evaluation and Monitoring of Approved State Plans.

Part 1955—Procedures for Withdrawal of Approval of State Plans.

Part 1956—State Plans for the Development and Enforcement of State

Standards Applicable to State and Local Government Employees in States without Approved Private Employee Plans.

Part 1960—Basic Program Elements for Federal Employee Occupational Safety and Health Programs and Related Matters.

Part 1975—Coverage of Employees under the Williams-Steiger Occupational Safety and Health Act of 1970.

Part 1977—Discrimination against Employees Exercising Rights under the Williams-Steiger Occupational Safety and Health Act of 1970.

Part 1990—Identification, Classification, and Regulation of Potential Occupational Carcinogens.

Part 2200—Review Commission Rules of Procedure.

Part 2201—Regulations Implementing the Freedom of Information Act.

Part 2202—Standards of Ethics and Conduct of Occupational Safety and Health Review Commission Employees.

Part 2203—Regulations Implementing the Government in the Sunshine Act.

Part 2204—Implementation of the Equal Access to Justice Act.

Part 2205—Enforcement of Nondiscrimination on the Basis of Handicap.

29 CFR Part 2700—Mine Safety and Health Review Commission, Rules of Procedure.

30 CFR Part 11—Respiratory Protective Devices; Tests for Permissibility; Fees.

Part 40—Representative of Miners.

Part 41—Notification of Legal Identity.

Part 43—Procedures for Processing Hazardous Condition Complaints.

Part 44—Rules of Practice for Petitions for Modification of Mandatory Safety Standards.

Part 45—Independent Contractors.

Part 46—State Grants for Advancement of Safety and Health in Coal and Other Mines.

Part 47—National Mine Health and Safety Academy.

Part 48—Training and Retraining of Miners.

Part 49—Mine Rescue Teams.

Part 50—Notification, Investigation, Reports and Records of Accidents, Injuries, Illnesses, Employment, and Coal Production in Mines.

Part 56—Safety and Health Standards: Surface Metal and Nonmetal Mines.

Part 57—Safety and Health Standards: Underground Metal and Nonmetal Mines.

Part 58—Health Standards for Metal and Nonmetal Mines.

Part 70—Mandatory Health Standards: Underground Coal Mines.

Part 71—Mandatory Health Standards: Surface Coal Mines and Surface Work Areas of Underground Coal Mines.

Part 74—Coal Mine Dust Personal Sampler Units.

Part 75—Mandatory Safety Standards: Underground Coal Mines.

Part 77—Mandatory Safety Standards: Surface Coal Mines and Surface Work Areas of Underground Coal Mines.

Part 90—Mandatory Health Standards: Coal Miners Who Have Evidence of the Development of Pneumoconiosis.

Part 100—Criteria and Procedures for Proposed Assessment of Civil Penalties.

42 CFR Part 37—Specifications for Medical Examinations of Underground Coal Miners.

Part 85—Requests for Health Hazard Evaluations.

Part 85a—NIOSH Policy on Workplace Investigations.

Mine Safety and Health Act of 1977 (Public Law 95-164).

Mine Safety and Health Regulations and Standards.

U.S. Bureau of Labor Statistics. Revisions to the 2012 Census of Fatal Occupational Injuries (CFOI) Counts. www.bls.gov/iif/oshwc/cfoi/cfoi_revised12.pdf. Accessed May 9, 2014.

United States Department of Labor. Occupational Safety & Health Administration: Frequently Asked Questions. www.osha.gov/OSHA_FAQs.html. Accessed May 9, 2014.

CHAPTER 3: LEGAL IMPLICATIONS FOR SAFETY

Arden, P. Create a corporate safety culture. *Safety and Health,* 147(2). 1993.

Ashforth, B.E. Climate formation: Issues and extensions. *Academy of Management Review*, 10, 837–847. 1985.

Bigoes, S. Back Injuries in Industry: A Retrospective Study; Employee Related Factors. *Spine,* Vol. 11, No.1, 1986.

Bodley, J.H. *Cultural Anthropology: Tribes, States and the Global System, New York*; McGraw-Hill, 1994.

Burns, C. *The role of trust in safety culture.* Unpublished Ph.D. thesis, University of Aberdeen, Aberdeen, 2004.

Chaudron, D. 2003. *Building a Framework: Begin at the beginning in organizational change.* www.organizedchange.com/decide.htm. Accessed Aug. 14, 2014.

Cooke, R.A., and Rousseau, D.M. "Behavioral Norms and Expectations: A Quantitative Approach to the Assessment of Organizational Culture. *Group and Organizational Studies*, 13, 1988.

Creek, R.N., "Organizational Behavior and Safety Management: Evolution of Safety." *Professional Safety*, 40, 1995.

Denison, D. and Mishra, A. "Toward a Theory of Organizational Culture and Effectiveness," *Organizational Science* 6(2):204–233, 1995.

Downey, H.K., Hellriegel, D., Phelps, M. and Slocum, J.W. Organizational climate and job satisfaction: A comparative analysis. *Journal of Business Research*, 2, 1974.

Fleming, M. 2000. *Safety culture maturity model.* The Keil Centre for the Health and Safety Executive (HSE). http://www.hse.gov.uk/research/otopdf/2000/oto00049.pdf. Accessed Aug. 14, 2014.

Geller, E.S. Ten principles for achieving a total safety culture. *Professional Safety*, 39(9), 1994.

Greenwood, J. and Wolf, H. Job Satisfaction Affects Rates of Occupational Accidents. *West Virginia News Digest*, November 1987.

Hale, A. "Organizational Culture and Safety." In *International Encyclopedia of Ergonomics and Human Factors (2nd ed., vol.3).* Boca Raton, FL: Taylor & Francis Group, 2006.

Hansen, L. Safety management: A Call for (R)evolution. *Professional Safety,* 38, 1993.

Hansen, L. "Re-braining" Corporate Safety and Health. *Professional Safety,* 40(10), 1995.

Hellriegel, D. and Slocum, J.W. *Organizational Behavior, 10th ed.* Mason, OH: Southwestern College Publishing, 2004.

Helmreich, R., and Merritt, A. *Culture at Work in Aviation and Medicine.* Aldershot: Ashgate, 1998.

Hirschhorn, L. *The Workplace Within.* Cambridge, MA: MIT Press, 1987.

Hudson, P. *Safety Management and Safety Culture – The Long, Hard and Winding Road.* Occupational Health and Safety Management systems – Proceedings of the First National Conference, Crown Content, 2001, Work Cover NSW, 2001.

Hudson, P. and van der Graaf, G.C. *Hearts and Minds: The Status After 15 Years Research.* Society of Petroleum Engineers (SPE 73941) International Conference on HSE in Oil and Gas Exploration and Production. Kuala Lumpur, 2002.

Hudson, P. "Applying the lessons of high risk industries to health care." *Quality and Safety in Health Care,* 12(Suppl 1), 2003.

INSAG. "Basic Safety Principles for Nuclear Power Plants." *Safety Culture Safety Series No. 76-INSAG-3.* Vienna, Austria: International Atomic Energy Agency, 1988.

James, L.R., and James, L.A. "Psychological climate and affect: Test of a hierarchical dynamic model." In C.J. Cranny, P.C. Smith, E.F. Stone (Eds.), *Job Satisfaction: How People Feel About Their Jobs, and How It Affects Their Performance.* New York: Lexington Books, 1992.

Kilmann, R.H., Saxton, M J., Serpa, R., and Associates. *Gaining control of the corporate culture.* San Francisco: Jossey-Bass, 1985.

Lewin, K. *Field Theory in Social Science; Selected Theoretical Papers.* D. Cartwright (ed.). New York: Harper & Row, 1951.

Martin, J., and Meyerson, D. Organizational cultures and the denial, channeling, and acknowledgement of ambiguity. In L.R. Pondy, R.J. Boland & H. Thomas (Eds.), *Managing ambiguity and change.* New York: Wiley, 1988.

Mayer, R.C. and Davis, J.H. The Effect of the Performance Appraisal System on Trust for Management: A Field Quasi-Experiment. *Journal of Applied Psychology,* 84, 1999.

Mayer, R.C., Davis, J.H., and Schoorman, F.D. An Integrative Model of Organizational Trust. *Academy of Management Review,* 20, 1995.

McLain, D.L. Responses to Health and Safety Risk in the Work Environment. *Academy of Management Journal,* 38, 1995.

Mead, M. *Mind, Self and Society.* Chicago, IL: University of Chicago Press, 1934.

Mearns, K.J. and R. Flin. "Assessing the State of Organizational Safety: Culture or Climate?" *Current Psychology,* 18, 1999.

Menzies, I.E.P. A Case Study in the Functioning of Social Systems as a Defense Against Anxiety. *Human Relations,* 13, 1960.

Petersen, D. *Techniques of Safety Management: A Systems Approach.* New York: Aloray, Inc., 1989.

Reason, J. *Managing the Risks of Organizational Accidents.* Ashgae, Kent, 1997.

Roethlisberger, F.J., and Dickinson, W.J. *Management and the worker.* Cambridge, MA: Harvard University Press, 1946.

Sarkus, D.J. "Safety and Psychology." *Professional Safety.* January 2001.

Schein, E.H. "Coming to a New Awareness of Organizational Culture." *Sloan Management Review*, 25, 1984.

Schein, E.H. Organizational Culture: Skill, Defense Mechanism or Addiction? In F.R. Brush and J.B. Overmier (Eds.), *Affect conditioning, and cognition*. Hillsdale, NJ: Eribaum.

Schein, E.H. *Organizational Culture and Leadership: A Dynamic View (2nd ed)*. San Francisco: Jossey-Bass, 1990.

Schein, E.H. *Organizational Culture and Leadership, 2nd ed*. San Francisco: Jossey-Bass, 1992.

Schneider, B. *Organizational Climate and Culture*. Oxford, England: Jossey-Bass, 1990.

Simon, S.I. and Leik, M. Breaking the Safety Barrier: Implementing Culture Change. *Professional Safety*, March 1999.

Skinner, B.F. *Science and Human Behavior*. New York: Macmillan, 1953.

Westrum, R. *Cultures with Requisite Imagination*. In Wise, Hopkin and Stager, 1993: Verification and Validation of Complex Systems: Human Factors Issues. NATO ASI Series. Spring-Verlag.

Westrum, R. Organizational Dynamics and Safety. In N. McDonald, N. Johnston, and R. Fuller (Eds.), *Applications of Psychology to the Aviation System*. Aldershot: Avebury, 1995.

Williams, J.C. "Safety Cultures: Their Impact on Quality, Reliability, Competitiveness and Profitability." In *Reliability*, R.H. Matthews, ed. London: Elsevier Applied Science, 1991.

CHAPTER 4: INJURY AND ILLNESS RECORD KEEPING, INCIDENCE RATES, AND ANALYSIS

American Society of Safety Engineers. *Dictionary of Terms Used in the Safety Profession*. 4th ed. Des Plaines, IL: ASSE, 2001.

Bird, F.E., Jr. *Management Guide to Loss Control*. Loganville, GA: Institute Press, 1980.

Bissell, D. *SPC for TQM*. New York: Chapman & Hall, 1994.

Deming, W.E. *Sample Design in Business Research*. New York: Wiley, 1990.

Duncan, A. *Quality Control and Industrial Statistics*. Burr Ridge, IL: Irwin, 1986.

Ferry, T.S. "Techniques of Operations Review (TOR)." In *Modern Accident Investigation and Analysis: An Executive Guide*. New York: Wiley, 1981.

Juran, J.M. *Managerial Breakthrough*. New York: McGraw-Hill, 1964.

National Safety Council. (Annual). *Injury Facts*. Itasca, IL: Author.

Petersen, D. *Techniques of Safety Management: A Systems Approach*, 4th ed. Des Plaines, IL: American Society of Safety Engineers, 2003.

Recht, J.L. "Bi-level Reporting." *Journal of Safety Research* 2(2), 51–54, 1970.

Tufte, E.R. *The Visual Display of Quantitative Information*, 2nd ed. Cheshire, CT: Graphics Press, (2001).

Van der Schaaf, T.W. "Near Miss Reporting in the Chemical Process Industry." Eindhoven, The Netherlands: Technische Universiteit Eindhoven, Proefschrift, (1992).

Weaver, D.A. "TOR Analysis: A Diagnostic Training Tool." *ASSE Journal*, 18(6):24-29, 1973, June.

Wheeler, D.J. *Advanced Topics in Statistical Process Control,* 2nd ed. Knoxville, TN: SPC Press, 2004.

Wheeler, D.J. *Understanding Statistical Control,* 3rd ed. Knoxville, TN: SPC Press, 2010.

CHAPTER 5: IDENTIFYING HAZARDS

Balge, M.Z., and Krieger, G.R., eds. *Occupational Health and Safety*, 3rd ed. Itasca, IL: National Safety Council, 2000.

Department of Defense. MIL-STD-882E, Department of Defense Standard Practice: System Safety, May 11, 2012.

Ferry, T. *Modern Accident Investigation and Analysis*, 2nd ed. New York: Wiley, 1988.

Firenze, R.J. *The Process of Hazard Control.* Dubuque, IA: Kendall/Hunt, 1978.

Gowen, L.D. "Using Fault Trees and Event Trees as Oracles for Testing Safety-Critical Software Systems." *Professional Safety* 41(4): 41–44, 1996.

Johnson, W.G. *MORT Safety Assurance Systems*. New York: Dekker, 1980. (Also available through the National Safety Council.)

MAS 611 Aviation/Aerospace System Safety. Daytona Beach, FL: Embry-Riddle University, 1998.

National Safety Council, 1121 Spring Lake Drive, Itasca, IL 60143.

Fundamentals of Industrial Hygiene, 5th ed., 2001.

Supervisors' Safety Manual, 10th ed., 2009.

U.S. Chamber of Commerce. *Analysis of WC Laws*. Washington, DC: U.S. GPO, 2012.

CHAPTER 6: LOSS CONTROL AND PREVENTION

American National Standards Institute, ANSI Z16-.3-1997, Recording and Measuring Employee Off-the-Job Injury Experience.

Board of Certified Safety Professionals of the Americas, 208 Burwash, Savoy, IL 61874. "Curricula Development and Examination Study Guidelines," Technical Report No. 1.

Boylston, R.B. "Managing Safety and Health Programs." Speech given before the Textile Section, National Safety Congress, October 1989.

Construction Advancement Foundation *Safety Manual*, 6050 Southport Road, Suite A, Portage, IN. National Safety Council, 2009.

Dennis, L.E., and Onion, M.E. *Out in Front: Effective Supervision in the Workplace.* Chicago: National Safety Council, 1990.

Factory Mutual Engineering Corp., 500 River Ridge Road, Norwood, MA 02062. *Factory Mutual Handbook of Industrial Loss Prevention and Loss Prevention Data.*

Firenze, R.J. *Guide to Occupational Safety and Health Management.* Dubuque, IA: Kendall/Hunt, 1973.

———. *The Process of Hazard Control.* Dubuque, IA: Kendall/Hunt, 1978.

———. *Safety and Health in Industrial/Vocational Education.* Cincinnati, OH: National Institute for Occupational Safety and Health, 1981.

Hogan, R.B. *Occupational Safety and Health Law.* New York: Lexis, 2000 Supp.

Johnson, W.G. *MORT Safety Assurance Systems.* New York: Dekker, 1980.

Kane, A. "Safety Begins the First Day on the Job." *National Safety News*, January 1979.

Larsen, R. *Workers' Compensation Laws.* New York: Lexis.

Manuele, F.A. "How Effective Is Your Hazard Control Program?" *National Safety News*, 53–58, February 1980.

———. *On the Practice of Safety*, 2nd ed. New York: Wiley, 1997.

National Association of Suggestion Systems, 230 North Michigan Avenue, Chicago, IL 60611.

Performance Magazine. Issued bimonthly.
"Suggestion Newsletter." Issued bimonthly.

National Safety Council, 1121 Spring Lake Drive, Itasca, IL 60143.

Fundamentals of Industrial Hygiene, 4th ed., 1996.
Injury Facts (formerly *Accident Facts*). Issued annually.
Management Safety Policies, Occupational Safety and Health Data Sheets, 12304-0585, 1995.
Supervisors' Safety Manual, 9th ed., 1997.

"You Are the Safety and Health Committee."

O'Reilly, J.T. *Product Warnings, Defects, and Hazards*, 2nd ed. New York: Aspen, 1999.

Peters, G.A. "Systematic Safety." *National Safety News*, September 1975, 83–90.

Rothstein, M. *Occupational Safety and Health Law*, 4th ed. St. Paul, MN: West, 1998. Updated annually.

U.S. Chamber of Commerce of the United States of America, *Analysis of Workers' Compensation Laws*, Annual Publication.

U.S. Department of Human Resources, National Institute for Occupational Safety and Health, Division of Technical Services, Cincinnati, Ohio. "Self-Evaluation of Occupational Safety and Health Programs," Publication 78-187, 1978.

U.S. Department of Labor, Occupational Safety and Health Administration. "Organizing a Safety Committee," OSHA 2231, June 1975.

U.S. Department of Transportation, Office of Hazardous Materials, Washington, DC.

"Newly Authorized Hazardous Materials Warning Labels," latest edition. (Based on Title 49 CFR, Parts 173.402, 403, and 404.)

Windsor, D.G. "Process Hazards Management." Speech given before the Chemical Section, National Safety Congress, October 17, 1979.

CHAPTER 7: SAFETY AND HEALTH TRAINING

The ADDIE Model, copyright 2013 InstructionalDesignExpert.com, www.instructionaldesignexpert.com/implementation.html. Accessed Aug. 14, 2014.

The American Society of Safety Engineers, "Safety Scope and Function,"copyright 1996 American Society of Safety Engineers. All rights reserved. www.asse.org/about/scope_function.php. Accessed Aug. 14, 2014.

The American Society of Safety Engineers, "Scope and Function," copyright 1996 American Society of Safety Engineers. All rights reserved. www.asse.org/about/scope_functionC.php. Accessed Aug. 14, 2014.

Brothers, S.K. "Game-Based e-Learning: The Next Level of Staff Training," *Long-Term Living*. March 1, 2007, www.ltlmagazine.com/article/game-based-e-learning-next-level-staff-training. Accessed Aug. 14, 2014.

Carr, C. *Smart Training: The Manager's Guide to Training for Improved Performance*. New York: McGraw-Hill, 1992.

Dennis, L.E., and Onion, M.E. *Out in Front: Effective Supervision in the Workplace*. Chicago: National Safety Council, 1990.

Didactic Systems. "A Catalog of Ideas for Action Oriented Training." PO Box 4, Cranford, NJ 07016.

DuPont. "Library of Programmed Instruction Courses." Education and Applied Technology Division, Wilmington, DE 20017.

Hendershot, C. "A Bibliography of Programs and Presentation Devices." 4114 Ridgewood Drive, Bay City, MI 48706.

Indiana University. Private study commissioned by QBInternational. Details available from QBInternational, 900 Larkspur Landing Circle, Suite 115, Larkspur, CA 94939.

Mager, R.F. *Preparing Instructional Objectives*, 2nd ed. Belmont, CA: Lake, 1984.

Mager, R.F., and Beach, K.M., Jr. *Developing Vocational Instruction*. Belmont, CA: Lake, 1984.

Mager, R.F., and Pipe, P. *Analyzing Performance Problems or You Really Oughta Wanna*, 2nd ed. Belmont, CA: Lake, 1984.

Merriam-Webster, definition of training, www.merriam-webster.com/dictionary/training. Accessed Aug. 14, 2014.

National Safety Council. *Supervisors' Safety Manual*, 9th ed. Itasca, IL: National Safety Council, 1997.

National Society for Programmed Instruction, PO Box 137, Cardinal Station, Washington, DC 20017.

"Questionnaire Design: Asking Questions with a Purpose," Ellen Taylor-Powell, Program Development and Evaluation Specialist, Program Development and Evaluation, University of Wisconsin-Extension, Cooperative Extension, G3658-2, http://learningstore.uwex.edu/assets/pdfs/g3658-2.pdf. Accessed Aug. 14, 2014.

Roberts, T.S. "The In-Basket Method." Bureau of Industrial Relations, Department of Training Materials for Industry, University of Michigan, Graduate School of Business Administration, Ann Arbor, MI 48104.

Science Research Associated. "Simulation Series for Business and Industry." Department of Management Services, 155 North Wacker Drive, Chicago, IL 60606.

Susan Harwood Training Grant Program,

"Best Practices for the Development, Delivery, and Evaluation of Susan Harwood Training Grants," September 2010, www.osha.gov/dte/sharwood/best-practices.html. Accessed Aug. 14, 2014.

U.S. Department of Labor, Occupational Safety and Health Administration, "Training Requirements in OSHA Standards and Training Guidelines," OSHA 2254 1998 (Revised) www.osha.gov/Publications/osha2254.pdf. Accessed Aug. 14, 2014.

U.S. Department of Labor. Training Requirements in OSHA Standards and Training Guidelines. OSHA No. 2254. Washington, DC: U.S. Government Printing Office, 1998. Available at local OSHA regional offices.

Zoll AA. *The In-Basket Kit*. Reading, MA: Addison-Wesley, n.d.

CHAPTER 9: FIRE PROTECTION

International Code Council, 500 New Jersey Avenue, NW, 6th Floor, Washington DC.
International Building Code®.

National Fire Protection Association, 1 Batterymarch Park, Quincy, MA

Fire Protection Handbook, 19th edition, A. Cote (editor), 2003.

Principles of Fire Protection, A. Cote and P. Bugbee, 1988.

NFPA 1, Uniform Fire Code.

NFPA 10, Portable Fire Extinguishers.

NFPA 11, Low-, Medium-, and High-Expansion Foam.

NFPA 12, Carbon Dioxide Extinguishing Systems.

NFPA 13, Installation of Sprinkler Systems.

NFPA 14, Installation of Standpipe and Hose Systems.

NFPA 15, Water Spray Fixed Systems for Fire Protection.

NFPA 16, Deluge Foam-Water Sprinkler and Foam-Water Spray Systems.

NFPA 17, Dry Chemical Extinguishing Systems.

NFPA 17A, Wet Chemical Extinguishing Systems.

NFPA 22, Water Tanks for Private Fire Protection.

NFPA 24, Installation of Private Service Mains and Their Appurtenances.

NFPA 25, Inspection, Testing, and Maintenance of Water-Based Fire Protection Systems.

NFPA 30, Flammable and Combustible Liquids Code.

NFPA 45, Fire Protection for Laboratories Using Chemicals.

NFPA 51B, Fire Prevention During Welding, Cutting, and Other Hot Work.

NFPA 68, Venting of Deflagrations.

NFPA 69, Explosion Prevention Systems.

NFPA 70, National Electrical Code®.

NFPA 72®, National Fire Alarm Code®.

NFPA 80, Fire Doors and Other Opening Protectives.

NFPA 80A, Protection of Buildings from Exterior Fire Exposures.

NFPA 90A, Installation of Air-Conditioning and Ventilating Systems.

NFPA 101®, Life Safety Code®.

NFPA 211, Chimneys, Fireplaces, Vents, and Solid Fuel-Burning Appliances.

NFPA 220, Types of Building Construction.

NFPA 253, Method of Test for Critical Radiant Flux of Floor Covering Systems Using a Radiant Heat Energy Source.

NFPA 326, Safeguarding of Tanks and Containers for Entry, Cleaning, or Repair.

NFPA 551, Evaluation of Fire Risk Assessments.

NFPA 600, Industrial Fire Brigade.

NFPA 701, Methods of Fire Tests for Flame Propagation of Textiles and Films.

NFPA 704, Identification of Hazards of Materials for Emergency Response.

NFPA 1081, Industrial Fire Brigade Member Professional Qualifications.

NFPA 1961, Fire Hose.

NFPA 5000, Building Construction and Safety Code®.

Society of Fire Protection Engineers, published by the National Fire Protection Association.

SFPE Fire Protection Engineering Handbook, 3rd edition, P. DiNenno (editor).

Occupational Safety and Health Standards *(Code of Federal Regulations)*.

Electrical, 29 CFR 1910, Subpart S.

Exit Routes, Emergency Action Plans, and Fire Prevention Plans, 29 CFR 1910, Subpart E.

Fire Protection, 29 CFR 1910, Subpart L.

Welding, Cutting, and Brazing, 29 CFR 1910, Subpart Q.

Process Safety Management of Highly Hazardous Chemicals, 29 CFR 1910.119.

Hazard Communication, 29 CFR 1910.1200.

Hazardous Waste Operations and Emergency Response, 29 CFR 1910.120.

CHAPTER 10: ELECTRICAL SAFETY

American National Standards Institute, 11 West 42nd Street, New York, NY 10036.

Attachment Plugs and Receptacles, ANSI/UL 498–2012.

Rubber Insulated Wires, ANSI/UL 44-1991.

National Electrical Safety Code, ANSI C2-1990.

Relays, Breakers, Switchgear Systems Associated with Electric Power Apparatus, ANSI C37.

Safety Requirements for Lockout/Tagout of Energy Sources, ANSI Z244.1–2003 (R2008).

American Society for Testing and Material, 1916 Race Street, Philadelphia, PA 19103.

Specifications for In-Service Care of Insulating Gloves and Sleeves, F496.

Specifications for Rubber Insulating Gloves, D120.

Specifications for Rubber Insulating Tape, D4325.

Canadian Standards Association, 178 Rexdale Boulevard, Rexdale, Ontario M9W 1R3, Canada.

Factory Mutual System Research Organization, 1151 Boston-Providence Turnpike, Norwood, MA 02062.

Illuminating Engineering Society of North America, 345 East 47th Street, New York, NY 10017.

National Fire Protection Association, 1 Batterymarch Park, Quincy, MA 02269.

Classification of Gases, Vapors and Dusts for Electrical Equipment in Hazardous (Classified) Locations, NFPA 497M, 2012.

Electrical Safety Requirements for Employee Workplaces, NFPA 70E, 2012.

National Electrical Code, NFPA 70, 2014.

National Safety Council, 1121 Spring Lake Dr., Itasca, IL 60143-3210.

Electrical Inspection Illustrated, 3rd ed., 1993.

Occupational Safety and Health Data Sheets:

Electrical Switching Practices, 12304–0544, 1991.

Electromagnets Used with Crane Hoists, 12304–0359, 1985.

Electrostatic Paint Spraying and Detearing, 12304–0468, 1991.

Flexible Insulated Protective Equipment for Electrical Workers, 12304–0598, 1991.

Industrial Electric Substations, 12304–0559, 1991.

Portable Reamer-Drills, 12304–0497, 1989.

Power Tool Institute, PO Box 818, Yachats, OR 97498

Underwriters Laboratories, Inc., 333 Pfingsten Road, Northbrook, IL 60062.

Insulated Wire, UL 44. "Electrical Appliance and Utilization Equipment Lists." Dimensions of Attachment Plugs and Receptacles, UL 498.

Electrical Construction Materials List.

Hazardous Location Equipment List.

U.S. Department of Commerce, National Institute of Standards and Technology, Gaithersburg, MD 20899.

Safety Rules for the Installation and Maintenance of Electric Utilization Equipment, Handbook H33.

U.S. Department of Labor, Occupational Safety and Health Administration, 200 Constitution Avenue NW, Washington, DC 20210.

29 CFR 1910.132–138, Personal Protective Equipment.

29 CFR 1910.145, Specifications for Accident Prevention Signs and Tags.

29 CFR 1910.331–339, Electrical Safety-Related Work Practices.

CHAPTER 11: CONSTRUCTION SAFETY

American National Standards Institute

ANSI A10.33, Safety and Health Program Requirements for Multi-Employer Projects, 1992.

ANSI A10.38, Basic Elements of a Program to Provide a Safe and Healthful Work Environment, 1991.

The Business Round Table. *Improving Construction Safety Performance.* Report A-3. September 1989.

Code of Federal Regulations. 29 CFR 1910.119 and 29 CFR 1926.64, Process Safety Management of Highly Hazardous Chemicals.

Connor, R.D. *The Agent Construction Manager's Liability for Safety Using a Pro-Active Approach to Manage Liability Exposure,* National Construction Management Conference, 1991.

Hislop, R. *Construction Site Safety.* Boca Raton, FL: CRC Press, 1999.

Keres, F. *Safety in Construction Contracts,* National Safety Council Congress and Exposition (1996).

MacCollum, D. *Construction Safety Planning.* New York: Van Nostrand Reinhold, 1995.

MacCollum, D. *Construction Safety Engineering Principles.* New York: McGraw-Hill, 2007.

National Society of Professional Engineers.

Code of Ethics, 1996.

Samelson, N., and Levitt, R.E. *Owner's Guidelines for Selecting Safe Contractors.* December 1982.

CHAPTER 12: BASICS OF INDUSTRIAL HYGIENE

American Conference of Governmental Industrial Hygienists (ACGIH). *Industrial Ventilation: A Manual of Recommended Practice.* Cincinnati, OH: ACGIH. Published biannually, even-numbered years.

———. *Threshold Limit Values (TLVs) and Biological Exposure Indices (BEIs).* Cincinnati, OH: ACGIH. Issued annually.

Balge, M.Z., and Krieger, G.R., eds. *Occupational Health and Safety,* 3rd ed. Itasca, IL: National Safety Council, 2000.

Burgess, W.A. *Recognition of Health Hazards in Industry.* New York: Wiley, 1981.

Cohrssen, B., and Rose, V.E., eds. *Patty's Industrial Hygiene and Toxicology,* 6th ed. Vols. I–III. New York: Wiley, 2011.

Cralley, L., and Cralley, L., eds. *In-Plant Practices for Job-Related Health Hazards Control.* Vol. 1, *Production Processes,* and Vol. 2, *Engineering Aspects.* New York: Wiley, 1989.

NIOSH. *Industrial Noise Control Manual,* rev. ed. NIOSH Publication No. 79-117, 1979.

Plog, B.A., ed. *Fundamentals of Industrial Hygiene,* 6th ed. Itasca, IL: National Safety Council, 2012.

CHAPTER 13: PERSONAL PROTECTIVE EQUIPMENT (PPE)

American College of Occupational and Environmental Medicine Noise and Hearing Conservation Committee. Guidelines for the conduct of an occupational hearing conservation program. *J Occup Med* 1987, 29:981–989.

American Conference of Governmental Industrial Hygienists, Building D–7, 6500 Glenway Avenue, Cincinnati, OH 45211.

A Guide for Control of Laser Hazards, 1976.

American National Standards Institute, 11 West 42nd Street, New York, NY 10036.

Occupational and Educational Personal Eye and Face Protective Devices, ANSI Z87.1-.

Industrial Head Protection, ANSI Z89.1.

Safe Use of Lasers, ANSI Z136.1.

Fall Protection Code, ANSI/ASSE Z359.

American Society for Testing and Materials, 1916 Race Street, Philadelphia, PA 19103.

Standard Specification for Performance Requirements for Foot Protection, ASTM F2413-05.

Respiratory Protective Devices Manual.

Compressed Gas Association, Inc., Crystal Gateway–1, Suite 501, 1235 Jefferson Davis Highway, Arlington, VA 22202.

Commodity Specification for Air, G–7.1.

Ellis, J.N. *Introduction to Fall Protection.* Des Plaines, IL: American Society of Safety Engineers, 1988.

Gasaway, D.C. *Hearing Conservation: A Practical Manual and Guide.* Englewood Cliffs, NJ: Prentice-Hall, 1984.

International Safety Equipment Association, 1901 North Moore Street, Suite 808, Arlington, VA 22209.

High-Visibility Safety Apparel and Headwear, ANSI/ISEA 107.

High-Visibility Public Safety Vests, ANSI/ISEA 207.

National Fire Protection Association, 1 Batterymarch Park, Quincy, MA 02269.

National Safety Council, 1121 Spring Lake Drive, Itasca, IL 60143.

Fundamentals of Industrial Hygiene, 6th ed., 2012.

Hearing Conservation in the Workplace, 1991.

Occupational Safety and Health Data Sheets (available in the Council Library):

Flexible Insulating Protective Equipment for Electrical Workers, 12304–0598.

National Institute for Occupational Safety and Health, Division of Technical Services. Cincinnati, OH.

Respiratory Protection—An Employer's Manual and Guide to Industrial Respiratory Protection, 1978.

Plog, B.A., ed. *Fundamentals of Industrial Hygiene,* 6th ed. Itasca, IL: National Safety Council, 2012.

SEI Certified Products. Safety Equipment Institute, 1307 Dolley Madison Boulevard, Suite 3A, McLean, VA 22101.

U.S. Department of Health and Human Services.

NIOSH Guide to Industrial Respiratory Protection, NIOSH Publication No. 87-116, September 1987.

NIOSH Respiratory Protection Program in Health Care Facilities. NIOSH Publication No. 99-143, September 1999.

U.S. Department of Health and Human Services. OSHA Technical Manual, Section VIII, Chapter 2, Respiratory Protection, Appendix B-1 to 1910.134 user seal check procedures, Occupational Noise Exposure, Revised Criteria 1998. NIOSH Publication No. 98-126, June 1998.

U.S. Department of Health and Human Services, Public Health Service, Centers for Disease Control, National Institute for Occupational Safety and Health.

Criteria for a Recommended Standard: Occupational Noise Exposure. Revised Criteria, June 1998.

29 CFR 1910.95, Occupational Noise Exposure.

29 CFR 1910.132–138, Personal Protective Equipment.

29 CFR 1926.52, Occupational Noise Exposure.

NIOSH Certified Equipment List, October 1986, Pub. 87–102. Washington DC: U.S. Superintendent of Documents, 1986.

U.S. Department of the Interior, 1849 C Street, NW, Washington DC 20240. 30 CFR Chapter 1, Subchapter B, Respiratory Protective Devices, Tests for Permissibility, Fees; Part 11. NOTE: The Code of Federal Regulations is available through the U.S. Government Printing Office, Washington DC 20402.

CHAPTER 14: LAB SAFETY

Alaimo, R.J., ed. *Handbook of Chemical Health and Safety.* Oxford, England: Oxford University Press, 2001.

American Conference of Governmental Industrial Hygienists, 1330 Kemper Meadow Drive, Cincinnati, OH 45240.

Documentation of the Threshold Limit Values and Biological Exposure Indices. Updated annually.

American National Standards Institute, 11 West 42nd Street, New York, NY 10036.

Emergency Eyewashes and Shower Equipment, ANSI Z358.1-2009.

Method of Testing Performance of Laboratory Fume Hoods, ANSI/ASHRAE 110-1995.

Occupational and Educational Personal Eye and Face Protection Devices, ANSI/ISEA Z87.1-2010.

IEEE C95.1-2005.

Safety Colors, ANSI/NEMA Z535.1-2006 (R2011).

Environmental Facility and Safety Signs, ANSI/NEMA Z535.2-2011.

Criteria for Safety Symbols, ANSI/NEMA, Z535.3-2011.

Product Safety Signs and Labels, ANSI/NEMA, Z535.4-2011.

Safety Tags and Barricade Tapes (for Temporary Hazards), ANSI/NEMA Z535.5-2011.

Product Safety Information in Product Manuals, Instructions, and Other Collateral Materials, ANSI/NEMA Z535.6-2011.

Standard for Safety Levels with Respect to Human Exposure to Radio Frequency Electromagnetic Fields, 3 kHz to 300 GHz, ANSI/IEEE C95.1-2005.

Balf, T., Churchill, F., Hall, G., Graham, Z.S., and Stuart, R. "Piloting an EMS-Based Regulation for Chemical Waste in Laboratories: A Lab XL Progress Report." *Chemical Health and Safety* 10(3): 22–28, 2003.

Centers for Disease Control and Prevention, Office of the Director/Administrator. "Laboratory Ergonomics." October 2002.

Centers for Disease Control and Prevention/National Institutes of Health. *Biosafety in Microbiological and Biomedical Laboratories*, 5th ed. Atlanta, GA: U.S. Department of Health and Human Services, Public Health Service, 2009.

Furr, A.K. *CRC Handbook of Laboratory Safety*, 5th ed. Boca Raton, LA: CRC Press, 2000.

Gollnick, D.A. *Basic Radiation Protection Technology*, 4th ed. Altadena, CA: Pacific Radiation, 2000.

Laser Institute of America, 12424 Research Parkway, Suite 130, Orlando, FL 32826.

American National Standard for Safe Use of Lasers, Z136.1-2014.

American National Standard for Safe Use of Optical Fiber Communication Systems Using Laser Diode and LED Sources, Z136.2-2012.

American National Standard for Safe Use of Lasers in Health Care Facilities, ANSI Z136.3-2011.

American National Standard for Recommended Practice for Laser Safety Measurements for Hazard Evaluation, ANSI Z136.4-2005.

American National Standard for Safe Use of Lasers in Educational Institutions, ANSI Z136.5-2009.

American National Standard for Safe Use of Lasers Outdoors, ANSI Z136.6-2005.

American National Standard for Testing and Labeling of Laser Protective Equipment, ANSI Z136.7-2008.

National Fire Protection Association, 1 Batterymarch Park, Quincy, MA 02269-9101.

Standard for Portable Fire Extinguishers, NFPA 10.

National Research Council. *Prudent Practices in the Laboratory: Handling and Disposal of Chemicals.* Washington, DC: National Academy Press, 2011.

NIOSH Publication No. 2007-107, School Chemistry Laboratory Safety Guide.

Noz, M.E., and Maguire, G.Q., Jr., *Radiation Protection in the Health Sciences*, 2nd ed. Hackensack, NJ: World Scientific, 2007.

Sliney, D., and Wolbarsht, M. *Safety with Lasers and Other Optical Sources: A Comprehensive Handbook.* New York: Plenum Press, 1985.

Stuart, R.B., and Moore, C. *Safety and Health on the Internet*, 3rd ed. Rockville, MD: Government Institutes, 1999.

Urben, P. *Bretherick's Handbook of Reactive Chemical Hazards*, 7th ed. Academic Press, 2006.

Varanelli, A.G. "Electrical Hazards Associated with Lasers." *Journal of Laser Applications* 7:62–64, 1995.

WEBSITES

Consumer Product Safety Commission Enforcement Manual and descriptive information, 16 CFR 1000 ff: www.cpsc.gov. Accessed Aug. 14, 2014.

U.S. Department of Justice, Civil Division, Office of Consumer Litigation: www.justice.gov. Accessed Aug. 14, 2014.

U.S. Department of Transportation, Federal Highway Administration and Federal Aviation Administration, and 49 CFR 10200 ff: www.dot.gov. Accessed Aug. 14, 2014.

Environmental Protection Agency, Office of Enforcement and Compliance Assistance, and Title 40 CFR, various sections: http://epa.gov. Accessed Aug. 14, 2014.

Mine Safety and Health Administration, and Title 30 CFR, Part 1 ff: www.msha.gov. Accessed Aug. 14, 2014.

U.S. Department of Labor, Occupational Safety and Health Administration, and Title 29 CFR, Part 1000 ff: www.osha.gov. Accessed Aug. 14, 2014.

U.S. Department of Justice, Civil Division, Office of Consumer Litigation: www.justice.gov. Accessed Aug. 14, 2014.

U.S. Department of Transportation, Federal Highway Administration and Federal Aviation Administration, and 49 CFR 10200 ff: www.dot.gov. Accessed Aug. 14, 2014.

U.S. Sentencing Commission Guidelines, reprinted in *18 United States Code Annotated*, Appendix. St. Paul, MN: West, 2000. www.ussc.gov. Accessed Aug. 14, 2014.

Index

Page numbers followed by *f* refer to figures and *t* refer to tables.

ABCD method of objective writing, 209
ABIH (American Board of Industrial Hygiene), 369
Accessible emission limits (AELs), 458
Accreditation Board for Engineering and Technology Inc. (ABET), 369
ACGIH (American Conference of Governmental Industrial Hygienists), 369, 372–373, 450
Acid hoods, 385
Acids, 425–426
Acoustic trauma, 386
Active fall arrest systems, 389, 391–394
Activity sampling, 168–169
Adapters, 316
ADDIE (Analysis, Design, Development, Implementation, and Evaluation) model, 203
Administrative controls, 376
Administrative law judges (ALJs), 27, 50
Adult learning needs, 211–215, 213*f*
AELs (accessible emission limits), 458
After-the-fact approach for incident examination, 167
AIDS/HIV, 364, 441
AIHA (American Industrial Hygiene Association), 356, 368, 369, 372
Airborne hazards, 360–361, 366–367, 396–397
Air-break switches, 310
Airline industry, regulatory directives in, 133–134
Air-purifying respirators, 398–399
Air-supplying respirators, 398
Aisles, requirements for, 94
ALARA (as low as reasonably achievable) exposures, 423, 447, 451
Alarm systems, 267, 282–288
Alcohol use, 339–340
ALJs (administrative law judges), 27, 50
All/multiple cause model, 135
Alpha-radiation, 445, 446–447
Alpha scores, 11
Alpha testing, 232–233
Altered environments, 461–463
Alveoli, 366, 367
American Board of Industrial Hygiene (ABIH), 369
American Chemical Society, 373
American Conference of Governmental Industrial Hygienists (ACGIH), 369, 372–373, 450
American Consulting Engineers Council, 133
American Industrial Hygiene Association (AIHA), 356, 368, 369, 372
American Institute of Chemical Engineers, 373
American National Standards Institute (ANSI)
    on confined spaces, 104
    on electrical safety, 308
    on eye protection, 382, 386
    on eyewash and shower stations, 428
    on fall protection, 395
    on fiber-optic safety, 461
    on head protection, 381
    on high-visibility clothing, 409–410
    on incident surveillance, 125
    on laser safety, 457, 458–459
American Optometric Association, 384
American Petroleum Institute, 373
Amperes, 303
Anaerobic chambers, 465
Analysis, Design, Development, Implementation, and Evaluation (ADDIE) model, 203
Analysis of Workers' Compensation Laws (U.S. Chamber of Commerce), 181
Analytical trees, 139–140, 140*f*
Anchorage points, 392
Animals, laboratory safety and, 435, 442*t*, 462–463
ANSI. *See* American National Standards Institute
APFs (assigned protection factors), 398
Apprenticeships, 221
Area Directors, 26
"Arising out of" requirements, 184–185
Arm protection, 402–405
Artifacts, 3
As low as reasonably achievable (ALARA) exposures, 423, 447, 451
Asphyxiation, 277, 306
Assault charges, 180
Assigned protection factors (APFs), 398
Assistant Secretary of Labor, roles and responsibilities of, 24, 25, 54
Audience identification/description, 207
Audiograms, 111
Audiometric testing programs, 386–387
Audits, 98
Aural inserts, 388
Authorized entrants, 102
Autoclaves, 439
Automatic fire detection systems, 283–286

Automatic sprinklers, 293–294, 295*t*
Auxiliary fire alarm systems, 287

Barriers, for machines, 309
Bases (chemical), 426
Beam hazards, 454–455
Before-the-fact approach for incident examination, 168
Behavior-based safety (BBS), 17–19
Behavior sampling, 168–169
Beta-radiation, 445, 447
Beta testing, 232–233
"Beyond a reasonable doubt" requirement, 178
Bilevel reporting, 124
Bioassay, 452
Biological exposure indices (BEIs), 373
Biological factors, in incident causation, 189
Biological hazards, 363–364, 397, 415–416
Biological safety, 432–444
    autoclaves for, 439
    for bloodborne pathogens, 440–441, 443–444
    containment practices for, 435–436
    guidelines for, 432–435
    labeling practices in, 443
    laboratory design and, 440
    personal protective equipment for, 439
    primary barriers for, 436–437, 439–440
    safety cabinets for, 436–437, 437*f*, 438*t*, 464
    secondary barriers for, 440
    training on, 443
    ultraviolet lights for, 439–440
    waste management and, 443
Biological safety cabinets (BSCs), 436–437, 437*f*, 438*t*, 464
Biosafety in Microbiological and Biomedical Laboratories (CDC/NIH), 433, 436
Biosafety levels (BSLs), 416, 433–436, 441–442*t*
Blankets, fire, 292
Bloodborne pathogens, 364, 433, 440–441, 443–444
BLS (Bureau of Labor Statistics), 24, 25–26, 29, 84
Body belts, 392
Bonding (electrical), 304
Brainstorming, 223
Branched-chain reactions, 264
Bricklaying, 71, 90
BSCs (biological safety cabinets), 436–437, 437*f*, 438*t*, 464
BSLs (biosafety levels), 416, 433–436, 441–442*t*
Buddy system, 220–221
Building Construction and Safety Code® (NFPA), 276
Bulb detection systems, 284
Bulletins, 123–124
Bureau of Labor Statistics (BLS), 24, 25–26, 29, 84
Bureau of Mines, 53, 54
Burns, electrical, 306, 307
"But-for" causation, 173
"By accident" requirements, 184–185

Calculative culture, 8, 9*f*
Canadian Centre for Occupational Health and Safety (CCOHS), 244, 250

Canal caps, 388
Carbon dioxide extinguishers, 291
Carbon monoxide, 264, 277
Cardiopulmonary resuscitation (CPR), 226, 307
Carr, Clay, 212
Case studies, 223–224
Causation, defined, 173
CBT (computer-based training), 216, 228–229, 251
CCOHS (Canadian Centre for Occupational Health and Safety), 244, 250
Center for Devices and Radiological Health (CDRH), 458
Center for the Protection of Worker's Rights, 339
Centers for Disease Control and Prevention (CDC), 432–433, 463
Central station service fire alarm systems, 288, 288*f*
Centrifuges, 466
Certified Industrial Hygienists (CIHs), 369, 372
CFR. *See Code of Federal Regulations*
Checklists, for inspections, 154–156
Chemical factors, in incident causation, 189
Chemical hazards, 360–361, 415
Chemical hygiene officers (CHOs), 415
Chemical hygiene plans (CHPs), 415, 431
Chemical Manufacturers Association, 373
Chemical safety, 421–432
    housekeeping practices in, 424
    labeling practices in, 72, 73*f*, 424–425
    laboratory design and, 427–430
    regulations for, 430–432
    sources of information for, 422–423
    storage considerations, 425–426
    training and documentation of, 423–424
    waste management and, 426–427
Chernobyl disaster (1986), 6
CHOs (chemical hygiene officers), 415
CHPs (chemical hygiene plans), 415, 431
CIHs (Certified Industrial Hygienists), 369, 372
Circuits, 303
Circumaural hearing protectors, 388–389
Citations, 46–47, 346
Citizen lawsuits, 177–178
Civil liability, 172–173, 180–187
Clarifications of standards, 37
Class A fires, 265, 289, 290, 292
Class B fires, 265, 289, 291
Class C fires, 265, 289–291
Class D fires, 265–266, 290
Classified locations, 317–321, 319*t*
Class K fires, 266, 290, 292
Clean rooms, 461–462
Climate, defined, 5. *See also* Safety climate
Closed circuits, 303
Closed-loop inspections, 156
Closing conferences, 43
Clothing, protective, 404, 407–410
CMs (construction managers), 326, 328, 342
Coaching, 220–221
Code of ethics, for industrial hygienists, 369, 370–371*f*
Code of Federal Regulations (CFR), 34–35, 60–61, 65, 125, 133

Coherent radiation, 453

Cold stress, 363

Cold-weather clothing, 409

Color-coded protective helmets, 382

Combined-events analysis, 139

Combustion gas detectors, 285

Combustion process, 262, 264. *See also* Fire and fire protection

Communication, organizational change and, 16–18

Comparative negligence, 183

Competent persons
 construction safety and, 335–336
 excavations and, 92
 scaffolding and, 89, 90, 92

Compliance audits, 98

Compliance safety and health officers (CSHOs), 29, 33, 39–43, 40*f*

Compressed-gas cylinders, 429–430

Compulsory compensation laws, 182

Computer-based training (CBT), 216, 228–229, 251

Computers and Internet, 241–260
 for data collection, 252
 discussion groups, 247, 249–250
 for maintaining awareness, 252
 in management system development, 252–253
 as networking tools, 248–250
 online training, 216, 228–229, 251
 overview, 242–243
 as program management tools, 252–253
 reference libraries on, 229, 251
 as reference tools, 243–248
 resources, 254–260
 as safety culture tool, 250–252
 search strategies, 244–248
 social media, 252
 Web tools, 244–245
 workstation ergonomics, 464

Concrete erection work, 70–71

Conductive clothing and footwear, 405, 410

Conductors, 310

Conference technique, 222–223

Confidentiality
 in Injuries and Illness standard, 105, 114–115
 trade secret provision and, 30, 41, 74, 98

Confined spaces
 defined, 99, 100, 103, 394
 OSHA standard for, 98–104, 101*t*

Confining fire, methods for, 279

Construction managers (CMs), 326, 328, 342

Construction safety, 325–354
 contractors and, 326, 328–329, 342–343, 345–351
 designated safety representatives for, 334–336
 discipline and, 336
 emergency procedures and, 340–341
 housekeeping practices and, 339
 incident reporting and investigations, 339
 inspections for, 336–337
 insurance and, 343–345
 integration into worksites, 341–342
 job safety analysis for, 332, 341, 343

management of, 326, 328, 329, 333–334
 policy statements for, 330–331
 procedures for, 331–332
 programs for, 326–330
 roles and responsibilities in, 332–334, 342–343
 substance abuse programs and, 339–340
 training on, 337–339

Construction Site Safety: A Guide for Managing Contractors (Hilsop), 327

Consumer Product Safety Commission (CPSC), 177

Contact lenses, 383–384

Contagious diseases, 110

Containment practices, 435–436

Contamination, radioactive, 446, 451

Content outlines, 230–231

Contested cases, 48–50

Continuous inspections, 150–151

Contractors
 citation history of, 346
 confined spaces and, 103
 construction safety and, 326, 328–329, 342–343, 345–351
 inspections by, 158–159
 investigations by, 350
 orientation programs for, 349
 Process Safety Management and, 97
 record keeping and reporting requirements for, 349–351
 references from previous employers, 346
 request for bids from, 347–350
 selection of, 345–351
 training for, 97, 103

Contributory negligence, 183

Controlled access zones, 70–71

Control of Hazardous Energy standard, 74–77, 321

Cooperative Compliance Program, 31

Cords, extension, 312

Correspondence courses, 229

Cost-effectiveness method of hazard analysis, 139

Covers, for open working surfaces, 94

CPR (cardiopulmonary resuscitation), 226, 307

CPSC (Consumer Product Safety Commission), 177

Craftsmen, construction safety for, 343

Criminal liability, 178–180, 187

Critical-incident technique, 168

Cryogenic liquids, 460

Cryostats, 465

CSHOs (compliance safety and health officers), 29, 33, 39–43, 40*f*

Culture. *See also* Safety culture
 climate vs., 5
 defining, 2–4, 15
 levels of maturity and, 3–4, 3*f*
 organizational, 2, 5–10
 subcultures, 4

Current (electrical), 302–303

Custom-molded aural inserts, 388

Cutaneous absorption, 367

Cyanide poisoning, 277

Daily participation, in discussion groups, 249

Databases, 246, 252
Deaf persons, alarm systems for, 286
Debris nets, 391
Decision making, in loss control and prevention, 192–194, 194*f*
Decision trees, 139, 140*f*
Deductive analytical methods, 139–140
Deluge sprinkler systems, 293, 294
Deming, Edward, 419
De minimis violations, 46–47
Demonstration method of instruction, 227
Demonstration Project program, 31
Department of. *See specific name of department*
Descent devices, 394
Designated safety representatives, 334–336
Dick and Carey model for training, 203
Diffusion flame fires, 263
Directives, system safety and, 133–134
Discipline, construction safety and, 336
Discussion groups, 247, 249–250
Disposable clothing, 410
Disposable respirators, 81
District of Columbia Workers' Compensation Act of 1982, 183
Documentation requirements, in OSH Act, 68
Dose–response relationship in radiation, 446, 446*t*
Dosimetry, 452
Double-insulated tools, 316
Drains, 282
Drill method of instruction, 226–227
Droplines, 393
Drugs and drug testing, 339–340
Dry chemical extinguishers, 264, 265, 291
Dry-pipe sprinkler systems, 293
Dry powder extinguishers, 291–292
Dual-capacity doctrine, 186
Dual-entry missions, 103
Dual training programs, 221
Dusts, 360, 396

Earmuff devices, 388
Earplugs, 388
Education vs. training, 198–199
Effective temperature (ET), 363
Egregious violations, 47–48
Elective compensation laws, 182
Electrical hazard footwear, 405–406
Electrical safety, 301–324
    equipment for, 308–314
    explosion-proof apparatus and, 320–321
    grounding systems and, 303–304, 314–317
    hazardous locations and, 317–320, 319*t*
    for high-voltage equipment, 321–322
    injuries from electrical contact, 304–307, 305*t*
    inspections for, 321–322
    in laboratory, 429
    maintenance and, 322
    OSHA standards on, 84–86
    overview, 302
    terminology, 302–304
    testing instruments for, 312–313, 313*f*, 315

training on, 323
Electric fields, 450
Electromagnetic radiation, 410, 444
E-mail, 248–249
Emergency action plans, 98
Emergency suits, 407–408
Employees. *See also* Training
    construction safety responsibilities of, 333
    inspections by, 158
    orientation programs for, 235–237, 337–338
    reference libraries for, 229, 251
    rights of, 31–34
    screening for, 166, 340
Employers, rights of, 29–30
Employment and Training Administration, 221
EMRs (experience modification rates), 344–345
Enclosed spaces, defined, 103
Enclosure hearing protectors, 388
Energy, hazardous, 74–77, 321
Engineering controls, 376
Entry process/system, 101–103
Entry supervisors, 102
Environmental factors, in incident causation, 189
Environmental Protection Agency (EPA), 156, 176, 387, 426
Environmental standards, regulations for, 56
Equipment grounding, 314–315
Ergonomics, 364–365, 463–466
Espoused values, 3
ET (effective temperature), 363
Ethical considerations, in system safety, 133
European Union, safety and health regulations for, 55–56
Evacuation strategies, 280
Evaluations, in safety and health training, 216–217, 227, 233–235
Excavations standard, 92–93
Exclusive remedy provisions, 185, 186
Exemptions for recording injuries and illnesses, 106
Exits, types of, 280, 281*f*
Experience modification rates (EMRs), 344–345
Experience ratings, 195–196
Explosion-proof apparatus, 320–321
Explosives, 95
Exposure protection, in fires, 278–279
Extension cords, 312
Extinguishing agents, 264, 265–266, 285–286, 288–296, 430
Eye injuries, 306–307
Eye protection, 382–386, 457–458, 458*t*
Eyewash stations, 428

FAA (Federal Aviation Administration), 156, 177
Facebook, 252
Face protection, 382–386
Facilitated discussions, 224–225
Facilitator-led training, 215–216
Factor analysis, 11
Failure mode and effect analysis (FMEA), 138, 190
Failure to abate penalties, 47
Fall arresting system (FAS), 393–394
Fall arrest systems, 69, 70, 90, 91, 389–395

Fall Protection standard, 69–71
Falls, injuries from, 307
Fatalities, in workplace, 23, 24, 84, 93, 338
Fault trees, 139, 140*f*
FDA (Food and Drug Administration), 177, 449, 458, 459
Federal Aviation Administration (FAA), 156, 177
Federal Aviation Regulation (FAR), 133–134
Federal Coal Mine Safety and Health Act of 1969, 54
Federal Employees' Compensation Act of 1916 (FECA), 183
Federal Employers' Liability Act of 1908 (FELA), 183
Federal Insecticide, Fungicide, and Rodenticide Act of 1947 (FIFRA), 176
Federal Metal and Nonmetallic Mine Safety Act of 1966, 54
Federal Railroad Administration (FRA), 118
Federal Register, 35–37, 60
Feedback, on organizational change, 16–17
Fiber-optic cables, 460–461
Field Operations Manual (OSHA), 45
Filters, respirator, 399
Finger stalls/cots, 403
Fire alarms and detectors, 267, 282–288
Fire and fire protection, 261–299
    building design and construction, 276–282, 281*f*
    chemistry of, 262–264
    classification of, 262–266
    controlling and suppressing, 263–264, 267–268
    detecting and responding to, 267, 282–288
    hazard analysis for, 268–271, 271*f*, 272–274*t*
    objectives of, 266
    overview, 262
    prevention strategies, 266
    recovering from, 268
    risk assessment, 268–271, 269*f*, 274–276, 275*f*
    site planning and, 277–279
    suppression and extinguishment, 264, 265–266, 285–286, 288–296, 430
Fire blankets, 292
Fire departments, access concerns for, 278
Fire doors, 280
Fire extinguishers, 264, 265–266, 285–286, 288–296, 430
Fire hoses, 295
Fire hydrants, 294–295
Fire Protection Handbook (NFPA), 268, 269, 296
Fire proximity suits, 408
Fire walls, 279
First aid, defined, 112
First-aid reports, 120
Fit tests, 79–80, 399–401
Fixed fire extinguishers, 288
Fixed guards, 83
Flame detectors, 284–285
Flame fires, 262–263
Flame-retardant gear, 292, 408
Flammability hazards, 95, 270, 273*t*, 425
Flash protection boundaries, 307
Flexible culture, 9
Floor drains, 282

Floor loading protection, 94
FMEA (failure mode and effect analysis), 138, 190
Food and Drug Administration (FDA), 177, 449, 458, 459
Footwear, 405–406
Ford Motor Company, 133
Forklifts, 86, 87
Formable aural inserts, 388
Formal databases, 246
Foundry footwear, 406
Four-point method of training, 218–220, 219*f*
FRA (Federal Railroad Administration), 118
Framework Directive (89/391/EEC), 56
Fraud, 179–180
Free radicals, 264
Full-body harnesses, 392
Fumes and fume hoods, 360, 396, 427–428, 464
Fundamentals of Industrial Hygiene (Plog), 364
Fuses, 310–311

Game-based learning, 235, 235*f*
Gamma-radiation, 445, 447
Gas cartridge extinguishers, 291
Gas cylinders, 429–430
Gases, 360, 367, 396–397
Gas-filled detectors, 451–452
Gas masks, 399
Geiger-Mueller (G-M) detectors, 451–452
General contractors. *See* Contractors
General Duty Clause of OSH Act, 67
General inspections, 153
Generative culture, 8–9*f*, 9
GFCIs (ground-fault circuit interrupters), 85, 311
Glasses, safety, 384, 457–458, 458*t*
Global Harmonization System (GHS), 422
Glove boxes, 465
Glove inflators, 322
Gloves, 322, 402–403
Goggles, 384, 457–458, 458*t*
G-1 powdered agents, 291
Gross negligence, 173
Ground-fault circuit interrupters (GFCIs), 85, 311
Grounds and grounding systems, 303–304, 314–317
Group behavior, influence on safety culture, 15
Group training methods, 217, 222–226
Guard devices, for machines, 82–84, 309–310
Guardrail systems, 69, 70, 90, 91, 94

Habit strength, 19
Half-life of radioactive material, 445
Halogenated hydrocarbons, 264
Hand protection, 402–405
Hard hats, 380–382
Hardware connectors, 393
Harnesses, 392
Hazard analysis, 131–163. *See also* Inspections
    benefits of, 191
    defined, 137
    factors involved in, 141
    for fire, 268–271, 271*f*, 272–274*t*
    job safety analysis and, 143-144*f*, 142–149, 145*f*

in loss control and prevention, 169–172, 191–192, 192*f*

methods of, 138–140, 140*f*

participants in, 141

system safety and, 132–137, 136*f*

uses for, 137–138

Hazard Communication standard (HCS), 32, 71–74, 73*f*, 422

Hazard control inspection inventories, 153–154, 157

Hazardous energy, 74–77, 321

Hazardous locations, 317–321, 319*t*

Hazardous materials, identification system for, 270–271, 271*f*, 272–274*t*

Hazards

    airborne, 360–361, 366–367, 396–397

    biological, 363–364, 397, 415–416

    chemical, 360–361, 415

    defined, 132, 169, 365

    flammable, 95, 270, 273*t*, 425

    health, 270, 272*t*

    instability, 270, 274*t*

    lasers, 454–455

    liquid, 360

    physical, 361–363, 416, 460–461

    ranking, 192, 192*f*

    smoke, 361, 397

    toxicity vs., 365–366

    wiring, 309–310

HBV (hepatitis B), 364, 441, 444

HCS (Hazard Communication standard), 32, 71–74, 73*f*, 422

HCV (hepatitis C), 364, 441

Head protection, 380–382

Health and Human Services Department, U.S., 24, 155

Health hazards, 270, 272*t*

Hearing impaired persons, alarm systems for, 286

Hearing protection, 362, 386–389

Hearing tests, 111

Heating, ventilation, and air conditioning (HVAC) systems, 427

Heat stress, 363, 408

Heinrich's dominoes model, 135

Helmets, 380–382

Hemorrhages, 306

Hepatitis B (HBV), 364, 441, 444

Hepatitis C (HCV), 364, 441

High-efficiency particulate air (HEPA) filters, 436

Highly hazardous chemicals (HHCs), 95–98

High-visibility clothing, 409–410

High-voltage equipment, 321–322

HIV/AIDS, 364, 441

Home-study courses, 229

Horizontal lifelines, 392–393

Hoses, fire, 295

Hot-work permits, 97

Housekeeping practices, 94, 339, 424

Human error, reduction of, 188

Human factors, in incident causation, 189

Human observers, as fire detection systems, 283

HVAC (heating, ventilation, and air conditioning) systems, 427

Hydrocarbon fuels, 95

Hygiene. *See* Industrial hygiene

IBCs (Institutional Biosafety Committees), 436

ICNIRP (International Commission on Non- Ionizing Radiation Protection), 450

Identification of the Hazards of Materials for Emergency Response (NFPA), 270–271, 271*f*, 272–274*t*

Immediately dangerous to life and health (IDLH) atmospheres, 398

Impervious clothing, 404

"In-basket technique," 226

Incident records, 117–130. *See also* Injuries and Illness standard

    annual reports, 123

    bilevel reporting and, 124

    calculation of incidence rates for, 126–128

    first-aid reports, 120

    investigation reports, 120

    monthly summary reports, 121, 121*f*, 123

    sentinel incidents and, 126, 129

    severity measures and, 128

    statistical measures and, 126

    surveillance systems and, 125–126

    systems for record-keeping, 119

    uses of, 118–119, 123–124

Incidents

    causation factors, 187–189

    defined, 170

    process case studies of, 224

    rates, calculation of, 126–128

Income replacement, 181–182. *See also* Workers' compensation

Indemnification clauses, 326

Independent study methods, 229

Individual civil liability, 180–186

Individual training methods, 217–218, 226–230

Inductive analytical methods, 138–139

Industrial hygiene, 355–374

    biological hazards and, 363–364

    certification and licensure in, 369, 372

    chemical hazards and, 360–361

    code of ethics for, 369, 370–371*f*

    consulting services on, 368–369

    defined, 356

    elements of practice in, 359–365

    ergonomics and, 364–365

    noise exposure and, 361–362

    physical hazards and, 361–363

    professional organizations for, 372–373

    radiation exposure and, 361

    role in health and safety program, 357–358

    temperature extremes and, 363

    toxicity and, 365–368

    vibration exposure and, 362–363

Industrial psychology, 166

Industrial Ventilation–A Manual of Recommended Practice (ACGIH), 373

Infectious agents, biosafety levels for, 416, 433–436, 441–442*t*

Informal knowledge, 246
Information technology. *See* Computers and Internet
Infrared detectors, 283, 285
Ingestion of chemicals, 367
Inhalation of chemicals, 366–367
Injection of chemicals, 368
Injuries. *See also* Liability; Workers' compensation
    data analysis of, 126–129
    from electrical contact, 304–307, 305*t*
    from falls, 307
    repetitive-motion, 464
    workers' compensation coverage of, 184–185
    in workplace, 23, 24, 75, 84
Injuries and Illness standard, 104–113
    classification standards, 113, 113*t*
    forms used in, 104, 106–107, 114–115, 121–122*f*, 121–123
    medical treatment and first aid, definitions of, 111–112
    privacy concern cases, 105, 114–115
    recordkeeping for, 104–108, 108*f*, 110–111
    restricted work activity and, 112–113
    work relatedness, determination of, 108–111
Inorganic acids, 425
Inspections, 149–161
    actors involved in, 157–159
    checklists for, 154–156
    for construction safety, 336–337
    corrective action following, 159–161
    for electrical safety, 321–322
    frequency of, 156–157
    philosophy behind, 149–150
    priorities for, 39–40
    procedures for, 40–44, 153–161
    purpose of, 150
    of respirators, 28, 402
    types of, 150–153
    warrants for, 38–39
Instability hazards, 270, 274*t*
Institutional Biosafety Committees (IBCs), 436
Instructional systems design (ISD), 203
Instructor-led training, 215–216
Insurance, 343–345. *See also* Workers' compensation
Intentional tort cases, 175, 186
Interior Department, U.S., 53–54
Interlocks, 309
Intermittent inspections, 152
Internal injuries, 306
International Building Code® (International Code Council), 276, 279
International Commission on Non-Ionizing Radiation Protection (ICNIRP), 450
International Organization for Standardization, 55, 56
Internet. *See* Computers and Internet
Internships, 221
Interval inspections, 151–153
"In the course of" requirements, 184–185
Investigations
    of chemical incidents, 97–98
    of construction sites, 339

    by contractors, 350
    reports of, 120
Ionization, 444–445
Ionization chambers, 451–452
Ionization detectors, 283
Ionizing radiation, 361, 444, 448, 449
ISD (instructional systems design), 203

Job analysis, 208
Job instruction training (JIT), 218–220, 219*f*
Job safety analysis (JSA), 142–149
    benefits of, 142, 148–149
    for construction sites, 332, 341, 343
    hazards and potential incidents, identification of, 145–146
    overview, 142, 143–144*f*
    selection process in, 142–144
    solution development, 147–148
    worksheet for, 145–146, 145*f*
"Job Safety and Health: It's the Law" poster, 34, 37*f*, 67
Job satisfaction, impact on safety climate, 12–13, 13*f*
Joint safety and health committees, inspections by, 158
JSA. *See* Job safety analysis
Just culture, 9

Keywords for searches, 246–247
Knee pads, 408
Knife switches, 310
Knowledge retention rates, 212, 213*f*, 235, 235*f*

Labeling practices, 72, 73*f*, 424–425, 443
Laboratory-acquired infections (LAIs), 432
Laboratory Chemical Safety Summaries (LCSSs), 423
Laboratory safety, 413–470. *See also* Biological safety; Chemical safety; Radiation
    administrative controls for, 415
    altered environments and, 461–463
    animals and, 435, 442*t*, 462–463
    biological hazards and, 415–416
    challenges of, 416–418
    chemical hazards and, 415
    closing and moving procedures, 467
    design considerations, 427–430, 440
    emergency planning and, 466
    ergonomics and, 463–466
    management tools for, 418–421
    overview, 414
    physical hazards and, 416, 460–461
    waste management procedures, 426–427, 443, 453, 466–467
Laboratory scale, 414
Laboratory Standard, 430
Labor Department, U.S., 24, 54, 221
Ladder standards, 88–89
Lagging indicators, 17
LAIs (laboratory-acquired infections), 432
Lanyards, 392
Laser-generated airborne contaminants (LGACs), 455
Laser Institute of America (LIA), 457, 458–459
Laser safety, 385, 453–460, 454*f*, 456*t*, 458*t*

Laser safety officers (LSOs), 459
LCSSs (Laboratory Chemical Safety Summaries), 423
Leaded clothing, 410
Learning culture, 9–10
Learning objectives, in safety and health training, 208–210
Learning pyramid, 212, 213f
Leather clothing, 403, 407
Lecture method, 225
Legal considerations. *See* Regulatory framework
Leg protection, 408
LGACs (laser-generated airborne contaminants), 455
Liability, 172–187. *See also* Workers' compensation
    civil, 172–173, 180–187
    criminal, 178–180, 187
    dual-capacity doctrine and, 186
    government penalty systems and, 175–177
    negligence and, 172–174, 180, 183
    organizational, 174–178
    prevention strategies, 186–187
    punitive damages and, 174–175
LIA (Laser Institute of America), 457, 458–459
Libraries, 229, 251
License to think, 8
Lifelines, 392–393
Life Safety Code® (NFPA), 276
Limited water supply sprinkler systems, 293
Linear sensor systems, 286
Liquid hazards, 360
Literacy levels, 211
Lith-X powder, 292
LLRWPA (Low-Level Radioactive Waste Policy Act of 1980), 453
Loans, for small businesses, 30, 50–51
Local fire alarm systems, 287
Lockout/tagout (LOTO) programs, 74–77
Log and Summary of Work-Related Injuries and Illnesses, 33
Loss control and prevention, 165–196. *See also* Liability
    corrective measures for, 194–195
    decision making in, 192–194, 194f
    environmental factors in, 189
    evaluating program effectiveness, 195–196
    hazard identification and evaluation, 169–172, 191–192, 192f
    history of, 166–167
    incident causation, techniques for examining, 167–169
    management support in, 167, 170, 192–194
    monitoring activities in, 195
    principles of, 190
    processes of, 191–196
    situational factors in, 189
    of unsafe practices and procedures, 187–188
Loss scenarios, 274–276, 275f
Lost workdays, 106, 123
LOTO (lockout/tagout) programs, 74–77
Low-Level Radioactive Waste Policy Act of 1980 (LLRWPA), 453
Low literacy levels, 211

LSOs (laser safety officers), 459
Lurking, 249–250

Machine guards, 82–84, 309–310
Magnetic fields, 450
Maintenance
    electrical safety and, 322
    of personal protective equipment, 379
    for respirators, 81–82, 401
Management. *See also* Supervisors
    construction managers, 326, 328, 342
    of construction safety, 326, 328, 329, 333–334
    criminal prosecution of, 179
    culture of safety promoted by, 7
    defined, 134
    inspections by, 157
    in loss control and prevention, 167, 170, 192–194
    organizational change, role in, 17, 18–19
    reports to, 123
    safety managers, 64, 202–203, 334–336
Manuals of policy and procedure, 210–211
Manufacturing-line process simulations, 226
Maritime workers, 183
Marshall v. Barlow's Inc. (1978), 38
Material Safety Data Sheets (MSDSs). *See* Safety Data Sheets (SDSs)
Maximum permissible exposures (MPEs), 457
Mechanical filter respirators, 399
Mechanical integrity, 97
Medical care
    defined, 111
    trade secret provision and, 74
    in workers' compensation, 182
Meeting technique, 222–223
Mental illness, 110
Mentoring programs, 221–222
Merit program, 31
MESA (Mine Enforcement Safety Administration), 54
Metatarsal footwear, 405
Met-L-Kyl, 292
Met-L-X powder, 292
Microbiological technique, 436
Microscopes, 464–465
Microtomes, 465
Mid-literacy levels, 211
Mine Enforcement Safety Administration (MESA), 54
Mine Safety and Health Act of 1977, 22, 53–55
Mine Safety and Health Administration (MSHA)
    administration of, 54–55, 59–60
    on incident records, 118
    on inspection frequency, 156
    on penalties for violations, 176
    respirator inspection by, 28
    role of, 22
    on training, 238
Mine Safety and Health Review Commission, 54
Mishap models, 134, 135–137
Mists, 360, 396
Mode of failure, 190
Molded aural inserts, 388
Monitoring activities, in loss control and prevention, 195

Monthly Summary of Injuries and Illnesses, 121, 121*f*, 123

Motors, 312

MPEs (maximum permissible exposures), 457

MSDSs (Material Safety Data Sheets). *See* Safety Data Sheets (SDSs)

MSHA. *See* Mine Safety and Health Administration

Musculoskeletal disorders (MSDs), 115, 364

National Advisory Committee on Occupational Safety and Health (NACOSH), 29

National Agricultural Chemical Association, 373

National Council on Compensation Insurance (NCCI), 344

National Electrical Code (NEC), 308, 309–310, 314–316, 320

National Electrical Safety Code (ANSI), 308

National Fire Codes® (NFPA), 279

National Fire Protection Association (NFPA)
    on building design, 276, 279
    classification of fires by, 264–265
    Fire Protection Handbook, 268, 269, 296
    on flash protection boundaries, 307
    hazardous material identification system of, 270–271, 271*f*, 272–274*t*
    Life Safety Code®, 276
    National Electrical Code of, 308
    on shock protection boundaries, 307
    Uniform Fire Code, 276

National Institute for Occupational Safety and Health (NIOSH)
    on best practices in safety, 6–7
    on hazard evaluations, 398
    respirator approval by, 78, 78–79*f*
    role of, 24, 27–29, 54

National Institute of Standards and Technology (NIST), 452

National Institutes of Health (NIH), 432–433

National Research Council, 423

National Safety Council, 155, 166–167, 227, 230, 268

National Training Laboratories, 212

National Voluntary Laboratory Accreditation Program (NVLAP), 452

Natural rubber latex (NRL), 403

NCCI (National Council on Compensation Insurance), 344

NEC (National Electrical Code), 308, 309–310, 314–316, 320

Needlestick injuries, 111

Negligence, 172–174, 180, 183

Negligence per se, 174

Nets, 391

Networking tools, computer and Internet as, 248–250

New injuries and illnesses, defined, 104

NFPA. *See* National Fire Protection Association

NIH (National Institutes of Health), 432–433

NIOSH. *See* National Institute for Occupational Safety and Health

NIST (National Institute of Standards and Technology), 452

Noise exposure, 361–362, 386–387

Noise-induced hearing loss (NIHL), 386

Noise reduction ratings (NRRs), 387

Nonbeam hazards, 455

Nonflammable solvents, 425

Nonionizing radiation, 361, 445, 449–453

Non-permit spaces, 103

Nontraining solutions, 200–202

Nozzles, for hoses, 295

NRL (natural rubber latex), 403

NRRs (noise reduction ratings), 387

Nuclear Energy Agency report (OECD), 6

Nuclear Regulatory Commission (NRC), 156, 177, 448, 449

NVLAP (National Voluntary Laboratory Accreditation Program), 452

Occupational exposure limits, 363

Occupational Safety and Health Administration (OSHA), 63–116. *See also* Occupational Safety and Health (OSH) Act of 1970
    on assigned protection factors, 398
    on bloodborne pathogens, 443
    citation history records, 346
    clarifications of standards, 37
    Confined Space Entry standard, 98–104, 101*t*
    Control of Hazardous Energy standard, 74–77, 321
    Electrical Safety standards, 84–86
    establishment of, 25
    Excavations standard, 92–93
    Fall Protection standard, 69–71
    Field Operations Manual, 45
    Hazard Communication standard, 32, 71–74, 73*f*, 422
    Injuries and Illness standard, 104–113
    on inspection frequency, 156
    Laboratory Standard, 430
    Ladder standards, 88–89
    Machine-Guarding standard, 82–84
    national and regional offices, 58–59
    posters from, 34, 37*f*, 67
    Powered Industrial Trucks standard, 86–88
    private sector input and, 35–36
    Process Safety Management of Highly Hazardous Chemicals standard, 95–98
    Respiratory Protection standard, 77–82
    roles and responsibilities of, 22, 25–26
    Scaffolding standard, 89–92
    on shock protection boundaries, 307
    on training, 237–238
    variances from standards, 36–37
    Walking/Working Surfaces standard, 93–95
    workplace inspection process, 38–44

Occupational Safety and Health (OSH) Act of 1970, 23–53. *See also* Occupational Safety and Health Administration (OSHA)
    administration and enforcement of, 24–29
    on citations, 46–47
    on contested cases, 48–50
    on employee rights, 31–34
    on employer rights, 29–30

enactment of, 22
on federal–state relationships, 51–53, 52f
General Duty Clause of, 67
history of, 23–24
on onsite consultations, 30
on penalties, 47
poster display requirements of, 34, 37f, 67
record-keeping requirements of, 37–38, 104, 118, 124–125
scope of, 64–65
on small-business loans, 50–51
on violations, 44–48, 176
on Voluntary Protection Programs, 30–31
on workplace inspections, 38–44
on written plans and documentation, 67–68
Occupational Safety and Health Review Commission (OSHRC), 24, 26–27
OD (optical density), 457–458
OECD (Organization for Economic Cooperation and Development), 6
Office of Apprenticeship, 221
OHA (operations hazard analysis), 138
Ohms, 303
Online Meeting platform, 216
Online training, 216, 228–229, 251
Onsite consultations, 30
On-the-job training (OJT), 216–222
Open circuits, 303
Opening conferences, 40–41
Openings, protection for, 94–95
Open-source software, 253
Operating controls, 82–83
Operations hazard analysis (OHA), 138
Optical cavities, 454
Optical density (OD), 457–458
Organic acids, 426
Organizational change, 15–19
Organizational culture, 2, 5–10
Organizational liability, 174–178
Organization for Economic Cooperation and Development (OECD), 6
Orientation programs, 235–237, 337–338, 349
OSHA. See Occupational Safety and Health Administration
OSH Act. See Occupational Safety and Health Act of 1970
OSHRC (Occupational Safety and Health Review Commission), 24, 26–27
Other-than-serious violations, 46, 47
Over-current devices, 303, 304, 310–311, 315
Overhand bricklaying, 71, 90
Oxidation, 262, 426
Oxidizing acids, 425–426
Oxygen deficiency, 101, 101t, 397

Paralysis, 306
Particle radiation, 444
Particulate respirators, 399
Passageways, requirements for, 94

Passive fall arrest systems, 389, 391
Path analysis, 13, 13f
Pathological culture, 8, 8–9f
Peer sharing and support, 419
PELs (permissible exposure levels), 401
Penalties, for violations, 47, 176
Pendant sprinklers, 294
Pendant switches, 310
Perception surveys, 10–11, 14–15
Performance analysis, 208
Performance-based training, 208
Performance objectives, 208–210
Performance testing, 233–235
Periodic inspections, 151–152
Permanent variances, 36
Permissible exposure levels (PELs), 401
Permit-required confined spaces, 98–103
Personal fall arrest systems. See Fall arrest systems
Personal injury requirements, 184–185
Personal protective equipment (PPE), 375–412
  for biological safety, 439
  clothing, 404, 407–410
  defined, 377
  employer obligation for providing, 379–380
  enforcement and disciplinary actions for, 379
  eye and face protection, 382–386, 457–458, 458t
  fall arrest systems, 69, 70, 90, 91, 389–395
  footwear, 405–406
  gloves, 322, 402–403
  hand and arm protection, 402–405
  head protection, 380–382
  hearing protection, 362, 386–389
  for high-voltage equipment, 322
  policy statements for, 377
  removal and disposal of, 404–405
  respiratory protection, 77–82, 395–402
  selection of, 377–378
  training on, 378–379
  use and maintenance of, 379
Personnel. See Employees
Personnel nets, 391
Petition for Modification of Abatement (PMA), 47
PHAs (process hazard analyses), 96, 97
Photoelectric smoke detectors, 284
Physical hazards, 361–363, 416, 460–461
Pipetting, 465
"Plan, Do, Check, Act" management systems, 419–421, 420f
Planned inspections, 151–153
Plea bargains, 178
Podcasts, 227–228
Point of operation, 82
Poisons, 426
Polarity plugs, 317
Policy and procedure manuals, 210–211
Policy statements, 330–331, 377
Portable fire extinguishers, 288–292
Positioning device systems, 392
Positive reinforcement, 19
Positive trees, 139

Posters, display requirements for, 34, 37*f,* 67
Posttests, 234
Powered Industrial Trucks standard, 86–88
Power transmission apparatus, 82
PPE. *See* Personal protective equipment
Pre-action sprinkler systems, 293–294
Precast concrete erection work, 70–71
Premixed flame fires, 262
Preponderance of the evidence, 173
Presignal feature alerts, 287
Pretests, 233–234
Prevent Blindness America, 383–384
Pre-work meetings, 339
Principles of Fire Protection (NFPA), 276
Privacy. *See* Confidentiality
Private rights of action, 177–178
Proactive culture, 8, 9*f*
Process, defined, 95
Process hazard analyses (PHAs), 96, 97
Process safety information (PSI), 95–96
Process Safety Management (PSM), 95–98
Productivity, 6, 6*f,* 171
Professional interpretations, 246
Profit motive, 132–133
Program management, computers and Internet as tools
    for, 252–253
Project safety managers, 334–336
Proprietary supervising-station fire alarm systems, 288
Protected-premises fire alarm systems, 287
Protective headwear, 380–382
Prudent avoidance, 450
Prudent Practices in the Laboratory (National
    Research Council), 421, 423, 426
PSI (process safety information), 95–96
PSM (Process Safety Management), 95–98
Public Health Service, U.S., 444
Punitive damages, 174–175
Push-button switches, 310
Pyrotechnics, 95

Qualified persons, scaffolding and, 89–91
Question-and-answer (Q&A) sessions, 225–226
Questionnaires, design of, 216–217
Quid pro quo, of workers' compensation law, 185

RACs (risk assessment codes), 192
Radiation, 444–453
    contamination control, 446, 451
    detection instrumentation, 451–452
    dose–response relationship, 446, 446*t*
    emission criteria, 449–450
    exposure limits, 448, 448*t,* 451
    half-life and, 445
    in laboratory, 416
    laser safety, 385, 453–460, 454*f,* 456*t,* 458*t*
    principles of, 444–445
    protection methods, 410, 447–448
    safety programs for, 450–453
    standards for, 448–449, 449*t*
    types of, 361, 381–382, 386, 444, 446–447

waste management and, 453
Radiation safety officers (RSOs), 450–451
Railroad workers, 183
Ranking hazards, 192, 192*f*
RCRA (Resource Conservation and Recovery Act of
    1976), 417
Reactive culture, 8, 9*f*
Receptacle-tension testers, 315
Record keeping and reporting. *See also* Incident
    records
    on construction sites, 339
    for contractors, 349–351
    exemptions for, 106
    forms for, 104, 106–107, 114–115, 121–122*f,*
        121–123
    for Injuries and Illness standard, 104–108, 108*f,*
        110–111
    for inspections, 159, 160
    OSH Act requirements for, 37–38, 104, 118,
        124–125
Recordkeeping Handbook (OSHA), 124
Reference libraries, 229, 251
References, from previous employers, 346
Reference tools, computer and Internet as, 243–248
Regional Administrators, 26, 37
Regulatory framework. *See also* Occupational Safety
    and Health Administration (OSHA); Occupa-
    tional Safety and Health (OSH) Act of 1970
    Code of Federal Regulations and, 34–35, 60–61, 65
    federal agencies involved in, 58–59
    Federal Register and, 35–37, 60
    for international standardization, 55–56
    Mine Safety and Health Act of 1977, 22, 53–55
    overview, 22
Rehabilitative care, 182
Reliability scores, 11
Remote supervising-station fire alarm systems, 288
Repeated violations, 46, 47
Repetitive-motion injuries, 464
Reporting. *See* Record keeping and reporting
Reporting culture, 9
Request for bids (RFBs), 347–350
Rescue service provisions, 99–100
Rescue systems, 394
Resistance (electrical), 303
Resource Conservation and Recovery Act of 1976
    (RCRA), 417
Respirators
    assigned protection factors for, 398
    certification of, 78, 78–79*f*
    cleaning and sanitizing, 401–402
    fit tests for, 79–80, 399–401
    in IDLH atmospheres, 398
    inspection of, 28, 402
    maintenance, storage, and replacement of, 81–82,
        401
    medical evaluations for, 80, 402
    purpose of, 77–78
    training on use of, 80–81, 402

types of, 398–399
user seal checks for, 80
written plans for, 79, 82
Respiratory protection, 77–82, 395–402. *See also* Respirators
Respiratory system, 366–367
Respondeat superior, 174
Restraint systems, 394
Restricted work activity, 112–113
Retaining devices, 93
Retention rates, 212, 213*f,* 235, 235*f*
Retracting lifeline devices, 392
Review tests, 234
RFBs (request for bids), 347–350
Risk, defined, 134
Risk assessment codes (RACs), 192
Risk management cycle, 135–136, 136*f*
Risk matrix, 275–276, 275*f*
Role-playing, 225
Root cause analysis, 200, 201
Routine job functions, 113
RSOs (radiation safety officers), 450–451
Rubber gloves, 322, 403–404

SAAs (satellite accumulation areas), 427
Safety
    construction, 325–354 (*See also* Construction safety)
    defined, 134
    electrical, 301–324 (*See also* Electrical safety)
    fire, 261–299 (*See also* Fire and fire protection)
    laboratory, 413–470 (*See also* Laboratory safety)
Safety and health training, 197–240
    adult learning needs in, 211–215, 213*f*
    apprenticeships, 221
    benefits of, 199–200
    brainstorming in, 223
    case studies used in, 223–224
    coaching in, 220–221
    computer-based, 216, 228–229, 251
    conference technique for, 222–223
    content outline for, 230–231
    demonstration method in, 227
    designing courses for, 210–217
    drill method for, 226–227
    evaluations in, 216–217, 227, 233–235
    facilitated discussions in, 224–225
    group training methods, 217, 222–226
    implementation of, 232–233
    individual training methods, 217–218, 226–230
    internships, 221
    job instruction training, 218–220, 219*f*
    learning and performance objectives for, 208–210
    lecture method in, 225
    literacy level considerations in, 211
    mentoring programs, 221–222
    models of, 203, 204*f*
    nontraining alternatives to, 200–202
    on-the-job training, 216–222
    question-and-answer sessions in, 225–226
    regulatory obligations in, 235–237

resources for, 237–238
    role-playing in, 225
    safety manager, in role of, 202–203
    seminars and workshops for, 230
    simulation devices for, 226
    training needs analysis in, 205–208
    video-based, 227–228
    written materials for, 229
Safety awareness, 329, 338
Safety climate
    defining, 5
    job satisfaction, impact on, 12–13, 13*f*
    measuring, 10–11, 14–16
    safety culture vs., 5
Safety culture, 1–20
    behavior-based safety models for, 17–19
    changing, 15–19
    computers and Internet in, 250–252
    defining, 2–3
    group behavior, influence on, 15
    importance of, 6–7
    for laboratory organizations, 421
    levels of maturity, 3–4, 3*f,* 7–10
    managerial role in promotion of, 7
    measuring, 10–11, 14–16
    origins of, 6
    safety climate vs., 5
    theoretical model of, 10–12*f*
    trust, impact on, 13–14
Safety Data Sheets (SDSs), 32, 71, 72–74, 270, 361, 422
Safety Equipment Institute (SEI), 378
Safety management systems (SMSs), 252–253, 419–421
Safety managers, 64, 202–203, 334–336
Safety net systems, 69, 70
Safety sampling, 168–169
SARs (supplied-air respirators), 398
Satellite accumulation areas (SAAs), 427
SBA (Small Business Administration), 30, 50–51
Scaffolding standard, 89–92
SCBA (self-contained breathing apparatus), 398
Scintillation detectors, 452
Screening of employees, 166, 340
SDSs (Safety Data Sheets), 32, 71, 72–74, 270, 361, 422
Search engines, 244–245
Secretary of Labor, roles and responsibilities of, 24, 25, 54
SEI (Safety Equipment Institute), 378
Selective participation in discussion groups, 249
Self-contained breathing apparatus (SCBA), 398
Self-paced training, 216
Seminars, 230
Sensor systems, 286
Sentencing Commission, U.S., 187
Sentinel incidents, 126, 129
Serious Injury Incidence Rates (SIIRs), 129
Serious violations, 45–47, 176
Setting analysis, 208
Severity measures, 128

Shock absorbers, 393
Shock protection boundaries, 307
Shower stations, 428
Sidewall sprinklers, 294
Simple negligence, 172–173
Simulation devices, 226
Site planning, for fire protection, 277–279
Situational factors, in incident causation, 189
Skin absorption, 367
Skin contamination, 446
Skin effect, 313
Skin injuries, 306–307
Skinner, B. F., 18
Small Business Administration (SBA), 30, 50–51
Small businesses
    loans for, 30, 50–51
    record-keeping requirements for, 38
Smart Training: The Manager's Guide to Training for Improved Performance (Carr), 212
SMEs (subject matter experts), 203
Smoke-control systems, 281–282
Smoke detectors, 267, 284
Smoke hazards, 361, 397
Smoke inhalation, 277
SMSs (safety management systems), 252–253, 419–421
Snaphooks, 393
Snap switches, 310
Social media, 252
Sole-puncture resistant footwear, 406
Solicitor of Labor, roles and responsibilities of, 26
Solvents, 425
Specific limit of 2 mG guideline, 450
Sprinkler systems, 267, 278, 282, 292–294, 295t
Stair enclosures, 279
Standard threshold shift (STS), 111
Standpipes, 282
Star program, 31
State plans for health and safety, 51–53, 52f, 65, 65–66f
Static dissipative footwear, 406
Storage
    of chemicals, 425–426
    of respirators, 81–82, 401
Stored pressure extinguishers, 291
Strict liability, 179
Structural ramps, 93
Structured on-the-job training, 216–222
STS (standard threshold shift), 111
Subcontractors. *See* Contractors
Subcultures, 4
Subject matter experts (SMEs), 203
Subrogation, of workers' compensation, 186
Substance abuse programs, 339–340
Superaural hearing protectors, 388
Supervising-station fire alarm systems, 287–288
Supervisors. *See also* Management
    bulletins to, 123–124
    construction safety responsibilities of, 333
    criminal prosecution of, 179
    inspections by, 157–158
Supplied-air respirators (SARs), 398

Surface contamination, 446
Surface fires, 263
Surveillance systems, 125–126
Switchboards, 311–312
Switches, 310
SWOT analysis, 200
System grounding, 314
Systems, defined, 134
System safety, 132–137
    defined, 134
    development of, 134–135, 136f
    directives and, 133–134
    ethical motives and, 133
    legal vulnerability and, 133
    mishap models and, 135–137
    profit motive and, 132–133
    terminology, 134

Tagout/lockout programs, 74–77
Technology. *See* Computers and Internet
Temperature extremes, 363
Temporary variances, 36
10 Safety Culture Maturity model, 2
Tension testers, 315
Testing instruments (electrical), 312–313, 313f, 315
Tests, in safety and health training, 216–217, 227, 233–235
Thermal burns, 307
Thermal comfort limits, 363
Thermal detectors, 283, 284
Thermoplastic helmets, 382
Three-light neon receptacle testers, 315
Three-wire adapters, 316
Threshold Limit Values (TLVs), 373, 401, 450
Toeboards, 91
Toe boxes, 405
Tort law system, 172, 175
Total safety culture, 7. *See also* Safety culture
Toxicity, 365–368
Toxic Substances Control Act of 1976 (TSCA), 176
Trade secret provision, 30, 41, 74, 98
Traffic considerations, in fire protection, 277
Trainer-led training, 215–216
Training. *See also* Safety and health training
    benefits of, 199–200
    on biological safety, 443
    on chemical safety, 423–424
    on confined spaces, 103
    on construction safety, 337–339
    for contractors, 97, 103
    defined, 198–199
    education vs., 198–199
    on electrical safety, 323
    on hazardous chemicals, 74
    on hazardous energy, 77
    on machine-guard devices, 84
    MSHA on, 238
    OSHA on, 237–238
    performance-based, 208
    on personal protective equipment, 378–379
    on powered industrial trucks, 87–88

on Process Safety Management, 96–97
on respirator use, 80–81, 402
on scaffolding safety, 90
Training Cycle model, 203, 204f
Training needs analysis, 205–208
Transportation considerations, in fire protection, 277
Transportation Department, U.S., 177, 453
Travel, injuries or illness during, 110
Trust, impact on safety culture, 13–14
TSCA (Toxic Substances Control Act of 1976), 176
Tuberculosis, 111, 397
Twitter, 252
Tylor, Edward, 15

Ultraviolet detectors, 285
Ultraviolet (UV) lights, 439–440
Ultraviolet (UV) radiation, 381–382, 386
Underwriters Laboratories (UL), 312, 313, 316, 320
Uniform Fire Code (NFPA), 276
Universal precautions, 364
Upright sprinklers, 294
User seal checks, 80

Values, 3
ValuJet, 132–133
Vapors, 360, 367, 397
Variances from standards, 36–37
Ventilation systems, 280, 282, 373, 427
Ventricular fibrillation, 306
Vertical lifelines, 393
Vibration exposure, 362–363
Video-based training, 227–228
Violations, 4–48, 176
Visually impaired persons, alarm systems for, 286
Voltage and voltage detectors, 303, 313, 313f
Voluntary Protection Programs (VPPs), 30–31

Walkaround provision, 33
Walking/Working Surfaces standard, 93–95
War games, 226
Warning signs, 309
Warrants, for inspections, 38–39
Waste management procedures, 426–427, 443, 453, 466–467
Water-level devices, 285

Water-reactive chemicals, 426
Water solution extinguishers, 290
Water-spray systems, 292, 294
Water supply, fire protection and, 278, 286
Water-temperature switches, 285
Watts, 303
Web-based training (WBT), 216, 228–229, 251
WebEx training platform, 216
Websites. *See* Computers and Internet
Weekly toolbox talks, 339
Welding, eye protection for, 385–386
Wet-bulb globe temperature (WBGT), 363
Wet chemical extinguishers, 292
Wet-pipe sprinkler systems, 293
WIFM (what's in it for me) statements, 212–215
Willful and wanton negligence, 173
Willful violations, 44, 47, 176
Williams-Steiger Act. *See* Occupational Safety and Health (OSH) Act of 1970
Windscreens, 90
Winter clothing, 409
Wiring hazards, 309–310
Workbenches, 464
Work environment, defined, 109
Workers' compensation, 180–186
    characteristics of, 182–183
    employment covered by, 183
    exclusive remedy provisions in, 185, 186
    income replacement in, 181–182
    injuries covered by, 184–185
    limitations on coverage, 183–184
    objectives of, 181
    overview, 180–181
    subrogation of, 186
Working/Walking Surfaces standard, 93–95
Work positioning systems, 394
Workshops, 230
Written plans
    for hazardous chemicals, 71–74
    OSH Act on, 67–68
    for respirator use, 79, 82
    for safety and health training, 229

X-ray radiation, 445, 447, 449